Microelectronic
Circuits
and
Applications

John M. Carroll
Formerly Managing Editor, ELECTRONICS

New York
San Francisco
Toronto
London
Sydney

M c G R A W - H I L L   B O O K   C O M P A N Y

BOOKS BY JOHN M. CARROLL

Mechanical Design for Electronics Production
Transistor Circuits and Applications
Modern Transistor Circuits
Design Manual for Transistor Circuits
Electron Devices and Circuits
Tunnel-Diode and Semiconductor Circuits
Microelectronic Circuits and Applications

Preface

Of the many new trends in the fast-moving field of electronics few have aroused the widespread excitement that microelectronics has aroused. The term microelectronics encompasses several approaches to the design and production of electronic circuits that result in circuits at least an order of magnitude smaller than could be realized with the conventional solid-state components of the early 1960s.

Microelectronics is, in fact, a new technology compounded of many incremental advances in solid-state physics, high-vacuum metallurgy, physical chemistry, electrical circuit design, and production engineering.

This new technology promises to cause profound changes in the electronics industry and in the profession of electronic engineering. Some manufacturers of conventional components will find their markets contracting as more and more equipment is designed to use microcircuits. But other component makers will become manufacturers of microcircuits and perhaps even make items of end equipment in which these microcircuits are used.

Conversely, manufacturers of electronic equipment may get into the business of making their own microcircuits either on a pilot-plant basis to measure the performance of their microcircuit suppliers, or to fulfill their in-house needs and perhaps to supply other manufacturers as well.

In both instances, however, the entry of companies into microelectronics will be restricted by the large outlay of capital required to acquire a microelectronics capability. There will be many more consumers of microcircuits than producers.

In many cases, solid-state physicists will become circuit designers, and the circuit designers who become involved in microcircuit design will have to acquire a deeper insight into solid-state physics than was required in working with discrete semiconductor components. Other circuit designers will find that their function has become largely one of specifying microcircuits and assembling them into equipment.

This book begins with a survey of the various approaches to microelectronics. These include assembling discrete components into micromodules, using complex semiconductor components such as multiemitter transistors, designing integrated semiconductor circuits and thin-film circuits. Integrated circuits are also called monolithic circuits because they are fabricated on and within a single block of silicon. Thin-film circuits are made up of micron-thick regions of conductive and resistive materials vacuum-deposited on some insulating substrate.

The bulk of the book consists of 78 technical articles that appeared in *Electronics* magazine during the years 1963–1964. Chapters 6 and 7 deal with integrated semiconductor circuits and cover both nonlinear and linear circuits. Chapters 8 and 9 deal with thin-film circuits and cover both active and passive circuits. Chapters 10 and 11 treat microcircuits using discrete components. Chapter 10 covers micromodules while Chapter 11 deals with the use of complex semiconductor components.

The remaining chapters treat subsidiary techniques useful in microelectronics. Chapter 12 is on optoelectronics or the use of light-sensitive and light-emitting materials to effect coupling in microcircuits. Chapter 13 covers micropower circuit techniques, the means for coping with problems that arise when circuit power levels are reduced an order of magnitude or more below those encountered in circuits using conventional semiconductor components. Chapter 14 is concerned with cryogenic or low-temperature thin-film circuits. Chapters 15 and 16 cover circuits using field-effect devices and other nonconventional semiconductor components.

The circuits described include oscillators, amplifiers, logic and switching circuits with applications in digital computers, hearing aids, servomechanisms, cathode-ray-tube displays, and such military apparatus as radar sets and loran receivers.

Most of the developments originated in the United States but there are also contributions from Great Britain, France, Japan, West Germany, the Netherlands, Italy, and Sweden.

This book is designed especially for the working engineer but may also find use as collateral reading in universities, colleges, and technical institutes. It supplements but does not duplicate material covered in *Tunnel-Diode and Semiconductor Circuits* and represents the fifth volume in a series of books on semiconductor electronics. The remaining books are *Transistor Circuits and Applications, Modern Transistor Circuits,* and *Design Manual for Transistor Circuits.*

Thanks are due my wife Billie and our son Jim for their help in preparing this manuscript.

John M. Carroll

Contents

PART ONE

A Survey of Microelectronics

Chapter 1

REASONS FOR MICROMINIATURIZATION

From the time Lee De Forest invented the three-element electron tube in 1907 until the close of World War II, the electron tube alone fulfilled the need of the electronics industry for an active circuit component that could amplify feeble signals to a level at which they could perform some useful function.

SEMICONDUCTORS VS TUBES—However, in the mid-1940s many disadvantages of the vacuum tube became apparent as new types of electronic equipment, principally automatic digital computers, began to appear. The hot filaments of electron tubes created a troublesome heat-transfer problem and their relatively fragile nature placed severe mechanical restrictions upon the design of mobile equipment. Even more disheartening, however, was the relatively low reliability of tubes compared to that of other electronic parts. The mean failure rate for JAN-type receiving tubes, both standard and miniature, is 1.70 failures per million operating hours as contrasted with, for example, 0.025 failure per million hours for carbon-composition resistors.

Clearly, the unreliability of electron tubes placed a limit on the size and complexity of electronic equipment that could be successfully maintained in operation since tube failures frequently rendered the gear inoperable.

However, the invention of the transistor by Shockley, Bardeen, and Brattain in 1948 gave the electronics industry a new lease on life by making possible the successful design and operation of large-scale digital equipment for military and commercial use. The transistor has no hot filaments and its construction is inherently rugged. Moreover, the mean failure rate for silicon transistors is only about 0.50 per million hours, less than one-third that of the best receiving-type electron tubes.

MICROELECTRONICS: COST, WEIGHT, AND SIZE —But as the United States guided-missile program advanced in technical sophistication and as digital computers, especially those designed for special military applications, grew increasingly more complex, even the low weight and enhanced reliability of silicon transistors became inadequate. By the late 1950s, the U.S. Air Force and Army Signal Corps were seeking new approaches to making electronic circuits smaller, lighter, and even more reliable. It was hoped also that these new approaches to circuit design, loosely lumped under the name of microelectronics, would reduce the cost of equipment and facilitate serial manufacture of complex circuits under uniform conditions. Hopefully, some of the new approaches would eventually admit the use of automatic production equipment. And the ability to pack more and more parts into a small space would make it possible to employ a technique known as redundancy to achieve even greater circuit reliability.

MICROELECTRONICS: RELIABILITY—Now component reliability, or the probability that a component will survive for a given period of time under the environmental conditions it was designed to withstand, is an exponential function of the failure rate of the component. Thus, when two components in a circuit are connected in series in a reliability sense so that the failure of either one will cause the circuit to malfunction, the failure rates of the compo-

nents are additive and the total circuit reliability is found to be the product of all the component reliabilities.

Given two components in series having reliabilities of R_1 and R_2 and failure rates of FR_1 and FR_2, the overall circuit reliability R_T is found to be

$$R_T = R_1 \times R_2$$

and the overall circuit failure rate is found to be

$$FR_T = FR_1 + FR_2$$

Now if $R_1 = R_2 = 0.90$, then the overall circuit reliability is only 0.81. However, if, for example, three components are connected in parallel in a reliability sense, the components are said to be redundant; that is, three components must fail before the circuit malfunctions. In this case (if the components have equal reliabilities), the circuit reliability is given by

$$R_T = 3R_1 - 3R_1{}^2 + R_1{}^3$$

when $R_1 = R_2 = R_3$ for the three components. If $R_1 = 0.90$, then R_T is equal to 0.999. An 11-percent improvement in reliability over one component is achieved at the cost of adding two redundant components.

Also suppose that the three-way redundant group of components must be placed in series with a fourth component so that at least two of the three redundant components must survive to avoid malfunctioning of the circuit, then

$$R_T = [3R_1{}^2 - 2R_1{}^3]R_4$$

If $R_1 = R_4 = 0.90$ then R_T is equal to 0.875. Such a circuit is said to use majority or voting logic. An 8-percent improvement in reliability over two components in series is achieved at the cost of adding two components.

These results arise from the fact that redundant reliability is calculated by use of the binomial distribution from mathematical statistics. Here the probability of there being x survivors out of a population of size n is given by

$$\text{Prob} = \frac{m!}{x!(m-x)!} p^x (1-p)^{m-x}$$

where p is the probability of survival of a single component. In other words, p is equal to the reliability of the component.

Now the probability of survival of a three-way redundant circuit is found by calculating the probability that one component, two components, and all three components will survive. The sum of these three probabilities is the probability of survival of the circuit. Thus

$$\frac{3 \times 2 \times 1}{1 \times 2 \times 1} p^1 (1-p)^2 = 3p - 6p^2 + 3p^3$$

$$\frac{3 \times 2 \times 1}{2 \times 1 \times 1} p^2 (1-p)^1 = 3p^2 - 3p^3$$

$$\frac{3 \times 2 \times 1}{3 \times 2 \times 1 \times 1} p^3 (1-p)^0 = p^3$$

$$\overline{3p - 3p^2 + p^3}$$

$$R_T = 3R_1 - 3R_1{}^2 + R_1{}^3$$

Now for the case of majority logic consider the probability of survival of three parallel components in series with another when at least two of the three redundant components and the component in series with the group must survive. Then, according to the binomial distribution, the probability of survival of the circuit is the sum of the probabilities that two or three of the redundant components and the fourth series component survive.

$$\text{Prob (2 survive)} = 3p^2 - 3p^3$$
$$\text{Prob (3 survive)} = \frac{p^3}{3p^2 - 2p^3}$$
$$R_T = [3R_1{}^2 - 2R_1{}^3]R_4$$

It is only fair to add that redundancy in and of itself is no panacea. One drawback to redundant reliability is the unreliability of the interconnections of the redundant components. However, this disadvantage can be overcome by using one of the new approaches to circuit design in which all the redundant components are fabricated as a single integral unit.

APPROACHES TO MICROMINIATURIZATION

The first approach to microminiaturization involved packing miniature components such as diodes, transistors, resistors and capacitors into encapsulated throw-away packages of uniform shape. The components were interconnected most frequently by resistance welding of their leads which are then tightly trimmed.

DISCRETE COMPONENTS, CONTROLLED SHAPE— Early welded modules were merely "rats' nests" of components fitted in every which way. However, manufacturers soon adopted a more orderly approach to welded-circuit design. Components were arranged with their leads parallel to each other and their bodies packed closely enough together to provide mutual support.

However, there is considerable variation in the size and shape of conventional components and the length of the longest component usually fixed the height of the circuit module. This state of affairs resulted in considerable wasted space within the circuit module. Accordingly, some manufacturers set about developing components of uniform size and shape for use in circuit modules.

Sometimes the sandwich construction technique was used and components were made in the form of pellets, disks, or cubes that could be inserted in plastic blocks specially drilled or milled to receive them. In other cases components were made in two-dimensional form on thin steatite wafers.

TIMM's, or thermionic integrated micromodules, are special circuit packages that make use of small heaterless electronic tubes which utilize the heat generated within the circuit to produce electron emission. TIMM's may become important in equipment designed to operate under high ambient temperatures and high levels of nuclear radiation since they do not use semiconductor components whose performance is degraded in such environments.

INTEGRATED SEMICONDUCTOR CIRCUITS—Some manufacturers have abandoned the use of discrete components altogether and adopted circuit-oriented approaches to microelectronics. There are two general circuit-oriented approaches: integrated semiconductor circuits and thin-film circuits.

In 1958 a research effort sponsored by the U.S. Air Force Aeronautical Systems Division sparked the development of semiconductor integrated circuits. In integrated cir-

cuits, a silicon slice is prepared as it is in the manufacture of transistors. Then appropriate impurities are diffused through masks into the silicon to produce a predetermined pattern of semiconductor p-n junctions.

A single p-n junction can be used as a semiconductor diode when it is forward-biased and as a capacitor when biased in the reverse direction. Both pnp and npn transistors have been produced in semiconductor integrated circuits and, depending upon bias conditions, these transistors can be used either as active devices to afford amplification or as high-resistance elements. Lower values of resistance are provided by the bulk of the semiconductor wafer itself. Interconnections are made by thermocompression bonding to vacuum-deposited metallic electrodes.

THIN-FILM CIRCUITS—In the thin-film approach, metallic films are vacuum-deposited upon a glass substrate through specially designed masks. Copper or gold alloys often provide conducting surfaces to make up interconnecting wiring, inductors, and the end plates of capacitors. Silicon monoxide or tantalum can be deposited to provide insulation or capacitor dielectrics while alloys of chromium or nickel are vacuum-deposited to function as the resistors

The metals are made into vapors within a vacuum bell jar either by evaporation induced by a hot filament (evaporation) or by using an electron beam or high electric field to pull the metallic atoms out of their lattice (sputtering). Silicon monoxide or even dioxide is formed as a vapor by reduction of some complex compound such as a silane.

The active components are chip semiconductors, that is, diodes and transistors that are operated without the usual hermetically sealed cases. Operation of semiconductor devices outside their cases has been made possible by using modern planar techniques to make these semiconductor components. These techniques can afford adequate surface passivation of the device so as to make the bulky hermetically sealed cases unnecessary.

Research is currently underway to produce active thin-film components. The most successful approach to date has used cadmium sulphide films to fabricate thin-film transistors. There is some evidence that p-n junctions may one day be successfully produced in thin films of cadmium sulphide, probably by the use of electron-beam techniques.

HYBRID MICROCIRCUITS—It is not possible to produce conventional inductors in semiconductor integrated circuits although inductors can easily be fabricated using thin-film techniques. In addition to solving the problem of producing inductance in microelectronic circuits, the thin-film approach has an additional advantage over semiconductor integrated circuits in that thin-film resistors can be made to exacting tolerances and in high values of resistance. Because of the advantages of thin films, there has been increasing interest of late in combining the thin-film and the integrated circuit approaches to microelectronics, since the integrated circuit approach makes it easy to incorporate large numbers of semiconductor junction devices in a microelectronic circuit without requiring a large number of thermocompression bonds for interconnection. When thin films and integrated circuits are combined, the upper surface of the completed silicon slice may be used as the substrate for the thin-film circuit by taking advantage of the insulating properties of the silicon dioxide layer that is formed on the silicon slice as the last step of the planar process. Such microelectronic circuits have been called hybrid circuits and show great promise for advancing the art of microcircuit design.

All the foregoing approaches to microelectronics are presently enjoying use throughout the industry. The component-oriented approaches are used where a moderate degree of miniaturization is desired at reasonable cost. The thin-film approaches are used in networks that are largely passive in nature, while integrated semiconductor circuits are used mostly in special-purpose digital computers for missile-borne applications.

Despite predictions that the component-oriented approaches would be adopted principally as an interim measure in the development of microelectronics during the time that thin-film and integrated circuits were slowly gaining acceptance, it now appears that development along all three lines will continue at an accelerated pace and that each type or combination of types of circuits will be developed with a view towards the application in which it will render optimum performance at minimum overall cost.

Chapter 2

CIRCUITS USING DISCRETE COMPONENTS

WELDED MODULES—Although many of the early welded modules were indeed "rats' nests" of conventional components with leads welded together and trimmed short, most welded modules today make use of a more orderly geometry.

In a typical module the components are arranged with their leads parallel and their bodies sufficiently close to afford mutual mechanical support. On the top and the bottom of the module prepunched dielectric films provide electrical insulation between component leads and help locate the components accurately before interconnection. In some cases, one or more components may be encased in a cylindrical sheath of thin dielectric film when additional electrical insulation between components is required.

Heat-producing components may be cemented to aluminum heat-transfer blocks. These blocks are brought out flush with the outer surface of the encapsulated module where they make contact with strips of aluminum foil inserted between the modules. The strips of aluminum foil lead, in turn, to some heat sink which may be the wall of the cabinet, part of a metal honeycomb structure used to retain stacks of modules, or a cold plate, that is, a flat, hollow structure through which a cooling liquid circulates.

Interconnection between components is accomplished by use of prewelded matrices or arrays of copper or nickel ribbon. Often several matrices are required to make all the required interconnections. The nickel-ribbon matrices are stacked in sandwich fashion on the top and bottom of the module with thin-dielectric-film sheets inserted between the matrices.

The welding process most often used for circuit modules is resistance spot welding. It is accomplished with light, bench-mounted welding equipment. In resistance welding, the component lead and metal ribbon are held between metal electrodes, pressure is applied and a high current passed between the electrodes and through the work. The current is turned on just long enough to enable the pressure of the electrodes to forge the metal pieces together. It is essential that the electrodes be in firm contact with the work before the current is turned on, to avoid vaporizing portions of the workpiece with explosive force. The flow of current is generally regulated by automatic timing equipment.

After welding, the entire module is encapsulated in an insulating thermosetting plastic that provides high compressive strength. The shape of the module is determined by the apparatus form factors selected by the manufacturers. Modules may be cubes, rectangular parallelepipeds, or slabs. Other shapes such as triangular "chips" or round wafers,

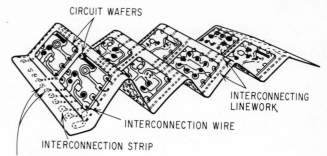

MISSILE GUIDANCE *computer has its circuit wafers mounted on a flexible interconnection strip that is folded accordion-fashion into a housing—Fig. 2*

have also been adopted for special applications.

When slab-shaped or wafer-shaped modules are used, provision is often made for a central mounting hole through the module. Then a stainless-steel rod threaded on both ends can be inserted in these holes and several modules held together in compression by nuts to form long stacks of modules or "sticks."

External electrical connections to the modules are made to pins protruding from the encapsulated body. These pins may merely be selected component leads trimmed long and constrained to protrude out of the module according to a predetermined basing pattern. Alternatively, portions of metal ribbon used to form the welded matrix for interconnecting components may protrude as tabs from the side of the module. Or, a dielectric mounting base with pin terminals may be incorporated as part of the circuit module.

Modules or even stacks of modules are almost always assembled to a "mother board." The mother board holds an array of female connectors designed to receive the terminal pins of the circuit modules or stacks. These female connectors are, in turn, often interconnected by prewelded matrices of nickel ribbon located beneath them and sandwiched between dielectric-film sheets that provide electrical insulation.

Interconnection between mother boards may be accomplished by fairing out the conductors of a multiconductor cable and making welded connections to the row and column ribbons of the prewelded interconnection matrix. Flat multiconductor cable may be used. Alternatively, the row and column ribbons of the matrix may be brought out to the wire-wrap terminals of a female connector and interconnection between mother boards effected by cables terminating in the multiconductor plugs.

A similar approach to the welded modules described dispenses with the prepunched dielectric-film masks and the welded nickel-ribbon matrices. Instead it uses conventional phenolic circuit boards on the top and bottom with the interconnecting wiring photoetched on them. The etched circuits incorporate plated-through holes in the boards to receive the component leads from the assembly of the parallel components sandwiched between the circuit boards.

The holes in the board serve both to locate the components accurately and to provide mechanical rigidity for the circuit assembly. The components are then made mechanically and electrically secure by a dip or flow soldering process.

Generally in these circuit-board sandwiches, conventional

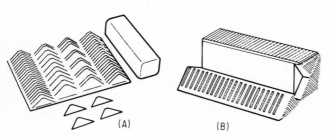

ASSEMBLIES OF *plug-in chips (A) may be folded to enclose a heat exchanger (B). Later, several of the resulting modules may be interconnected to form the electronics portion of a digital differential analyzer—Fig. 1*

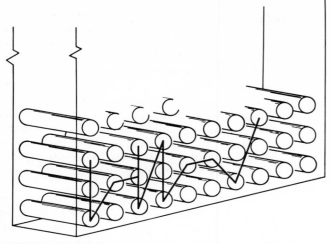

POPULAR SHAPES *for uniform circuit components are pellet or cordwood-type cylinders*—Fig. 3

printed-circuit connectors are attached to one of the circuit boards to facilitate mounting the circuit modules on the mother board.

In order to prevent damage to certain critical components by expansion and contraction of the circuit module due to heat, these critical components may be given a thin rubber coating. As usual, the circuit module is encapsulated in epoxy filled with some insulating material such as asbestos, paper, cotton, or wool fibers. Glass fibers are often used because of their low water absorption and excellent physical characteristics.

Many epoxy resins are based on the reaction products of an aromatic diphenol with epichlorohydrin. In the uncured state at room temperature the epoxy resin is a viscous amber-colored fluid. Fluidity increases at elevated temperatures and, for ease of mixing, the resin may be warmed to 55 deg C before it is cured.

When the curing agent is added, the resin turns brown and increases progressively in viscosity. The curing reaction is exothermic; that is, it gives off heat. Even so, many curing cycles are carried out in ovens at temperatures of from 150 to 300 deg F. These curing cycles last about two hours.

UNIFORM COMPONENTS—As discussed earlier, there is a wide variation in the dimensions and form factors of electronic components. Accordingly, some manufacturers have suggested that these components be standardized in form and size. For example, N. V. Philips of Holland has demonstrated how the design of a radio set may be simplified when all the components are fabricated as uniform rectangular parallelepipeds for mounting on an etched circuit board. Although not strictly a microminiaturization technique, this approach achieves some of the same results in terms of reduced cost and size of equipment and in enhanced ease of maintenance.

In other modular circuit approaches to microminiaturization, the components are fabricated as tiny cylindrical pellets or as wafers. The components are assembled by dropping the pellets into recesses drilled in a printed-circuit board. The interconnections are already defined on the bottom of the board by a conventional photoetched circuit.

The resulting flat circuit boards may be assembled in extremely compact style such as folded accordion fashion to make up a complete equipment subassembly.

MICROMODULES—One of the most popular microcircuit approaches uses two-dimensional circuit components that are mounted on wafer-like insulating substrates. The wafers are assembled into stacks and held securely by riser wires that provide interconnecting wiring and also mechanical support. The ends of the riser wires become the terminal pins of the circuit module.

This approach may be used for many years to come inasmuch as thin-film and integrated semiconductor circuits may be mounted on micromodule wafers and complete equipment subassemblies fabricated using this method.

The micromodule approach grew out of Project Tinkertoy. This effort was carried out in the early 1950s to permit the automatic manufacture of sonobuoys, an item of equipment required by the Navy in large quantities.

As originally devised, the wafer approach used a $\frac{7}{8}$-inch-square, $\frac{1}{16}$-inch-thick steatite wafer as the basic substrate. The wafers used today are made of glass or ceramic material. They are 0.310 inch square and 0.010 inch thick.

The original wafers used the adhesive-tape resistors designed by the National Bureau of Standards in 1948. Today's micromodules make use of deposited alloy and metal-film resistors. The early circuits were designed to accept 7- and 9-pin miniature electron tubes in ceramic sockets. But today, transistors and semiconductor diodes, sometimes in multiple-component assemblies, are used as the active elements of micromodules.

Other microelements that have been successfully built on wafer substrates include general-purpose, precision, and tantalum-electrolytic capacitors, inductors (including transformers and chokes using both powdered-iron and ferrite cores), and piezoelectric crystals.

The micromodules have twelve riser wires, three to a side. The riser wires are retained in notches cut in the wafer substrate. The conductors to which the riser wires are soldered are vacuum-deposited in predetermined patterns on the ceramic substrates. However, in some designs, there are no notches cut for riser wires. Instead, interconnections are made by flat metal ribbons.

A departure from the micromodule approach is the thermionic integrated micromodule (TIMM) that uses small heaterless electron tubes as the active elements instead of transistors or semiconductor diodes. The heat generated

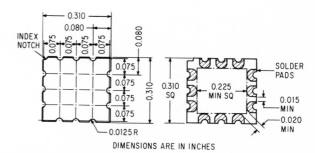

DIMENSIONS ARE IN INCHES

LAYOUT OF A *typical microelement showing the placement of solder pads. This type of wafer is the basic building block of micromodules*—Fig. 4

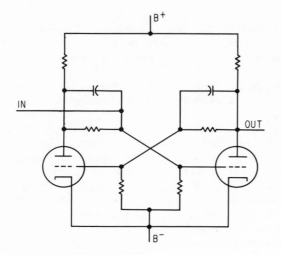

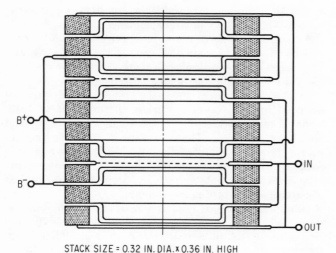

STACK SIZE = 0.32 IN. DIA. x 0.36 IN. HIGH
SPACE OCCUPIED = 0.04 IN.³

CROSS-SECTIONAL VIEW *of stacked thermionic integrated micromodule (TIMM) circuit showing electrical connections and the corresponding circuit schematic of a bistable multivibrator—Fig. 5*

by the circuit itself is utilized to produce electron emission from the cathodes of the electron tubes. Titanium electrodes provide continuous gettering action for the tubes.

The thermionic micromodules are cylindrical in shape and measure 0.32 inch in diameter. They are assembled by stacking appropriate ceramic rings one on top of the other. Interconnection between components (or ceramic rings) is achieved by metal ribbons or riser wires connected to tabs protruding from the ceramic rings.

The circuits are stable and reliable, rugged in construction, and tolerant of nuclear radiation. Devices have operated in atomic reactors for 1,600 hours without deterioration. Transconductances up to 2,000 micromhos per ampere have been achieved at low plate voltages.

PACKAGED CIRCUITS—The basic idea that an entire electronic circuit could itself be a component or basic part goes back at least to the pre-World War II radio business when manufacturers began to package all the interstage elements of i-f amplifiers within an r-f transformer housing.

During the war packaged units such as delay lines and pulse-forming networks for radar sets were manufactured in large numbers. Later, all sorts of passive circuits such as filters of all kinds, tuning elements and coupling circuits were made up from assemblies of basic parts and encapsulated in plastic.

With the advent of the transistor and other semiconductor devices, it became feasible to package active components as well as passive components in circuits and handle entire circuits as single components of larger circuits. Electronic choppers for converting direct current into alternating current by means of transitorized multivibrator circuits could now be packaged so as to be direct physical replacements for electromechanical choppers designed to accomplish the identical function.

Today, these packaged circuits used in conventional circuit design have been escalated downward in size and weight by at least an order of magnitude. It is not uncommon, for example, to package an active semiconductor circuit within a size TO-5 hermetically sealed case such as that used to house single conventional transistors. Actually the inside of a transistor case is mostly empty space. So if the case is fitted with, for example, nine instead of three leads, it becomes possible to incorporate perhaps two transistors and possibly a semiconductor diode or two within the single container.

Several of these complex semiconductor components are being marketed and others are in the developmental stage. Two matched *npn* silicon transistors for use in electronic choppers are packaged with their collectors tied together. Such packages are available in 5-pin TO-5 or TO-18 cases. Chopper pairs matched for offset voltage have all of their six terminals brought out to external pins. Dual chopper sets utilizing four *npn* silicon transistors are available. The collectors of each transistor pair of the quad are connected together and the assembly is packaged in a 10-pin TO-5 case.

A very popular packaged semiconductor circuit is the Darlington amplifier. The Darlington amplifier consists of two *npn* silicon transistors with their collectors tied together. The emitter of the second transistor is tied to the base of the first and the whole assembly is housed in a 3-lead TO-18 case. The external pins contact the common collector, the emitter of the first transistor, and the base of the second. One variation of this circuit is packaged in a 4-lead TO-5 or TO-18 case and makes the emitters of both transistors available at the external terminals of the case. Another variation makes the two bases available for external connection although the emitter of only the first transistor and the common collector connection are similarly available.

Another packaged circuit containing two transistors ties together the collectors and the bases of the units and makes each emitter available for external connections. Several matched-pair assemblies are marketed which have all six electrode terminals available externally. The transistors are specially selected and matched. Some are recommended for use as Darlington amplifiers; others are recommended for use as differential amplifiers. All connections are, of course, made externally to the case.

In another packaged circuit, a device called the nonlinear resistance element (NRE) is realized by packaging a complete transistor amplifier with a feedback circuit incorporated as part of it. The NRE provides the nonlinear resistance characteristics of, for example, a four-layer *pnpn* diode

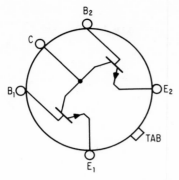
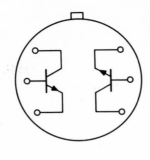
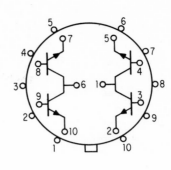

PACKAGED TRANSISTORS *for chopper applications (changing direct to alternating current) may have collectors tied together or be simply a matched pair. A dual chopper set has collectors of each pair tied together—Fig. 6*

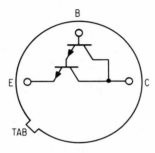
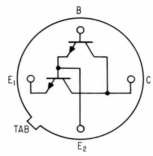
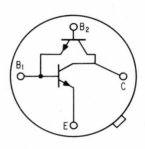

THREE PACKAGED VERSIONS *of the popular Darlington amplifier: basic circuit, variation with two external emitter connections, and with two base connections—Fig. 7*

but is much more versatile in its circuit application.

In still another application, a Zener or avalanche breakdown diode is connected in the emitter circuit of an *npn* silicon transistor. This arrangement provides a convenient voltage-regulating module.

It also has been possible to realize the characteristics of the so-called constant-current diode, a diode that regulates in the current mode rather than in the voltage mode, by packaging two amplifier transistors in a single case.

An interesting packaged circuit is the optoelectronic switch. This consists of a light-emitting gallium arsenide diode and a transistor. The light-emitting diode constitutes the input circuit of the switch. Forward current flowing in the diode causes it to emit light in the deep-red and infrared regions. This light, falling on the exposed base region of the transistor, makes available a great number of charge carriers. The transistor, which has no base connection, now conducts heavily. The transistor is, of course, part of the output circuit of the switch. These

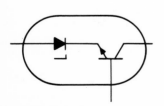
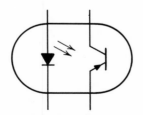

PACKAGE VOLTAGE *regulating element consists of an avalanche transistor and a transistor. Optoelectronic switch consists of a light-emitting diode and a transistor—Fig. 8*

optoelectronic devices provide absolute isolation between the input or control and the output or power circuits.

Actually, some of the semiconductor integrated circuits known as micrologic circuits may be classified as packaged semiconductor components.

These micrologic circuits are packaged in multilead TO-5 cases and consist of a number of chip semiconductor components (transistors or diodes) arranged in a circle around a centrally located microcircuit on which the passive elements of the logic circuits—resistors, capacitors, and interconnecting wires—are realized by thin-film vacuum deposition on a ceramic substrate or by a combination of deposition and diffusion of appropriate metals and solid-state impurities on and into a silicon wafer.

SUMMARY—The microelectronic circuits discussed thus far have the following in common: examine any of them closely enough and you can identify the discrete elements that provide values of inductance, capacitance, and resistance or the functions of amplification and rectification in the circuit.

This is true whether the circuit is fabricated from conventional components, from components specially manufactured with uniform form factors or whether the circuit consists of several uncased or "chip" semiconductors packaged within a single hermetically sealed case. In the remaining approaches to microelectronics the circuit components lose their identity. This is the distinguishing feature of true thin-film and integrated semiconductor circuits.

Chapter 3

INTEGRATED SEMICONDUCTOR CIRCUITS

As early as 1953 the U.S. Air Force's Aeronautical Systems Division at Wright–Patterson Air Force Base, Dayton, Ohio, foresaw that even the size and weight advantages of transistors and semiconductor diodes would not be adequate to meet the requirements for packing components into weapons systems then in the proposal stage. They visualized electronic circuits fabricated on and within a single tiny block of silicon.

The ASD contracted with several universities and with two manufacturers: Westinghouse Electric in Youngwood, Pa., and Texas Instruments Incorporated in Dallas. By 1958, both companies had produced prototype integrated semiconductor circuits.

MANUFACTURING—The element silicon is admirably suited for use in integrated circuits. It has a higher melting point than germanium and has lower electron and hole mobilities (1,500 and 500 square centimeters per volt second, respectively). It has a higher band gap than germanium (1.1 electron volts as compared to 0.7 electron volt). Thus silicon is less sensitive to thermal effects. And this is important in microcircuits where many components must be jammed together in a very restricted space.

Primarily, however, silicon has a stable oxide (silicon dioxide) which forms on the surface of a silicon slice when it is heated in an oxidizing atmosphere. The formation of this oxide literally encapsulates an integrated circuit in glass. Furthermore, it can be utilized to effectively and selectively mask portions of the silicon slice during intermediate processing operations.

Most high-purity silicon used today by the semiconductor industry is produced by an integrated process that entails the chemical reduction of trichlorosilane. This compound is reduced by the action of hydrogen in a heated environment. The reduction products are silicon and hydrochloric acid.

The purity of semiconductor silicon is measured by its resistivity—the higher the resistivity the purer the metal. Pure polycrystalline silicon is available in rod form with a resistivity of 1,000 ohm-cm. Monocrystalline silicon prepared by the vacuum floating zone method is available with resistivities greater than 1,000 ohm-cm but the material used in industry has much lower resistivity.

Monocrystalline silicon grown by pulling a seed crystal out of a melt of silicon in a silicon dioxide (or silica) crucible (Czochralski technique) usually has a resistivity of about 20 ohm-cm. After background doping with boron (for p-type material) or phosphorus (for n-type material), resistivity is about 2 ohm-cm for silicon to be used in manufacturing transistors.

In the manufacture of integrated circuits, it is customary to begin with a substrate of p-type silicon having a resistivity of some 10 ohm-cm. Upon this substrate is grown an epitaxial layer in and on which the microcircuit is formed. The epitaxial layer is n-type silicon whose resistivity is chosen to be somewhere between 0.1 and 0.5 ohm-cm.

In epitaxial deposition, a thin film of semiconductor material is grown upon a smooth substrate by depositing atoms that build integrally upon the crystal lattice structure of the substrate. One difficulty in making epitaxial material lies in growing a uniform layer on the substrate. To do this successfully, the substrate must be carefully sliced, lapped, and polished.

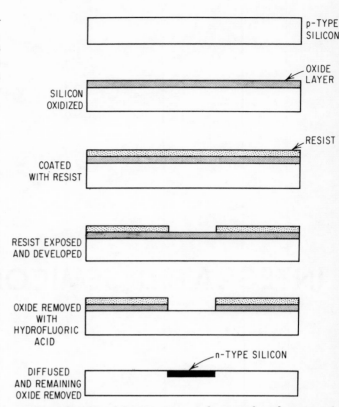

THIS FIVE-STEP *diffusion process is basic in the fabrication of monolithic semiconductor circuits—Fig. 9*

The atoms of silicon to be deposited on the substrate are introduced in a carrier gas, usually silicon tetrachloride. The substrate is first heated in a hydrogen atmosphere to 1300 deg C for ten minutes. Then the temperature is reduced to 1185 deg C and the silicon tetrachloride is introduced. The epitaxial film is permitted to grow long enough to get the desired thickness of film. The silicon tetrachloride is doped with phosphorus to produce an n-type epitaxial region. The introduction of phosphorus pentoxide helps produce a masking film of silicon dioxide over the n-type epitaxial film. This silica coating protects the surface of the slice from impurities.

The next step is called isolation diffusion. In this step the n-type epitaxial region is isolated into individual islands by diffusing a pattern of barriers consisting of heavy concentrations of p-type impurity through the epitaxial layer until they connect up with the p-type substrate.

The slice is first coated with photoresist. This is a compound that becomes insoluble in a developing solution after it has been exposed to light. A pattern is prepared in which the islands are defined as black rectangles on a white sheet of pasteboard. A photographic negative is made of the pattern board and reduced photographically 50 to 100 times to achieve a mask having the desired dimensions. This photographic negative mask is registered over the slice and the assembly is exposed to ultraviolet light.

The photoresist is then developed and washed. By this process the desired island areas are protected by insoluble photoresist while the remaining areas are simply bare silica. The slice is now selectively etched by hydrofluoric acid which eats through the unprotected silica but does not

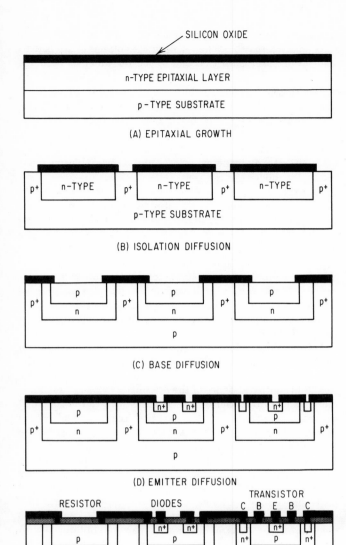

← SILICON OXIDE

n-TYPE EPITAXIAL LAYER

p-TYPE SUBSTRATE

(A) EPITAXIAL GROWTH

(B) ISOLATION DIFFUSION

(C) BASE DIFFUSION

(D) EMITTER DIFFUSION

(E) ALUMINUM METALIZATION

SEQUENCE OF *photoresist and diffusion processes illustrates the manufacture of a typical monolithic circuit making use of isolation diffusion—Fig. 10*

bodies of resistors, the p regions of semiconductor diodes or the bases of npn transistors.

The unprotected borosilicate glass film is selectively etched away with hydrofluoric acid. A shallow diffusion of boric acid is performed to achieve these desired p-type regions. This shallow diffusion may be achieved by using a shorter time than the previous p^+ isolation diffusion, less elevated temperatures or both.

The concentration of boric acid in the atmosphere of the diffusion furnace is less concentrated than before. As a by-product of this p-type diffusion, another protective layer of borosilicate glass forms all over the surface of the slice.

The final diffusion is called the emitter diffusion. It forms the emitter regions of npn transistors and the n regions of semiconductor diodes. A photographic negative mask is prepared defining these regions, the slice is again coated with photoresist and the mask is registered on the slice. After exposure to light and subsequent washing only the desired n-type regions remain unprotected. The slice is once again selectively etched and a shallow n^+ diffusion is performed in a furnace whose atmosphere has a heavy concentration of phosphorus pentoxide. A protective layer of silicon dioxide is formed as a by-product of the diffusion process.

In a typical unit, the background impurity concentration of the n-type island might result in a resistivity of 0.1 ohm-cm. The diffusion cycle would be adjusted to produce a sheet resistance of 200 ohms per square in the p-type base region at a junction depth of 2.7 microns. Since the n-type emitter diffusion is doped much more, it produces a sheet resistance of 2.2 ohms per square at a junction depth of 2 microns. This results in a net physical base width equal to only 0.7 micron.

The final step in producing a microcircuit is aluminum metallization. The contact areas of the n, p, and n^+ regions are defined on a photographic negative mask and the protective film of silica is selectively etched away to reveal the underlying silicon surface. The silicon slice is then registered with a metal mask that provides for expanded contact regions around the regions of exposed silicon and the assembly is subjected to vacuum deposition of aluminum.

The wafer can now be scribed and broken into individual microcircuit chips. These can, in turn, be assembled on headers in multilead TO-5 transistor cans or in microcircuit flatpacks. The connections to the leads of the package are made by 1-mil gold wires thermocompressively bonded to the external leads of the package and to the appropriate metallized contact regions of the microcircuit chip.

CIRCUIT DESIGN—Circuit elements that can be realized within and upon a monolithic slice of silicon include resistors, capacitors, resistance-capacitance networks, semiconductor diodes, bipolar or conventional transistors, and unipolar or field-effect transistors.

There are two means for realizing resistors in monolithic circuits: as bulk resistors or as diffused resistors.

The resistance of a semiconductor bulk resistor is obtained from the familar relationship

$$R = \rho\ell/A$$

where the resistance R is in ohms, the resistivity ρ is in ohm-centimeters, the length ℓ is in centimeters, and the area A is in square centimeters. Considering the small size

attack the photoresist nor the silicon underlying the unprotected layer of silica which is removed.

Now the diffusion of p-type material around the islands is accomplished in an atmosphere of heavily concentrated boric acid. The diffusion takes place at elevated temperatures and requires several hours to produce the p^+ isolating regions that surround the n-type islands and connect up with the p-type substrate. As a by-product of the boron diffusion, a protective layer of borosilicate glass is formed over the slice to exclude unwanted impurities.

In the next step, base regions are defined in the n-type islands. Again a photographic negative mask is prepared and registered upon the slice that has once again been coated with photoresist. After the assembly is exposed to light and washed, the unprotected regions are those into which it is desired to diffuse p-type impurities in order to form the

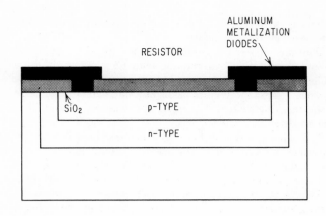

RESISTOR

ALUMINUM
METALIZATION
DIODES

SiO₂ p-TYPE

n-TYPE

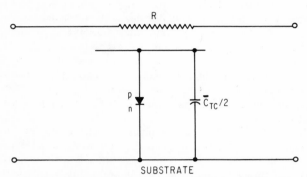

DIFFUSED RESISTOR *and its equivalent circuit—Fig. 11*

It has distributed diode properties as well as a linear resistance characteristic. When a positive voltage is applied to one end of the resistor that end of the p-n junction becomes forward-biased allowing just enough current to flow to supply the reverse leakage current to the back-biased isolation diode. The rest of the p-n junction remains reverse-biased since all the n-type material is essentially at the same potential.

There are two means for realizing capacitance in monolithic circuits: as oxide capacitors and as back-biased semiconductor diodes.

An oxide capacitor may be formed by depositing a film of silicon dioxide over the n^+ diffused "emitter" region and then depositing a film of aluminum over the silicon dioxide. One plate of the capacitor is the aluminum top film; the other plate is the low-resistance (heavily doped) n^+ "emitter" region. The silica film is, of course, the dielectric. These oxide capacitors are very stable and their values are independent of the value of voltage impressed across the parallel plates. As a rule of thumb: the capacitance per unit area of an oxide capacitor having an oxide film 500 angstroms thick is 0.35 picofarad per square mil.

Actually the oxide capacitor is a resistance-capacitance network which consists basically of the capacitance of the aluminum, silica, and silicon sandwich in series with the small but finite resistance of the n^+ emitter region. Furthermore, the oxide capacitor has in series with it the so-called parasitic capacitance of the isolation region, which arises because there is a back-biased p-n junction between the n-type "collector" region and the p-type substrate.

Oxide capacitors are used where linearity is important or where reverse bias cannot always be maintained. They have temperature coefficients of capacitance well below 100 parts per million per deg C, low voltage coefficients and excellent stability with time. Capacitances of 50,000 picofarads per square centimeter can be obtained with 50-volt breakdown ratings. However, the requirement for extreme miniaturization in monolithic circuits means that the maximum realizable values of oxide capacitors must range from only 500 to 1,000 picofarads.

and the relatively low resistivity of monolithic circuits, it becomes apparent that only very small values of resistance can be obtained by taking advantage of the bulk resistance properties of the semiconductor material.

A more fruitful approach is to realize the desired values of resistance by diffusion. Here the resistive element is actually the resistance of the p-type base region which has been diffused into the isolated n-type "collector" region or island. The resistor also includes the resistance of the ohmic contacts of the aluminum film deposited on the p-type diffused region.

The resistance of a diffused resistor is obtained from the relationship

$$R = \sigma[\ell + K]/w$$

where R is the resistance in ohms, σ is the sheet resistance of the semiconductor junction in ohms per square, ℓ is the length of the diffusion region in mils, w is the width of the region in mils, and K is a correction factor based upon the geometry and material of the metallized contacts.

There is no absolute limit on the resistance values which can be produced by diffusion techniques. However, size restrictions and typical material resistivities make it desirable to limit maximum values of bulk resistors to about 40,000 ohms.

Resistors produced by either process have extremely favorable noise properties because they are formed from single-crystal material and conduction does not take place between individual particles of resistive material.

Typically, a diffused resistor consists of a long, narrow region of p-type base diffusion on an n-type collector region.

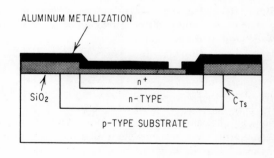

ALUMINUM METALIZATION

SiO₂ n⁺

n-TYPE C_{Ts}

p-TYPE SUBSTRATE

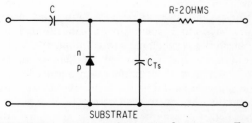

OXIDE-TYPE *capacitor and its equivalent circuit—Fig. 12*

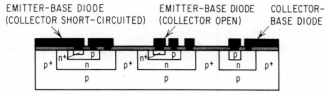

CROSS-SECTIONAL *representations of the three basic cross sections of a semiconductor diode—Fig. 13*

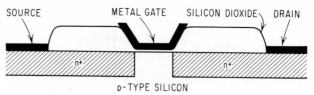

INSULATED-GATE *field-effect transistor made by diffusion processes—Fig. 15*

A reverse-biased *p-n* junction may be used as a capacitor. Here the depletion region at the junction serves as the dielectric. For a given material, the capacitance is a function of the width of the depletion region and the area of the junction. In silicon, capacitance values up to 200,000 picofarads per square centimeter are possible and breakdown voltages of several hundred volts can be obtained with a low temperature coefficient.

The value of a semiconductor junction capacitor is calculated from the expression

$$C = cA/V^{1/n}$$

where *c* is the junction capacitance per square mil at one volt of reverse bias, *A* is the junction area in square mils, *V* is the back-bias voltage and *n* is equal to two for step junctions and three for graded junctions.

The conventional emitter-base diffusion yields a capacitance of approximately 0.7 picofarad per square mil at 1.0 volt reverse bias. Not only the emitter-base diode but also the collector-base junction can be used as a capacitor by itself or in parallel with the base-emitter junction. However, because of the high series resistance and high relative shunt isolation capacitance at the collector, the collector-base junction capacitor is usually found to be impractical.

Since the width of the depletion region changes with applied voltage a nonlinear response results. This effect has proved advantageous in many applications but these capacitors are not suitable for high-level linear circuits. Furthermore, the capacitors are polarized and must be connected so that the junction is not forward-biased.

Distributed-constant resistance-capacitance networks are readily formed in monolithic silicon circuits. In fact, it is impossible to make a resistor without some capacitance and likewise a capacitor also incorporates a certain amount of resistance.

These RC networks may be used to advantage in circuits that utilize their properties to realize low-pass filters or phase-shift networks. A distributed RC network used as a low-pass filter will have much sharper cutoff characteristics

than a three-stage lumped-constant network and will provide more attenuation for a given RC product. Distributed phase-shift networks will have more phase shift for a given attenuation than a lumped-constant equivalent.

Diodes and transistors can be made by either diffusion or alloying although the former process is most widely used today. The diffusion process permits fabricating the highest power and highest frequency devices. Both *npn* and *pnp* transistors have been produced. Unipolar or field-effect transistors, tunnel diodes, *pnpn* devices, solar cells, and thermoelectric and photoelectric elements are all possible.

There are three basic types of diodes available: a collector-base diode, an emitter-base diode, or a transistor connected as a diode by shorting the collector to the base with a metallized connector.

Collector-base diodes consist of *p*-type base diffusion into an *n*-type collector. They have high collector-base voltage breakdown ratings in the collector (about 12 volts) and lend themselves to the common cathode configuration within a single isolation area. Common anode arrays can also be made using collector-base diffusion for a common anode pair. Each diode requires a separate isolation area and anodes must be connected by metallizing.

As long as the reverse voltage requirement does not exceed the lower base-emitter voltage-breakdown characteristic, diodes may be formed by emitter-base diffusion. Common anode arrays may easily be made using this approach to realize a multiemitter transistor in a single-isolation region. The collector may either remain floating or be connected to the base. Such diodes exhibit good matching characteristics.

The highest conduction is provided by a diode-connected transistor in which the collector and base comprise the anode and the emitter is the cathode. Reverse-recovery characteristics of this diode are good due to transistor action which eliminates collector shortage. This diode connection results in the most favorable diode of the three basic types where its lower breakdown voltage can be tolerated.

In integrated circuits transistors must be electrically isolated from each other and their collector contacts must be brought out from the top surface for interconnection. Since collector current flows laterally, these devices have a higher saturation collector resistance than do discrete resistors. Furthermore, the isolation junction adds capacitance to ground which can become a limiting factor in the performance of the device.

If the collector junction is close enough to the isolation junction *pnp* transistor action can occur between base, collector, and isolation. This effect can be beneficial inasmuch as it helps to control collector charge storage in

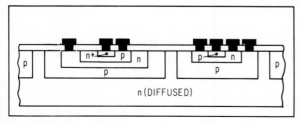

COMBINED *npn and pnp transistor structures—Fig. 14*

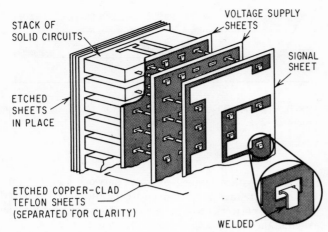

STACK OF SOLID CIRCUITS

VOLTAGE SUPPLY SHEETS

SIGNAL SHEET

ETCHED SHEETS IN PLACE

ETCHED COPPER-CLAD TEFLON SHEETS (SEPARATED FOR CLARITY)

WELDED

ONE METHOD *for interconnecting monolithic semiconductor circuits—Fig. 16*

saturation by collecting charge carriers injected into the base region. But it can be detrimental inasmuch as the inputs to certain transistor logic gates will be shunted to ground by the *pnp* action of the transistor.

Diffused devices may incorporate both *pnp* and *npn* transistors. A *p*-type substrate is used and isolation regions are formed by *n* diffusions. The transistors are then fabricated in the isolated *p* regions.

Only inductors present a problem in monolithic circuits. Inasmuch as inductance is a measure of flux-linkages per unit current and a finite volume is required to link lines of flux, extreme miniaturization is incompatible with achieving large values of inductance.

Nevertheless, under certain conditions, some semiconductor diodes can provide the circuit equivalent of a high-Q large inductance in series with a large resistance. Furthermore, it is possible to realize an inductive reactance between terminals by the use of active circuit techniques.

The need for inductance in monolithic circuits can often be side stepped, for example, by using semiconductor delay lines to replace inductors in a time-delay circuit or by using RC networks to replace LC tuned circuits. Field-effect devices may be used to replace chokes and impedance matching may be achieved by circuit design rather than by using coupling transformers.

Nevertheless, when the designer requires large values of inductance or where the selectivity of an LC circuit is essential for proper equipment performance, he must go to a hybrid unit—perhaps one that uses a thin-film inductor deposited upon an insulating layer of silicon dioxide grown on the silicon substrate.

INTERCONNECTION—Microcircuits are commonly packaged in either modified JEDEC TO-5 transistor cans or in flat packs. The TO-5 can is cylindrical. Its base measures 0.355 to 0.370 inch in diameter by 0.020 to 0.030 inch high. An insulator protrudes 0.015 to 0.045 inch below the base. The can itself is 0.170 to 0.180 inch high and 0.315 to 0.325 inch in diameter. The can may have 8, 9, 10, or 12 leads equally spaced on a circle around a central header. The leads are 0.016 to 0.019 inch in diameter and at least 0.75 inch long.

A typical flat pack is ¼ inch square and ⅟₁₆ inch wide. It may have 10, 12, or 14 leads. The leads are flat ribbons 0.015 to 0.018 inch wide, 0.004 to 0.006 inch thick, and 0.235 to 0.260 inch long. They are weldable and solderable and extend axially from two opposing sides of the square package.

The body of the package is a square of Corning 7052 hard glass with a shallow cavity formed in one face to accommodate the silicon circuit chip. The gold-plated Kovar leads are fused in position through the sidewalls when the body is formed. The ends of the leads inside the cavity are exposed for connection to the circuit chip. A flat Kovar pad, which is an extension of one of the leads, provides both a secure mouting for the silicon chip and a convenient connection to the substrate. When the flat Kovar lid is fused in place, a wide uniform shoulder of glass around the periphery of the package provides a reliable hermetic seal.

The silicon circuit chip is fused to the Kovar mounting pad with a gold preform. Connections between the circuit chip and the external leads are made by thermocompression ball bonding and microwelding. In thermocompression bonding gold wires are positioned over metallized contacts and a fine chisel is used to press each wire into the contact. Heat is simultaneously applied to raise the temperature to about 300 deg C thus forming the bond. Ball bonding results in an even more reliable thermocompression bond.

To complete the package, the Kovar lid is fused to the glass shoulder by a devitrifying glaze. This is accomplished in a nitrogen atmosphere within a dry box where water vapor content is below 10 parts per million. Fusing is accomplished by momentary application of heat and pressure to the Kovar lid to form a high temperature seal although the internal temperature of the package remains safely lower.

Microcircuit flat packs are furnished with grooved slides of molded plastic to serve as carriers, and to protect the package and its leads during storage, shipping, and testing. Contactor assemblies are used that accept these plastic carriers. The contactor assembly has a conventional printed circuit connector to hook the microcircuit up to test equipment for electrical inspection.

One way to interconnect microcircuits is to stack them on a mother board. Sheets of 2-mil-thick copper-clad Teflon are used to provide interconnection between circuits. However, because of the close spacing between leads, all the wiring cannot be provided in a single plane, therefore multiple sheets are used.

Each required supply voltage is connected to a separate sheet. Each sheet has, in turn, a grid pattern with holes providing electrical and mechanical clearance for some of the leads. Thus a lead may either pass straight through a sheet and be insulated from it or be bent over and welded to make an electrical connection.

When all the supply-voltage sheets have been sandwiched together with the proper connections made, a top sheet is added to the assembly. The signal paths are etched on this top sheet. If crossovers of signal paths are required, a second sheet with signal paths etched on it can be used.

Individual copper-clad sheets may be used for r-f shielding or to form a ground plane. And in very high-frequency applications, the copper-clad Teflon sheets could become two-dimensional strip transmission lines.

APPLICATION—Monolithic integrated circuits have received a much more favorable reception than even their staunchest supporters anticipated when they were first introduced. They have received their principal impetus from military electronics, especially the Minuteman intercontinental ballistic missile program. But they are now finding use in industrial, commercial, and even consumer equipment. One manufacturer has announced that 18 types of integrated circuits designed for the Minuteman program are now commercially available on an off-the-shelf basis. Together these circuits comprise between 75 and 95 percent of the circuitry typically needed to build a military general-purpose computer.

The Minuteman guidance and control system uses integrated circuits in its computer, inertial measuring unit, and flight control. Use of integrated circuits has reportedly more than doubled the system's operational capability. To accomplish this using conventional components would have required tripling the number of components used. Instead, the new Minuteman computer is $33\frac{1}{2}$ pounds lighter in weight, occupies 40 percent less space, uses only half as many parts and operates on about half as much power as an earlier version which used discrete components.

Chapter 4

PASSIVE THIN-FILM CIRCUITS

In thin-film circuits there is usually a one-to-one correspondence between the thin-film components and their lumped-constant equivalents even though the thin-film areas do not resemble conventional components. But a given area is uniquely a resistor, a capacitor, or an inductor.

Both conductive, resistive, and dielectric films are used in thin-film circuits. They may be laid down by reactive deposition (such as by hydrogen reduction of trichlorosilane to deposit a film of silicon), by vacuum evaporation, sputtering, electron-beam technology, photolithographic techniques, chemical etching, electron beam or laser machining, and many combinations of these techniques.

Multilayer films are used in the fabrication of resistive, capacitive, and inductive networks. Unencapsulated transistors and diodes are attached to the wafers by thermocompression bonds.

MATERIALS—Glass wafers are most frequently used as substrates of thin-film circuits. But circuits have also been laid down on silicon wafers that have been coated with a film of silicon dioxide. Some ceramic materials have also been used as thin-film substrates.

Conducting areas such as interconnections, capacitor plates, ground planes, and shields are made by deposition of aluminum, copper, gold, or gold-copper alloys. Aluminum has a tough, transparent oxide that grows naturally on its surface or can be produced by anodizing.

Several materials are used to form resistors. Of these, chromium has the highest sheet resistance, from 500 to 30,000 ohms per square. Other resistive materials are nickel-chromium (Nichrome) at 200 ohms per square; tantalum, 100 ohms per square; tantalum nitride, 200 ohms per square; titanium, 500 to 2,000 ohms per square; tin oxide, 500 ohms per square; cermets at up to 20,000 ohms per square; and carbon-resin ink at 10,000 ohms per square.

Materials for capacitor dielectrics include tantalum oxide, titanium dioxide, silicon monoxide, and silicon dioxide. Silicon monoxide and silicon dioxide are used also as insulators.

PROCESSES—Thin films are usually evaporated on the substrate; this is done within a vacuum produced inside a large bell jar. The jar is evacuated by use of an oil diffusion pump and a backing pump. Vacuums at present range to about 10^{-6} mm of mercury and will probably range down to 10^{-10} mm of mercury.

To obtain a satisfactory deposit, the substrate must be absolutely clean. Coarse high-power electron beams can be used for thorough surface preparation such as the fusion of the film-receiving surface to achieve the ultimate in molecular cleanliness and surface activation as well as ultrasmooth fused surfaces. But whether or not such an elaborate procedure is to be used, the surface must be washed clean of any trace of grease and dried in alcohol to remove moisture.

Except when dealing with refractory metals, evaporation is the preferred method for depositing thin films. Aluminum, for example, can be evaporated after it has first been coated upon a spiral of thin tungsten wire. In a typical application, little U's of 1-mm-diameter aluminum wire can be squeezed onto a spiral of clean 0.5-mm-diameter tungsten wire. The filament is then placed in the bell jar, the jar is evacuated and the filament heated to about 800

to 1000 deg C by alternating current so that the aluminum forms beads on the tungsten wire.

Next the glass substrate that has been washed and dried is inserted into the jar and the jar is evacuated to a low vacuum by the action of backing pumps. Before turning on the oil diffusion pumps to obtain high vacuum, a potential of 15 kilovolts is applied between the insulated electrode and the metal base-plate to bombard the surface of the glass and remove any thin water or grease films remaining.

After cleaning, the jar is quickly pumped down to less than 10^{-4} mm of mercury by diffusion pumps and the tungsten spiral is heated repeatedly to 1400 deg C for thin-film deposition.

An alternative process for evaporation involves heating the metal to be evaporated in a graphite crucible surrounded by a tungsten spiral. The spiral is heated to 2300 deg C to emit electrons that then bombard the crucible. The crucible is maintained 1,000 volts positive with respect to the spiral. This high-velocity electron bombardment heats the crucible and the metal inside to evaporation temperature.

Silica may also be evaporated in vacuum to make thin dielectric films. A silicon rod 1 mm in diameter inside a closely fitting spiral of 0.5-mm-diameter tungsten or tantalum wire will evaporate slowly. Alternatively, fused silica may be evaporated in a small tantalum crucible heated by electron bombardment from a heated tungsten spiral.

Certain other metals such as copper and silver are best deposited as thin films by the technique of cathodic sputtering. Here the bell jar is evacuated by a combination of backing and diffusion pumps to a pressure of less than than 10^{-5} mm of mercury. Then a slow trickle of hydrogen or argon gas is admitted through a needle valve.

A disk of the metal to be laid down is suspended above the substrate to be coated and a potential of 1,000 to 2,000 volts is applied between the disk and the metallic base-plate underlying the substrate. The metal to be sputtered is the cathode terminal for the process.

An alternating potential is applied and the positive ions of gas produced by the resulting glow discharge impinge on the cathode where their momentum is sufficient to dislodge aggregates of atoms from the cathode so that the substrate beneath the cathode becomes covered with a film of the cathode metal.

The rate of sputtering increases with ion current density, with cathode potential and the molecular weight of the positive ions. In an argon atmosphere, the rate of sputtering of metals, in descending order is: cadmium, silver, lead, gold, antimony, tin, bismuth, copper, platinum, nickel, iron, tungsten, zinc, silver, aluminum, and magnesium.

Electron beams show considerable promise in thin-film technology. The possibility is foreseen of using beams for substrate preparation to enhance the probability of crystal-film deposition. Coarse electron beams (30 to 100 mils in diameter) would be used for bulk material evaporation and thin beams (1 to 3 mils) for precise remelting and recrystallization.

Hard vacuums down to 10^{-10} mm of mercury are needed for electron-beam deposition. Coarse beams permit vacuum deposition of refractory metals impossible to vaporize by tungsten filament or hot crucible techniques. Ultrafine diameter beams can be used in machining vacuum-deposited film to define precisely the pattern of residual film material.

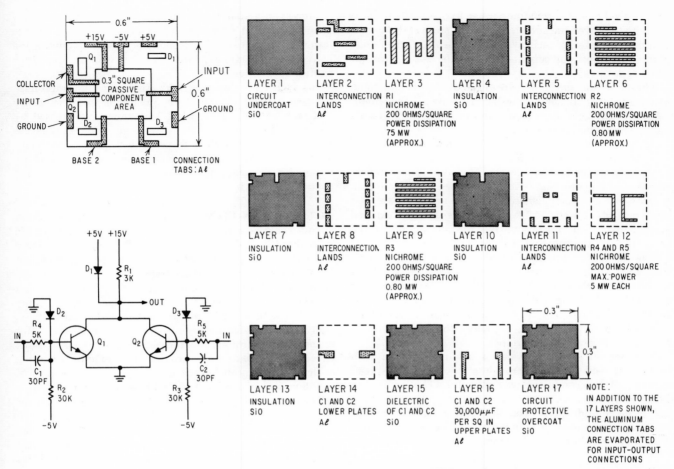

THE ARRAY OF *vacuum deposition masks used in fabricating a multilayer thin-film circuit. Chip semiconductors are welded to control area—Fig. 17*

Furthermore, beams can be used to join or alloy material of different composition in the vacuum chamber or to heat-treat vacuum-deposited material to achieve desired surface perfection and crystal structure. Beam-deflector control by programmed magnetic tape may result in unlimited choice of shape, high accuracy, and tight control of machining depth.

The laser, or quantum mechanical light amplifier, shows promise for application to thin-film and other microelectronic circuit fabricating procedures such as welding strips to printed-circuit boards, micrologic can lids, wire to metal pads, and thin-film materials. Also drilling thin-film resistors and silicon disks and removing metal from semiconductors and thin-film resistors.

FABRICATION—There are two general methods of thin-film circuit fabrication: masking and selective etching.

In the masking technique, the layout topology, based upon the geometrical capabilities of the deposition process, is undertaken first. The masks are designed and fabricated by photoetching, arc erosion or milling. It is essential to hold close tolerances.

Next the substrate is prepared by screening the wafers for imperfections, then cleaning the selected substrates chemically and ultrasonically. At least one manufacturer chooses, at this point, to vacuum-deposit an undercoat of silicon monoxide.

Next the conductors are deposited in a pattern of interconnecting bands of aluminum. Gold and copper can also be used as conductors but aluminum is most compatible with an undercoat of silicon monoxide. Conductors are between 5,000 and 50,000 angstrom units thick.

Next dielectric film regions of silicon monoxide or silicon dioxide are deposited with gaps left in the insulator film to permit conductive connection between layers.

Additional layers of conductive or insulating film are deposited through successive masks. A final layer of silicon monoxide is deposited over the entire structure except for land areas to which other circuits or chip semiconductors are to be attached. These are attached usually by thermocompression bonding.

When the individual circuits have been electrically tested they are attached to a connection plate by soldering, conductive adhesives or by thermocompression bonds. Joints can also be made by solder reflow in which pretinned areas on the connection board are placed in contact with pretinned land areas on the circuit modules and the entire assembly baked briefly in a vacuum oven until the solder fillers reflow.

Final packaging measures can range from applying a conformal coating of silicon monoxide to hermetic sealing of the whole assembly in a container.

In a typical selective etching process a layer of resistive material such as chromium or cermet (for example, four parts by volume of chromium powder to one part silicon) is deposited all over the substrate. Then an overall layer of conductive material such as chromium-gold, cermet-gold, chromium-copper, or cermet-copper is deposited over the resistive layer.

The chromium and cermet are evaporated from aluminum oxide crucibles with spiral tungsten filaments used as radiant heaters. The gold and copper are evaporated from resistance-heated molybdenum boats.

After both metal depositions, the wafers are dip-coated with photoresist. The wafers are then exposed to ultraviolet light through a photographic negative of the complete circuit. The photoresist is then developed, for example, in a spray of trichloroethylene that washes away the areas of photoresist that were not exposed to light. The exposed areas harden and resist both the washing action of the developer and the subsequent etching.

Now the wafers are etched and the metal film removed from all areas that are neither conductor nor resistor. Gold is removed with a commercial gold stripper. Copper is removed with ferric chloride. Chromium or cermet is removed with hydrochloric acid into which an aluminum wire has been introduced. Finally, the photoresist is removed with photoresist stripper.

As a second step, the wafer is again dip-coated with photoresist and exposed through a photographic spread negative of the conductor pattern only. The wafers are developed, rinsed, and etched using only the gold stripper and ferric chloride. This completes the circuits except for removing the remaining photoresist. Then semiconductor components can be attached by thermocompression bonding.

CIRCUIT DESIGN—Thin films look promising for small-volume linear circuits where high performance and close tolerance components are needed. Thin-film resistors can go as high as 1 megohm and be individually adjusted to 5 percent tolerance or even less.

Practical-sized tantalum capacitors of 0.1 microfarad and 5 volts working voltage can readily be obtained. In one circuit, a relatively small feedback capacitor was formed by using the full thickness of the ceramic structure as its dielectric, larger coupling capacitors were made up as internal multiple electrode capacitors while the large filter capacitors were solid tantalum units inlaid within cavities of the substrate.

Moreover, actual hybrid integrated circuits consisting of passive thin-film elements deposited on a silicon dioxide insulating region of a semiconductor block containing the active elements are especially attractive in certain servo control applications.

In realizing inductance with thin films a compromise between inductance and Q, or quality, must be made for each application. Thus when inductance is increased by increasing the number of turns, it is necessary to decrease the film resistivity such as by using thick high-conductivity silver films. Alternatively, inductance can be raised by improving the magnetic permeability of the surrounding medium such as by using a ferrite substrate.

ACTIVE THIN-FILM DEVICES—The ideal thin-film circuit would be one in which all elements of a circuit could be realized by thin-film processes. This goal will require development of active solid-state devices perhaps different from the conventional bipolar transistor.

One such device is the tunnel triode. This consists of a metal emitter deposited on an insulating substrate. On top of this is a thin insulating layer, then a thin metal base, another thin insulating layer, and a metal collector. Hot or energetic electrons tunnel through the insulators. Tunnel triodes are hard to make because they require insulating oxide films 20 to 50 angstrom units thick and capable of handling field strengths of 10^7 volts per centimeter.

The metal-base triode consists of a semiconductor emitter on an insulating substrate, a thin metal base and a semiconductor collector. The Schottky barrier emits hot charge carriers. With 10-micron thick layers, this device should oscillate in the 100-Gc region. Although present structures use single-crystal semiconductors, it is thought that the devices can be made by evaporation processes.

The space-charge-limited triode consists of a metallic cathode and anode separated by an insulator having a metallic grid structure embedded in it. One approach to realizing this device is to use a cadmium sulphide insulator with an oxide-encased gold grid. Theoretically these devices could operate up to 900 Mc, but fabrication problems are extremely difficult.

The field-effect triode has exhibited the most successful performance thus far. The thin-film version of the FET consists of a film of cadmium sulphide deposited on an insulating substrate. The source and drain electrodes are

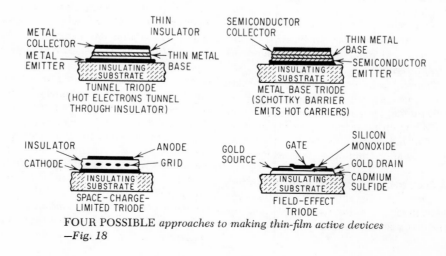

FOUR POSSIBLE *approaches to making thin-film active devices*
—*Fig. 18*

gold stripes making ohmic contact with the cadmium sulphide. The gate electrode is insulated from the cadmium sulphide by a film of silicon monoxide. These thin-film FET's operate in both the enhancement and depletion modes as do their discrete silicon counterparts.

Several approaches to thin-film active devices are still very much in the research stage. One is the depletion layer transistor. It consists of a cadmium sulphide collector region upon which there is an aluminum base, an insulating film of aluminum oxide, and a gold emitter. Carriers are injected directly into the space-charge region at the collector surface. Attempts have also been made to grow single-crystal semiconductors directly onto both single-crystal or amorphous substrates. One manufacturer has tried to form thin-film silicon p-n junction devices on ceramic substrates by rheotaxial growth. There is also a project under way to build micron-sized field-emission vacuum triodes and tetrodes.

REFERENCES

J. M. Carroll, Semiconductor Circuits, "Tunnel-Diode and Semiconductor Circuits," chap. 9, McGraw-Hill Book Company, Inc., New York, 1963.

Reliability: 1962, ELECTRONICS, Nov. 30, 1962.

What's New in Semiconductors, ELECTRONICS, Sept. 29, 1961. "Mechanical Design for Electronics Production," chaps. 7, 10, 11, McGraw-Hill Book Company, Inc., New York, 1956.

"Fairchild Microcircuits Handbook," Fairchild Semiconductor, Mountain View, Calif., 1964.

G. T. Jacobi and S. Weber, The Impact of Microelectronics, ELECTRONICS, New York, 1963.

M. M. Perugini and N. Lindgren, Microminiaturization, ELECTRONICS, Nov. 25, 1960.

PART TWO
Circuits and Applications

Chapter 5
INTRODUCTION TO MICROELECTRONICS

INSPECTING NEW metalizing mask for production of integrated circuits at Motorola Semiconductor Products division

ADVANCES IN MICROMINIATURIZATION

From promise to practice in just four years, a whole new technology for electronics heralds a change in the face of our industry. The question is no longer when and why microminiaturization, but how

By MICHAEL F. WOLFF, Senior Associate Editor

"WE'RE GOING MICRO." These words are being echoed throughout the industry in 1963—what was scoffed at in some quarters four years ago is now a reality.

Today production of microminiature equipment is underway for important military and space missions. Speculative talk about ultimate wonders, playing "the numbers game"—these are largely gone. Engineers are grappling with engineering problems: how best to fabricate, design, test, specify and demonstrate reliability. They emphasize that in microminiaturization they are not interested in size reduction for its own sake—rather engineers see a whole new technology of microelectronics that will bring low cost and high reliability as its most im-

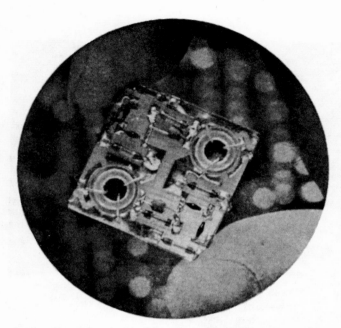

ONE OF FOUR standard wafers that comprise the logic in Arma's 20-lb space computer

(A)

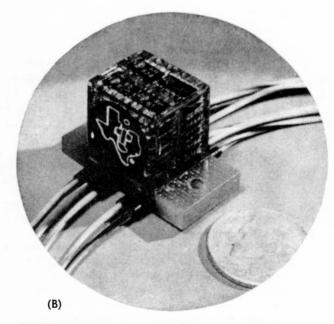

(B)

DIGITAL DATA signal conditioner for State University of Iowa experiment in first Orbiting Geophysical Observatory (A) uses 102 Texas Instruments semiconductor networks for all logic functions. Counter-scanner-programmer (B) uses 36 such networks, is undergoing laboratory evaluation for NASA

portant benefits. Now, at the start of microelectronics' first real production year, the major concern is with the practical problems of how best to realize these potentials.

APPROACHES

APPROACHES—Three approaches to microminiaturization still claim the major effort: component, thin-film and semiconductor integrated circuits.

Discrete microcomponents are widely used in soldered or welded modules. These will continue to be important where moderate size reduction is needed along with proven reliability and the design flexibility of choosing from a wide range of commercially available parts.

Smaller size with discrete components is obtained by attaching parts to "2-D" passive substrates or inserting parts in cavities in printed circuit boards. Arma's 20-lb guidance computer is an example of what can be done with the former. This 1-Mc computer is a serial, binary stored program computer designed to handle a variety of space navigation problems. It occupies 0.42 cubic foot and requires 50 w.[1] Second technique is also in production, has been used in several linear and nonlinear systems such as proximity fuzes and timers built for Army Ordnance under the Micram program.[2]

Standard component form factors have been derived for the micromodule program and pellet, or dot, concept. Micromodule production capabilities will be demonstrated this year as applications in Army communications and computer equipment are stepped up. In contrast to many other techniques, micromodules have an impressive amount of reliability data: RCA reports 3,493,940 element hours of life testing on 96 10-element communications modules has given an mtbf of 381,000 hours at 60 percent confidence, 16,568,650 element hours on 176 digital modules has given an mtbf of 528,000 hours.

By next year RCA estimates micromodule costs will drop below $8 a logic circuit in quantities of 300,000. In some cases costs will be less this year than those of equivalent circuits with military-type components.

During the next few years new microelectronic techniques will also be incorporated in the micromodule package as they become feasible and are required. Experimental packages incorporating integrated circuits have been built. A new package is under development to give, in the same size, the additional interconnections these higher density techniques will need. Package would use electron-beam-welded ribbons on 25-mil centers.

Pellet approach is scheduled to be introduced into General Dynamics' manufacturing program this year. It is an interconnecting process that can use either discrete components or integrated circuits if they are packaged as pellets. Design survey indicates that 78 to 96 percent of the electronic circuits produced at General Dynamics/ Astronautics can either be directly pelletized or pelletized with approximately 5 percent redesign, compared with 60 percent for thin films. Plans for a computer controlled automatic assembly system are underway.[3]

Thermionic integrated micromodules (TIMM's) could play an important role in high temperature and radiation environments. GE claims long-term, stable operation is possible from −65 to 500 deg C under total integrated flux of 10^{18} fast neutrons. Typical NOR circuit draws 3½ mw at 12-16 v. Nuclear power supplies in space, nuclear rockets and long-life (5 years or more) space communicanications systems are seen as possible applications.

INTEGRATED CIRCUITS—While component-oriented approaches will be around a long time, momentum seems to be toward thin-film and semiconductor integrated circuits where "circuit elements are inseparably associated on or within a continuous body to perform the function of a circuit."[4] Feeling within the military and NASA is that these techniques will bring the reliability, maintainability and performance per dollar they consider necessary to perform their missions. Some spokesmen show little interest in discrete component approaches.

Feeling now is that semiconductor integrated circuits are satisfactory for most digital data processing functions, especially those requiring large volumes of standard circuits. Major limitation has been speed. Maximum clock rates are now generally limited to about 6 Mc but these will improve as design techniques to minimize parasitic coupling are applied and faster logic schemes introduced; 10 to 20 Mc is considered feasible on a production basis this year.

COST AND RELIABILITY—Cost has come down an order of magnitude in the last two years but yield is still considered too low. This will improve with better inspection and process control, packaging and interconnection techniques. Some observers say that yields and uniformity are good enough now that the cost of an individual transistor in a silicon integrated circuit is close to the cost of a discrete transistor. And while overall circuit costs are greater than those of comparable printed circuit boards with discrete components, the crossover point could come in the next year or two. Meanwhile introduction into commercially competitive systems will be slower than for military and space applications.

Practical limit in the complexity of a single integrated circuit that can be economically achieved is presently set by materials processing technology at around the shift-register level (about 15 transistors and 21 resistors) in the opinion of R. B. Seeds of Fairchild Semiconductor.

Increased understanding of the underlying silicon technology has led to widespread confidence in eventual high reliability of these circuits. Evidence coming in indicates this confidence may not be misplaced. Texas Instruments reported failure rate of 0.13 percent per 1,000 hours at 85 C in April 1962, estimates 0.04 percent for third quarter 1962 and predicts less than 0.01 percent by the end of this year.

Bureau of Naval Weapons feels semiconductor integrated circuits on the whole have demonstrated they are more reliable than average discrete components and expects 1-Mc devices to be available shortly with certified parameters and reasonable cost. In linear applications they feel 10 to 20 percent of present circuits can be realized with silicon integrated circuits but that here proof of reliability is not yet available.

APPLICATIONS—Semiconductor integrated circuits are already being introduced into several aerospace digital computers, but the significant boost to their application has come from the selection of Texas Instruments' semiconductor networks for the guidance and control electronics in the improved Minuteman. Observers say this program could run to ten's of millions of dollars, may eliminate the need to sell people on microelectronics.

MICROMINIATURIZATION 1963

Discrete components will always be important, but the tide is toward the circuit and function-oriented approaches. This means:

● Designers of systems, circuits and devices, will have to work closer together to generate the new circuit design and fabrication techniques that are needed. Each must know more about the other's problems than he does now

● Manufacturers will find the thin-film and semiconductor techniques complementary in their application—not competitive. But the key to the profits inherent in these technologies is careful attention to process control

● Users will find greater performance per dollar rather than small size and weight the rationale for microsystems. Eventually microminiaturization will allow attaining new levels of performance, such as duplicating biological systems

To realize fully the promise of microminiaturization, however, solving such problems as manufacturer-user cooperation, specification, testing and standardization will be just as important as solving the purely technical ones

Autonetics, associate prime contractor for Minuteman, also plans integrated circuits for inertial navigation systems under design and is evaluating them for a spacecraft radar with a 10,000-hour mtbf. Other programs planning semiconductor integrated circuits include: Apollo guidance computer, EGO and POGO satellite digital-data signal conditioners, an all-weather Naval avionics system for helicopters and VTOL aircraft, radar computer indicator for Navy's W2F-1 early-warning aircraft, and some Air Force pcm telemetry systems.

THIN FILMS—Considerable progress is being made in linear silicon circuits; however, at this time thin films appear more promising for complex and small-volume-production linear applications where high performance and relatively close tolerance components are needed. Diffused silicon resistors are generally limited to around 50,000 ohms and 20-percent tolerances, while thin-film resistors can be individually adjusted to less than 5 percent and go as high as 1 megohm. Practical-size silicon-dioxide capacitors are considered limited to around 1,000 pf, while 0.1 μf is readily obtainable in metal films, especially tantalum where 1 μf can be obtained at 5 v. Common film characteristics are tabulated on p 48.

Research group at Bendix Radio feels applications requiring reproducibility and rigidity will employ the early thin-film techniques. Examples are phased-array radar (because of the great number of identical receivers) and complex filter networks. Bendix wants stable circuits at uhf and above, is presently fabricating a 400-Mc i-f strip with a gain of 80 db and 100-Mc bandwidth. All resistors, capacitors and inductors will be thin film.

ITT Federal Laboratories expects to go into pilot production on tantalum film communications circuits this year. One application they are considering is a 70-Mc i-f

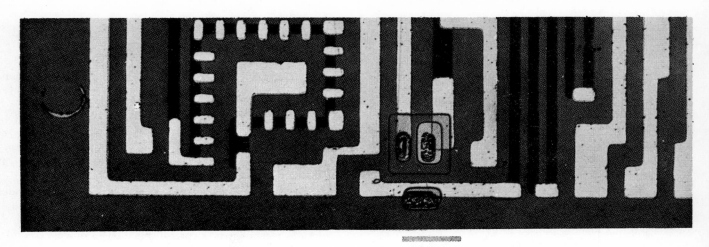

(A)   10 MILS

MICROCIRCUIT for a meteorological satellite differential amplifier (A) and NOR gate (B) built by CBS Labs. Hybrid construction employs

amplifier for parametric receivers, feeling tantalum film components can be used to about 100 Mc.

Kearfott is going into pilot production of a ¼-cubic-inch 5-watt servo amplifier that has a gain adjustable to around 1,000 at 400 cps. Some hearing aids now use films.

Battery-operated 15-Mc pulsed f-m receiver is under development at Johns Hopkins Applied Physics Laboratory for use by the National Institute of Mental Health in experiments on brain stimulation of animals. The thin-film receiver is on three 1×1-inch substrates, would be mounted on a monkey's head.

Thin films are also being used in specialized digital systems by those who claim the following advantages over semiconductors: design flexibility, faster fabrication of prototype systems, and higher speeds and pulse rise-times. GE is fabricating a 1,500-component digital decoder for a Navy missile; a 200-module digital computer built by Lear Siegler has been tested in a satellite. An 18-

lb airborne computer is scheduled for delivery by IBM this year under a Naval Avionics Facility contract.

Titanium metal technology is being pursued at Lockheed to meet space environmental requirements, particularly radiation. They report less than 5 percent change of resistor characteristics under 2×10^{16} neutrons per sq cm[5], have used titanium components in a sequencer subsystem for a space telemetry multiplexing system. The 0.894-cubic-inch unit draws 450 mw.

HYBRID APPROACHES—Major problem with thin-film circuits is the lack of compatible active components. At present, semiconductor diodes and transistors must be attached in what is considered a transitional hybrid that is generally larger, more expensive and less reliable than its equivalent in semiconductor integrated circuits. Real promise of the thin-film approach lies in its automation potential, but until deposited-film active components make this feasible, the trend is to use thin-film passive

TABLE — THIN-FILM RESISTORS AND CAPACITORS[a]

RESISTORS	Ohms per sq	TCR (ppm/deg C)	Dissipation (w/in.² of film @ rating)	Tolerance (%)	Stability (% @ 1,000 hr)
Chromium[b]	500 — 30,000	50	25	±0.1	0.5
Nickel-Chromium[c]	to 200	±50	12	±0.1	<0.1
Tantalum[c]	to 100	±200	20	±0.01	1
Tantalum Nitride[c]	to 200	−75 ±25	20	±0.01	<0.1
Titanium[d]	500 —2,000	+120 to −110	12.5 — 25	±1	0.8 — 1.5
Tin Oxide[e]	Approx 500	±300	15 — 25	±2	1
Cermets[f]	to 20,000	±250	to 20	±1	2
Carbon Resin Ink[g]	10,000	500 — 1,000	1	±10	5 — 10

Capacitors	Leakage Current (@ working voltage)	Working Voltage	TCC (ppm/deg C)	μf/cm²	Dissipation Factor (%)	Tolerance (%)	Stability (% @ 1,000 hr)
Tantalum Oxide[c]	10⁻⁷ amp/μf	100V max	250	0.1 @ 50V	1	±3[h]	Approx 1 @85C
Titanium Dioxide[d]	2.5 x 10⁻⁷ amp/μf	50V	800	0.01	<1	±2	0.5
Silicon Monoxide[i]	<10 μ amp	6V	j	0.5	1	±10	j
Silicon Dioxide[k]	—	50V	<100	0.004	0.2	±10	j

(a) Representative manufacturable values variable with specific fabrication process (b) Xerox, on ceramic (c) Bell Labs (d) Lockheed (e) Corning Glass Works (f) International Resistance (g) Harry Diamond Labs (h) Without adjustment (i) IBM (j) Not available (k) General Instrument

(B)   **10 MILS**

silicon transistors, nickel-chromium resistors on silicon oxide, and gold interconnections—Fig. 1

components with semiconductor integrated circuits in such a way as to get the most from both approaches.

Most aerospace companies are maintaining a balanced research effort. Some want an in-house thin-film assembly capability with purchased semiconductor integrated circuits for standard functions because they feel the complexity of the semiconductor technology and its inherent application to volume production preclude it as an in-house technology for the military and space electronic system assemblers.[6]

In addition to complementary usage of the two technologies there will be the actual hybrid integrated circuit consisting of semiconductor and thin film components. A promising hybrid technique is to deposit metal-film passive elements on a silicon-dioxide insulating region of a semiconductor block containing the active elements. Leads from passive to active components are then evaporated. This will be widely used wherever film passive components are required to perform a function that cannot be obtained in a silicon integrated circuit. It is seen especially attractive for 0-to-20-Kc servo control applications because there would be little problem with stray capacitance from the thin-film elements.

Figure 1A shows one of two identical patterns that make up a differential amplifier built this way for a 10-track digital tape recorder to be used in an advanced meteorological satellite. Circuit has three resistors adjustable to one percent and a transistor; amplifier can be placed inside the recorder next to the record-playback head for increased noise immunity.

Desire for greater flexibility with semiconductor integrated circuits is also leading to hybrid approaches here. These involve putting passive or active semiconductor components or both on top of an insulating substrate and interconnecting by metalization, wire bonding or both. Entire circuit is encapsulated in a single package.

While slightly more expensive than the single-block approach, this technique overcomes the problem of the inherent incompatibility of silicon transistors and resistors in the same block. Also, it minimizes capacitive coupling, permits easier testing, and is considered especially useful for small quantities of custom-made circuits where quick changes and modifications may be required. Some people

are going to this in any amplifier with more than three transistors where they need maximum speed. General Instrument is working on a technique to modify the mask so that resistors on a passive component chip can be selectively changed on the production line.

Bell Labs finds this hybrid approach reduces the number of leads made on the external circuit board by a factor of three in computer-type circuits. They are also using it in exploratory pcm circuits. In such circuits getting stable gain at 200-Mc bandwidths requires feedback. At these frequencies this feedback can best be accomplished in microelectronic circuits because otherwise the propagation time around the loop would be too great. (This points up an inherent functional advantage that many feel will give microelectronics an important role in nanosecond circuits.)

Figure 2 shows an operational amplifier built this way, which because of parasitics could not have been built satisfactorily in a single silicon block. Comparison with the cordwood equivalent showed that in addition to getting much more stable closed-loop gain, open-loop performance began to degrade at 130 Mc compared to 50 Mc for the conventional. All components in the signal path are integrated except the precision feedback resistor.

DESIGN PROBLEMS

DESIGN PROBLEMS—Microelectronics will require changes in the designer's thinking. Circuit, equipment and systems engineers will have to work much more closely if an optimum microelectronic design is to result.

On the system level, decision to go micro will require a new look at solving the system transfer function. For example, digital integrated circuits might make it practical to switch to a digital command link and airborne data reduction.

Then there's the problem of devices that can't be miniaturized. In a typical airborne system mechanical components and electronic components with moving parts occupy half the volume and have a greater failure rate than pure electronic components. Arinc Research Corp. estimates that if only the latter are microminiaturized and their reliability assumed to be unity for the life of the system, the system failure rate would only decrease by approximately 17 percent. They recommend microelectronics be used only in equipments that can be built almost entirely this way. Thus, designers will need to be alert to new ways of performing electromechanical functions more compatibly with microelectronics, such as solid-state relays, transducers and inertial components.

Active thin-film devices will not be replacements for transistors in thin-film circuits—they will have different characteristics and therefore require different approaches to circuit design. Similarly silicon integrated circuits differ from ordinary circuits in that transistors and diodes are cheaper than the passive components, and some components such as inductors are not even available. Also there will be advantages in linear circuits because of the ability to match components formed during the same diffusion and to have thermal tracking of parameters.

LOGIC—Integrated circuit logic is one of the most controversial subjects. With no microelectronic logic scheme yet applied extensively on a system basis, the user is often hard put to select the best for his needs.

Each logic scheme has advantages and disadvantages for both producer and user. From the user's standpoint no specific type is presently clearly superior to all others; in each case he should select to fit total system requirements, taking into account such factors as operating environment, cost, size, weight and power consumption. Moreover tradeoffs between power dissipation, switching speed, fan-in and fan-out, and component tolerance must be considered.

Several military and industrial groups are presently evaluating the different types of logic, indicated in Fig. 3. U. S. Naval Air Development Center has evaluated DTL, RCTL, DCTL, and ECTL. Of these they find DCTL the simplest for semiconductor integrated circuits. It is relatively easy to fabricate and can handle 1-Mc clock rates. Major disadvantage is current hogging where varying base to emitter characteristics of the load elements prevent even current distribution among the loads. Adding a resistor to the base of each transistor minimizes current hogging, but at the expense of operating speed.

DCTL is also sensitive to input noise which is injected directly into the base of the transistors. This is not the only noise mode that may affect microelectronic logic however, and the Center plans to investigate others.

Desire to eliminate current hogging and still maintain a relatively simple system led to ECTL (emitter-coupled transistor logic). This is a form of current-mode logic, which is presently gaining a lot of attention.

Present ECTL assemblies may use a few more parts than their DCTL equivalents but still contain only transistors and resistors. In ECTL the input base-to-emitter resistance is a function of the transistor β. Thus, the base current varies inversely with β, permitting higher fan-out. This advantage together with improved noise immunity is obtained with two power supplies compared to one in DCTL. GE claims a 2-Mc shift rate for shift registers.

Flip-flop clock rates of 20 Mc are claimed by Motorola for their current-mode logic. For a fan-out of 1, stage propagation delay, rise time and fall time are 4 nsec with a 20-pf shunt capacitance. Maximum fan-out is 26, noise

VIDEO AMPLIFIER consisting of six silicon planar resistors and two epitaxial transistors on ceramic substrate is fabricated at General Instrument, has been used in prototype navigational aids equipment. Typical values for a representative amplifier are on schematic

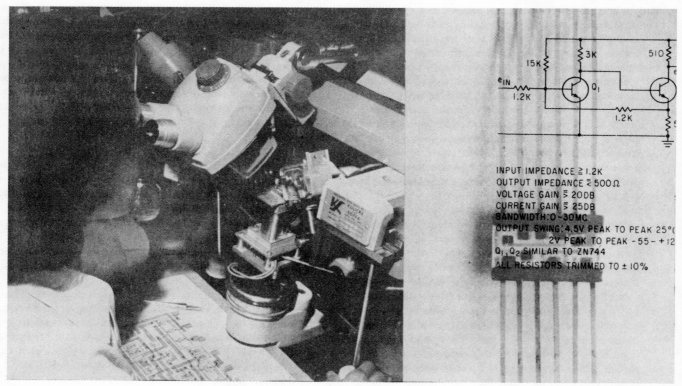

voltage at the input can be half the input voltage before confusing the logic.

DTL is another relatively simple system to fabricate, is being used in many new semiconductor integrated circuits. It operates on relatively low voltage swings (4v) and is fast (3-6 Mc clock rates). Furthermore, immunity to noise can be 50 percent.

Most complex system now used is RCTL. The capacitors increase base current for fast collector current turn-on and minimize storage time by supplying a charge equal to the stored base charge. RCTL units have been quite insensitive to input noise and supply voltage variation but relatively slow (about 500 Kc), the Center finds.

Another type of logic becoming increasingly popular is TCL. This is similar to DTL and may be used with common bases and collectors (multiple emitter coupling). Claim is that TCL does not have the DCTL current hogging problem, has better noise rejection, and for constant power dissipation has about the same speed.[7]

Simplest logic is probably RTL. Because it needs resistors with ±5 percent overall tolerance, however, it may be more suited to thin films. Also the resistors make it less efficient in terms of power dissipation.

LOGIC NETS—New concept of integrated logic nets is considered by RCA to offer the most economical way of meeting most digital requirements. Here arrays of 2,000 insulated-gate field-effect transistors (see Fig. 4) are fabricated on a 1-inch-square silicon substrate. These transistors are majority-carrier devices fabricated by diffusing heavily doped source and drain contacts into the silicon

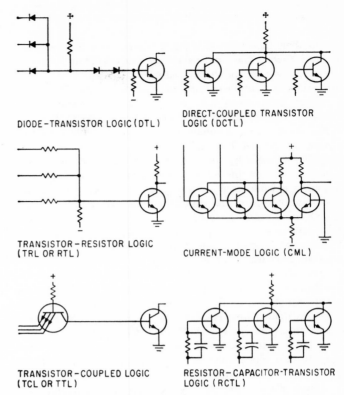

DIODE–TRANSISTOR LOGIC (DTL)

DIRECT-COUPLED TRANSISTOR LOGIC (DCTL)

TRANSISTOR–RESISTOR LOGIC (TRL OR RTL)

CURRENT-MODE LOGIC (CML)

TRANSISTOR–COUPLED LOGIC (TCL OR TTL)

RESISTOR–CAPACITOR–TRANSISTOR LOGIC (RCTL)

SIX FORMS of integrated circuit logic are illustrated for a fan-in of three—Fig. 3

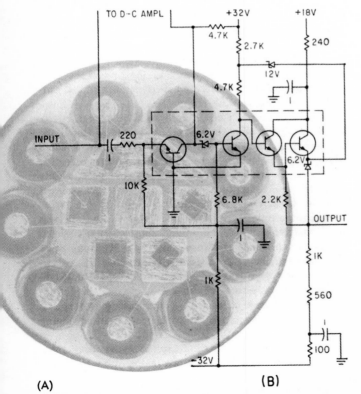

(A)

(B)

INTEGRATED CIRCUIT package (A) for Bell Labs high-frequency operational amplifier module (B) contains two experimental 2-Gc planar epitaxial transistors and two silicon zener diodes. External d-c stabilizing circuits and feedback loops are not

SOME STRAIGHT TALK ON DESIGNING

Our rate of progress will be determined by the rate engineers can invent circuits that utilize the unexploited unique features of silicon rather than by simply avoiding the fundamental limitations of the silicon substrate says C. D. Simmons, director of Philco's microelectronics laboratory. For example, while the tolerance of individual diffused resistors is poor, new avenues of design are offered by the fact that differential tolerance can be reduced to 1 or 2 percent.

R. E. Lee, executive vice president of Siliconix, points out that some companies new to integrated circuits have been using the almost brute force method of trying to realize a circuit in a silicon block by part-for-part translation from what was a good optimum circuit in the discrete component domain. "This is not the ideal way to design an integrated circuit," he says, adding "integrated circuit design requires the combined experience of circuit-oriented people who can range over the entire scope of alternate designs to accomplish a given circuit function, joined with solid-state physics and device people who know what can and can't be done in a semiconductor block as far as device structures are concerned"

and then thermally growing a silicon dioxide layer between them. The contacts are then metalized and a metal gate put on top of the insulator.

Electrons flow between source and drain parallel to the surface only when the gate is biased positively. This allows direct coupling between successive stages in what can be regarded as voltage controlled relay logic. Equivalent of the DCTL load resistor can be obtained in a similar element by forming an n-type channel under the oxide between the source and drain. In addition the source is connected to the gate, giving a two-terminal nonlinear resistor that simulates a constant-current source with more rapid charging and better noise immunity than a linear resistor. Supply voltage is coupled through the nonlinear resistor to the drain, which is then connected to the next transistor gate.

Result is the ability to have series—parallel logic with unlimited fan-out and without shifting voltage levels between stages. With a 10,000-ohm load resistor, typical gate switching time is estimated at roughly 40 to 50 nsec and power dissipation at 40 mw. Computer clock rates of 10 Mc are seen with present devices. Scaling laws apply and clock rates of 20-200 Mc are predicted as device size comes down.

RCA claims laboratory yields exceed 90 percent, that the devices are highly uniform. They expect this technique to lead to an order of magnitude price reduction over other integrated circuit techniques. The transistor chains, nonlinear resistors, fingers and crossover insulation are made on a general array basis so that almost always only one layer of evaporated gold wiring is needed to complete the desired circuit.

Major failure mode reported so far is short-circuited gates. Major problem to be resolved is the long-term stability; however, researchers believe they will be able after a few months to show characteristics won't drift.

Technique may also lead to nanowatt computer memories. Here the transistors would be used with their hole-conduction equivalents in a flip-flop type memory (see Fig. 4D). Hole conduction occurs with n-type silicon and a $p+$ source and drain. (Logic circuits using similar complementary devices have been reported by Fairchild Semiconductor to consume less than 10 nw standby power per node and switch in less than 20 nsec[8].)

Presently two applications are under development (see the front cover). One is an eight-neighbor NOR gate for a 2-D data processing panel being built at Air Force Cambridge Research Laboratories. Panel will use a checkerboard array of the gates. Each nodal unit input is tied to eight neighbors; by changing the gate voltage it is possible to select which of the neighboring logic signals is to be OR-gated into the output.

Possibility of replacing the eight control leads with optical coupling is also being studied. This would be done by energizing the gate from a deposited photovoltaic cell, might eventually lead to adjustable computers that could change their logic functions by optical command.

Second application is a series of resettable decade ring counters that will divide by any of 28,000 integers in a 2-to-30-Mc ssb equipment under construction. There will

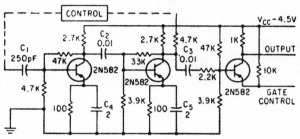

be five decks in a package expected to occupy 1 cubic inch and draw 2½ watts. Total number of interconnections is estimated at 105 compared with the 1,136 that would be required if the comparable circuit was fabricated with integrated circuits in 8-lead cans.

INDUCTORS—Fabrication of inductors still remains a major problem in designing integrated circuits. For within a limited volume, inductance can be raised only by increasing the number of turns and their cross-sectional area or improving the magnetic permeability of the surrounding medium.

Problem is to find the best compromise between inductance and Q for each application. Example of this is the diode-switched tuner shown in Fig. 5. Here the isolated resistors and capacitors are on the same substrate so that glass is used instead of ferrite. Since low permeability of glass requires more turns enclosing a larger area of pancake spiral coil, the conductor length of the larger coils is approximately 400 times the width. It was therefore necessary to make the film resistivity much lower than the usual thin-film conductor. By using thick high-conductivity silver films, the larger coils of this circuit have Q's near 100 and inductance of about 0.25 μh.

The spiral inductors require a crossover to the center; a transformer can be made by interleaving two spirals or placing one on top of the other with an insulating layer between them.

Limitations of thin-film inductors prevent using them at audio frequencies. Above a few tenths of a microhenry or below 100 Mc you must replace deposited film inductors with discrete inductors or design around them by (1) attaching piezoelectric resonators, (2) using the simulated inductance in a forward-biased p-n junction together with negative resistance devices like tunnel diodes or (3) designing notch filters and distributed R-C net-

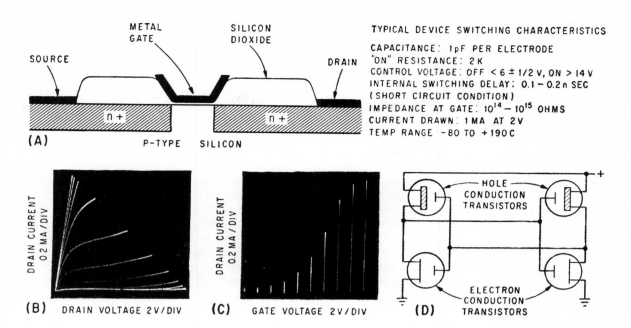

TYPICAL DEVICE SWITCHING CHARACTERISTICS

CAPACITANCE: 1pF PER ELECTRODE
"ON" RESISTANCE: 2K
CONTROL VOLTAGE: OFF < 6 ± 1/2 V, ON > 14 V
INTERNAL SWITCHING DELAY: 0.1 – 0.2 n SEC
(SHORT CIRCUIT CONDITION)
IMPEDANCE AT GATE: 10^{14} – 10^{15} OHMS
CURRENT DRAWN: 1 MA AT 2V
TEMP RANGE – 80 TO +190 C

INSULATED-GATE field-effect transistor (A) has output characteristics of (B) and transfer characteristics of (C) when gate bias is varied in 2-v steps from 0 to 20 v. Load is 10,000 ohms and supply is 20 v. Complementary pairs of transistors could be used in the memory cell designed by P. K. Weimer of RCA Labs (D) whose two stable states would have essentially no dissipation—Fig. 4

works. Latter have been used in thin-film form to make band-pass amplifiers and phase shift oscillators; a frequency discriminator with a Q of 0.22 and an output linear over ±17 percent has been designed.[9]

Obtaining selective frequency response without inductors is generally difficult, however, because it leads to instability. The higher the Q the more sensitive it is to element variations. For a standard twin-T null circuit components must maintain tolerances of about ±0.1 percent over the entire range of operating conditions in order to attain a Q of 50 within ±10 percent.[10]

DISCRETE INDUCTORS—Wound toroids are satisfactory up to 200 Mc; Q's of 50 to 100 can be obtained and the magnetic field is contained so there is little interaction with other circuits.

Shielded 1-mh solenoids 0.1 inch in diameter and ¼ inch long with a Q of about 40 are being developed by Nytronics. Shielding is provided by a new magnetic powder molding process. Values to 100 mh in a year are projected. They are also working toward modular power transformers to fit micromodule wafers.

Equivalent performance of a resonant circuit in much smaller volumes and at lower cost is expected from materials such as lead-titanate-zirconate now being studied for use with metal members as thin-film piezoelectric filters.

Deposited resonators are needed in the 500-Mc region, where the required Q's of 1,000 are presently unobtainable except with various forms of lines. Engineers at Harry Diamond Laboratories feel the helical cavity resonator is best from the volume standpoint. They have built 0.01-cubic-inch units with unloaded Q's of approximately 230 at 500 Mc for the preselector of a command receiver. The receiver has screen-printed wafer circuits, occupies 0.75 cubic inch, and when completed is expected to have 60-db image rejection, approximately 3-db bandwidth at 5-6 Mc and 3-db insertion loss.

One possible solution to the inductance problem is to fabricate an integrated circuit out of piezoelectric material such as gallium arsenide. Junctions in gallium arsenide have high resistivity and theoretically could be used as resonators—but so far no one claims to know how. Furthermore, much more work is needed in alloying and diffusing so that other components could be made in gal-

DIODE-SWITCHED tuner developed at General Instrument applied research laboratory covers range of 50 to 200 Mc—Fig. 5

lium arsenide, which is expected to allow higher frequency operation than silicon. However, it might be possible to grow a gallium arsenide junction heteroepitaxially in a certain spot on a silicon substrate.

FIELD-EFFECT DEVICES—Need to design around large resistors and capacitors is leading to field-effect transistors for raising impedance, thereby allowing smaller coupling and bypass capacitors.

Where large R-C time constants are required for coupling in low-frequency linear circuits, a field-effect transistor in series with a bipolar transistor can give high input impedance as well as high current gain. These devices can be diffused simultaneously into a silicon block to give input resistances over 1 megohm and, by cascading, g_m's on the order of 1 mho.

Westinghouse Electric has fabricated an audio amplifier this way that uses a matched pair of unipolar transistors as a high-impedance input and nonlinear bias resistor for three Darlington-connected bipolar transistors. Typical amplifier gives 3 w out for ½ v rms in at 2½ percent distortion; frequency response is flat to nearly 1 Mc.[11]

TEMPERATURE COMPENSATION — Semiconductor integrated circuits need built-in temperature compensation because diffused silicon resistors are not as stable as ordinary resistors. Negative feedback is widely used for this. Operating point is stabilized in a typical two-stage common-emitter amplifier because the ratio of emitter resistance to feedback resistance is maintained in spite of temperature variations since both resistors are made from the same piece of silicon and have the same TCR (temperature coefficient of resistance). Westinghouse engineers feel this technique allows designing practical linear circuits with good frequency response, low distortion, and stability comparable to that of ordinary circuits.

ISOLATION—Parasitic capacitance arising from use of reverse biased p-n junctions to isolate transistors and other regions in integrated circuits has been another important problem, particularly at high frequencies. Recent progress in alternately applying epitaxial growth and selective diffusion points to improved isolation, however. One technique considered useful up to 100 Mc is to diffuse p-type impurities through an n-type layer epitaxially grown on a lightly doped p-type substrate.[12]

NONELECTRICAL EFFECTS—Phenomena other than electrical should also be watched for in designing semiconductor integrated circuits. Figure 6 shows how thermal feedback can reduce the temperature variation of a Zener diode voltage reference. Resistors R_1 and R_2 establish a constant potential of approximately 0.4 v on the base of transistor Q_1; this is insufficient for conduction at room temperature. When the supply voltage is turned on, current through R_3 flows into the base of Q_2, resulting in Q_2 dissipating enough power to raise the substrate temperature. As the temperature of Q_1 increases, the base-to-emitter voltage required for conduction decreases until Q_1 starts conducting. Current flowing into Q_1 then reduces the current at the base of Q_2 and the dissipation decreases until an equilibrium temperature is reached.[13]

There is also the possibility of exploiting the relation between frequency characteristics and distance for such devices as filters and oscillators. If a sinusoidally varying

heat source is attached to a uniform silicon bar, the propagation velocity of the resulting temperature wave is frequency dependent. Mathematical analysis indicates that varying the bar length and, hence, the transit time of the wave, will vary the oscillating frequency of a closed-loop system. Aeronautical Systems Division of Air Force Systems Command (ASD) is presently investigating thermal characteristics of silicon to see if this effect can be exploited for oscillators and band-pass filters.

MICROPOWER—You can expect increased emphasis on microwatt electronics, for progress in power reduction has not kept pace with other areas of microelectronics.

NASA ranks requirement for low power in space directly after reliability, has found silicon integrated circuits consume three times the power of standard circuits in applications like flip-flop memories and counters. This results largely from lack of large resistors and single-block complementary circuits. However, possibility of complementary insulated-gate field-effect transistors as well as recent demonstration that pnp and npn transistors can be fabricated in the same block (see Fig. 7) now makes zero-watt logic look more realizable.

Several circuits that operate at microwatt supply power levels have been built at CBS Labs with the hybrid approach, which they feel offers the greatest versatility, least temperature sensitivity and highest speed for a given power level. These techniques are considered promising at 50-Kc clock rates, adequate for many satellite applications. The NOR gate in Fig. 1B consumes about 50 microwatts in a satellite 7-bit analog-to-digital converter.

For still lower power levels, researchers want nanowatt devices. Sperry Semiconductor has made transistors with common-emitter current gain of 20 at 1 namp and noise figures of about 1 db, feels they can be incorporated in a 1,000-transistor computer that would dissipate 5 mw.

While power gain has been obtained in nanowatt circuits, it is felt an order of magnitude size reduction is needed for significant speed through, perhaps, a filamentary transistor to cope with lead capacitance.[14]

Present logic schemes are being investigated at U.S. Army Electronics R & D Laboratory (USAERDL) to determine the tradeoffs that would occur at microwatt levels. James Meindl points out we can't assume relative merits and limitations at present milliwatt levels will be the same at microwatt. However, he cites the follow-

TUNNEL-EMISSION device fabrication program at Burroughs Laboratories has produced these diodes with 30-40-angstrom-thick oxide layers. Current density of 175 amp/cm^2 can be maintained and devices have worked with 35 ma d-c

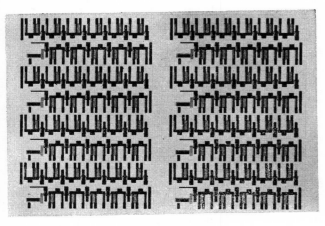

(1) Resistor Matrix of Cr-SiO

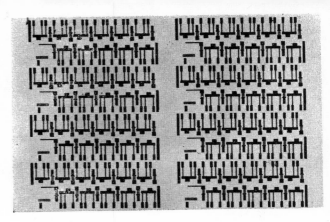

(2) Resistor Lands, Some Cu Interconnections

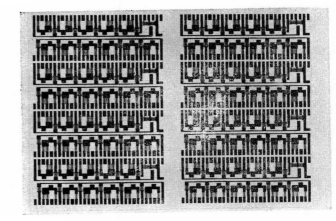

(3) SiO Capacitor Dielectric

(4) Interconnections, Upper Capacitor Cu Plate

THIN-FILM PILOT production system built by IBM for Naval Avionics Facility at Indianapolis fabricates passive networks on SiO-coated 3¾ × 5-3/16-inch substrates continuously in a four-stage deposition process. Equipment is first step toward what Navy hopes will eventually be a pilot production capability for complete thin-film circuits

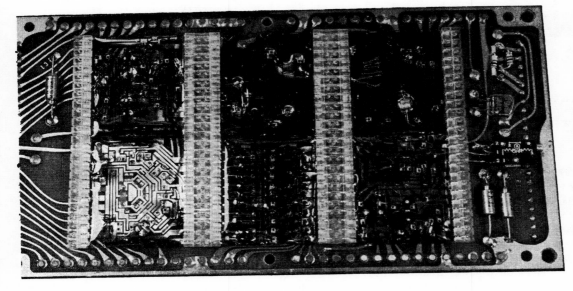

THIN-FILM COUNTER assembly occupies 9 cubic inches, was delivered to Army Ordnance, Frankford Arsenal, by Martin-Orlando in 16 weeks. Counter has maintained frequency stability in system of 0.05 percent over an operating temperature range of −45 to +55 C

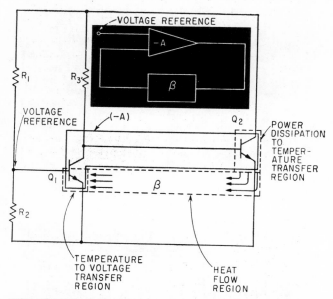

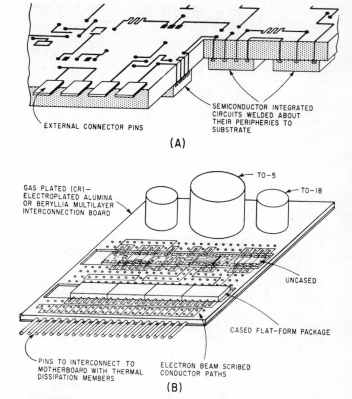

HOW THERMAL FEEDBACK reduces temperature variation of a voltage reference for analog-to-digital conversion in the telemetry encoder Texas Instruments is building for ASD—Fig. 6

CONCEPTUAL illustration of unencapsulated hermetic header for intra-interconnection of semiconductor integrated circuits (A) and interconnection—packaging system for joining cased and uncased circuits and assembling systems (B) under study at Hamilton Standard div. of United Aircraft for ASD—Fig. 8

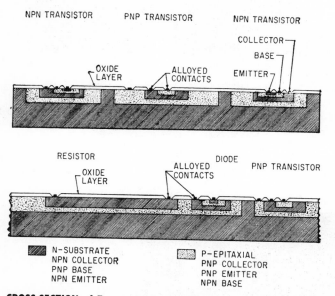

CROSS-SECTION of Texas Instruments' recently-announced series 52 linear amplifier illustrates how npn and pnp transistors can now be diffused into a single block of silicon—Fig. 7

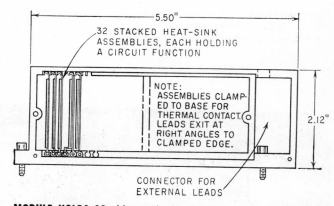

MODULE HOLDS 32 chips and occupies 13 cubic inches in this packaging technique by Autonetics—Fig. 9

ing problems microwatt logic designers will face regardless of the logic they select.

• Leakage currents with silicon transistors can be significant compared with operating current, I_{CBO} of 0.1 to 1 microampere is possible depending upon how high a temperature circuit is designed for. But germanium transistors will not be feasible.

• Current gain of ordinary micropower transistor will be more temperature sensitive than that of milliwatt transistors.

• Because microampere currents are obtained at essentially the same junction voltages as milliampere cur-

rents, a high impedance circuit will result. This circuit will be slower in almost direct proportion to the current drop—if a 1-mw circuit operates at 1 Mc, then the 1-microwatt version will operate at approximately 1 Kc.

• In designing microwatt logic circuits it will be absolutely necessary to minimize stray and parasitic device capacitance. Also, maximum speed in the 1-100 microwatt range will require minimizing voltage swing to roughly 0.1 v to 0.4 v by tightening tolerances and controlling temperature.

INTERCONNECTION AND PACKAGING — Most

often cited as problem number one, size and power drain of interconnections still thwarts the goal of microelectronics and could be the determining factor in the practical success of a particular technique. However, thin-film technology may provide the answer.

Electron beam welding of semiconductor integrated circuits to a ceramic substrate is being studied by Hamilton Standard for ASD Electronic Technology Laboratory. Direct welds as well as bonds with intermediate materials such as chromium and titanium thin films will be used to hermetically seal all active surfaces while at the same time dissipating heat and providing for interconnections with minimum parasitic coupling (Fig. 8A).

Production processes are also being developed and an unbalanced production line set up for the ASD Manufacturing Technology Laboratory to interconnect present semiconductor integrated circuit systems. As shown in Fig. 8B, cased (or future uncased) circuits are attached to a grooved ceramic wafer of high thermal conductivity. A conductive matrix for interconnecting the packages, thin-film passive elements, and external circuits is fabricated by electron beam etching. Plated-through vertical feedthroughs permit crossovers, matrix design allows additional horizontal-vertical layers to be added to yield a multilayer matrix of horizontal networks.

Hughes feels its electroless copper plating process developed for pellet circuits will provide a mass interconnection technique as reliable as printed circuit wiring. No high temperatures are involved.

Near term will see greater use of flexible conductors, and also flat packets and stacked thin-film wafers. Packaging technique for semiconductor networks (which have flat form factor and leads) used by the Apparatus division of Texas Instruments on several equipment contracts is built around 1.5-inch-wide printed circuit boards with welded connections. On one contract, a computer unit has been delivered on which 49 boards are mounted in a package that weighs about 1½ lb, occupies about 22 cubic inches and meets environmental specifications for airborne operation per MIL-E-5400.

Figure 9 shows a packaging concept under study for Autonetics armament control circuits and systems.

Optical soldering techniques have been used to fabricate modules for flat packages as shown in Fig. 10.[15] A system has been conceived and partially realized using this concept that will contain 35 circuits, dissipate 100 mw at 3.3 v, occupy 0.45 cubic inch, weigh 0.02 oz.

There is also considerable effort to eliminate thermocompression bonds, particularly in high vibration environments like space. One technique under study is a ceramic sandwich where evaporated wiring on one wafer would be fused to circuit contacts on the other.

TESTING—Whole area of specification and testing faces change as we head toward microelectronics. With component junctions largely inaccessible, users want new measurements they can perform to check temperature stability and major device parameters. Failure rates which have largely been gathered on the component level are now needed on a circuit level. Manufacturers expect that if the circuit environment and application are known then worst case tests on terminal pins can be specified that will satisfy users. Some feel meaningful acceptance tests can be performed externally by evaluating characteristics that are the sum of internal parameters, rather than

evaluating the parameters themselves.[16]

A major problem for users according to Harry Knowles, general manager of Westinghouse Electric's molecular electronics division, is how to demonstrate reliability that may approach one failure per billion circuit hours in a few years. He sees the answer in giving users visibility into the process control and providing an analytical capability for overstressing devices. Then by determining the predominate failure modes in a run the user can extrapolate for his mission.

Advanced linear circuit design will also call for cooperation between device manufacturers and systems people in writing specs for such things as high-frequency properties, which can be measured only on the completed circuit. Inability to measure within the wafer may require more designing statistically for a class of devices.

Biggest day-to-day problem for designers could come from the high-frequency circuits that work only in the final encapsulation. Conventional breadboarding techniques fall down here and there is no possibility of trouble-shooting economically. Bell Labs engineers say designers will therefore have to operate more precisely than they have, possibly do more computer simulation or low-frequency analog work to be certain of their design.

THE FUTURE

THE FUTURE—By 1970 new forms of integrated circuits will undoubtedly arise that bear little resemblance to those presently under development. Key research areas to watch include: optoelectronics, new materials phenomena, active thin-film device research, homogeneous semiconductors, bionics, and advanced fabrication techniques like selective epitaxial growth.

Semiconductor integrated circuits are limited by present diffusion and epitaxial techniques to three or four layers. One approach that might lead to the next generation is in the early research stages at ASD. They envision fabricating a "three-dimensional" circuit by selective epitaxial growth, diffusion and vacuum deposition of both active and passive components. This would allow growing complex circuits of many layers and then depositing the metallic interconnections on the surface as the final step. Connections within the block could be by low-resistivity semiconducting material.

One way to fabricate a 3-D circuit might be to grow a number of epitaxial layers and isolate the active elements by high-resolution selective machining with molecular beams. Because the beam melts as it cuts, however, this would probably require later etching to remove shorts across junctions formed by subsequent refreezing.

Long-range goal at Norden division of United Aircraft is automatic synthesis and manufacture of optimized circuits or systems within a crystal. According to M. W. Aarons, chief of the applied physics branch at Norden, it is conceivable that in the future a description of the desired output in terms of the data supplied to the circuit will be typed into a computer. From this point on, manufacturing as well as business decisions would be computer-controlled.

One technical approach might be a laser beam servo-positioned over a substrate for controlled local heat. Various organometallic gases could then be synchronously valved to the growth chamber so as to epitaxially produce devices with maximized characteristics, at their proper position upon the substrate. The substrate would have large anisotropic thermoconductivity so that heat could flow only normal to its plane. Such a technique would allow the selective growth of many presently incompatible devices of different materials and frequency characteristics over a broad conductivity range, Aarons says.

Optical techniques and devices will become increasingly important in microelectronics.

If a 3-D circuit could be fabricated out of a material with photoconductive properties, such as gallium arsenide, then connection within the block could be done optically. Such a scheme is shown in Fig. 11. Here the intrinsic and *n*-type material is transparent to the coupling light frequency and the *p*-type material is opaque. Thus, light conducting paths can be made by varying the doping.

At infrared wavelengths semiconductors such as indium antimonide, lead selenide, lead sulfide and silicon exhibit photoelectric, photovoltaic and photoconductive properties when exposed to the proper wavelength of light energy. Several of the photoconductive semiconductors can be fabricated into resistive areas that are variable when light is incident on the surface. Diffused resistors are also possible with these same materials and can be fabricated to a precision of ±20 percent.

ACTIVE THIN-FILM DEVICES—Desire for a compatible technology that permits fabricating complete thin-film circuits with their interconnections in large volume and low cost is spurring widespread research on majority-carrier amplifiers and other active thin-film devices shown in Fig. 12.[17, 18] Where there is to be competition between thin-film and semiconductor integrated circuits, it will come when these devices can be fabricated reproducibly—but few expect this before 1965. Here's a rundown of their status:

• Tunnel triodes—Absence of semiconductors has brought research support for this hot-electron tunneling device from such groups as Harry Diamond Labs, USAERDL and NASA who hope for high radiation resistance. Problems are formidable, however, and nobody has yet reported power gain. One must fabricate 20-to-50 angstrom oxide films to handle 10^7 volts per cm, and find

a collector material with the right barrier height and mobility that electrons can be collected with useful efficiency. Philco is trying to control barrier height by varying the ratio of cadmium to zinc in a layer of cadmium-zinc sulfide evaporated between base and collector.

Sylvania has formed contact rectifiers using titanium oxide as a semiconductor with current rectification ratios to 100 at 1 v.

• Metal base triode—Because of high input capacitance, presently conceived tunnel triodes are not expected to exceed the performance of a good high-frequency transistor. The metal base triode might, however. For a given emitter charging time it can operate at current densities two orders of magnitude lower than the tunnel triode, and its characteristically low base resistance gives the metal base triode a power gain-bandwidth product about two orders of magnitude better. With 10-micron layers, it should oscillate in the 100-Gc range.[19]

Although present structures use single-crystal semiconductors, the device may be evaporable. Even if it is not, however, it could be important in high-frequency hybrid circuits if a base metal is found that injected carriers can traverse without losing too much energy.

• Space-charge-limited triode—Although power gain or current transfer have yet to be reported, there is the possibility of 900-Mc operation. Difficult fabrication problems at the micron dimensions include properly placing the overlays to obtain isolated grid-base and grid-collector structures. GE Electronics Lab is studying evaporated cadmium sulfide devices containing an oxide-encased gold grid. In future experiments the cadmium sulfide may be replaced by zinc oxide to allow better control of trap density, which must be made very small.

• Field-effect triode—Most successful performance to date has been obtained with the cadmium sulfide thin-film transistor (TFT). This insulated-gate field-effect transistor operates in enhancement and depletion modes similarly to the silicon insulated-gate device. If performance can be improved and repeatable stable devices made, then the TFT would have the same potential for voltage controlled relay-type logic.

In the enhancement mode TFT's have had g_m's greater than 10,000 micromhos and 12-Mc gain-bandwidth

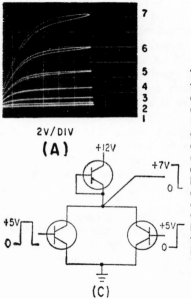

2V/DIV

(A)

TWO RCA TFT's with typical characteristics as shown in (A) are used with a common load resistor in NOR gate (B); a 5-v pulse applied to input of either TFT gate (C) causes output to drop by 3 v (D). Two-stage audio amplifier (E) has circuit (F) which is not yet fully operative but has first stage waveform shown for 10-Kc input in (G)—Fig. 13

(C)

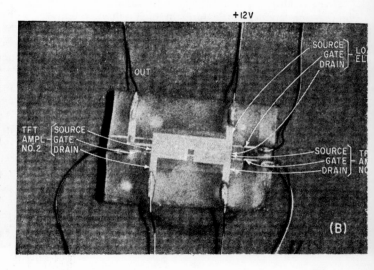

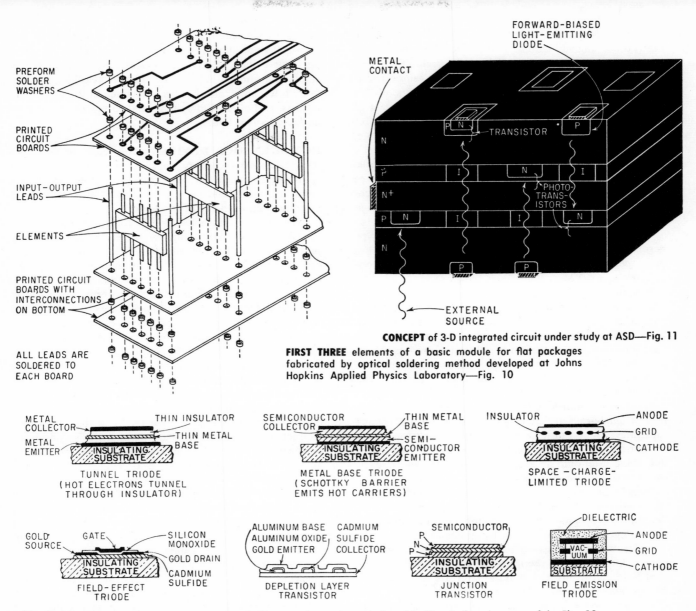

PREFORM SOLDER WASHERS

PRINTED CIRCUIT BOARDS

INPUT–OUTPUT LEADS

ELEMENTS

PRINTED CIRCUIT BOARDS WITH INTERCONNECTIONS ON BOTTOM

ALL LEADS ARE SOLDERED TO EACH BOARD

METAL CONTACT

FORWARD-BIASED LIGHT-EMITTING DIODE

N

P̄

N+

P

N

TRANSISTOR

I

N

I

PHOTO-TRANS-ISTORS

P

P

EXTERNAL SOURCE

CONCEPT of 3-D integrated circuit under study at ASD—Fig. 11

FIRST THREE elements of a basic module for flat packages fabricated by optical soldering method developed at Johns Hopkins Applied Physics Laboratory—Fig. 10

METAL COLLECTOR

THIN INSULATOR

THIN METAL BASE

METAL EMITTER

INSULATING SUBSTRATE

TUNNEL TRIODE
(HOT ELECTRONS TUNNEL THROUGH INSULATOR)

SEMICONDUCTOR COLLECTOR

THIN METAL BASE

SEMI-CONDUCTOR EMITTER

INSULATING SUBSTRATE

METAL BASE TRIODE
(SCHOTTKY BARRIER EMITS HOT CARRIERS)

INSULATOR

ANODE

GRID

CATHODE

INSULATING SUBSTRATE

SPACE–CHARGE-LIMITED TRIODE

GOLD SOURCE

GATE

SILICON MONOXIDE

GOLD DRAIN

CADMIUM SULFIDE

INSULATING SUBSTRATE

FIELD–EFFECT TRIODE

ALUMINUM BASE
ALUMINUM OXIDE
GOLD EMITTER

CADMIUM SULFIDE COLLECTOR

DEPLETION LAYER TRANSISTOR

SEMICONDUCTOR

P
N
P

INSULATING SUBSTRATE

JUNCTION TRANSISTOR

DIELECTRIC

ANODE

VAC-UUM

GRID

CATHODE

SUBSTRATE

FIELD EMISSION TRIODE

TRUE INTEGRATED thin-film circuits could result if research on these active thin-film devices is successful—Fig. 12

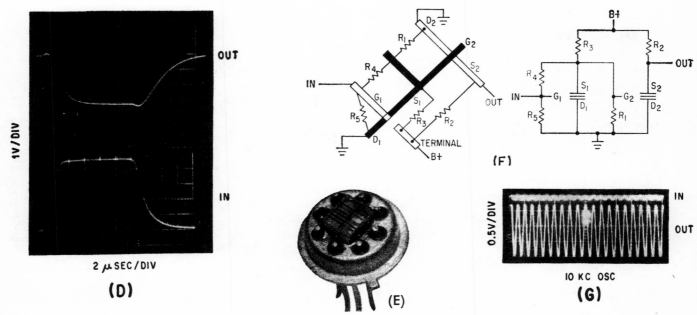

1V/DIV

OUT

IN

2 µSEC/DIV

(D)

D₂

R₁

G₂

R₄

S₂

IN

OUT

R₅

G₁

S₁

R₃

R₂

D₁

TERMINAL

B+

B+

R₃

R₂

OUT

R₄

S₁

G₂

S₂

IN

G₁

D₁

D₂

R₅

R₁

(F)

(E)

0.5V/DIV

IN

OUT

10 KC OSC

(G)

products.[20] Materials other than cadmium sulfide have been used, higher mobility of some 3-5 compounds may make these more promising. Typical TFT's (see Fig. 13A) have $g_m \approx 3,000$ micromhos/v, source resistance $\approx 15,000$ ohms and amplification factors of 30. They have recently been used under an ONR contract to fabricate complete circuits such as a NOR gate (Fig. 13B) and an audio amplifier with a gain of 20 db up to 70 Kc.

• Depletion layer transistor—Raytheon is studying a field-effect device analogous to the depletion layer transistor. Carriers are injected directly into the space charge region at the collector surface; by adjusting base potential it is believed feedback can be prevented and high frequency operation result.[21]

Philco has a similar device with single-crystal n-type germanium as the collector. Power gain of 10 db has been measured at 10 Mc and oscillation has been observed above 40 Mc.[22]

• Some feel growing single-crystal semiconductors onto single-crystal or amorphous substrates will be more fruitful than trying to build majority-carrier amplifiers.

Sylvania is attempting to form thin-film silicon p-n junction devices on ceramic substrates by rheotaxial growth. They have deposited laboratory diodes and transistors, latter giving alphas of approximately 0.985 and betas of about 60 at $V_{ce} = 5$ v and $I_B = 0.1$ ma.[23]

General Dynamics/Astronautics is researching deposition of single-crystal semiconductor films on amorphous substrates. They fabricate 500-angstrom-thick seed crystal films on a soluble substrate by direct epitaxy, then float the crystal onto an amorphous substrate and thicken by pyrolytic decomposition.

Melpar has deposited tunnel diodes pyrolytically on fused silica substrates. Martin is studying depositing germanium heteroepitaxially on sodium chloride and then separating the germanium film by sublimation.

• Vacuum thin-films—Most ambitious and original approach may well be the four-year-old program at Stanford Research Institute to build micron-size field-emission triodes and tetrodes.[24] Sponsored by USAERDL and ONR, aim is a one-cubic-inch data processing machine with 10^{11} amplifying, switching, storage and transducer elements. Devices would be fabricated from refractory metals by electron-beam-activated machining, are expected to withstand 900 C temperature, operate at less than 100 v and support (at micron size only) 10^7 to 10^8 w per square inch. While no devices have been built yet, simulation studies indicate the idea is feasible. Resolution of 300 angstroms has been obtained in the machining process, and a vacuum system built to reach 10^{-12} mm of mercury in two hours.

HOMOGENEOUS DEVICES—This class of junctionless devices may someday yield the true function-oriented approach to microelectronics, where discrete circuit elements are absent and the electronic function is performed by some bulk property of the material.

One that has attracted considerable attention is the cadmium sulfide ultrasonic amplifier, which uses the piezoelectric effect for electric-to-sonic coupling. Bell Labs is presently studying ways to suppress spontaneous oscillations so it can operate c-w, possibly at 100's of Mc.

Immediate plan is to use it as a booster in a broadband delay line. However, if better transducers can be devised it might be a high-frequency transistor substitute. This would require transducers with large conversion efficiencies at losses below 6-10 db. Diffusion-layer transducers, where copper forms a high resistivity layer in conductive cadmium sulfide, might be the answer here.

Other homogeneous devices include the cryosar, oscillistor and helicon. Latter is under study at Ecole Normale Superieure in Paris, works by a traveling-wave interaction in a semiconductor plasma. It is considered promising as a low frequency isolator, has operated at 50 Mc. Active geometrics are also being sought.

Combinations of materials phenomena may also lead to new types of function-oriented devices. One presently under preliminary investigation by ASD is photoferroelectricity—the varying of ferroelectric characteristics of materials by incident light. Devices utilizing photopiezoelectricity are also anticipated.

Navy and others feel not enough work is being done in bioelectronics and self-organizing systems. Stepped-up effort in these areas could have an important influence on microelectronics, lead to capability for high component redundancy, self-diagnosis and healing through exploitation of such areas as electrochemical phenomena, organic semiconductors and artificial neurons.

REFERENCES

(1) E. Keonjian and J. Marx, The Arma Micro Computer for Space Applications, Spaceborne Computer Conference, Anaheim, Calif., Oct. 1962.
(2) A. Gross, Cleveland Metal Specialties, private comm., Nov. 6, 1962.
(3) G. Mealey, General Dynamics Astronautics, private comm., Dec. 1962.
(4) EIA Microsystem Electronics Bulletin No. 1, Recommended Terminology in Microsystem Electronics, Dec. 1962 (definitions formulated by MCA-1 and 2 subcommittees).
(5) W. D. Fuller, Lockheed Missiles and Space Co., private comm., Nov. 27, 1962.
(6) W. D. Fuller, Production Techniques for Integrated Electronics, 6th National Conference on Product Engineering and Production, San Francisco, Nov. 1962.
(7) W. W. Eckess, Pacific Semiconductors, private communication, Nov. 30, 1962.
(8) F. M. Wanless and C. T Sah, Nanowatt Logic Using Field-Effect Metal-Oxide Semiconductor Triodes, paper to be presented at 1963 International Solid-State Circuits Conference, Philadelphia.

(9) P. S. Castro, A Thin-Film Frequency Discriminator, East Coast Conference on Aerospace and Navigational Electronics, Baltimore, Oct. 1962.
(10) W. E. Newell, Proc IRE, p. 2, 517, Dec. 1962.
(11) H. C. Lin, M. J. Geisler, and K. K. Yu, A New Unipolar-Bipolar Transistor Configuration for Integrated Audio Amplifiers, paper to be presented at 1963 International Solid-State Circuits Conference, Philadelphia.
(12) D. S. King, G. R. Madland, and W. J. Carrigan, Methods of Isolation of Active Elements in Integrated Circuits, IRE PGED meeting, Wash., Oct. 1962.
(13) A. D. Evans, Molecular Electronics Telemetry Encoder, Texas Instruments Interim Engineering Report 02-62-4 under contract No. AF 33(616)-8339, Jan. 1962.
(14) W. W. Gaertner, Nanowatt Devices, IRE PGED meeting, Wash., Oct. 1962.
(15) G. J. Veth, High Density Microelectronic System Realization, National Winter Convention on Military Electronics, Los Angeles, Jan. 1963.
(16) R. H. Norman and R. C. Anderson, Testing of Micrologic Elements, WJCC, Los Angeles, May 1961.
(17) P. K. Weimer, Thin-Film Active Devices, East Coast Conference on Aerospace and Navigational Electronics, Baltimore, Oct. 1962.
(18) W. Tantraporn, How Good Are Thin-Film Triodes, ELECTRONICS p 29, Dec. 28, 1962.
(19) M. M. Atalla, The Hot Electron Triode with Semiconductor-Metal Emitter, Northeast Electronics Research and Engineering Meeting (NEREM), Boston, Nov. 1962.
(20) H. Borkan and P. K. Weimer, Characteristics of the Insulated-Gate-Thin-Film Transistor, NEREM, Boston, Nov. 1962.
(21) J. M. Lavine and A. A. Iannini, The Metal Interface Amplifier, NEREM, Boston, Nov. 1962.
(22) R. F. Schwarz et al, A Tunnel Emission Triode, IRE PGED meeting, Washington, Oct. 1962.
(23) E. Rasmanis, Thin Film Semiconductor PN Junction Devices, NEREM, Boston, Nov. 1962.
(24) M. M. Perugini and N. Lindgren, Microminiaturization, ELECTRONICS, p 77, Nov. 25, 1960.

PROGRESS AND PITFALLS IN
Microelectronics

Two of the most important problems in microelectronics are to resolve the difficulties of making transistors and diodes with thin-film deposition techniques, and conversely, of forming resistors and capacitive components with techniques developed for semiconductor work.

By J. J. SURAN

Electronics Laboratory, General Electric Company, Syracuse, New York

AMONG the objectives of microelectronics are reduction of size, weight and cost, plus increased reliability, improved power utilization and more functional capabilities per unit volume of equipment. Size and weight reduction is to be achieved by new fabrication techniques such as electrolytic deposition, or evaporation of thin films. Increased reliability will come through use of fewer solder connections, or through their replacement by chemically bonded material interfaces, by improved control of materials and processes used in fabricating the circuit elements, and finally, by increased use of redundancy on the componenet or circuit level. Cost reduction will be a by-product of improved construction and assembly techniques. The vast efforts in material technology may also lead to basic new devices ultimately superseding the transistor and related devices because of improved performance and more efficient power utilization.

To appraise the objectives of microelectronics, it is first necessary to consider that the end result of microelectronics is equipment and systems, not devices. To realize the best possible microelectronic system it is necessary to maintain a high degree of flexibility in the choice of component technologies and to appreciate that any technology selected for implementation must be subject to manufacturing process control, production standardization, acceptance testing and must be compatible with other technologies used in the same system.

APPLICABLE TECHNOLOGIES —The gamut of technologies applicable to microelectronics includes semiconductors, dielectrics, magnetics, superconductors, thermionics, metallic films and optoelectronics, and others that may become significant as time goes on. It will probably be necessary to integrate several of these technologies in microelectronics to achieve op-

DIFFICULTIES *of fabricating semiconductors making use of thin film techniques are overcome in this thin-film flip-flop*

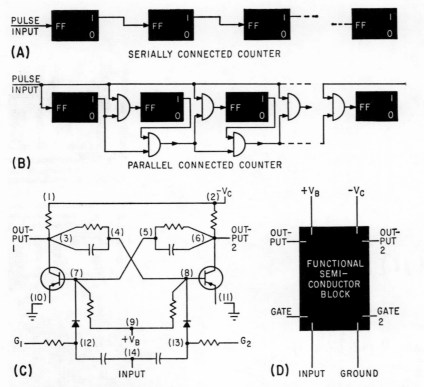

(A) SERIALLY CONNECTED COUNTER

(B) PARALLEL CONNECTED COUNTER

(C)

(D) FUNCTIONAL SEMI-CONDUCTOR BLOCK

LOGIC *in a serial counter (A) is considerably simpler than in a parallel counter (B); the serial version has fewer interconnections. Bistable circuit from individual components has 14 connection points (C); functional block arrangement has 8 (D)—Fig. 1*

ABILITY OF FOUR TECHNIQUES TO FULFILL CIRCUIT FUNCTIONS—TABLE I

Component	Semiconductor	Metallic Film	Ferrite	Optoelectronic
Inductor.............			✓	
Transformer.........			✓	
Memory.............		✓	✓	
Resistor.............		✓		
Capacitor...........		✓		
Diode..............	✓			
Switch.............	✓			
Amplifier...........	✓			
Display.............				✓

timum system results. For example, Table I shows how four of these technologies: semiconductors, metallic films, ferrites and optoelectronics, fulfill nine device functions. None of the four technologies meets all the requirements for components in conventional electronic systems. Hence an optimum design will select from the available techniques to best fulfill its needs.

SYSTEM CONSIDERATIONS— Figure 1 illustrates two binary-counter configurations capable of performing the same counting function. One is a serially connected counter, the other parallel

connected. Although the parallel configuration is more complicated, it is used where the serial counter's propagation time prevents operation at high speed. Comparing a 10-stage counter assembled from conventional, discrete components with a counter made up of functional semiconductor circuits emphasizes their relative complexity. Figure 1 also illustrates the two building blocks used for comparison. The semiconductor functional circuit allows a 45-percent reduction in interconnection nodes.

Table II shows the total number of interconnection nodes for the serial and parallel counter config-

urations, with both types built first from discrete components, and then from functional blocks. The functional block version of the serial counter produces a 50-percent reduction of interconnections, while the functional block parallel counter produces only a 28-percent improvement. The difference between the 28-percent and 50-percent advantage of the functional block configurations comes through the extra connections required for additional logic in the parallel design.

An example of how undue component constraints can obviate the advantages of microelectronics on the system level can be shown by considering the use of direct-coupled transistor logic (DCTL) in applications which are clearly not advantageous for it. The DCTL principle is attractive because it attempts to realize all logical functions using only resistors and transistors. However, the DCTL approach sometimes leads to considerable system complexity through lack of capacitors and diodes, which often contribute to a more straightforward design.

Figure 2 shows a DCTL flip-flop configuration, commercially available in microelectronic form, which performs the same function as the Eccles Jordan flip-flop and pulse transmission gate shown in Fig. 1. Even on the circuit level, the DCTL flip-flop is more complicated than the flip-flop of Fig. 1. Table III illustrates the additional system complexity encountered by using DCTL for the 10-stage binary counter. Considering the serial counter configuration, the first two entries in the table show the number of interconnection nodes required when the counter is realized with discrete components using resistors, capacitors, diodes and transistors and when only resistors and transistors are used in DCTL circuits. The significant increase in complexity due to DCTL is impossible to overcome even if semiconductor functional blocks are used.

RELIABILITY—Another question commonly arising in microelectronics depends upon component tolerances for a solution. What constitutes an allowable tolerance for a deposited resistor or transistor in a functional block? From a circuit point of view, most component

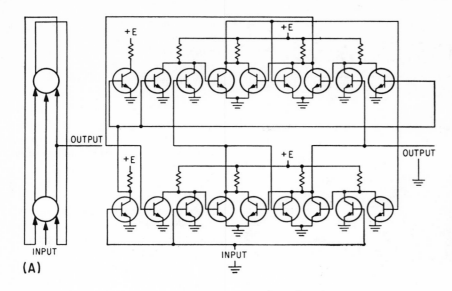

(A)

(B)

DESIGN TOLERANCE

DIRECT-COUPLED *transistor logic often brings added complexity and increased interconnections that could be avoided with capacitors or inductors, (A). Optimum circuit design implies tolerances that are not so loose that drift may prevent operation, nor so tight that increased stress may cause catastrophic failure (B)—Fig. 2*

COMPARISON OF CONNECTIONS IN FUNCTIONAL BLOCK AND SEPARATELY WIRED BINARY COUNTERS—TABLE II

Ten Stage Binary Counter	Discrete Components	Semiconductor Functional Blocks
Serial Configuration		80
Parallel Configuration	227	

COMPARING INTERCONNECTIONS FOR BINARY COUNTERS USING THREE TYPES OF LOGIC—TABLE III

Ten Stage Binary Counter	Discrete Components		Semiconductor Functional Blocks
	RCDTL	DCTL	
Serial Configuration		500	
Parallel Configuration	227	690	230

tolerances or drift can be taken into account in circuit design with increased dissipation as the price paid for broader tolerances.[1] Some minimum power dissipation exists in every circuit, even if ideal components with zero tolerance are used. But as component tolerances increase, more power must be dissipated if the circuit is to work despite the component variations. As circuit power levels are increased, however, the components themselves become subject to greater stresses and consequently the higher power levels may lead cumulatively to an increase in component catastrophic failures. An optimum design tolerance, therefore, balances drift failures against catastrophic failures, as illustrated in Figure 2. Overdesigned circuits may fail catastrophically, while underdesigned circuits may be subject to too many component-drift failures. A great deal has been published about designing micropower circuits to increase packing densities in microelectronic systems. However, considering the relationship between system reliability and circuit power dissipation, micropower circuits may well sacrifice reliability to accommodate com-

ponent packing densities. In a review article on microelectronics, it was stated, "Recent in-microcircuit transistor failures tend to fall in the out-of-spec rather than the catastrophic category."[2] This could indicate that the microcircuits re-

BACK TO THE BEGINNING

Just when transistor technology has evolved empirical but valid rules for designing reliable circuits, we land back into the laboratory with microelectronic methods of synthesizing systems.

Microelectronics cannot be dismissed as just a method of building transistor circuits along conventional lines only under a microscope. New fabricating techniques have been developed for preparing active and passive components. And new methods must be produced to resolve their incompatibilities.

Although much of microelectronic knowledge draws heavily on thin-film deposition techniques, and on methods developed by semiconductor manufacturers over the past decade, microelectronics is more than the sum of its individual parts. It offers many future advantages including increased reliability, small size and reduced cost per system

ferred to have been underdesigned from a reliability point of view.

Besides concluding that an optimum tolerance design point exists for maximum system reliability, implying in turn an optimum circuit power level, the reliability penalty for overdesign or underdesign becomes increasingly worse as the system complexity increases. And for a given system reliability, it is necessary to tighten component tolerances as the complexity of the system increases.

Redundancy as a cure for tolerance troubles is much easier to suggest than to apply in practice. Reserve components must be connected to allow the system to work even if components fail catastrophically. Some degree of inetrnal feedback should be employed in the system to protect against drift failures if the component tolerance problem is to be solved without use of cooling or without exceedingly tight component tolerance control. Furthermore, a means for testing the redundant blocks after production must be devised to make certain that all of the internal components are functioning properly. This requirement is important because, by the nature of redun-

TIMM SHIFT REGISTER MODULE

THERMIONIC *integrated module is one way to find a use for heat generated by electronic components. The module works like a package of vacuum-tube circuits, withstands high temperature and radiation—Fig. 3*

SEMICONDUCTOR DESIGN *used in fabricating a functional circuit flip-flop. It achieves the highest packing density of present day micro-electronic techniques—Fig. 4*

RESISTORS *and capacitors are deposited on an insulating substrate using thin-film techniques. Microdiodes and microtransistors are then attached to the deposited passive components—Fig. 5*

dancy, it would be possible to have many components fail in production while terminal measurements before shipment indicate that the system is operational.

PRESENT AND FUTURE—The capability in microelectronics spans the gamut from vacuum tubes to semiconductor functional components. The tube approach is to use thermionic integrated micromodules (TIMM) that permit operation at high temperatures and in high-radiation ambients, Fig. 3. In fact, the thermionic approach may be the only microelectronic technology at the present time capable of operating reliably at temperatures exceeding 150 deg. C or in radiation fields exceeding 10^{16} nvt. Another feature of the TIMM technique is that it is the only microelectronic technology today that actually utilizes heat as an operational component in the system. However, the thermionic approach has disadvantages as well as advantages. At the present time, the TIMM tubes have limited gain-bandwidth and, consequently, are of comparatively low speed. The high temperature required to operate TIMM components severely limits the types of components that can be used, particularly capacitors. Other disadvantages include the difficult maintenance procedures encountered because of the heat environment and also the necessity for a finite warmup time.

A second present capability is the semiconductor functional circuit illustrated in Fig. 4. Shown here is a flip-flop fabricated on a silicon wafer 70 mils square. The principal advantage of the semiconductor approach, as distinct from the thin-film deposition approach, is that it comes closer than any other device technology in achieving the high packing density and small number of interconnections expected from integrated electronics. In addition, the semiconductor functional circuit is fabricated from well-controlled materials with well-understood fabricating processes based upon some 10 years of transistor experience. Among the disadvantages of semiconductor functional approaches to microelectronics are the isolation problems encountered by packing many components on a noninsulating substrate. Other disadvantages include the limited range of passive components particularly resistors and capacitors and the difficult testing procedures required to determine whether or not closely-packed components fall into specified tolerance ranges.

A third production capability is the deposited integrated circuit illustrated in Fig. 5. Shown here is a flip-flop circuit consisting of six evaporated resistors and four evaporated capacitors, with two microdiodes and two microtransistors attached to the deposited passive components. The principal advantage of the deposited integrated circuit is that it starts with an insulating substrate, thus providing excellent isolation between all components. It also provides the greatest flexibility for fabricating different types of resistors and capacitors. From a speed point of view, the highest frequency circuits can be obtained with this approach. The principal disadvantage of the deposited integrated circuit is the need to interconnect separately-fabricated semiconductor elements, thus increasing the number of interconnections over the semiconductor functional circuit approach.

Considering the limitations of the present state-of-the-art in microelectronics, it is reasonable to expect laboratory efforts under way to play a significant role in the future of microtechnology. Present research and development effort in microelectronics is aimed at overcoming the disadvantages inherent in any one of these approaches. For example, semiconductor technology offers the best way of realizing active elements and diodes while thin metallic films offer the best approach to resistors, capacitors and memory elements. It is natural, therefore, to expect r&d efforts to be aimed at combining these two technologies into a compatible integrated approach to microelectronics. Several laboratories are experimenting with deposited metallic resistors and capacitors on passivated semiconductor substrates. If this effort is successful, it should be possible to combine transistors and diodes in semiconductor functional arrays directly with deposited metallic-film passive components, without the need of welding or soldering connections

ACTIVE ELEMENTS *such as diodes and transistors are most easily fabricated by conventional techniques. However, this matrix of 64 diodes was deposited onto its substrate by thin-film techniques—Fig. 6*

between them. This would combine the advantages of semiconductor active devices with the greater capability of the metal-film art in making passive components. A second approach to consolidate the semiconductor and metal-film technologies is aimed at depositing single-crystal semiconductors on insulating substrates. If this can be achieved successfully, technology will have advanced to a state where advantages of both metal-film and semiconductor devices would be available in integrated form while the disadvantages of either approach alone would have been overcome.

Other research and development efforts under way in several laboratories are aimed at overcoming the deficiency of metal films in the diode and active triode areas. Some success has already been achieved in evaporating metal film diodes on insulating substrates. Shown in Fig. 6, for example, is a matrix consisting of 64 diodes designed to operate as a commutator in a telemetry system.

It may be possible to make an active triode by combining evaporated metallic and insulating films to produce a device analogous to a vacuum tube or thin-film tunnel triode. Ultimate success of these approaches will depend on controlling a deposition process for films of the order of 10 atomic layers thick. Several approaches are being explored in an attempt to produce usable active triodes not requiring such ultrathin films but which are compatible with thin metallic-film components. These other ap-

proaches include research and development in the deposition of cadmium sulfide layers to achieve space-charge and field-effect triodes.

CONCLUSIONS — Considerable progress has been made in developing fabrication techniques for microelectronic circuits. However, no single approach available today achieves all the system advantages that comprise the general goals of microelectronics. Considerable research and development is under way to combine the semiconductor and thin-metallic film technologies and also to increase the capability of each. The introduction of microelectronic techniques and devices to practical systems will probably progress in evolutionary stages, starting today with arithmetic and logic sections of military computers and ultimately spanning the entire gamut of electronics as both economic realities and technological advances catch up with expectations.

The author is grateful to many colleagues for information and discussion, and acknowledges the assistance of L. Ragonese and B. Rutter of the Electronics Laboratory, M. Clark of the Semiconductor Products Department, J. Crittenden of the Receiving Tube Department and G. Siegel of the Light Military Electronics Department.

REFERENCES
(1) J. J. Suran, Circuit Considerations Relating to Microelectronics, *PROC. IRE,* p 420 Feb., 1961.
(2) *Electronic Design,* Feb., 1962.

LONG-RANGE DATA *transmission is one of the key research areas at IBM's recently dedicated La Gaude Labora-tory near Nice, France. Circuit costs may be cut with thin-film logic elements that are under development*

MICROELECTRONICS
AROUND THE WORLD

European and Japanese manufacturers are looking to integrated circuits for industrial computers, process control systems and—in a few cases—consumer items

An ELECTRONICS Staff Report

LARGE-SCALE APPEARANCE of microelectronics on the commercial scene may come first in Europe and Japan. Major companies there are taking a hard look at integrated circuits for industrial electronics applications. This could bring about the volume requirements that U. S. manufacturers predict will reduce integrated circuit prices below that of conventional components.

An on-the-spot check by McGraw-Hill World News correspondents confirms reports of "tremendous" interest in applying integrated circuits to commercial computers and process control systems (ELECTRONICS, p 22, May 10). This interest is spurred, especially in Europe, by the newness of their facilities and the strong push to automation arising from the shortage of skilled labor and climbing wage scales.

While actual applications are limited at present, some prototype equipment is being developed and most electronics companies expect significant applications to appear within the next five years. However, they are reticent to reveal details on specific equipment or techniques.

Like their U. S. counterparts, European and Japanese firms cite expectations of reduced cost, increased reliability and small volume as the main reasons for their interest in microelectronics. There is also general agreement that substantial consumer usage is further off. However, some Japanese firms are already fabricating prototype microelectronic items for the consumer market.

Here are the highlights of reports from six countries:

GREAT BRITAIN

Multimillion-dollar industrial electronics market predicted for microcircuits

LONDON—Silicon integrated circuits are on the verge of large-scale acceptance by British equipment makers. Strangely enough, first applications are likely to be more prolific in professional equipment than in military systems. But at present no one is saying what these commercial applications will be or even which firms are actively experimenting with integrated circuit designs.

The same close-mouthed attitude covers thin-film circuit applications. Only one manufacturer, Elliott-Automation Ltd., has announced any production uses for these techniques. In their new 503 computer, thin-film circuits will be used experimentally in the computer peripheral equipment. Another application is the switchover to thin-film RCTL sub-units for Elliott's Minilog package logic system. Third application revealed by Elliott uses thin-film units in a gyro stabilizer system.

In the integrated circuit area, the only announced applications come from Government research establishments. At the Royal Armament Research and Development Establishment, integrated circuits are being used in a high-speed tape comparator, Fig. 1, to locate and display differences between two 5-digit tapes. The Royal Radar Establishment has a tunable solid-state filter operating between 15 and 90 Mc. The filter makes use of the distributed capacitance associated with a diffused silicon resistor to form a twin-T network whose center frequency is shifted by altering the voltage on the voltage-dependent *p-n* capacitance.

But while few applications have been disclosed, there is plenty going on under the surface with five major companies, Standard Telephones and Cables Ltd. (an ITT subsidiary), Ferranti, Plessey, Texas Instruments and SGS-Fairchild offering silicon integrated circuits. Well advanced commercially is Texas Instruments with prototype applications already under test on industrial digital servos, commercial computer designs, airborne radar units, aircraft surface control systems and navigation computers. Plessey is finalizing a fast logic application for a 30-Mc counter and developing multi-emitter logic with good noise rejection capabilities.

THE MARKET—All five suppliers assess today's integrated circuit potential as lying firmly within

ON THE SCENE

Electronics is an international business and its coverage requires international footwork. This point is demonstrated by the accompanying story which resulted from the efforts of McGraw-Hill World News correspondents in six nations who contacted 50 electronics companies and filed 7,000 words of copy—all within a few weeks. The reporters: Derek Barlow (London), Charles Cohen (Tokyo), Arthur Erikson (Paris), Marc Messina (Milan), Richard Mikton (Bonn), and Robert Skole (Stockholm). Their copy was coordinated in New York by Senior Associate Editor Michael F. Wolff

the professional equipment rather than military systems. Confirming this view are current studies on integrated circuit applications for electronic telephone exchanges. One manufacturer says that compared to commercial applications of integrated circuits in the U. S., the U. K. commercial market will appear faster and be broader based.

British circuit suppliers are confidently talking about a multimillion dollar market in the U. K. Guesses as to when the upsurge will start vary from manufacturer to manufacturer. One company, Semiconductors Ltd., (a subsidiary of the Plessey group) anticipates its turnover in 1967 in integrated circuit sales will top $3 million. Other firms, like Texas Instruments, see a more rapid growth with the major boom occurring in 1964-5. Growth rate of the market is not expected to follow the normal smooth exponential rise but will be a step function when after this 1963-4 assessment period involving quantities of a few hundred integrated circuits, the production phase from 1965 on will call for thousands, a fact that has production men worried.

Paradoxically it is the lack of a heavy military program in the U. K. that has caused this ready acceptance of commercial integrated circuit applications. With little call for the microminiaturization afforded by the circuits, reliability and economic advantages are considered their chief selling points. This emphasis is causing changes as manufacturers seek ways to recoup their development costs. In place of the original thrust on logic circuits, British designers are switching to linear circuits and hybrid systems.

LINEAR CIRCUITS—Highest priority is on linear circuit development as offering the widest market potential. All manufacturers currently offer amplifiers with gains adjustable by feedback resistor variation, solid-state demodulators, phase splitters, and emitter followers. Typical of these circuits are Plessey's single chip amplifiers (gain of 25, 6-7 Mc bandwidth).

Main applications of linear circuits are foreseen in instrumentation and sections of communications equipment. At first, hybrid configurations are an-

THREE VERSIONS *of tape verifier designed at the British Government Research Establishment shows size reduction achieved between tube version (left), transistor and integrated circuit where all components are within the control unit—Fig. 1*

ticipated using both integrated circuit elements and conventional components. But this imposes economic problems on the manufacturer since cost of linear circuit elements must be comparable to the component assembly it replaces. Cost is currently the main sales feature because integrated circuits form only a part of the overall equipment and, therefore, the increased reliability stemming from their use is limited. Solid-state costs in the U. K. are expected to be comparable with conventional techniques by 1964-5.

An alternative approach finding favor with many users is a hybrid circuit where a thin-film substrate acts as a mechanical base for the silicon integrated circuits. The economics of this approach look promising as thin-film costs are expected to be equivalent to conventional techniques by next year. With heavy Government backing British thin-film production is growing rapidly; by the end of the year it is estimated that Mullard Ltd., Welwyn Electric Co., and STC will have a joint production capacity of 30,-000 thin films per week. But none of the manufacturers is saying just what the demand will be.

Solid-state logic elements—initially thought to have an immediate sales outlet—are not expected to get to full production for 2 or 3 years. Around 1967-8 the full production of electronic telephone systems, increased military applications and the commercial computer usage will push integrated circuit logic. But for the next couple of years the

majority of clock rates for computers in production will be in the kilocycle rather than megacycle range and suppliers will find it tough going to offer solid logic with its megacycle capability at prices competitive with conventional components. In the next computer generation now on the drawing board, solid logic elements will be used. Manufacturers claim this will be within 2 or 3 years.

Another factor slowing down acceptance of solid logic is the multiplicity of logic configurations currently available on the U. K. market: DTL (Ferranti), DCTL (Texas Instruments), RCTL (Welwyn and Elliott) together with multi-emitter logic. Most likely long-term solution seems to be the multi-emitter system. One manufacturer, Plessey Ltd., is already in pilot production of a single-chip multi-emitter transistor configuration providing two-level logic. The circuit, Fig. 2, performs AND operations on the multiple-emitter transistors and an OR-INVERT in the amplifiers. Propagation time for a 40-stage parallel adder is 1 microsec.

Consumer applications in the U. K. of integrated circuits for domestic radio and tv look far out. Reasons quoted by manufacturers range from excessive costs of integrated circuits to lack of requirements for the increased reliability. Only investigation reported underway, and this rather desultorily, is the application to hearing aids.

ITALY

Semiconductor microcircuits planned for commercial computers, are already in some prototype office equipment

MILAN—Italy's electronics industry—both home grown and foreign affiliated—shares the opinion that a "tremendous interest" exists throughout Western Europe in applying integrated circuits to commercial computers and process control systems. But the consensus is that actual commercial application of integrated circuits in these fields in Europe—and particularly Italy (excluding some specific NATO military contracts)—is still extremely limited—particularly so when compared to integrated-circuit progress in the United States.

Major electronics firms using or studying the use of semiconductor or thin-film integrated circuits in Italy include Olivetti, IBM Italia, Cea-Perego (electronics affiliate of the giant Edison company) and the Compagnia Generale di Elettricita (CGE), Italian affiliate of the American General Electric Co.

Giorgio Sacerdotti, director of Olivetti's electronic research laboratories in Rho says Olivetti has no intention of introducing integrated circuits in its existing machines as it would not be economically sound. However, the company is studying both semiconductor and thin-film integrated circuits for commercial computers and office equipment now in development. Several prototype commercial calculators use the new systems, but he said Olivetti could not release details at the present time.

Semiconductor integrated systems rather than thin-film systems are being favored in Olivetti's planning because of the former's more widespread

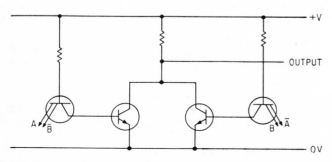

EXCLUSIVE-OR *integrated circuit developed at Plessey uses multiple-emitter transistors—Fig. 2*

(A)   (B)

MICROCIRCUITS *from Siemens (A) and Telefunken (B)*

use and consequent proven experience.

Industry sources suspect Olivetti will introduce its new semiconductor integrated circuit computers only when the company feels it can sell them at a profit. This may range from one to five years.

OTHER MANUFACTURERS—Cea-Perego's electronic computer expert Giorgio Quazza says his company is working on semiconductor integrated circuits for prototype computers it has under development. The firm also feels integrated circuits will have an important place in other process control devices it is developing.

Quazza says it will be one or two years before Cea Perego would consider using thin-film integrated circuits, which are still in the initial stages of development.

Enrico Chiesa, chief engineer for CGE, reports his firm is developing semiconductor circuits for eventual use in the computer and process control systems it manufactures as GE's Italian affiliate. He feels that since this type of integrated circuit has undergone more proven experience than that based on thin films, it will hold the lead over thin-film systems for at least the next few years.

Italy's largest semiconductor manufacturer, Societa Generale Semiconduttori, is currently marketing Fairchild's integrated circuits. But according to SGS sales manager Donald Rogers, Fairchild plans to build its Micrologic systems in Europe by 1964 utilizing SGS's Agrate facility and another plant in London. Rogers expects dollar volume of Fairchild affiliate sales in the U. K. and Western Europe this year to run from $1.5 million to $2 million. He says SGS is working with about eight large computer manufacturers in Europe.

SGS plans to do some thin-film work, and Rogers feels the future of integrated circuits will be in hybrid systems utilizing a combination of semiconductor and thin-film devices.

Although SGS plans to do some work in radio circuits, Rogers believes it will be "quite some time" before component manufacturers can slash the price of their product to the low price necessary to meet the "cheap cost" demands of the radio and tv manu

facturers. The manufacturers of these "low cost" consumer products will accept only very low-cost electronic components for their products, he says.

Among advantages cited by Rogers are lower cost resulting from less design time required to plan integrated circuit systems, fewer parts, smaller boards, and so forth. SGS estimates semiconductor integrated circuits, although they may be more expensive per individual unit will cut costs as much as 25 percent in setting up overall electronics systems.

Siemens Elettra SpA, Italian affiliate of the West German Siemens Group, imports semiconductors from Germany where the company has been building commercial computers and process control systems since 1956, and where they are now applying semiconductor integrated circuits to these products

Engineer Arnaldo Moruzzi says Siemens is working with semiconductors rather than thin-films, feels thin films are still 'too costly too sophisticated, too refined" to be accepted by the average Italian company

Siemens is counting on something like $10 million in computer sales for fiscal 1963-64 but Moruzzi emphasizes the company is still in the groundwork stage He feels integrated circuits are an "absolute necessity" to meet the needs of advanced electronics systems. The cost is "still rather high priced," but microelectronic systems are "fulfilling high-priced functions." He adds that the cost of integrated circuits is still "far toc high" for consumer items.

WEST GERMANY
Integrated circuits are under development for both industrial and consumer applications

BONN—Leading West German electronics companies are of the opinion that progress here in solid-state and thin-film integrated circuits is presently at a stage that was reached in the U. S. some two years ago. However, all of the large firms — including Siemens, Telefunken, Standard Elektrik Lorenz and Grundig—report substantial laboratory development work on integrated circuits for applications varying from computers through aerospace equipment to industrial electronics and consumer goods Siemens expects to use integrated circuits in the model 3003 commercial computer it is now building but will not change over its present 2002 model.

Telefunken says its offering three months ago of seven solid-state circuits for computer applications has met with gratifying success. Telefunken's progress in this sector is typical of a cautious but hopeful policy by German electronics manufacturers of developing components and finding applications in order to be prepared when the first really substantial demand occurs in three to five years' time. DCTL and ECTL circuits are out of the laboratory stage at Telefunken and available as samples for computer, data-processing, aerospace, instrumentation and military applications, where their small size and high order of dependability argue against their relatively high cost. The company says a small but technically important market already exists in Europe in the military and satellite fields.

CONSUMER APPLICATIONS — Widespread consumer goods applications cannot be expected for another five years, in the opinion of several companies whose plans include immediate market penetration in those sectors where the circuits' advantages overshadow their higher cost. Standard Elektrik Lorenz reports it is well along with laboratory testing of thin-film circuits employing tantalum (among other materials), concentrating on amplifiers, power supplies and passive circuits. The company expects to make its first deliveries in 1964, having already discussed a range of possible uses with various equipment manufacturers.

First area of application should be in data processing equipment, although SEL says it is concentrating just as heavily on tv, radio and tape recorders. Although it is still too early to give even an approximate estimate of the market for such circuits, SEL engineers feel acceptance will be rapid once the first deliveries are on the market in consumer goods. Primary advantages for integrated circuits, in their opinion, is cost-cutting of mass-produced goods and increased dependability.

Grundig says its research labs are actively pursuing integrated circuit applications in both consumer goods as well as industrial equipment. The company's primary interest lies in items such as integrating apparatus, closed circuit tv cameras— where the present tendency is to smaller dimensions —and various types of office equipment (Grundig owns the Olympia company, one of West Germany's largest office machine manufacturers).

Grundig reports that all its development work at present is intended for application in its current product line (radios, tv sets, tape recorders). Management emphasizes they are only in a research phase and that application of developments is still far off. Circuits in development are not being discussed.

JAPAN

Microcircuits planned for telephone switching equipment and several consumer products

TOKYO—All Japanese semiconductor companies are studying integrated circuits, but most seem to be

(A)

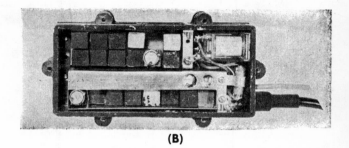

(B)

(C)

(D)

PROTOTYPES OF *consumer items in which Yaou Electric plans to use integrated circuits are pocket radio (A), transceiver (B), radio microphone (C) and pencil radio (D)*

waiting to see what types of circuits the Americans use for what, and their success, before committing themselves. With cost still a big stumbling block most people feel use of integrated circuits in any but the most specialized products is at least three to five years away. Nevertheless, some companies are pushing ahead on prototype development.

Middlesized Yaou Electric plans to develop several consumer items such as a pocket radio, pencil radio, transceiver, car radio, radio microphone, and radio page. The company also plans to use integrated circuits for industrial items such as tv cameras and tv broadcasting equipment including camera, auxiliary amplifier and synchronizing signal generator. The consumer items will probably use silicon circuits, while thin films look most suitable for the industrial products.

Sony's chief engineer says his company is starting to think about using integrated circuits in consumer equipment but has not yet made any definite plans.

TELEPHONE EQUIPMENT—Oki Electric Industry Co. is interested in using integrated circuits in computers and telephone exchanges. It considers speed one of the greatest advantages of applying integrated circuits to computers and is therefore looking toward all-thin-film integrated circuits for this application. On the other hand, semiconductor integrated circuits are expected to provide the increased reliability and small size considered important for telephone exchanges. Electronic telephone exchanges are expected to greatly reduce present need for expensive secondary facilities.

Although it is difficult at present to foresee the size of the market, Oki is convinced the economic feasibility of producing its integrated circuits will depend on demands for its computers and telephone exchanges. At present, trial production of semiconductor circuits is underway and thin-film circuits are being researched. Future plans include developing active thin-film elements, and trial manufacture of thin-film memories.

Nippon Electric plans to apply semiconductor integrated circuits to computers, telephone exchanges, carrier terminal equipment and others. It anticipates that by 1970 half the semiconductor devices for such equipments will be replaced by integrated circuits. Silicon circuits look most likely to be used because of their reliability.

Other companies studying integrated circuits for computers include Hayakawa Electric, Matsushita Electric Industrial Co. and Mitsubishi Electric. Matsushita is researching the introduction of thin-film circuits into some commercial computers that are presently all-transistorized. Thin films are expected to appear shortly in switching circuits, later in other portions. The company reports similar plans for consumer items like transceivers and tape recorders.

Mitsubishi is experimenting with various types of circuits but considers details company secret. Hayakawa is researching thin films primarily for small computers at this time because of the present high cost.

INTEGRATED CIRCUITS IN U. S. TELEPHONE SYSTEMS?

When informed of Japanese intentions to use integrated circuits in telephone switching equipment, two U. S. firms told **ELECTRONICS** they had no similar plans at this time but were actively studying the possibility.

Electronic switching system No. 1 being installed by Bell Telephone Labs at Succasunna, N. J., is using discrete components because present cost of integrated circuits is too high, according to R. W. Ketchledge, director of Bell's electronic switching lab. However, he foresees the need for integrated circuits in the future when machines must work faster and consequently be made much smaller to reduce delay times. Integrated circuits look promising for such applications and an exploratory development program is underway in which several basic types are being evaluated, he said.

Automatic Electric Company, a subsidiary of General Telephone & Electronics, is studying the use of silicon integrated circuits in telephone switching equipment, and believes that such usage will someday be feasible. With extreme compactness not so important in commercial telephone equipment, emphasis of the study will be on the expectations of greater reliability and (ultimately) lower cost than existing circuits using discrete components

SWEDEN

Integrated circuits under close scrutiny for industrial computers

STOCKHOLM — Standard Radio & Telefon AB, Bromma, is planning to use semiconductor integrated circuits in military and industrial type computers for series production starting 1967-68. Extensive use of integrated circuits is considered dependent on the reduction of present prices that is foreseen in the near future. The requirement for the individual circuit element is fairly moderate in logic circuits and will thus promote a good yield of the production of integrated circuits in these applications, the company feels.

Svenska Aeroplan Aktiebolaget (SAAB) reports that for the past couple of years it has been working on an integrated circuit technique in designing an airborne digital computer. SAAB, most famous for its jet fighter planes and rally-winning automobiles, has an electronics division that produces computers for civil and military use.

Viggo Wentzel, head of the computer department, says that as a result of this integrated circuit work "we have gained a lot of experience and we also feel that we have been successful in using integrated circuits for that particular project. Having this background it is quite natural that we are now studying the integrated circuit technology in order to find out if, and when, we can use this technology in our future commercial computers. From the same point of view, we are also interested in thin-film

CENTRAL DIGITAL COMPU-TER *and system control desk is type of equipment in which Sweden's Standard Radio & Telefon plans to use integrated circuits*

circuits or possibly in hybrids. The latter may be a more optimum technique at this time. As a consequence of our interest in this circuit technology, we have now started suitable evaluation work on the matter."

Wentzel adds that the basic advantage SAAB foresees for integrated circuits in commercial digital computer applications lies in increased reliability. He also says that during SAAB's early work with integrated circuits, they found that the assembly cost will be considerably reduced when the prices of integrated circuits "come down to a reasonable level."

"We have also found that layout and draft work was eased because the integrated technique allowed a more standardized logical symbolism," Wentzel says.

Speaking for L. M. Ericsson Co., the telecommunications firm, Percy Broomé says that his company has not introduced integrated circuits into any equipment manufactured by the firm "and we have no decisive plan to do so." He adds, however that the company is keeping abreast of developments in this field and has discussed the possibilities of using integrated circuits in certain control units in airborne equipment. This would be the first step in a coming chain of introducing integrated circuits in airborne and later on in ground equipment, both for military and civil purposes, Broomé says.

FRANCE

Major market is still military

PARIS—France seems to be an exception to the foregoing industrial electronics picture. Although all the heavyweights of the French electronics industry see high promise for integrated circuits, no one is far enough along with them to talk specifics about the potential commercial market.

True, by the end of the year the semiconductor manufacturing subsidiaries of CSF, Thomson-Hous-

ton and Philips all will have pilot production lines started up, or just about ready to start, but for the next two or three years only military applications seem likely. In fact, French Air Force research funds have financed the bulk of integrated-circuit R&D done so far.

The computer makers, too, are taking a hard look at these circuits. Bull, for example, says it's cooperating closely with component manufacturers to develop planar silicon circuits, and is working on superconducting thin films in its own laboratories. A top research engineer at Bull predicts a mass entry of integrated circuits in the computer field within the next five years, but refuses to be more specific than that.

At IBM-France, integrated circuits rate as just one of several avant-garde techniques that may one day cut down the cost of computers. At its La Gaude research center, for example, thin-film parametric cells are under development. They have relatively slow switching times but exceptional cost-cutting potential. However, IBM-France's research chief flatly states there's no prototype computer in the works for the moment.

SILICON DOMINATES—A look at the pilot-production units slated to go on the market next year shows the silicon integrated circuit dominating. CSF's subsidiary COSEM is setting up a line to produce logic circuits by the planar technique. And CSF has developed an experimental NOR circuit with four field-effect transistors plus passive components diffused into a silicon slab 1 mm by 1.5 mm. Still, a CSF engineer working on integrated-circuit research thinks that for the long haul the hybrid circuit shows the greatest promise because you can't get very high resistance and capacitance values in a silicon slab.

At SESCO (Societe Europeenne des Semi-conducteurs), the Thomson-Houston semiconductor subsidiary, silicon integrated circuits will start coming off a pilot production line early in 1964. The circuits and the technique used to produce them are very similar to General Electric's—SESCO will begin production using GE masks.

Still a third company, the Philips group subsidiary COPRIM (Compagnie des Produits Elementaires pour Industries Modernes) recently put on the market preproduction prototypes of hybrid integrated logic circuits using oxide films on a glass base for the passive elements. Like CSF and SESCO, COPRIM sees only military applications—notably airborne computers—in sight for the moment.

With military computer applications the only imminent potential market, French integrated-circuit manufacturers generally cite reliability first and component density second when talking about the advantages of integrated circuits. And all three agree that computers look far and away the most likely commercial application, but not until the price is right.

As far as consumer items go, the French feel that integrated circuits won't start to find their way into radio and tv sets until they're cheaper than conventional circuits. Right now, that seems several years off.

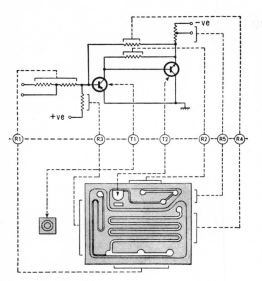

INTEGRATED *silicon microcircuit by Ferranti Ltd. is constructed from two silicon chips and contains two transistors and six resistors. Photo of circuit at right shows mounting in a reduced height JEDEC TO-5 case*

Microcircuits Are Busting Out in Britain

Production starts in thin film and integrated circuits

By DEREK BARLOW,
McGraw-Hill World News

LONDON — Microminiature units cheaper than conventional component assemblies, new modular construction methods, high power waveguide loads and calorimeters, a new piezoelectric ceramic material and microminiature 300 Mc planar transistors were the highlights of the recent British Radio and Electronic Component Exhibition held here. Attendance at the show was a record-breaking 49,000, while over 250 exhibitors represented Britain's burgeoning component industry.

Component output in Britain is now running at 3,000 million components a year, with a sales value of $384 million for 1962/63—an increase of more than 6 percent over 1961.

THIN FILMS — Greatest talking points of the show was industry's commercial adoption of microminiature elements and the number of companies offering either production thin film units, or fully integrated solid state circuits. Of the British companies now in full production on thin films, the Welwyn Electric Co. is producing 1,000 circuits a week and expect to produce 10,000 a week by the end of the year. Welwyn anticipate that in five years 50 percent of all their turn-over will be from thin film circuits, with main applications in logic elements.

Another manufacturer, Elliott Brothers Ltd., is switching over its Minilog logic system entirely to thin film circuits; this step alone will require $\frac{1}{4}$ million thin film units next year.

The Welwyn system uses high alumina ceramic as the base of the film substrate. The advantages claimed over glass substrates include higher strength, production in any geometry, higher thermal conductivity giving uniform heat distribution without hot spots, and better control over surface smoothness allowing better film adhesion. Films of nickel alloy are deposited with resistance from 10 ohms to 50 kilohms with 1.5 watt per sq. in. dissipation. At this power, resistance does not change after the first 1,000 hours more than 0.04 percent per thousand hours. Capacitors are formed from aluminum plates and silicon dioxide dielectric. While costs of the substrate are 25 to 50 percent higher than for the individual unwired conventional components, thin films are cheaper when compared with final wired assemblies of conventional components.

Also in production with thin film circuits for industrial applications is Mullard Ltd. Using a glass substrate 30 × 20 mm, Mullard is currently achieving packing densities of 350,000 components per cubic foot. Circuits developed to date include 50 Mc oscillators and 65 Mc video amplifiers. In the oscillator a 0.7 microhenry inductor was vacuum deposited.

CIRCUIT PACKAGING — While not giving packing densities anything like thin films, a new component packing system, Ministac, developed by Standard Telephones and

Cables Ltd. (ITT subsidiary) consists of two side mouldings each carrying the required circuit configuration on a two layer grid system with slotted solder terminals on a 0.1 in. pitch for mounting components. The side mouldings are supported by a pair of end plates which carry the external module terminals. Internal connections to these terminals are made by the end tags on the side assembly, with a maximum of four connections per end. End plates can also be mounted within the module.

The wiring pattern is formed from a 0.01 in. thick nickel-silver sheet punched with a standard pattern. To form the wiring pattern, the unwanted portions are cut away and the remainder is mounted on the moulding to form an interconnecting side assembly.

MICROWARE — Integrated circuits too are moving from research and development into production. Already Hughes, Texas Instruments, and SGS-Fairchild are marketing units in Britain. But new to the integrated circuit field is the British firm, Ferranti Ltd. Developed with only minimal government backing, the Ferranti system does not rely on integrating all circuits in one silicon chip. Often multiple chips are used, interconnected by thermocompression bonded gold wires. Linear amplification units and high speed logic circuits are now available. The linear units include a servo amplifier, demodulator and a 100 Mc linear amplifier with a 7.5 current gain. In addition to conventional single and double entry NOR gates and emitter followers, a transient memory unit is under development to allow serial machines with clock rates up to 5 Mc. Typical delay times of the gate units are less than 12 nsec.

FASTER SEMICONS—One experimental microminiature 300 Mc silicon planar transistor developed by Mullard is only 0.05 inch in diameter. A three-lead *npn* device for direct soldering on microcircuit substrates, the transistor has an amplification factor of 40 to 120 with 10-ma collector current. An experimental planar diode, also from

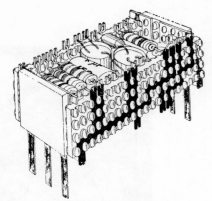

TYPICAL *ministac circuit with wiring on side mountings; dark side-sections are wiring punched from standard material*

Mullard, is claimed to have better piv rating, forward drop and shunt capacitance characteristics than present devices. Its recovered charge is less than 20 picocoulombs at 10 ma and it has a piv of 50.

Other new semiconductor devices on view include first U.K. production avalanche rectifiers. An STC 1.25-amp rectifier operates with a 1,000-v reverse working voltage and 4-kw energy dissipation; an Associated Electrical Industries 1,200-v all diffused rectifier handles 10 amps.

Application of Boff snap action diodes in pulse shaping networks sharpens up the leading edges of the pulse. A new diode developed by Ferranti obtains rise times of one nanosecond from 20-ns pulse generators. In the diode, the magnitude of the forward current control the delay time of the high reverse conduction period up to 100-ns. Transition from this state to reverse blocking takes 0.8-ns.

PIEZOELECTRIC IGNITION—In the other component areas the most significant innovation was a new high sensitivity ceramic piezoelectric material capable of generating automobile ignition sparks directly. Developed by Mullard, the substance, primarily a lead zirconate titanate, generates 400 v per millimeter of thickness when subjected to a 7,000 lb. psi pressure. Piezo sensitivity up to 100 v/mm per kg/mm^2 is controllable by the amount of polarization imparted to the material during manufacture.

Highlights from the remainder

of the show include:

• High power microwave loads and power meters developed by Marconi's Wireless Telegraph Company Ltd. now allow on-line measurements up to 3-kv. The new load, shown for the first time, consists of a ceramic compound moulded integrally into a normal length of waveguide to produce a taper from all four internal corners of the waveguide. This new ceramic absorbs power at a much higher rate than other types of load material, while the shape of the moulding produces an even absorption of power throughout the material. Maximum power dissipation is governed by surface temperature. Specially brazed and reinforced ends allow waveguide pressures up to 60 lb./in^2 while surface temperature maximum is now 300C, although up to 450C can be tolerated under certain conditions.

The power meter operates up to the same power level and comprises a high power waveguide load surrounded by an oval-shaped water jacket maintaining good thermal contact between the waveguide wall and the cooling water. Thermocouples mounted at the inlet and outlet water connections measure the water temperature rise.

• Vacuum capacitors now being manufactured by the English Electric Valve Company will handle up to 40 amps and provide tunable capacitance ranges of 5 to 750 pf. Other types extend the range to 2,000 pf.

Development is under way to raise current capacity to 75 amps.

• A new component fixing technique that eliminates all circuit board punching or drilling has been successfully developed by J & S Engineers Ltd. The hydrostatic method employed enables relatively soft objects to be punched through harder materials. The component being inserted acts as its own punch and locks itself securely within the circuit board. Special brass terminations are swaged onto the component lead wires, which are then cropped and formed to shape before punching.

On punching, the termination secures itself mechanically and connects electrically with the printed circuit wiring.

Chapter 6
NONLINEAR INTEGRATED CIRCUITS

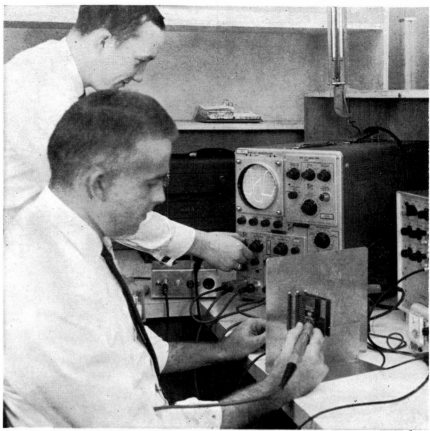

BREADBOARD CIRCUITS *of semiconductor networks are checked out*

*To apply
semiconductor networks
in digital equipment,
the designer has
to understand
the application rules
and design points
brought out here*

DESIGNING

DIGITAL EQUIPMENT WITH

Semiconductor Networks

By THOMAS COOPER and GENE McFARLAND, Engineers, Texas Instruments Inc., Dallas, Texas

ALTHOUGH semiconductor networks are still new to many equipment designers, the logic layouts and circuit functions are well-known. The techniques for implementing logic equations are similar to those used with discrete component circuits.

A series of these semiconductor networks, called Series 51, has been fabricated for application in digital equipment designs. Each network is a complete electronic circuit fabricated within a single piece of silicon (Solid Circuit). Fabricated using planar diffused structures with oxide protection and deposited leads on the surface to connect the components within the bar in the desired circuit configuration, the network bar is placed in a hermetically sealed package $\frac{1}{4}$ in. $\times$ $\frac{1}{8}$ in. $\times$ $\frac{3}{32}$ in. with 10 lateral leads.

LOGIC—This series of networks uses the RCTL (Resistor-Capacitor-Transistor-Logic) NOR/NAND configuration. This logic was selected because RCTL is widely used in present equipment design and be-

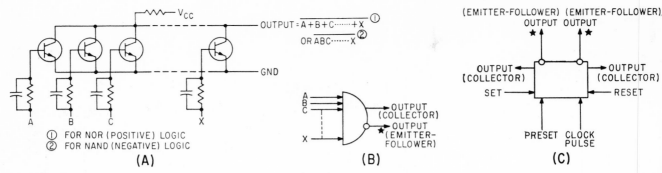

(A)

① FOR NOR (POSITIVE) LOGIC
② FOR NAND (NEGATIVE) LOGIC

OUTPUT = $\overline{A+B+C\cdots+X}$ ①
OR $\overline{ABC\cdots X}$ ②

(B)

(C)

RCTL is the basic circuit configuration (A). Logic symbol for the NOR/NAND gate (B), and logic symbol for R-S flip-flop (C)—Fig. 1

cause RCTL lends itself to good power-speed compromises. Also, wide tolerances of component values can be used without affecting circuit performance.

The NOR/NAND configuration is shown in Fig. 1A. The logical symbol for the RCTL NOR/NAND gate is shown in Fig. 1B. The star on the gate output designates the emitter-followers available on the

SN 511 and SN 513 (see Fig. 2). Also among the networks is a reset-set (R-S) flip-flop shown in Fig. 1C.

For implementing binary algebra, two logic assignments are possible, either NOR or NAND. In one system, NOR, a logical *one* is represented by a voltage level and a logical *zero* is represented by no voltage. The NAND system results if

the assignments are reversed:

	Binary 0	Binary 1
NOR	Low voltage	High voltage
NAND	High voltage	Low voltage

A gate can be used as either a NOR or NAND gate, depending upon the logic system selected. The transfer functions of the gates are:

	Inputs	Outputs
NOR	$A, B, \ldots X$	$\overline{A\,B\ldots X}$ or $\overline{A+B+\ldots+X}$
NAND	$A, B, \ldots X$	$\overline{A+B+\ldots+X}$ or $\overline{AB\ldots X}$

The two logic systems are duals with the NOR logic favoring maxterm type equations and the NAND logic favoring minterm type equations. (A maxterm equation is one in which the logic is arranged as a product of sums, that is, $(A + B)(C + D)$; in the minterm type equation, the logic is arranged as a sum of products, that is, $AB + BC$.) Implementing an equation with its favored type of logic ordinarily results in the best system with respect to economy and speed. It is sometimes possible to reduce the number of gates connected in series, hence increasing speed at the expense of using extra networks.

Any equation may be readily reduced to its simplest minterm form; however, it is often difficult to expand an equation in minterm form into a maxterm type that is reduced to the optimum form for implementation. For this reason, NAND logic is usually preferred. Further, the input equations of the R-S flip-flop (SN 510-511) (see Fig. 2) are defined to be compatible with NAND logic.

Logic types should be chosen after giving consideration to the requirements of a particular system. A combination of the two types is often used, especially where a

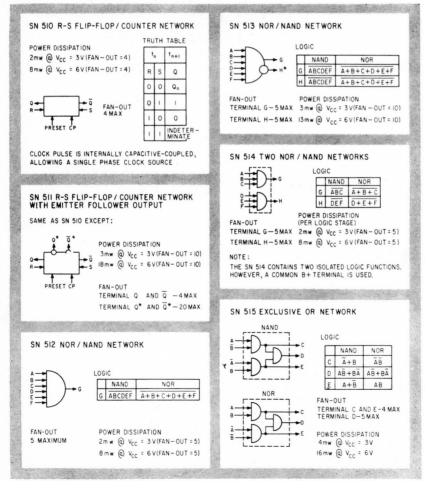

LOGIC, schematic, fan-out and power drain for semiconductor networks applicable to digital equipment—Fig. 2

60

TABLE–FAN-OUT CAPABILITIES

	D-C Fan-Out	A-C Fan-Out Clock Frequency <500 Kc	A-C Fan-Out Clock Frequency >500 Kc
SN510	4	5	Use SN511
SN511	20	5	5 (from e-f output)
SN512	5	5	Use SN513
SN513	25	5	5 (from e-f output)
SN514	5	5	Use 513
SN515 (each gate)			
Exclusive on	5	5	Use SN513
Auxiliary	5	5	Use SN513

subsystem interface requires a change in logic levels.

EQUIPMENT DESIGN — Specifications applicable to all these networks are: supply voltage, 3 v to 6 v d-c; operating temperature range, − 55 deg C to + 125 deg C. The individual logic, schematic diagrams, fan-out and power drain are shown in Fig. 2.

The flip-flops can be used either in synchronous or asynchronous systems and can, without additional steering, be connected as either counter or shift-register stages.

For digital equipment design, the designer may set up application rules for each circuit to be used. In this way, the connection pattern that conforms to the rules will operate properly and no individual pattern analysis is required. The rules that must be established are: (1) maximum fan-out to be allowed; (2) maximum fan-in available; (3) maximum number of gates which may be connected in series between clocked flip-flops.

FAN-OUT & FAN-IN — Fan-out represents the number of parallel loads that can be driven from one output node as shown in Fig. 3A.

A load, which for these networks is a d-c load, can be represented by the equivalent circuit in Fig. 3B.

Any of these networks will drive any other network in the series. For high fan-out requirements ($N = 20$-25), emitter-followers can be used on the flip-flop (SN 511) and gate (SN 513). If maximum d-c fan-out of the emitter-follower output on SN 511 or SN 513 is used, fan-out from the collector output is not available; otherwise, a combination of loading from the emitter-

SEMICONDUCTOR NETWORKS FOR DIGITAL EQUIPMENT

All the semiconductor networks discussed in this article are encased in the hermetically sealed package shown here.

This 0.001 cubic inch package weighs 0.05 gram. A Kovar-glass seal around the leads and metal-to-metal bond of the final package creates the hermetic seal.

Leads are gold-plated Kovar allowing bonding to external conductors by either welding,

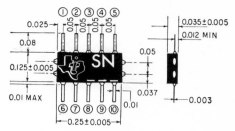

ALL DIMENSIONS IN INCHES

soldering or thermocompression bonding. The center-to-center lead spacing of 0.05 in. is a unit multiple of preferred spacing for many interconnection techniques

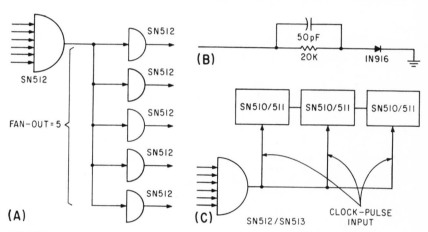

GATE *with a fan-out of 5 (A); equivalent circuit for one d-c load (B); and example of a-c loading on a gate (C)—Fig. 3*

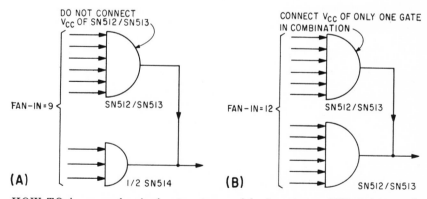

HOW TO *increase fan-in for two types of logic gates, a SN514 (A), and a SN512 (B)—Fig. 4*

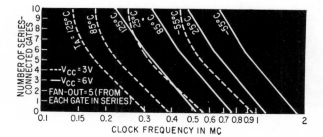

NUMBER of *gates that can be connected in series between clocked flip-flops plotted against operation frequency—Fig. 5*

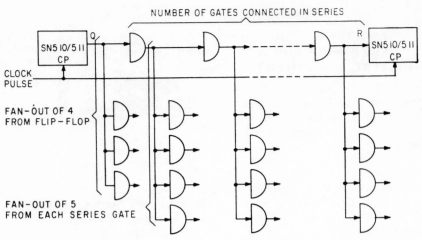

LOGIC ARRANGEMENT *used to determine the maximum clock frequency*
—*Fig. 6*

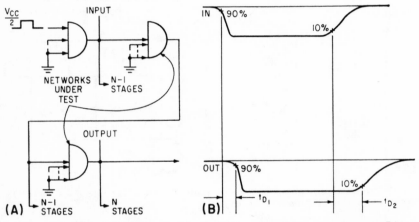

PROPAGATION DELAY *test circuit (A) and voltage waveforms (B)—*
Fig. 7

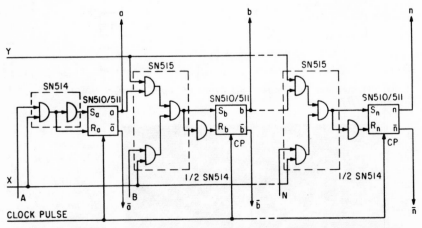

SHIFT REGISTER *having parallel read-in and serial read-out, with transfer at each clock pulse—Fig. 8*

follower and collector outputs can be used. All gate inputs and the reset, set, or preset inputs of the flip-flop are considered d-c loads.

Alternating-current loading of a network occurs when its output drives the clock-pulse input of a flip-flop (Fig. 3C). The effect of the added capacitance (approximately 100 pf per clock pulse input) limits a-c fan-out from the networks to 5. Also, at clock rates above 500 Kc, only emitter-follower outputs should be used when driving a-c loads.

A summary of the fan-out capabilities over the — 55 deg C to + 125 deg C operating temperature range is shown in the Table.

In certain cases, simultaneous fan-out into both d-c and a-c loads from the same gate is required. If a gate is driving the maximum number of a-c loads (5) it can simultaneously fan-out into 60 percent of the maximum number of d-c loads. For example, maximum loading (a-c and d-c simultaneously) for SN 512 is 5 a-c loads + 3 d-c loads, and for SN 513 is 5 a-c loads + 15 d-c loads.

Fan-in represents the number of inputs that can be connected to a logic network that will give one output. The fan-in for a logic gate can be increased by connecting the output nodes of two gates and using only one common load resistor (Fig. 4A and Fig. 4B).

PROPAGATION DELAY—In design of digital equipment, it is normally necessary to know the maximum number of gates that can be connected in series between clocked flip-flops. This is a function of the frequency of operation, the supply voltage, the fan-out of the gates connected in series and the temperature range for which the equipment is designed. For the Series 51 networks, this function is shown in Fig. 5 at $V_{cc} = 3$ v and at $V_{cc} = 6$ v. Fig. 6 shows the logic arrangement used to determine the maximum clock frequency. A fan-out of 5 from each series gate is used, which is probably more severe than normal systems require. Maximum clock pulse frequencies will be increased (average propagation delay decreased) if the fan-out is less than 5 from each gate in series. Also an increase of 10 to 20 percent in clock frequency can be obtained if the emit-

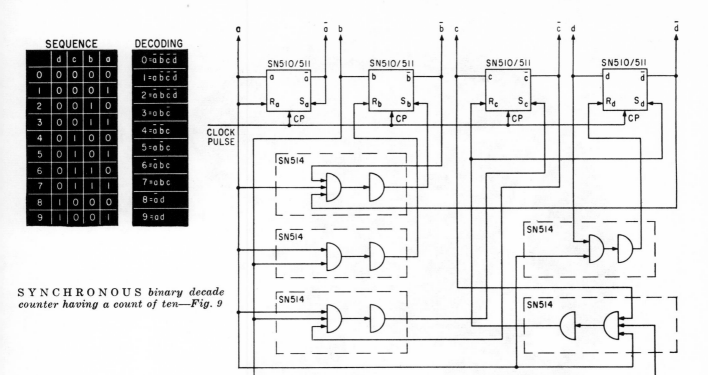

SEQUENCE					DECODING
	d	c	b	a	
0	0	0	0	0	$0 = \bar{a}\bar{b}\bar{c}\bar{d}$
1	0	0	0	1	$1 = a\bar{b}\bar{c}\bar{d}$
2	0	0	1	0	$2 = \bar{a}b\bar{c}\bar{d}$
3	0	0	1	1	$3 = ab\bar{c}$
4	0	1	0	0	$4 = \bar{a}\bar{b}c$
5	0	1	0	1	$5 = a\bar{b}c$
6	0	1	1	0	$6 = \bar{a}bc$
7	0	1	1	1	$7 = abc$
8	1	0	0	0	$8 = \bar{a}d$
9	1	0	0	1	$9 = ad$

SYNCHRONOUS *binary decade counter having a count of ten—Fig. 9*

ter-follower outputs of the SN 513 are used for the gates connected in series between clocked flip-flops rather than the collector outputs.

The propagation delay of a gate is defined as the time required for a signal to propagate through a gate and is shown in Fig. 7A and Fig. 7B. Average propagation delay equals $(t_{d1} + t_{d2})/4$ for 2 stages, $(t_{d1} + t_{d2})/2$ for a single stage.

APPLICATIONS — The following illustrations show how these networks can be used to implement logic designs. NAND logic is used for these illustrations; however, NOR logic can also be implemented to perform the same functions.

For a shift register having parallel read-in and serial read-out, with transfer at each clock pulse, the logic is

$$\text{1st stage} \begin{cases} S_a = AX \\ R_a = \bar{S}_a \end{cases}$$
$$\text{2nd stage} \begin{cases} S_b = BX + aY \\ R_b = \bar{S}_b \end{cases}$$
$$\text{typical stage} \begin{cases} S_n = NX + (n-1)Y \\ R_n = \bar{S}_n \end{cases}$$

The block diagram is shown in Fig. 8 where: X = parallel transfer gate; Y = shift gate; $A, B...N$ = word to be transferred into shift register; and $a, b...n$ = bit positions of shift register.

This register will shift or transfer at every clock pulse. When X and Y are both zero, the entire

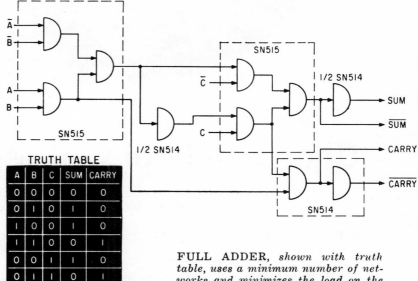

TRUTH TABLE

A	B	C	SUM	CARRY
0	0	0	0	0
0	1	0	1	0
1	0	0	1	0
1	1	0	0	1
0	0	1	1	0
0	1	1	0	1
1	0	1	0	1
1	1	1	1	

FULL ADDER, *shown with truth table, uses a minimum number of networks and minimizes the load on the input circuit—Fig. 10*

register will be reset to 0. Unless a reset of this type is desired, the functions X and Y may be the Q and $\bar{Q}$ outputs of a control flip-flop. The condition $X = Y = 1$ is not permitted.

A synchronous binary decade counter may be modified to a count of ten as in Fig. 9. Its logic is

$$\text{1st stage} \begin{cases} S_a = \bar{a} \\ R_a = a \end{cases}$$
$$\text{2nd stage} \begin{cases} S_b = a\bar{b}\bar{d} \\ R_b = ab \end{cases}$$
$$\text{3rd stage} \begin{cases} S_c = ab\bar{c} \\ R_c = abc \end{cases}$$
$$\text{4th stage} \begin{cases} S_d = abc = R_c \\ R_d = ad \end{cases}$$

A full adder is shown in Fig. 10. Its logic is

$$\text{SUM} = [(A\bar{B} + \bar{A}B) + C][(AB + \overline{A\bar{B}}) + C]$$
$$\text{CARRY} = (A\bar{B} + \bar{A}B)C + AB$$

This adder uses a minimum number of networks and minimizes the load on the input circuit.

If minimum propagation delay is an important factor, adders and subtracters can be assembled which have a maximum of three gates in series, but these require more total networks.

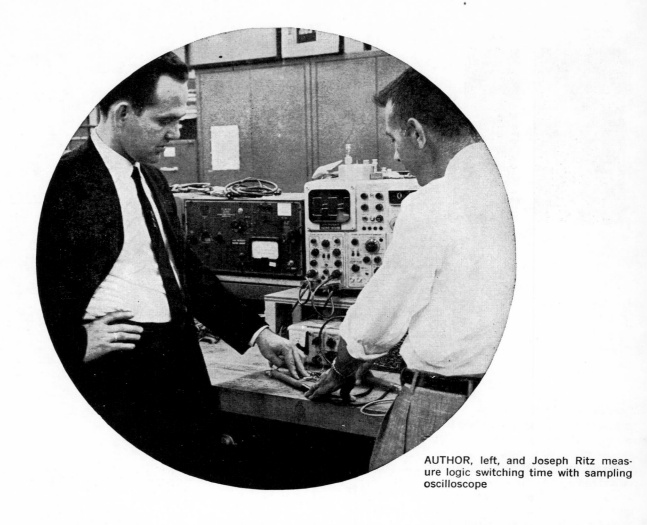

AUTHOR, left, and Joseph Ritz measure logic switching time with sampling oscilloscope

Choosing Logic for Microelectronics

Engineers make a systematic study of available microelectronic logic. Their conclusion: none is inherently superior

By **ALEX E. SKOURES**, U. S. Naval Air Development Center, Johnsville, Penna.

IN SOLID STATE integrated circuits—those formed principally by diffusion of active and passive components in doped silicon chips—two conditions must be met before a circuit may be successfully fabricated.

• The circuit should function satisfactorily with relatively wide component tolerances. This requirement is basic since it affects both performance and yield.

• The circuit should use relatively few components. This requirement establishes the econom-ical yield and influences reliability.

Greatest success with solid state integrated circuits has thus far been achieved with digital logic circuits.

Even though many logic schemes may be realizable, several factors must be considered in choosing a logic system for a particular application. The panel (next page) lists the major considerations.

Logic Function—The main function of any logic circuit is to arrive at a logical decision and deliver the decision, or its complement, to one or more loads. In delivering this decision the circuit appears as a signal source supplying power to a load. A typical elementary circuit, Fig. 1A, can also be represented as shown in Fig. 1B.

In the first state ($I_b = 0$ or S open) current is supplied to the load through R_1 and load voltage V_L is derived from the voltage divider action between load and R_1. In the second state (I_b large or S closed) V_L is zero, or virtually so, and the load is essentially isolated. In each case, however, current

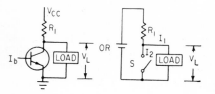

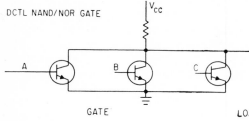

◄ CURRENT FLOWING in R₁ in (A) and (B) when load voltage is zero sets power dissipation limit—Fig. 1

CURRENT FLOWING in R_1 in (A) and (B) when load voltage is zero sets power dissipation limit—Fig. 1

▼ DCTL LOGIC is popular because of simplicity, but small variations in thresholds cause wide variations in load currents, resulting in current hogging—Fig. 2

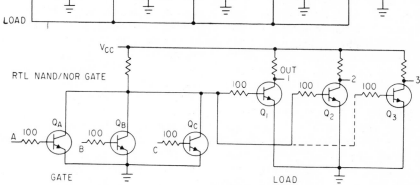

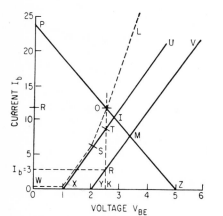

TWO UNEQUAL diode type loads in parallel leads to unequal load currents in DCTL logic. See text for discussion—Fig. 3

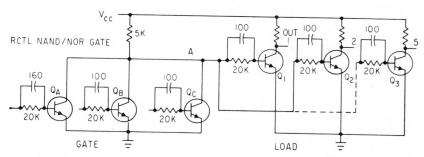

ADDING RESISTANCE in the base changes DCTL logic to RTL, reducing waste current but also speed—Fig. 4

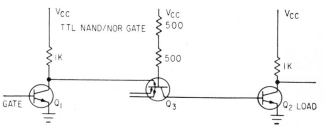

CAPACITORS and resistors in base circuits give relatively high fan-out and low operating power—Fig. 5

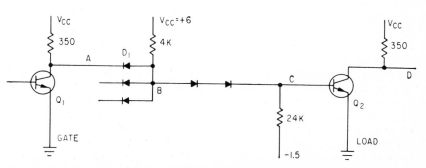

CIRCUIT ACTS to bring transistor out of saturation quickly, thus increasing operating speed—Fig. 6

GATE HAS high immunity to noise and no limitation on fan-in—Fig. 7

FACTORS TO CONSIDER IN CHOOSING A LOGIC SYSTEM

Logic Capability—Fan-in; inversion capability; availability of both normal and complemented outputs

Maximum Fan-Out—Number of loads which the logic element supplies.

Maximum Frequency of Operation—Determined by rise, fall, delay, storage and recovery times

Packing Density—Power dissipation, operating temp., heat sink temp.

Isolation—Signal propagation between channels of the same circuit

Directionality—Degree of signal propagation from output to input

Interconnection Interaction — Signal propagation from one line to another.

Limiting—Restandardization of the signal extremities corresponding to logical one or zero

Threshold Level—Limits at which circuit amplifies information but rejects certain noise signals

Stability—Degree of freedom from errors resulting from regeneration within a circuit

Signal Amplitude—Minimum limits of signal level used to communicate from one circuit to another

flows through R_1 and power is dissipated.

This power dissipation is the irreducible minimum and is one of the most important factors in the design. Power dissipation determines the packaging density, and the addition of a cooling requirement will reduce the benefits of microelectronics. The effect of the temperatures resulting from this power dissipation on drift and reliability must also be considered.

An ideal logic coupling network should provide infinite isolation impedance between inverting stages, have zero signal propagation time, and dissipate no power. Furthermore, the use of relatively few component is desirable.

DCTL—The Direct Coupled Transistor Logic (DCTL) NAND/NOR gate, shown in Fig. 2, is popular due to its simplicity. The threshold function is achieved through the base-to-emitter V-I characteristic of the load transistors. This characteristic is of the diode type. Whenever any of the inputs of the gate is at a high state, the output, point A, is low and the output of each of the load transistors, Q_1 through Q_5, is high. To achieve a logic fan-out, several threshold devices must be connected in parallel. These devices constitute the total load seen by the gate element. The gate element should, ideally, supply the same amount of current to each of the loads. However, relatively small variations in threshold characteristics result in a wide variation in the current supplied to the loads.

The poor distribution of current in the load elements can be understood from Fig. 3. Line WXU represents the V-I characteristic on an idealized diode type load. Line WYV represents the V-I characteristic of another diode type load having a different forward voltage drop. The combined characteristic of these devices in parallel is $WXSL$. If the signal source must supply a minimum of three units of current to each of the diode loads, the source must supply a voltage represented by WK (2.5 voltage units) to the combined loads. To meet this condition, and to insure minimum dissipation, the combined diode characteristic must intercept their load line at O. Total current supplied to the loads is represented by KO (12 units), with KR (3 units) being supplied to one load and RO (9 units) supplied to the other. One load is therefore supplied with three times its required current.

Also, if the minimum current requirement is reduced to near zero, the power supplied to one load approaches zero while that supplied to the other approaches the product of voltage WY and current YS.

This current represents waste, and the condition is called current hogging. Current hogging limits the loading capability of DCTL gates and limits their application except where the base-to-emitter characteristics of the load transistors can be closely matched. Figure 2 also shows that when the gate is not conducting, a small negative noise voltage introduced between A and any of the loads will turn that particular transistor off, since the base-to-emitter voltages are small.

RTL—If a small resistance is introduced into the base of each transistor in the DCTL system, the coupling mechanism becomes Resistor-Transistor logic, or RTL. This is shown in Fig. 4. A 100-ohm resistance reduces the spread of the diode type load characteristic, reduces the waste current, and increases the fan-out capability. Noise rejection, however, will still be relatively low. Operating speed is reduced to below that of the DCTL gate, but it is still relatively high. Logic swing is about one volt and power consumption, although less than DCTL, is relatively high per shift.

RCTL—If the base circuit is modified to that of Fig. 5, the result is Resistor-Capacitor-Transistor logic (RCTL). The high base resistance greatly reduces the spread of the diode type load characteristic, but also reduces operating speed. The capacitor increases the base current for fast turn on and minimizes storage time by supplying a charge equal to the store base charge. At low temperatures the noise rejection may be reduced. Normal noise rejection is high because of a logic swing of about two volts; there is no current hogging problem. The low base current permits relatively high fan-out and operating power typically is low.

TTL—Transistor Coupled Transistor logic (TTL) is shown in Fig. 6. When Q_1 is cut off, the base current of coupling transistor Q_3 is steered into the base of inverting transistor Q_2. In this condition the emitter of Q_3 sees approximately 500,000 ohms and the current goes through the collector; Q_3 therefore acts as a diode. When Q_1 is saturated, the base current of Q_3 is steered into the collector of Q_1, clamping the base of Q_2 to a low potential. This cuts off Q_2, and the emitter of Q_3 is clamped at almost ground potential through saturated Q_1. In this condition the V_{BE} of Q_3 is much smaler than the V_{BC} of Q_3 plus the V_{BE} of Q_2 so the base current of Q_3 would be steered through the emitter. This gate is capable of high-speed operation; logic swing is about 0.4 volt.

One factor that must be considered with this type of logic is the inverse beta (β_{in}) of Q_3; β_{in} must be low since it is a measure of the leakage current of the input emitter. If each emitter is connected to a different driving source, which could be at different potentials, the high leakage currents become analogous to current hogging and limit fan-out. Also, $V_{CE(SAT)}$ of Q_1 must be low at high collector currents or noise at any of the inputs of Q_3 could influence operation. For example, if Q_1 is conducting and has a high $V_{CE(SAT)}$ and Q_2 is cut off, a positive noise introduced between Q_1 and an emitter of Q_3 will turn Q_2 on. For stability in noise

$$(V_{CE(Q_1SAT)} + \text{Noise} < V_{BC(Q_3)} + V_{BE(Q_2)})$$

DTL—The fifth coupling network to be considered is Diode-Transistor logic or DTL, as shown in Fig 7. If Q_1 is cut off, the voltage at A is almost equal to V_{cc}. Current flows from V_{cc} through the two series diodes and then through the parallel path formed by the 24,000-ohm resistor and the base to the emitter of Q_2. The voltage at point B is therefore 6 volts minus the drop across the 4,000-ohm resistor, and the voltage at C is the voltage at B minus the forward drops of the two series diodes. The voltage at C, being well above ground, drives Q_2 into saturation, and the voltage at D equals $V_{CE(SAT)}$.

In this situation a positive noise picked up between A and D_1 will not affect the operation of the gate since it will only increase the back bias on D_1. A negative noise, however, if sufficient to overcome the forward and reverse voltage of D_1, and the voltage necessary to turn Q_2 off, will affect operation. When Q_1 is conducting and Q_2 is cut off, the voltage at B is equal to the $V_{CE(SAT)}$ of Q_1 plus the forward voltage drop of D_1. The voltage at C is at or below ground, and the base of Q_2 is back biased. In this situation a positive noise between A and D_1 must overcome the forward drop of the two series diodes and the base-to-emitter drop of Q_2.

This gate has a relatively large noise immunity, provides diode isolation, and has no fan-in limitation. It does, however, require two power supplies for a high degree of noise immunity; logic swing is typically 1.7 volt, which is not too high for fast operation nor too low to be affected by noise of less than a volt.

ECTL—One logic system available in integrated circuit form but not evaluated is Emitter Coupled Transistor logic (ECTL). The principal advantage of ECTL is that it retains the manufacturing simplicity of DCTL without current hogging. ECTL does, however, utilize more components than DCTL and requires two power supplies. An ECTL AND gate is shown in Fig. 8. The resistances are selected so that with a V_{ref} of 0.4 volt, and point X at -0.3 volt, Q_D will conduct and Q_A, Q_B and Q_C will be off when any of the inputs at A, B, or C are 0.2 volt or below. Increasing any of the inputs, say A, to 0.7 volt will cause Q_A to conduct; Q_A will conduct more heavily than Q_D by virtue of its lower collector resistance (none, versus 3,000 ohms). The relatively large current flowing through Q_A will increase the voltage at X from -0.3 volt to zero. This in turn reduces the V_{BE} of Q_D from 0.7 to 0.4, which will cut off Q_D and present a high output voltage.

This gate circuit inherently tends to eliminate current hogging. Assuming the inputs initially are less than 0.2 volt, Q_A, Q_B, and Q_C are cut off, and Q_D is conducting. Current I_R is

$$I_R = \frac{[(-0.3)-(-3.5)]}{(2/3)R} = 1.6 \text{ ma}$$

Current I_{CD} is

$$I_{CD} = (V_{CC}-V_c)/R = [3-(-0.2)]/3$$
$$= 1.07 \text{ ma}$$

Since $I_c = \beta I_b$, and in this case $I_b = I_R - I_{CD}$

$$\beta = I_c/(I_R - I_{CD}) = 1.07/(1.6-1.07) \approx 2$$

Thus a transistor with a β of only two is required.

When any of the inputs, A for example, is 0.7 volt, Q_A will conduct and I_R becomes I_R'.

$$I_R' = \frac{V_Q-(-3.5)}{(2/3)R} = \frac{0+3.5}{(2/3)3} = 1.75 \text{ ma}$$

Since $I_R' \approx I_c$

$$I_R' = \beta I_b, \text{ and } I_b = (1/\beta)I_R'$$

The base current required for switching therefore varies inversely with the β of each transistor. This has an effect on the current drawn by each diode type load. From Fig. 8, emitter resistance is ⅔ the collector resistance. Base-to-emitter resistance for each diode type load therefore becomes $(⅔) \times R \times \beta$. For a transistor with β of 10 the diode type load would be 20,000 ohms, and for a transistor with a β of 5 it would be 10,000. Thus as β increases, the slope of the load line decreases, so the current drawn by the diode type load varies as $1/\beta$.

This means that—unlike DCTL—the base to emitter resistance varies with β and base current varies as $1/\beta$. Therefore, the transistor with the high β will take less current from the source than those with low β. This permits a higher fan-out capability than with DCTL. The fact that only one transistor in the gate is driven to saturation, in addition to a small logic swing, makes high speed operation possible. The small logic swing, however, reduces noise immunity.

No one logic type stands out as being inherently superior: each has its advantages and its disadvantages. Table I lists typical worst case operating conditions.

The scope of this article has been limited to solid state integrated logic circuits that have been evaluated by the U. S. Naval Air Development Center. Many of the observations and conclusions must therefore be considered interim.

The opinions expressed are not necessarily those of the U. S. Naval Air Development Center or the Navy Department.

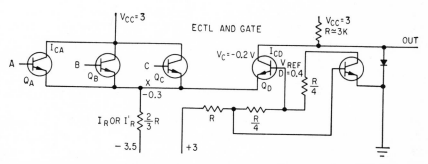

GATE has manufacturing simplicity of DCTL and is free from current hogging but uses two supplies—Fig. 8

Worst Case Conditions for Logic Gate Types—TABLE I

RTL Gate—$T = 125$ C. Fan-Out $(N) = 4$. $f = 1$ Mc.
Propagation Delay $(T_{pd}) = 40$ ns. Rise Time $(T_r) = 15$ ns.
Fall time $(T_f) = 22$ ns.
Power Dissipation: $(P_d) = 15$ mw per gate and 15 mw per shift register.

RCTL Gate—$T = 125$ C. $N = 5$. $V_{cc} = 3$V. $f = 0.1$ Mc.
$T_{pd} = 200$ ns. $T_r = 0.3$ μsec. $T_f = 1.4$ μsec.
P_d (for $V_{cc} = 3$v) $= 3$ mw per gate and at $V_{cc} = 6$v, 7 mw per shift register.

DTL Gate—$T = 125$ C. $V_{cc} = 5$ v. $N = 4$. $f = 7$ Mc.
$T_{pd} = 42$ ns. $T_r = 39$ ns. $T_f = 56$ ns.
$P_d = 6$ mw per gate and 23 mw per shift register.

TTL Gate—$T = -55$ C. $V_{cc} = 4$. $f = 5$ Mc.
$T_{pd} = 55$ C. $V_{cc} = 4$. $f = 5$ Mc.
$T_{pd} = 90$ ns. $T_r = 13$ ns. $T_f = 15$ ns.
$P_d = 12$ mw per gate and 60 mw per shift register.

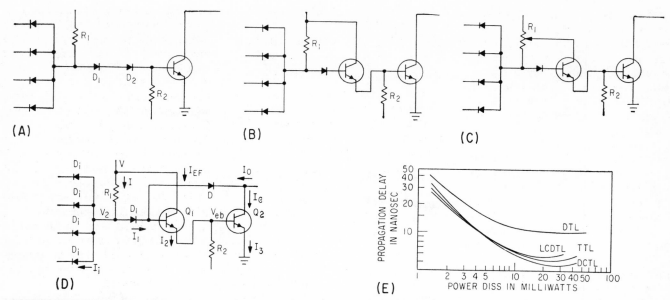

CONVENTIONAL DTL *circuit (A); high-gain DTL (B); high-gain, resistor-controlled DTL (C); load-compensated DTL (D); and power-speed curves for the various switching circuits (E)—Fig. 1*

For integrated circuits, LCDT logic is shown to offer many advantages— including short propagation delay at low power dissipation, high fan-out levels with loose component tolerances, and minimal crosstalk

High Speed Integrated Circuits With

FOR SEVERAL REASONS integrated logic circuits are usually designed as low-power, high-speed devices. First, of course, these goals are desirable in themselves. Second, since integrated circuits aim at high component packing density, the power dissipation per component must be low. Third, small device size makes it possible to process a large number on a single slice of silicon and to maximize the probability of any given device being good. Since transient delays due to both capacitive and minority carrier effects are related to current densities rather than total currents, small device geometry implies low power operation.

With the trend towards low power levels, it is desirable to use logic circuits that operate satisfactorily with small voltage differences between true and false states. Saturating current-steering circuits satisfy the requirement for small line voltage swings. They can also be used at low voltage levels, which further reduce power consumption. Their disadvantages are minority carrier storage effects and their need for low saturation resistance. The former can be made small in comparison with capacitance effect by gold doping techniques, particularly at low power levels.

But low saturation resistances are difficult to realize in integrated circuits since all contacts are usually at one side of the device—collector currents must therefore flow along increased path lengths. The low power requirement alleviates this problem, but does not eliminate it because of small device geometries. Low saturation resistance can be satisfactorily achieved only with epitaxial growth techniques.

LOGIC CIRCUITS—Diode-transistor logic (DTL), direct-coupled transistor logic (DCTL), and transistor-transistor logic (TTL) have all been scrutinized for their applicability in integrated circuit design. Conventional DTL (Fig. 1A) offers the desired high speed at low power levels. It has a relatively high saturation resistance tolerance but the current available for turning off the inverter transistor must flow either as recovery current in diodes D_1 and D_2 or through R_2. A compromise is thus forced between circuit gain and speed, which is particularly severe if R_2 is grounded to avoid a second power supply.

Logic modes DCTL and TTL offer higher speeds at lower operating voltage level than DTL when the

LCDT INTEGRATED CIRCUIT *in plan view shows functional areas called out*

ARGUMENT FOR LOGIC

In this article author Murphy argues the case for LCDT versus other types of logic such as DTL, DCTL and TTL for applicability to integrated circuit design. By modifying a DTL circuit with a clamping diode—thus forming the load compensated circuit—he shows that certain speed and power dissipation problems of the other circuits are overcome

β_{MIN} FOR FAN-OUT AND RESISTOR TOLERANCES–TABLE I

		3–VOLT SUPPLY			4–VOLT SUPPLY		
	F.O.	5	15	25	5	15	25
TOLERANCES	5%	5	7	9	4	6	7
	15%	6	8	10	4	6	8
	25%	6	10	12	5	7	9

By BERNARD T. MURPHY
Siliconix Inc., Sunnyvale, Calif.

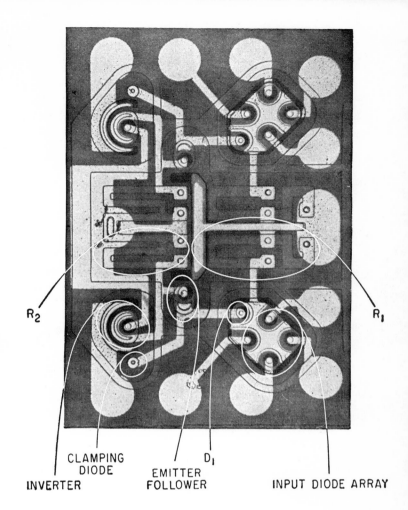

CLAMPING DIODE
D_1
EMITTER FOLLOWER
INVERTER
INPUT DIODE ARRAY
R_2
R_1

Load-Compensated Diode-Transistor Logic

same inverter is used in all three, primarily because of the smaller voltage difference between their true and false states. However, since they have a lower tolerance to saturation resistance, a slower transistor is generally needed for adequate d-c stability. The d-c stability and logical gain of these circuits is further compromised by cross-talk. Current hogging, which is severe in DCTL, can be reduced to acceptable levels by using resistive coupling, but only by sacrificing switching speed. A similar situation exists in TTL due to inverse gain in the logic transistors, and the requirement of low inverse β conflicts with the requirement of low offset voltages. Thus, a confusing situation exists as to the relative suitability of the foregoing circuits in integrated circuit form.

In an integrated DTL circuit, it is convenient to form one or both of diodes D_1 and D_2 (Fig. 1A) as the emitter-base diode of a transistor. This transistor also can be used to increase the total gain of the circuit to a point at which gain no longer presents a problem. The transistor can be used as an emitter follower (Fig. 1B), or as a quasi emitter follower (Fig. 1C) in which saturation is also prevented. In Fig. 1B, the power dissipation is high and gain dependent; in Fig. 1C, power dissipation is high but resistor controlled, as is the additional gain. In both, the overdrive is excessive at low fan-out values; but the circuit of Fig. 1C could be used as a buffer element to complement the conventional lower fan-out DTL circuit, provided the inverter were redesigned (larger geometry) for low saturation resistance.

Speed and power dissipation problems posed by the above circuits can be overcome by using a clamping diode as a shunt around the amplifying stages, as in Fig. 1D. Here the excess current from R_1 (which causes overdrive in the previous circuits) flows through the clamping diode, while the emitter follower draws just enough current from the power supply to sustain the load current. As load current increases, the driving current also increases and, in this sense, the circuit is load compensated. The current drawn from the power supply by the emitter is

$$I_{EF} = \left\{ \frac{V_{eb}}{R_2} + \frac{I_c}{\beta_1} \right\} \Big/ \left\{ 1 + \frac{1}{\beta_2} \right\}$$

The clamping diode considerably improves switching

speed by restricting the line voltage swing. Speed improves also because the lower limit of R_2 is not now set by gain requirements. Minority carrier storage in the transistor collector region is also avoided, but the clamping diode introduces a similar effect, so that gold doping is still needed to control minority carrier lifetime. Transistor coupling could decrease the effect of carriers stored in the diode, but crosstalk problems would be introduced by this mode of coupling.

At first sight, it appears that d-c stability of the load-compensated circuit must always be inferior to that of conventional DTL. This probably will be the case if the best switching speeds are to be attained; however, to obtain the fastest switching speed with DTL, the transistor design should be such that the saturation resistance is close to its maximum permissible limit, which gives minimum permissible d-c stability. Furthermore, the load-compensated version (LCDTL) clamps at an output voltage which can be adjusted by introducing series resistance effects into the diode shunt path (this is easy to do in the integrated circuit). Thus, considerable design freedom is possible in balancing d-c stability and speed requirements, while retaining the load compensation feature of the circuit.

To summarize, the LCDT circuit can be used with line voltage swings similar to those of DCTL and TTL. At the same time, it has the relatively high tolerance to saturation resistance of DTL. Switching speed and d-c stability can be traded by introducing resistance in series with the clamping diode. The number of components used is greater than in any of the single-stage circuits, but their tolerance are considerably looser, which makes the device particularly suitable for integrated circuits. The circuit seems to combine the good features of the more conventional saturating circuits, while eliminating their weaknesses. A detailed description of the circuit and its integrated version follows.

LCDT LOGIC—The most interesting circuit characteristics are d-c stability at various values of fan-out and switching speed. The former can be calculated if the ideal diode equation is assumed. The latter is dependent on minority carrier storage effects in the diodes and transistors and also on current flow in R_1 and R_2 during the ON-OFF and OFF-ON transients. Such a transient analysis would be a study in itself; information presented here is based on direct measurements.

Two requirements need to be satisfied for the circuit to operate at a given value of fan-out; namely, the overall gain should be high enough and the output voltage at that fan-out should be low enough to turn off the next stage with an adequate margin of stability ΔV.

The maximum output current from the circuit under worst-case conditions is:

$$I_{0\,max} = \beta_1\beta_2\left\{\left(\frac{V - V_{2\,max}}{R_{1\,max}} - I_i\right) - \frac{1}{\beta_1}\cdot\frac{V_{eb\,max}}{R_{2\,min}}\right\} \quad (1)$$

where β_1 = current gain of the emitter follower, β_2 = current gain of the inverter, I_i = worst-case input current ON, and V, V_2 and V_{eb} are the voltages indicated in Fig. 1D. Voltage $V_{2\,max}$ is the maximum V_2 ever occurring in the circuit.

The worst-case input current when the circuit is being held OFF is:

$$I_i = \frac{V - V_{2\,min}}{R_{1\,min}} - \frac{V_{eb\,min}}{\beta_1 R_{2\,max}} \quad (2)$$

Voltage $V_{2\,min}$ is the lowest V_2 that can occur when the input is at the highest permissible false voltage.

Since both the emitter follower and the inverter are formed simultaneously in proximity on the device, it is a good approximation to assume that they have the same gain. Then, using Eq. 1 and 2, Table I gives the minimum gain values at −55 deg C for various values of fan-out and resistor tolerances. Values for V_2 and V_{eb} were measured on a circuit using silicon diodes and transistors; $R_{2\,nominal}/R_{1\,nominal}$ is taken to be 1.5, which was found to give optimum speed power balance. In an integrated circuit, the required β_{min} values will be lower than those given in Table I, particularly for the looser resistor tolerances, since resistors R_1 and R_2 tend to increase or decrease together in the same circuit.

Assuming that the circuit has sufficient gain, its output voltage when fully loaded is determined by the forward voltages across the emitter-base diodes

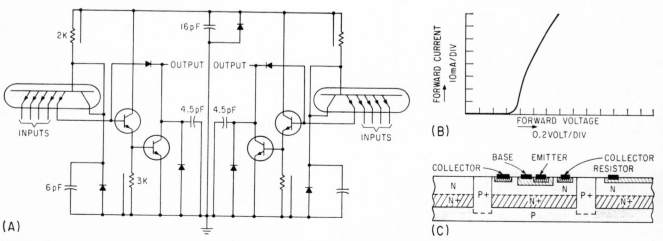

EQUIVALENT CIRCUIT *of LCDT logic device (A), and cross-section of the actual device (C); in (B) appears the forward characteristic of transistor used as a diode—Fig. 2*

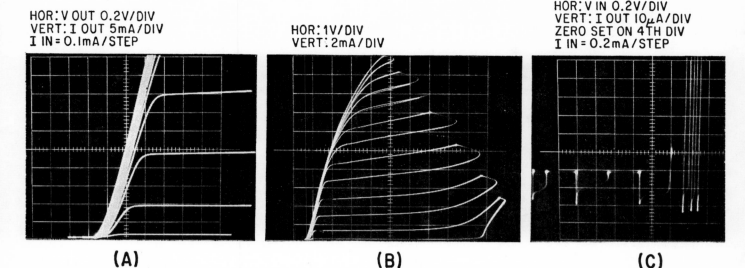

(A)   **(B)**   **(C)**

OUTPUT CHARACTERISTICS *of LCDT integrated circuit, 4-v supply (A and B). In (A), max permissible load current at 1.1 v is 37 ma. In (B), saturation effects set in at 100 ma output current, breakover occurs at over 10 v. Input characteristics of LCDT circuit (4-v supply, 4-v output) shown in (C)—Fig. 3*

of Q_1 and Q_2 and the clamping diode D.

$$V_0 = V_{eb}(Q_1) + V_{eb}(Q_2) - V_D$$

Similarly, the maximum permissible false voltage at the input is

$$V_F = V_{eb}(Q_1) + V_{eb}(Q_2) + V_{D1} - V_{Di}$$

The d-c stability margin ΔV is the difference between the worst-case values of V_F and V_0. Using the ideal diode equation

$$\Delta V = \frac{kT}{q} \left\{ \log \frac{I_3''}{I_{S3}} + \log \frac{I_2''}{I_{S2}} + \log \frac{I_1''}{I_{S1}} - \log \frac{I_i''}{I_{Si}} \right\} - \frac{kT}{q} \left\{ \log \frac{I_3'}{I_{S3}} + \log \frac{I_2'}{I_{S2}} \right\} + V_D$$

where subscripts are as in Fig. 1D. Single primes indicate worst-case ON values, double primes indicate worst-case OFF values; I_S values refer to the saturation current of the various diodes.

Rearranging this expression, and noting that to a good approximation

$$\text{Fan-out (FO)} = I_3'/I_i''$$

then

$$\text{FO} = \left[\frac{I_2'' I_3'' I_1''}{(I_i'')^2 I_3'} \right] \left[\exp \frac{q}{kT} (V_2 - \Delta V - \Delta V') \right]$$

The term $\Delta V'$ accounts for two effects. First, it includes the difference in forward voltage across diodes D_i and D_1 at the same current level. For maximum stability D_i should have a low forward voltage relative to D_1. Second, it includes the forward voltage tolerances from circuit to circuit on the emitter diodes in Q_1 and Q_2.

The current level in the emitter of Q_2 varies enough from ON to OFF that the ideal diode equation is unlikely to hold over the whole range; departure from the ideal equation will be in a direction to reduce F.O. However, even if the ideal equation does not hold exactly, it does give some measure of the effects of various circuit parameters on the overall d-c stability.

POWER-SPEED CURVES—Figure 1E shows the power-speed curve for the LCDT gate using a 2N743

inverter, an FD829 clamping diode and a 4-volt supply. Similar curves are shown for DCTL, TTL and DTL, using in each case a 2N743 inverter and a 4-volt supply. These curves cannot be directly related to integrated versions of the four circuits, since the transistor design and optimum power supply voltage would vary from circuit to circuit. The lower supply voltages which are permissible with TTL and DCTL tend to compensate for the higher saturation resistances which are permissible with DTL.

Two further points are worthy of note. First, integrated circuits eliminate the contribution of packaging capacitance to collector-base and clamping-diode capacitance. This is of more significance in DTL and LCDTL than in DCTL and TTL, since turn-off currents are more limited in the former. Second, DCTL requires the use of as many inverters with separate bases and low saturation resistances as there are inputs. These transistors require more layout space and provide more stray capacitance in integrated circuit form than the input transistor-diodes of DTL, TTL and LCDTL. This tends to counter-balance the low component count of DCTL.

TOPOLOGY—In designing an integrated circuit to perform LCDTL, it is important to minimize stray capacitances and to avoid cross-overs. The device was planned as a four-input dual NAND for maximum packing density. An equivalent circuit, including principal stray capacitances, is shown in Fig. 2A. Low isolation capacitances, including 1.3 pf of pin capacitance, were realized with adequately low saturation resistances by use of epitaxial growth techniques and tight masking tolerances.

A plan view of the device (see photo) shows the function of the different areas. In accordance with the principles outlined, the device was designed for minimum junction areas to allow high-speed operation at low power levels, to obtain as many devices per silicon wafer as possible, and to increase the percentage yield. Thus, the total size for the dual gate is 37×28 mils. The inverter transistor has a slightly

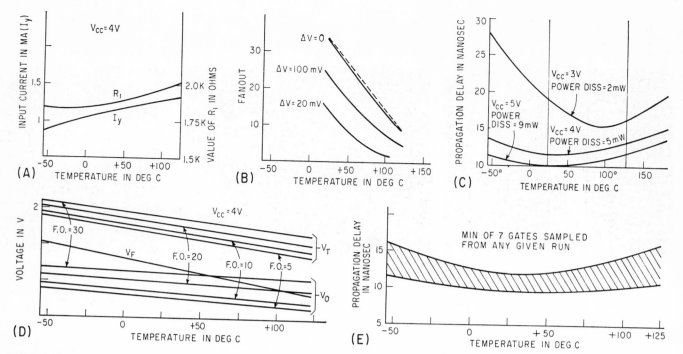

INTEGRATED LCDT PERFORMANCE: *resistor and input current variations with temperature (A); worst case F.O. as function of d-c stability and temperature (B); propagation delay as a function of voltage and temperature (C); variation with F.O. and temperature of true and false thresholds and fully loaded output voltage (D); and envelope of all 4-v propagation delay measurements obtained on 6 different runs (E)—Fig. 4*

smaller geometry than the 2N709 transistor.

The input diode array was formed as a transistor array with a collector-base short for convenience in fabrication, but the arrangement also has operational advantages. Good diode action is obtained in that the ideal diode equation is obeyed over a wide range of forward-current values. This is because most of the forward current flows by transistor action through the collector until the transistor saturates. At that point, which is well outside the operating range, the diode characteristic shows an inflection, as in Fig. 2B. The collector-base short avoids inverse transistor action.

To obtain maximum d-c stability, the clamping diode and diode D_1 were made as small as was consistent with reproducibility. From this point of view, it would also be desirable to make the input diodes large, but this requirement conflicts with that of minimizing the recovery effects in these diodes and with small total device size; thus a compromise must be made.

The sizes of the emitter follower and inverter are unimportant from the point of view of stability, provided that resistive effects are avoided, since each affects both the output and input voltages.

FABRICATION—Epitaxial techniques have been used to minimize junction capacitance while maintaining an adequately low saturation resistance. There are many ways of using epitaxial growth techniques to fabricate integrated circuits. As is standard practice in transistors, the best ones employ a heavily doped layer beneath the surface for current carrying purposes and a lightly doped surface layer in which p-n junctions can be formed for transistors,

resistors or diodes with minimal capacitance effects. The heavily doped layer can be predeposited either uniformly or selectively, using epitaxial growth or diffusion techniques, or it can be formed as part of a composite layer by proper control of the dopants in the gas stream entering the reaction furnace. Contact can be made to the n^+ layer either through the n layer by a special diffusion through it, or by pre-arranging the surface so that the n^+ layer appears at certain points.

The substrate will generally be high resistivity p-type silicon, and isolation between component areas can then be obtained by either etching troughs between them or by a p-type diffusion. Etching minimizes capacitance effects but exposes junctions and creates problems in making the desired interconnections between component parts. Isolation by diffusion is simpler, gives planar junctions, and for the purposes of the low-power circuit in hand, gives only marginally more isolation capacitance with adequate values of saturation resistance. The latter technique was used in this design; a cross-section of the device is shown in Fig. 2C.

Sheet resistivity and depth of the boron diffusion affects the circuit in a number of ways. The range of useful values of sheet resistivities is generally confined to 100 to 300 ohms/sq., although for special purposes, the limits of this range can be exceeded. Higher values generally are more suitable for forming resistors with small junction areas and obtaining high gain in the transistors. Lower values are more suitable for minimizing resistive effects in the transistors and diodes. Lower resistivities also maintain high forward voltage drops in the various diodes that determine the threshold voltage V_T and hence indi-

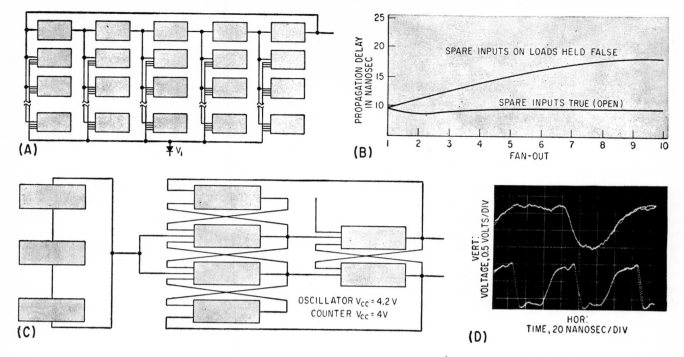

LOADING ARRANGEMENT *for propagation delay measurements (A); effect of loading on propagation delay (B); ring oscillator and counter arrangement (C) in which counting proceeds at a 15 Mc rate; input and output waveforms of counter are shown in (D). With better techniques and a better waveform on the clock pulse, a higher counting rate should be achieved—Fig. 5*

rectly the maximum permissible saturation resistance in the transistor. Shallow diffusion depths are necessary to obtain fast switching, since the transit time must be kept small both for its own sake and to minimizes the effect on gain of the heavy gold doping required for low storage effects. For the LCDT gate, resistor values are small, gain requirements are at minimum, and, at the same time, resistive effects in the various diodes must be minimized. Thus, a relatively low ρ_s value of 140 ohms/sq was chosen. Junction depths of 1.8 to 2.1 microns for the base layer and 1.2 to 1.6 microns for the emitter gave satisfactory gains and switching speeds. Based on all units measured to date, a 15 percent tolerance can be maintained on resistors with 93 percent yield.

Gold doping is necessary to minimize minority carrier storage effects in the transistors and diodes. One of the more fortunate facts about the diode-coupled logic circuit is that capacitance effects are worst at low temperatures, while minority carrier storage effects are worst at high temperatures. If the gold doping is adjusted correctly, switching speeds can be made worst-case at both high and low temperatures with optimum performance near room temperature and with a minimum of overall variation.

INTEGRATED CIRCUIT PERFORMANCE—The d-c characteristics of the LCDT gate can be studied most simply with a transistor curve tracer. The output, one input, and the ground leads are connected to the collector, base, and emitter posts of the curve tracer; the B⁺ lead is connected to an appropriate supply voltage. Displays of output voltage against output current with negatively stepped input cur-

rent, and input voltage against output current for negatively stepped input current are the most informative. These displays give: (a) the worst-case output voltage under full load and worst-case input current, (b) the maximum "false" voltage for worst-case output OFF current, (c) the minimum "true" input voltages for various load currents, (d) the value of resistor R_1, and (e) the worst-case input current. Typical displays are shown in Fig. 3A, 3B and 3C. Figures 4A and 4D show how these parameters as measured on a typical device vary as a function of temperature. One of the desirable features of DTL is that the variation in input current and power dissipation due to variation of R_1 with temperature is partially compensated for by variation in the diode forward voltages with temperature.

The LCDT integrated circuit will operate over a minus 55 deg C to plus 125 deg C range at supply voltages between 3 and 6 volts. It seems unlikely, however, that such a wide voltage variation will be experienced by any one device. Preliminary studies indicated that a 4-volt supply was optimum in that

OFF CURRENT CHOSEN FOR OPERATING TEMPERATURES—TABLE II A

T °C	−55	+25	+70	+100	+125
I_0 μA	5	10	20	40	40

I_L CHOSEN FOR OPERATING TEMPERATURES—TABLE II B

T °C	−55	+25	+70	+100	+125
I_L μA	0.05	0.1	0.3	1	2.5

component tolerances were loose and that speed and power dissipation varied little with temperature at this voltage. Thus the circuit was designed primarily for operation at 4 volts, d-c and dynamic studies on the device were made primarily at this operating voltage.

The following test program was carried out on a large number of units sampled from 20 different production runs. First, an output current level I_o' was chosen for each temperature at or below which the device was defined as being OFF (see Table IIA), and the input voltage V_F at which this current would flow was measured on all units. Second, input currents at various temperatures were measured, and worst-case values set which gave a good yield. Third, a leakage specification I_l (see Table IIB) was set at each temperature for the input diodes, to be measured with the full B^+ voltage applied to the input with the device ON. Fourth, output voltage V_o was measured at various fan-out values and temperatures on all the units with an input current I_i, where

$$I_i = \text{Fan-In} \times \{I_0' + (FO - 1)I_L\}$$

These results were used to choose values of V_F and V_o at 125 deg C that would guarantee a d-c stability $\Delta V = 100$ mv at a fan-out of 5 with maximum yield. Units were selected which would pass this test and plots drawn of their worst-case V_o vs F.O. at each temperature. From these plots, the values of F.O. were obtained for which

$$V_0 = V_{FW} - \Delta V$$

where V_{FW} = lowest value of V_F measured on any unit at each temperature. The curves in Fig. 4B, showing fan-out as a function of temperature and d-c stability level, were obtained in this way.

If the fan-out values given in Fig. 4B are to be realized, saturation resistance of the inverter transistor should be lower than V_o at the maximum fan-out at each temperature. Saturation would have two effects. First, V_o would be increased; such an increase would be detected in the tests already described. Second, the power drain from the supply would be increased, since any increase in V_o above the natural clamping level will divert current from the clamping diode into the emitter follower, even though the increased V_o is within specifications. Power drain at maximum fan-out must be measured to safeguard against this effect.

Specifications for the epitaxial layer were chosen to avoid saturation at all temperatures. The following measurements were made to check this. First, the saturation resistance of the inverters on a large number of gates were measured at room temperature with 20 percent overdrive. Nearly all units fell within the range 0.25 to 0.35 volt at 10 ma collector current. Second, the collector current on a worst-case inverter was measured at a collector voltage of $V_o' = V_{FW} - 200$ mv with 20 percent overdrive at various temperatures; V_o' was chosen in this way so that it would be below the clamped output voltage of any unit. Finally, the fan-out values to which these collector currents corresponded were plotted to give the broken line in Fig. 4B.

Breakdown effects in the device are consistently above the operating voltage range of the device. The input diodes, being emitter-base junctions, have breakdown voltage of 6.5 to 7 volts at 10 μa. Isolation and collector-base junctions (including the clamping diode, which is formed at the same time as the collector-base of the transistor) have breakdown voltages typically in excess of 25 volts at 10 μa, and both the emitter follower and inverter transistor have breakover voltages of 8 to 10 volts.

DYNAMICS—Propagation delays in the device were measured using a five-stage ring oscillator. No significant difference was observed between delays measured across two stages of the ring (average of the delay per stage between 50 percent points) and measurements based on the frequency of oscillation.

The dependence of average propagation delay on voltage, temperature and fan-out are illustrated in Fig. 4C, 4E and 5B. The effect of increasing fan-out depends on whether or not the spare input diodes on the additional loads are connected to other gates which remain ON during the 0 to 1 transient. If such a connection is assumed, recovery effects in the input diodes slow down the propagation. Figure 5A illustrates how this effect was simulated to obtain the results given in Fig. 5B. Care was taken to ensure that voltage V_1 was such as to give worst-case effects in these measurements. Grounding V_1 produced a situation very close to the worst-case. The rise time (0 to 1 transient) varies from 10 nanosec at 4 volts (with a single load), to 18 nanosec with 10 loads ungrounded or 30 nanosec with 10 loads grounded. The fall time (1 to 0 transient) varies from 5 nanosec at 4 volts with a single load, to 20 nanosec with 10 ungrounded loads and 20 nanosec with 10 grounded loads.

The LCDT gate is shown interconnected as a counter, driven by a ring oscillator and counting at a rate of 15 Mc in Fig. 5C and 5D. The interconnection techniques were poor, which accounts for the poor wave form. With better techniques, and a better wave form on the clock pulse, a higher counting rate should be achieved.

One final point of note concerning the dynamic characteristics of the device is that when overdriven with a low impedance generator, ringing is observed. Although related to the large recovery currents that would flow in the input diodes under such circumstances, the mechanism propagating the ringing is not fully understood. The ringing can be avoided by using a transistor on the generator output.

CONCLUSIONS—LCDT logic offers a way of achieving high-speed propagation delay at low power dissipation, and high fan-out levels with loose component tolerances, particularly at temperatures below 100 deg C. Cross-talk is virtually nonexistent, and the circuit has a relatively high saturation resistance tolerance. Extra d-c stability is achieved by a small resistance in series with the clamping diode to depress the clamped output voltage, at a sacrifice in speed and saturation resistance tolerance.

The author acknowledges the invaluable contributions of W. F. Perrine, H. L. Schoger and W. R. Faleschini in the development of the LCDT integrated circuit.

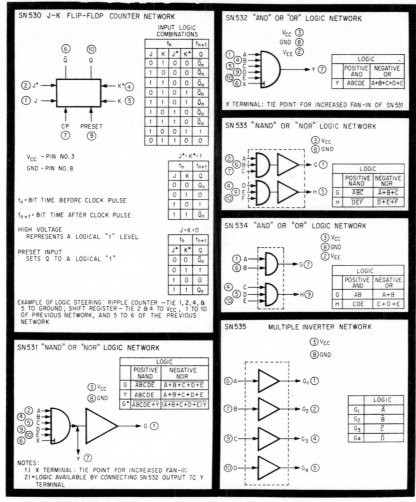

LOGIC DIAGRAMS for Series 53 semiconductor networks—Fig. 1

NEW SEMICONDUCTOR NETWORKS

Reduce System Complexity

Fabrication and design features allow 1-Mc speed of operation and fewer networks per system. Series consists of six standard devices

By **CHARLES R. COOK, JR.**
Senior Project Engineer

BILLY M. MARTIN
Design Engineer

Semiconductor-Components Div.
Texas Instruments Incorporated
Dallas, Texas

SEMICONDUCTOR integrated circuits are becoming a familiar product in design applications, particularly in the digital computer area. A new series of Solid Circuit semiconductor networks, called Series 53, has been developed that is designed to operate above 1 Mc.

Series 53 is designed for application in general-purpose computers. Of particular note is the excellent loading capabilities of the individual networks, which together with the ability to cascade the non-inverting gates minimizes the number of units required to perform logic operation. Further, through the use of dual gates, inverter and a complete J-K flip-flop/shift register in one network package, system usage of networks can be often substantially re-duced with Series 53 as compared to other integrated circuit types. The fewer networks required per system can have real impact on reliability—minimizing connections, size, and weight, as well as cost.

Presently, Series 53 (see the front cover) consists of six standard high-speed digital devices: SN530, a single-phase *J-K* flip-flop; SN531, a 5-input NAND gate; SN532, a 5-input AND gate; SN533, a dual 3-input NAND gate; SN534, a 2-and-3-input AND gate; and SN535, a 4-inverter package. Logic diagrams are shown in Fig. 1. Flexibility of the "master slice" concept makes it simple to add devices to the line as the need appears.

Series 53 Structure—The Series 53 uses a triple-diffused process to produce the four-layer silicon structure shown in Fig. 2. P-type starting material forms the substrate into which subsequent collector, base, and emitter diffusions are made to form isolated *npn* transistors. The collector diffusion also forms the base of the common-collector (substrate) *pnp* transistors, resistor isolation regions, capacitor areas, and crossover tunnels. The base diffusion forms *pnp* emitters, resistors, and capacitor areas. The emitter diffusion dopes a collector ring on the *npn* to reduce R_{cs}, lowers resistivity of crossover tunnels, and forms capacitor areas.

The collector diffusion uses a two-step process to optimize both *npn* and *pnp* structures. In the first step, only the *npn* collectors are doped, whereas the second step dopes both *npn* collectors and *pnp* bases. This produces *n*-type collector diffusions of different depths to optimize *npn* R_{cs} and *pnp* h_{FE}. The deep region forms the collector of the *npn* while the shallow region forms the base of the *pnp*'s (Fig. 2).

The triple diffusion process produces *npn* transistors with R_{cs} of 50 ohms or less. It is possible to produce integrated transistors with improved characteristics by using epitaxial techniques, but these processes are significantly more expensive up to the point of packaging and testing. Although the cost of packaging and testing presently overshadows material preparation cost, automation of packaging and testing will soon leave material processing as the significant part of total cost. This should give the triple-diffused process a definite cost advantage.

Use of PNP Action—Present integrated circuit techniques require a four-layer structure to produce isolated transistors on a single substrate. The first two diffusions into a *p*-type substrate produce a *pnp* transistor (Fig. 2). The utilization of the substrate in forming the *pnp* structure can be helpful if these diodes (base-emitter junction of *pnp* transistor) are used for particular circuit components. For example, the junction formed by the first two diffusions may be used for gate input diodes, as shown in Fig. 3A. They will appear as "diodes with current gain" (*pnp* emitter followers) as shown in Fig. 3B. On the other hand, if they are used for the output diodes of Fig. 3A, current will be shunted into the substrate as shown in Fig. 3C. For this reason the out-

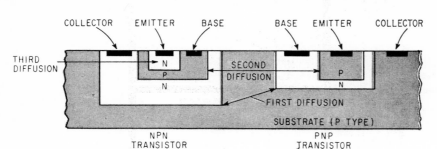

NPN/PNP triple-diffused structure—Fig. 2

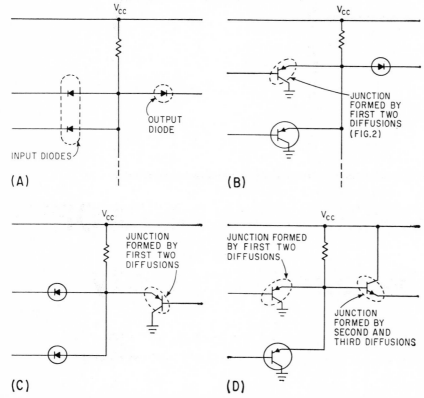

DIODE AND/OR gate (A); input diodes replaced with pnp (common collector) transistors (B); output diode replaced with pnp (common collector) transistor (C); input diode replaced with pnp and output diode replaced with npn transistor (D)—Fig. 3

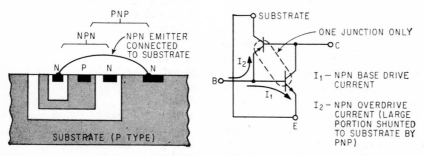

PNP ACTION in npn transistor can limit saturation—Fig. 4

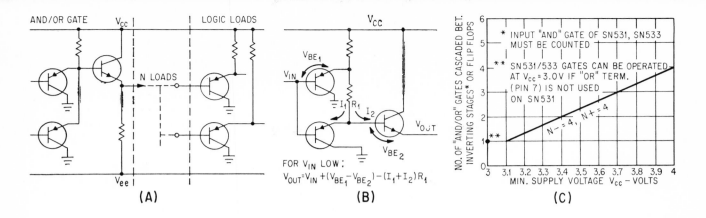

FANNING OUT from AND/OR gate (A); Series 53 gate input circuit (B); number of cascaded AND/OR gates permitted (C)—Fig. 5

put diodes cannot use the first two diffusions, but must use the last two (B-E junction of *npn* transistor, see Fig. 2).

If the first diffused layer of the structure (the collector of the *npn*) is connected to V_{cc} as in Fig. 3D, the output diodes will also exhibit "current gain" (*npn* emitter follower). It is possible to kill the lifetime in the base of the common-collector *pnp* so that current lost to the substrate will be small. This would allow the first two diffusions to be used for output diodes, but would also eliminate the current gain in the input diodes (Fig. 3B).

The *pnp* action inherent in a triple-diffused *npn* transistor can limit saturation. Figure 4 shows the four-layer device fabricated with three diffusions. The substrate and emitter will normally be connected together as shown. As the base-collector diode becomes forward biased, the overdrive current will be shunted to ground, thus limiting saturation. This gives the same effect as minority carriers drifting across the collector and being collected at the substrate.

Series 53 Logic—The basic Series 53 logic gate is a straightforward AND/OR gate. It is similar to diode logic, but improvements have been made by replacing the input diodes with *pnp* transistors and the output diodes with *npn* transistors (Fig. 3D). This produces a device with higher d-c input impedance and lower d-c output impedance.

The input sink currents of the Series 53 gates are considerably reduced from that of diode logic (current gain of input *pnp*'s), so that it is possible to fan out from a non-

inverting AND/OR gate (Fig. 5A). In addition, resistor tolerances can be wide since variations here can be absorbed by the transistor gains. The low output impedance (*npn* emitter follower) also gives this gate the capacity to fan out to loads that require a source drive. Some of the other Series 53 devices require this type drive.

Series 53 non-inverting gates can be cascaded before restoring logic levels in an inverter. A dual transistor input circuit (Fig. 5B) is used to ensure that logic levels are maintained in cascaded gates. This is necessary to guarantee that $V_{out} \leqq V_{in}$ when V_{in} is at a low level. On the other hand, there will also be a voltage drop through the device when the input is high. This drop limits the number of cascaded gates. The number allowed depends on the supply voltage used (Fig. 5C).

NAND Gate—The NAND gate is the same as the AND gate described previously followed by an inverter (Fig. 6A). This gate has a fan-in of five, but may be increased to a maximum of twenty by supplementing it with standard AND gates (Fig. 6B). In addition, this gate may be "ORed" with AND gates by connecting the AND output to the Y output of the NAND gate (Fig. 6C).

The triple transistor inverting output stage (Fig. 6A) is designed to have "low output impedance" (approximately 50 ohms) for both source and sink loads. Source currents are supplied by the *npn* emitter follower when the output voltage is high, while sink currents are shunted to ground by the saturated common-emitter transistor when the output voltage is low. The same

output stage is used on all Series 53 inverting outputs.

Flip-Flop—The Series 53 flip-flop operates on a single-phase clock and performs *J-K* logic. (See Fig. 1.) A *J-K* flip-flop is one in which simultaneous application of logic "1"s at the inputs results in a defined change of state. All logic states are defined and no indeterminate condition

Maximum Output Drive Capability of Series 53 Networks—TABLE I

	Max. Allowable Loading	
	N⁺ Loads	N⁻ Loads
SN530 Output........	10	10
SN531 [1]		
Inv. Output........	10	10
Y Output..........	2	4 [2]
SN532 Output........	4	4
SN533		
Each Gate Output..	10	10
SN534		
Each Gate Output..	4	4
SN535		
Each Inverter Output.	10	10
4 Inv. in Parallel....	40	40

[1] If both the inverter and Y terminals are being used as outputs, maximum loading from both is allowed   [2] n⁻ fan-out is allowed only if the Y output is being "ORed" with an SN532 or SN534

Weighted Value of Loads Represented by One Input of Particular Series 53 Network—TABLE II

	Weighted Value of Each Input	
Network	n⁺ Loads	n⁻ Loads
SN531, 532, 533, 534....	0	1
SN531 (Inverter Only)...	2	1.5
SN532, 534 Outputs.....	0	1.5
(Output appears as a load when performing "OR" function)		
535 (Each Input)......	2	0
535 (4 Inv. in parallel).	8	0
SN530 (Logic Inputs).....	1	0
Clock Pulse..........	2.5	2.5

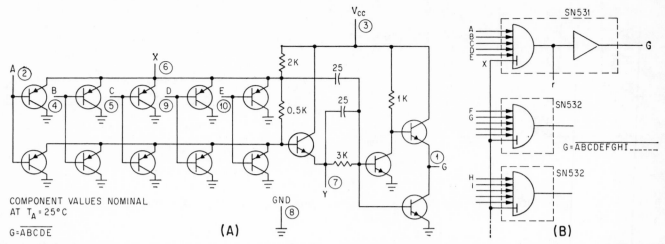

SN531 NAND logic gate (A) can have fan-in increased by supplementing with AND gates (B). In addition, the gate may be as shown in (C)—Fig. 6

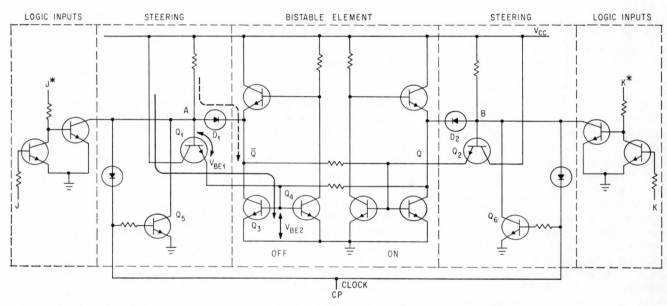

SN530 J-K flip-flop consists of bistable element, steering and and logic input sections—Fig. 7

exists. Such *J-K* flip-flops have been widely used in logic design, but have not previously been available in integrated form. Complementary inputs have also been provided, so that full *J-K* operation can be obtained for positive and negative logic. In practical designs, use of the complementary inputs will result in a substantial reduction in the number of gates or inverters required.

The *J-K* flip-flop has been designed to operate without the conventional storage capacitors. Intermediate storage is provided by control of propagation through the input stages rather than a precise *R-C* circuit, permitting reliable operation at high speeds. Circuit operation can best be understood by dividing

the flip-flop into the three basic sections shown in Fig. 7—the bistable element, steering, and logic inputs.

Bistable Element — The bistable element is composed of two low-impedance inverters with *R-C* cross coupling. Both Q and $\overline{Q}$ outputs, therefore, have good drive capabilities for both source and sink loads. Output stages of this type with large voltage swings not only provide good drive sources for other devices in Series 53, but also are excellent for driving capacitive loads and various interface loads.

Steering — The flip-flop uses a unique steering method that does not require input capacitors. Turn-on

switching action is controlled by the bases of common-collector transistors Q_1 and Q_2—points A and B respectively. For analysis, assume that output $\overline{Q}$ is high. Since this is a turn-on circuit, the device may be switched by steering the clock pulse (*CP*) to apply drive current to the bases of Q_3 and Q_4. In other words allowing point A to assume a level $V_A = V_{BE1} + V_{BE2}$. Disregarding transistors Q_5 and Q_6, an equation may be written describing the logic for points A and B:

$$A = (J + J^*) (Q) (CP)$$
$$B = (K + \overline{K}^*) (Q) (CP)$$

Notice that switching is dependent

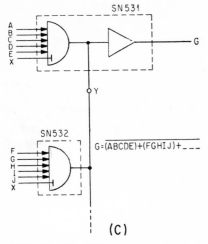

SN 531

SN 532

$G = (ABCDE) + (FGHIJ) + \_\_\_$

(C)

"ORed" with AND gates connected

POINT A INHIBITED BY TRANSISTOR Q5 (FIG 7)

A — LOW

B — LOW

CP — LOW

$\overline{Q}$ — HIGH — LOW

Q — LOW — HIGH

(A)

V_{cc}

SINK CURRENT

N−

(B)

N+

LOAD CURRENT

(C)

FLIP-FLOP switching waveforms (A); n− load (B) and n+ load (C)—Fig. 8

Component Count—TABLE III

Transistors

Type	Quantity
npn......................	28
pnp (common collector-substrate)..	10

Capacitors

Value	Quantity
25 pf......................	4
15 pf......................	1
Total capacitance—115 pf	

Resistors

Value	Quan.	Taps
8 k.......	2	1.5–1.5–5.0
4 k.......	2	1.0–2.0–1.0
4 k.......	2	1.5–1.5–0.3–0.7
3 k.......	2	1.5–1.5
3 k.......	4	2.0–1.0
2.5 k.....	2	1.0–1.0–0.5
2.0 k.....	2	1.0–1.0
3.9 k.....	2	1.5–0.25–0.15–2.0
0.7 k.....	2	None
0.3 k.....	6	None

Total resistance—70.0 k
Tunnels (crossover paths)—13
(In addition, capacitors may serve as tunnels)

on the present state of the flip-flop (outputs Q and $\overline{Q}$) as well as the logic inputs—thus J-K action.

For d-c stability, points A and B cannot be allowed to assume a high level together. For this reason, transistors Q_5 and Q_6 are used to inhibit points A and B respectively a short time (propagation delay) after the occurrence of a positive clock pulse. Voltage waveforms (Fig. 8A) show the time relations of points A, B, clock pulse (CP), and outputs Q and $\overline{Q}$ when switching output $\overline{Q}$ from off to on.

Transistor Q_1 serves as a low-impedance drive to the bases of Q_3 and Q_4 to turn the inverter on (solid line in Fig. 7). Once the inverter is on, however, base current is di-

verted from Q_1 by clamp D_1 (shown by the dotted line), so that the overdrive is reduced.

Logic Inputs—Flip-flop logic inputs are common-emitter stages. Complementary inputs are supplied on both J and K for increased versatility. Intermediate signal storage on the J and K inputs is sufficient for reliable shift register operation. These steering inputs require a d-c drive source and can be driven from either inverting or non-inverting gates.

Series 53 Loading—In general there are only two types of d-c loads that must be considered:

n− load—requires a current sink (Fig. 8B).

n+ load—requires a current source (Fig. 8C).

The Series 53 has inputs that require both of these type drives. For example, the gate inputs require a driver to act as a current sink only (n− load) while the flip-flop steering inputs require a driver only to supply current (n+ load). If a driver can act as both a sink (output voltage low) and a source of current (output voltage high), then it can drive both types of load. Each Series 53 output and input is rated for n− and n+ drive capabilities (Table I) and drive requirements (Table II), respectively. All possible combinations of loads can be recognized by using these two tables.

Master Slice—The Series 53 master slice component count for each 65

× 150 mil bar is given in Table III. Each component is isolated and all interconnections are made with evaporated aluminum. The large number of components available makes it possible to place complex circuits on a single bar without bonded interconnections.

None of the circuits use all of the components, but some use more than others. The relative difficulty of producing a working circuit is dependent on the total junction area used and the area of surface covered by aluminum.

Circuits produced on the master slice require widely differing combinations of component specifications and tolerances. For example, one circuit may require low R_{cs} npn transistors while it can tolerate wide resistor tolerances. On the other hand, another circuit may require closer tolerances on resistors but may not be critical on npn R_{cs}. The master slice concept permits assignment of the best material to each of these circuits without loss of any material. In addition, a single device may have different evaporated lead patterns which may be used to select resistor taps and thereby adjust resistance values if resistors are running high or low.

Given this flexibility, it is possible to use resistors with tolerances of ± 50 percent, npn h_{FE} from 15 to 1,000, pnp h_{FE} from 0 to 1,000, and R_{cs} up to 300 ohms. In short, it is possible to use all material that is ready for evaporated aluminum leads. This is a distinct advantage of the master slice fabrication technique.

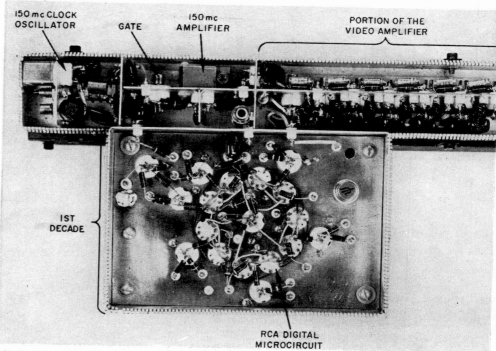

150 mc CLOCK OSCILLATOR — GATE — 150 mc AMPLIFIER — PORTION OF THE VIDEO AMPLIFIER — 1ST DECADE — RCA DIGITAL MICROCIRCUIT

COUNTER frequencies and rise times demand careful circuit layout and miniaturization to minimize parasitics

USING MICROCIRCUITS IN

High-Resolution Range Counters

High-frequency decade of this counter is a digital microcircuit to save space and power. Snap-off diodes designed into the driver help produce pulse widths of about 2 nanoseconds at clock rates as high as 250 Mc

By **L. C. DREW**
Systems Support Engineering,
Radio Corp. of America,
Burlington, Mass.

REAL-TIME RANGING SYSTEMS

One of the problems of rendezvous in space is determining distance between vehicles. Here is a range counter which operates at a 150-Mc clock rate or ±1 meter resolution. It has operated successfully in stringent environments and shows promise for satellite docking, surveying and long range determinations

RANGING SYSTEMS of high resolution can be built, if the latest in circuit techniques and devices are designed into compatible circuits. Here is a range counter system operating at 150-Mc clock rate or ±1 meter resolution. Typical of the advanced techniques used: a digital microcircuit as the 150-Mc first decade; and, snap-off diodes in the critical high-frequency driver. The feasibility model of this counter system has operated successfully under environmental conditions similar to military specs, and shows promise for many uses, both here on earth and in space.

The block diagram (Fig. 1) shows a straight-forward counter with a gated clock controlled by start-stop pulses. Counter time reference is a crystal-controlled oscillator whose period corresponds to desired range resolution. If desired range interval is ±1 meter, the

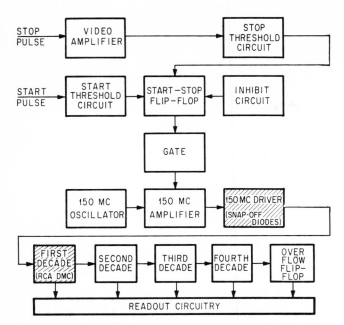

COUNTING SCHEME is normal, but critical 150-Mc driver turns off and recovers in under 3.5 nanoseconds. Snap-off diodes do it. First decade is digital microcircuit—Fig. 1

oscillator must operate at 150 megacycles. Oscillator output is gated to the counting circuits by the start-stop flip-flop. This flip-flop is turned on by a start line pulse and turned off by a stop line pulse.

The counting flip-flops are arranged into decades. Each decade has reached some count when the stop pulse occurs. When the start-stop flip-flop goes off, a 0.8-second one-shot multivibrator is started. This initiates the readout period resulting in each decade count being presented on a separate Magneline readout. Each decade count is converted, by relays, to an appropriate drive signal for display. Once the display has reached final readout position, no further maintaining power is required; this provides infinite type storage. As a result, all power can be removed from the readout circuits when the one-shot period is over. An overflow flip-flop is also included, to indicate the lack of a return pulse to stop the counter. When the counter has reached its maximum capacity, the overflow flip-flop indicates that the reading obtained is invalid. The inhibit flip-flop circuit prevents the counter from being turned off before an adjustable length of time. After this time, the inhibit flip-flop changes state, allowing the next stop line pulse to turn off the start-stop flip-flop. The inhibit flip-flop insures that noise external to the system, which can be high enough to turn off the counter, will not negate the function of the system. Complete counter reset is automatic, with manual reset included.

Circuits—Counter system high frequencies and fast rise times demand careful component selection and circuit construction. Circuit configurations must optimize the performance of all devices. Careful mechanical layout and miniaturization minimize parasitic inductance and capacitance. Shunt feedback, as an example, is used around each stage of the video amplifier, causing low input and output impedances

which, in turn, require extremely short leads to minimize stray inductance. In Fig. 1, the high-frequency circuits to note are—the clock-oscillator, amplifier and gate, the video amplifier, and the high-frequency or first decade of the counter and its driver.

Since the maximum possible range of the counter is 9,999 meters (four decades) and resolution is ± 1 meter, the oscillator should have a stability of one part in 10^5. This insures the maximum error to be the counter error of ± 1 cycle. Therefore, the 150-Mc oscillator must be a crystal-controlled oscillator. A seventh overtone crystal oscillator was chosen, over a lower frequency oscillator and multiplier, because it conserves space and power.

The 150-Mc amplifier is necessary for two reasons —it acts as a buffer; and it is able to provide at least 3 volts peak at driver input. A grounded-base stage, with matching network, is used on both input and output for good isolation. Several methods are explored in gating this amplifier, only one was successful. Main cause for failure—the impedance of a saturated transistor or diode is not low enough, at 150-Mc, to act as a shunt or series switch, and so causes on and off levels to be nearly equal.

Figure 2 shows the 150-Mc clock-gate, amplifier, and driver. The gate-amplifier circuit uses a current-robbing technique for operation. When the gate transistor Q_1 (2N2368) is turned on, the emitter of Q_2 is held positive: Transistor Q_2 is off providing more than adequate isolation. This method also proved capable of switching from one state to another within one cycle of the clock, preserving counter resolution.

Video Amplifier—Included in the stop line is a 60-db, 200-Mc bandwidth current amplifier, to handle the low-level stop pulse (as low as 2-8 μ amp). The 200-Mc bandwidth preserves stop pulse rise time and counter resolution.

This video amplifier has its gain time programmed (tpg) from the start-stop flip-flop to reduce false triggering. This tpg circuit, similar to agc, allows amplifier gain to range from approximately unity (at time = 0) to full gain at maximum range. This is possible since the stop line signal strength varies inversely with time. This time-programmed function is achieved by controlling, with RC networks, the conductance through a set of diodes in shunt with the input.

The basic video amplifier was designed with six stages, using individual parallel voltage feedback and emitter degeneration and peaking. This approach produced the desired bandwidth (200-Mc) and approximately 54-db of gain. In addition, a common-emitter input stage (providing an added 6-db gain) was included to reduce the input impedance to its lowest possible value. Using 2N918 transistors biased at optimum operating point, the video amplifier achieved the desired characteristics.

The output of this video amplifier drives a threshold device (diode-transistor gate) which, when threshold is exceeded, provides a pulse to trigger the start-stop flip-flop. Since the start line has a similar threshold device, the differences in delay, approximately 15 nanoseconds, in the start and stop line are caused primarily by the video amplifier.

Decade Operation—The first decade accepts the clock rate of 150-Mc, with each flip-flop within the decade operating at $\frac{1}{5}$ the bit rate. A typical 5-stage decade, consisting of five flip-flops and ten AND gates, is shown in Fig. 3A. The flip-flop outputs are cross-coupled to opposite input gates in a ring formation. Figure 3B illustrates the idealized output waveforms of each flip-flop.

The counter (3A) is shown in the reset position with all right sides on, and the clock line held to ground. The various gates are enabled by the off side of the previous flip-flop in the ring and the input positive clock pulse.

The left side of the first stage is turned on by the first pulse, which enables the left side gate of the next flip-flop such that the second pulse will turn off the second stage, etc. If the input signal gets through a gate, it can only turn a flip-flop from 1 to 0. If the flip-flop is already in the on state, no switching can occur. Thus there are four enabled gates which do not switch as their flip-flops are already in the on state. Each succeeding input pulse switches a succeeding stage off until the fifth pulse. The sixth pulse starts again with the first stage, turning it on. Succeeding pulses turn on succeeding stages until the counter is back in the reset position after the tenth pulse. According to Zoltan Tarczy-Hornoch[1] and our experimental tests, this scheme depends primarily on gate sensitivity and rise time, not on flip-flop speed.

Critical Driver—The counter's most critical feature is the driver (Fig. 2), which must turn off and recover within one cycle of the clock rate. The propagation-rise-fall time, as well as the pulse width, must be less than one-half cycle or approximately 3.5 nanoseconds. Since the driver transistor is biased in the saturated condition, the above conditions are difficult to achieve. Using snap-off diodes, drivers were designed capable of producing a pulse width, at the base, of approximately 2 nanoseconds at a clock rate as high as 250-Mc. This driver circuit is normally saturated holding the clock line grounded. Both the FD600 and the SSD558 are snap-off diodes. They reshape the incoming 150-Mc sinewave to a fast rising negative pulse which turns off the 2N709. This produces the fast positive clock pulse necessary to trigger the TTL flip-flop. The snap-off diodes are necessary for pulse shaping to take advantage of the 2N709 optimum switching speed.

The normal minimum sensitivity of the driver is 2-3 volts peak; however, it will operate more reliably with a 4-6 volt input. Such a driver was developed and used with the above counting scheme to successfully test a 250-Mc counter, insuring reliable counting circuits in this 150-Mc counter.

Microcircuits—Using the above logic scheme, various circuit designs of the gates and flip-flop were tried—namely, RCTL, DCTL, RCTL in a current mode, and TTL. All appeared to operate successfully, however, the TTL was deemed the most feasible, and packaged in the RCA digital microcircuit format (RCA DMC), because it conserves power and space. The packaging technique was also found to increase the speed of previous breadboard counters by a factor of almost 2.

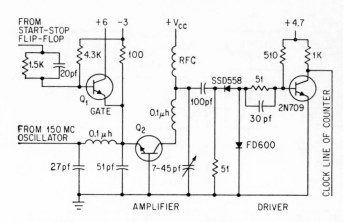

CURRENT robbing gate-amplifier operation makes the amplifier a good buffer. Driver snap-off diodes shape fast negative pulse turning off 2N709; sends fast positive trigger to first decade—Fig. 2

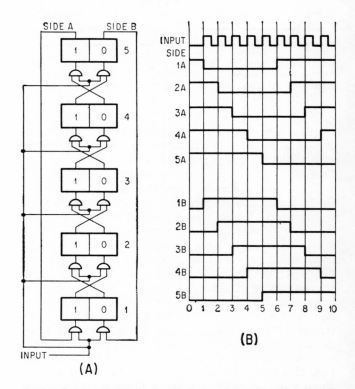

DECADE COUNTER stages (A) in reset condition or side B conducting. Output waveforms (B) of flip-flops—Fig. 3

The other three decades of the counter, consisting of 4 flip-flops each, use a conventional, universal RCTL flip-flop.

The readout of all four decades is performed by the output of each flip-flop driving a relay driver. The relay contacts form the decoding logic, switching each Magneline readout unit to the proper decade number.

The author thanks Harold F. King and Donald H. Landry for their assistance in this article.

REFERENCE

(1) Zoltan Tarczy-Hornoch, "Five Binary Counting Technique Makes Faster Decimal-Counting Circuits," *Electronic Design*, Jan. 1961.

TYPICAL CIRCUIT module using digital microcircuits and a few discrete components. Digital techniques allow cockpit operation of Loren-C receiver for first time

DIGITAL LORAN-C RECEIVER Uses Microcircuits

Redesigning an analog receiver to use digital techniques requires a new approach to system design. Even servo loops and filters are digital, and only r-f amplification remains analog

By **ROBERT L. FRANK** and **ALAN H. PHILLIPS**, Sperry Gyroscope Co., Great Neck, New York

REDUCED SIZE, weight and power consumption combined with simpler operation are the results of marrying digital techniques and microcircuits in a new Loran-C receiver for general aircraft use. But digital circuits could not be substituted for analog circuits on a straightforward function-by-function basis. Complete redesign of the receiver on a system-function basis was necessary. Some of the design techniques developed have applications in radar and communications systems.[1]

The basic Loran-C navigation system consists of a master station and two associated slave stations. Each station transmits precisely timed pulses on a carrier freqency of 100 kc, which results in usable ground-wave signals to 1,900 n.m. over water and 1,500 n.m. over land.[2]

A Loran-C receiver in the aircraft measures the time difference between the reception of a signal from the master and each of two slaves to establish two unique hyperbolic contours or lines of position with the stations as foci. The intersection of the two lines locates the aircraft, as indicated in Fig. 1.

As a result of a completely new system and circuit design that maximizes the use of digital integrated microcircuits and eliminates all moving parts, it has been possible to obtain the following advantages.

• Operator controls are reduced

from 26 to 6 and the usual crt is eliminated, making cockpit operation feasible for the first time.

• Weight is 20 lb instead of 100.

• Power consumption is 150 watts instead of 500.

• Reliability is increased by a factor of three.

Signal characteristics—Loran-C signals are complex and many factors are involved.

• Each Loran-C chain broadcasts a group of eight pulses, with the signals of the master followed by two or more slave station signals in sequence. Each chain uses a different repetition rate.

• The pulses are carrier-phase coded for station identification and to permit compression of the eight

NOW: LORAN IN THE COCKPIT

Although the Loran-C navigation system was developed approximately 12 years ago, widespread aircraft use for general navigation was not likely until the receiving equipment was simple to operate, could be installed in the cockpit, and could provide information similar in form to that from DME, VOR, or TACAN. A digital Loran-C receiver showed promise of meeting the requirement, since digital logic could substitute for operator logic—making the receiver simple to operate—and microelectronics could reduce size and weight

ORIGINAL LORAN-C equipment, left, and new digital system

pulse groups into one higher energy pulse.

• All except the first three cycles may be contaminated by skywave signals reflected from the ionosphere. Skywaves may be as much as 30 db larger than the desired ground-wave signal.

• The signals may be immersed in atmospheric noise as much as 20 db above the ground wave, and in interference as much as 35 db above the ground wave.

• The signals may have an amplitude anywhere within a 120-db range, depending on distance from the stations.

• Aircraft motion produces a doppler shift up to 0.2 cps at 1,200 knots.

With such signals, the Loran-C receiver must make phase measurements without ambiguity to an accuracy of 0.1 μsec, which is 1/100 of a carrier cycle.

Requirements — Receiver operation is indicated in Fig. 2. Master search requires examination of the entire 100,000 μsec loran interval to find and identify the master signal arriving at an unknown time. Slave search requires tracking on the master (since slave identification is determined by approximate timing in relation to the master), but only a small time delay range must be examined.

Settling requires that the receiver tracking gates settle on the signal in spite of doppler shift. Furthermore, the settling must determine first the groundwave signal, then a particular cycle of the groundwave.

Tracking requires that the receiver integrate the information over a 10-sec period (800 pulses) to give the accuracy to overcome noise

and c-w interference, and to follow aircraft maneuvers. Readout requires a presentation of measured time difference to an accuracy of 0.1-μsec over a 100,000 μsec interval.

For data processing, serial operation at 1-Mc is adequate, except for storing loran signal timing (necessary for coherent detection) and measuring the loran time-difference; both these require a precision of 0.1 μsec. Computing at 10-Mc was not possible with available integrated microcircuits so a hybrid design was developed. The loran signal-timing reference is stored in real time with a few 10-Mc chip circuits performing simple operations; the remainder of the functions are performed on a special purpose 1-Mc computer operating independently of loran time.

System — A simplified block dia-

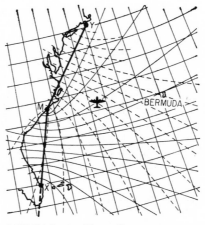

LORAN-C position lines are generated by master and slave transmitters. Photographic overlay shows analog receiver equipment and new digital equipment designed to replace it and make cockpit operation feasible—Fig. 1

gram is shown in Fig. 3. The r-f amplifier, of necessity analog, amplifies the Loran-C signals from a level as low as 5 μvolts to the 1-volt range.

The r-f signals are sampled directly and converted to digital form. Quadrature-channel operation required for coherent detection is provided by sampling separated by 2½ μsec (90 degrees at the carrier frequency). For the cycle resolution, an envelope derivation network forms a zero point on the leading edge of the received pulse envelope. Five samplings are made on each pulse: two guard samples ahead of the signal to resolve skywaves and ground waves, one for cycle phase, one envelope sample to resolve cyclic ambiguity, and one for automatic gain control.

The data processor performs smoothing, integrating, transfer, timing, and threshold-detection functions. A circulating memory with a magnetostrictive delay line is used. This data processor is controlled by a synchronizer and programer. Outputs from the data processor control the r-f amplifier gain (through a D/A converter), the various mode registers, and the loran timers.

Sampling is controlled by three loran timers—one for each station. The timers run from a 10-Mc oscillator and form a real-time memory of the expected time of arrival of the loran signals. They can be shifted in small steps under control of the data processor. A pulse counter and coder combines signals from the three timers and introduces proper phase coding.

Time difference indication is provided by a readout counter started by the master timer and stopped by a selected slave timer. The count (in cycles of 10 Mc) provides the loran time difference, and is displayed on numerical display tubes in the control-indicator unit.

Computer — Digital, integrated microcircuits are used in all digital functions. A plug-in card containing up to 250 individually replaceable microcircuits is shown in one of the photographs.

The disparate requirements of master search and other modes are handled by a completely reorganized computer between these modes.

In modes other than master search, the memory is organized into three sectors corresponding to the three loran signals to be tracked. In each sector, the words store data deprived from the five samplings of each signal and secondary data derived therefrom.

The required data processing is accomplished with only addition and subtraction operations. Scaling is accomplished by (1) programing the memory into which the input data bits are inserted and (2) programing the memory bits examined for threshold and selected for transfer into secondary data words.

The digital functions include nine digital servo loops of various degrees of complexity and ten smoothing filters that operate threshold detectors.

Extensive time sharing is used in the A/D converters, digital-processing elements, mode registers, and D/A converters for agc.

Digital Servo Loops—The receiver has functions equivalent to nine servo loops, six of which were electromechanical in earlier Loran-C receivers. The most complex are the three phase-lock loops.

Analysis indicated the receivers required a second-order (zero velocity lag) tracking loop with bandwidth switching to meet the noise reduction and maneuver requirements.

A simplified diagram of the Loran-C digital phase-lock loop, Fig. 4, shows that the sampling pulse output of the digital loop for e μsec error is

$$\left(\frac{aen}{bP} + \frac{aen^2t}{bPQ} \right) \mu\text{sec/sec}$$

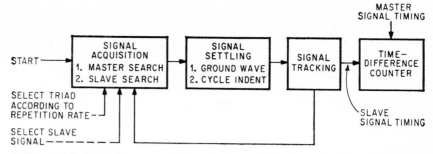

RECEIVER OPERATION requires identification of master and slave signals and determination of time relationships between them—Fig. 2

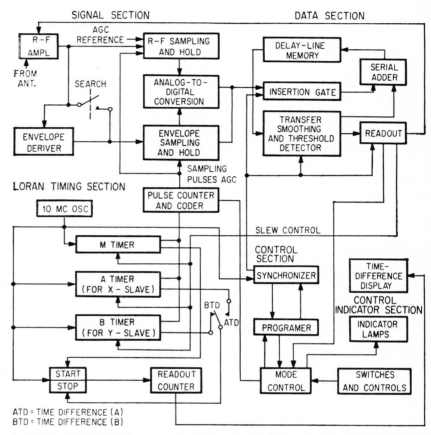

DIGITAL OPERATIONS are accomplished with 839 microcircuits consisting of five types of II series 53 circuits: flip-flops, single and dual **ord** gates and single and dual **nord** gates—Fig. 3

where the terms are defined in the diagram.

The equivalent Laplace transform of the loop, Fig. 5, shows an output of $(Ae + Aket)$ μsec/sec for a fixed error of e-μsec, where A and K are coefficients in the equivalent Laplace transform.

The equating of the coefficients of e and et yields

$$A = an/bP$$
$$AK = an^2/bPQ$$

Therefore $K = n/Q$. Transient response, noise bandwidth, and signal-to-noise improvement of the system can be computed from Laplace transform theory.

The block marked cycle word in Fig. 4 is instrumented as follows. The sampled phase error is fed in digital form into the insertion gate (Fig. 3). From there it is shifted into the adder and, at the proper time, is added serially to the cycle word in the memory. The addition takes place for each sample of the signal (n times per sec). The cycle word continues to increase in value (if the error persists) until it overflows, returning to zero. The overflow is detected by the threshold detection and readout and is fed to the slew control, which causes a change of a μsec in the timing of the

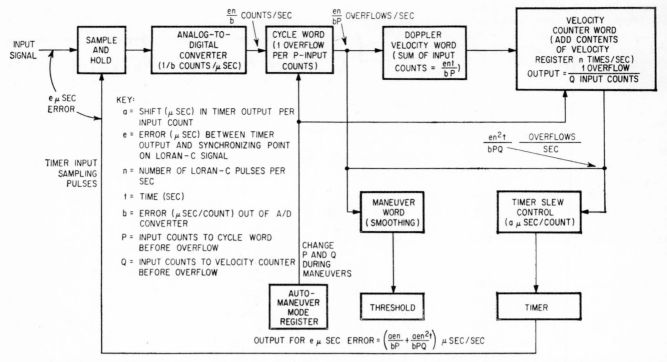

$\frac{en}{b}$ COUNTS/SEC $\frac{en}{bP}$ OVERFLOWS/SEC

| INPUT SIGNAL → | SAMPLE AND HOLD | → | ANALOG-TO-DIGITAL CONVERTER (1/b COUNTS/µ SEC) | → | CYCLE WORD (1 OVERFLOW PER P-INPUT COUNTS) | → | DOPPLER VELOCITY WORD (SUM OF INPUT COUNTS = $\frac{ent}{bP}$) | → | VELOCITY COUNTER WORD (ADD CONTENTS OF VELOCITY REGISTER n TIMES/SEC) OUTPUT = $\frac{1\ OVERFLOW}{Q\ INPUT\ COUNTS}$ |

e µ SEC ERROR

TIMER INPUT SAMPLING PULSES

KEY:
a = SHIFT (µ SEC) IN TIMER OUTPUT PER INPUT COUNT
e = ERROR (µ SEC) BETWEEN TIMER OUTPUT AND SYNCHRONIZING POINT ON LORAN-C SIGNAL
n = NUMBER OF LORAN-C PULSES PER SEC
t = TIME (SEC)
b = ERROR (µ SEC/COUNT) OUT OF A/D CONVERTER
P = INPUT COUNTS TO CYCLE WORD BEFORE OVERFLOW
Q = INPUT COUNTS TO VELOCITY COUNTER BEFORE OVERFLOW

$\frac{en^2t}{bPQ}$ $\frac{OVERFLOWS}{SEC}$

CHANGE P AND Q DURING MANEUVERS

MANEUVER WORD (SMOOTHING)

TIMER SLEW CONTROL (a µ SEC/COUNT)

AUTO-MANEUVER MODE REGISTER

THRESHOLD

TIMER

OUTPUT FOR e µ SEC ERROR = $\left(\frac{aen}{bP} + \frac{aen^2t}{bPQ}\right)$ µ SEC/SEC

DIGITAL PHASE-LOCK servo loop, of which three are used. A total of nine servo loops are used, of which six were electro-mechanical in previous equipment—Fig. 4

---

sampling pulses. The overflow is also stored and put into the insertion gate at the proper time to be added to the doppler-velocity word.

The doppler-velocity word is added to the velocity-counter word n times per sec. The velocity-counter word precedes the doppler-velocity word in the memory. The doppler-velocity data are transferred to the velocity-counter word by bypassing a one word shift register (marked transfer in Fig. 3). The least significant bits come into the adder coincident with the least significant bits of the velocity-counter word.

After Q input counts to the velocity-counter word, the word overflows and returns to zero. Each overflow jumps the timer by a µsec (by way of the threshold detection and readout and the timer slew control).

The stored-cycle-word overflow is also added to the maneuver word (through the insertion gate). The maneuver word is a smoothed version of the cycle servo-error signal. The most significant bits of the maneuver word are subtracted from its least significant bits as described in the next section on smoothing. Thus the maneuver word, if it exceeds a threshold, puts a *1* into the automaneuver register and

causes the previously described changes in P and Q. These changes are brought about because the auto-maneuver register causes a change in the synchronizer that, in turn, changes the time of insertion of the A/D converter output into the memory. The error signal is added to more significant bits in the cycle word and causes a higher gain (larger P). There is also a change in the gating of the velocity-counter word bit (changing Q).

Digital Smoothing—The Loran-C receiver must render decisions based on the presence or absence of certain signals that, at the input, may be submerged in noise and interference. Thus a low-pass filter is used to average the input over a length of time to enable the signal component to integrate sufficiently above the noise level to be identifiable. The simplest filter is a resistance-capacitance network with

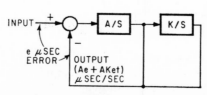

INPUT + ⊖ — → A/S → K/S
e µ SEC ERROR
OUTPUT (Ae + AKet) µ SEC/SEC

EQUIVALENT Laplace transform of servo loop shown in Fig. 4—Fig. 5

a time constant $\tau = RC$. This type of filter is readily mechanized as a digital filter using the dynamic data processing loop consisting of the tapped shift register, a serial adder, and the magnetostrictive delay-line memory. The digital filter and its analog equivalent are shown in Fig. 6.

The impulse response $\exp[-t/\tau]$ is derived in the data processor by the application of exponential decay to an infinite memory storage loop. Infinite memory allows all inputs to be lumped into a simple storage cell. The exponential decay is applied as a decrement to the lumped inputs by the single operation of subtracting a fraction of the data from the data itself. The decay factor is adjustable from multiple tap positions on the shift register (as shown in Fig. 6B) and is identified as factor r in

$$x_n + 1 = x_n (1 - 1/2^r)$$

where x_n is the smoothed output after the nth iteration.

By applying 2's complementation in the subtractor (complementator) a simple serial subtraction is accomplished. The filter equation is

$$x_n + 1 = x_n (1 - 1/2^r) + x_i$$

where x_i is the instantaneous $x(t)$ input, and x_n is the accumulation of past inputs.

Three fundamental rules apply to

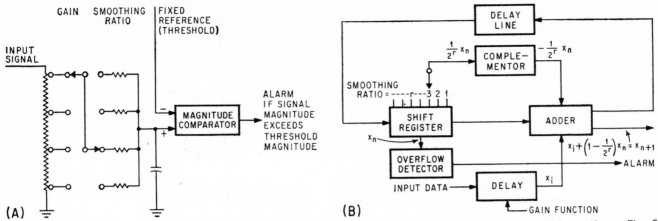

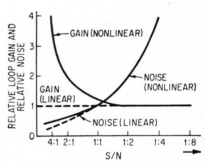

ANALOG FILTER (A) and digital equivalent (B). Signal to noise enhancement is a function of smoothing ratio r—Fig. 6

the digital smoothing functions:

(1) The filtered signal approaches the limit of $2^r \times A$ for an input of average value (A) as the number of samples approach infinity.

(2) The effective time constant (τ) of the digital filter is equal to the sampling period (T) multiplied by the factor 2^r or $\tau = T \times 2^r$.

(3) The signal enhancement (S/N improvement factor) = $2^{(r+1)}$.

Threshold Detection — Threshold detection involves the identification of a quantity according to whether it exceeds a fixed magnitude. Since the data may be bipolar according to sign-bit storage, magnitude detection consists of detecting overflow into certain most-significant-bit positions in the data word by testing each of these bits for opposite polarity from the sign bit.

In the signal it was possible to adjust the input-gating-gain parameter (timing) so that the threshold could be set at discrete binary levels. This greatly simplifies the threshold detector.

Dynamic Range—The resolution required affects the design of discrete systems. This is reflected in the number of binary bits required to represent a specific quantity, and, in turn, the complexity of the analog-to-digital interfaces or converters. The fineness of the resolution (smallness of unit quantum) is a measure of how closely the discrete system approaches a true linear system. The usual concept of the resolution requirement is that the data be quantized into steps no greater than the smallest increment of data of interest in the output or

in the control process. This, in fact, applies to the three timers that maintain the loran time references. Six binary decimal decade counter sections are required to quantize the 100,000-μsec repetition interval of the loran signal in units of 0.1 μsec for time difference readout accuracy. However, in the digital filter and digital (sampled data) feedback loops, the unit quantum can be much larger than the increment of signal to be detected.

The required 0.1 μsec instrumental precision is obtained by a data-sign conversion separate from the level quantization. The sign is determined to a very small fraction of the unit-quantization level.

In the presence of noise or c-w interference, these extraneous random processes provide effective interpolation between levels, and a linear system action results. For clean signals, the servo loops tend toward a hard-limiting type of operation. This side effect of coarse quantization gives a desirable adaptive behavior, as shown in Fig. 7.

System Simulation—The Loran-C digital receiver lends itself readily to simulation on a digital computer. The processes taking place in the computer can be made to correspond exactly to the processes that take place in the data section (Fig. 3) of the receiver. Quantization of the error signal and jumping of the timer in discrete jumps are also simulated exactly.

In Fig. 3 the time delay of the input signal from the antenna is represented by a number, as is the time delay of the sampling pulses. The output of the A/D converter is a function of the difference of these

LOOP GAIN of digital servo shows adaptive behavior, decreasing as signal to noise ratio falls—Fig. 7

time delays. Since a sample is taken of the pulse-modulated r-f signal, the output of the A/D converter is a pulse-modulated sinusoidal function of the difference of the time delays. This function is stored in the digital computer memory. The output of the A/D conversion of the envelope deriver is a different function, also stored in the computer memory. The effect of vehicle motion is simulated by causing the time delay of the input signal to vary as a function of time. Response of the output and various intermediate points in the system are printed out.

Digital system design of the AN/ARN-7 receiver is, to a great degree, the result of work by Sperry research engineer James Meranda. He was assisted by the engineers in the Radio Navigation Equipment Department.

REFERENCES

(1) E. S. Lurin, Digital Radar Techniques, *Sperry Engineering Review*, 15, No. 3 p 10, (Winter 1962).
(2) E. Durbin, Recent Developments in Loran C, *Navigation*, 9, No. 2, p 138, (Summer 1962).
(3) S. Claypoole and J. King, Loran-C Inertial Navigation, *National Aerospace Electronics Conference Proceedings*, May 1963.

Integrated circuits shrink a doppler radar system

Integrated circuit functions, used most often in digital computer applications, are slowly invading analog circuitry. Here is how off-the-shelf miniaturized components were designed into the linear circuits of an airborne radar system to be flight tested soon

By E.M. Pacifico and Stanley King

Senior Engineers, GPL Division-General Precision Aerospace, Pleasantville, N.Y.

It now seems clear that integrated circuits improve the reliability, maintainability and effectiveness of military electronic equipment by nearly an order of magnitude. At the same time they reduce the size and weight of airborne gear by even more than that amount. So far, most of the successful applications of such microelectric circuits have been in digital equipment, like the computers for the Minuteman missile guidance system, and only few accomplishments have been reported miniaturizing analog circuits this way. General Precision Aerospace has now designed and built a microelectronic dopplar radar navigation system. The major circuits of a radar system, of course, are basically analog.

This program demonstrates a procedure for designing analog circuits with integrated circuits. The equipment is markedly smaller and lighter; more reliable, better performing, easier to maintain, and less expensive. The approach is applicable to most radar systems.

Seventy percent of the General Precision radar has been microminiaturized with off-the-shelf microelectronic integrated circuits (MICs). Application of this technique to the remaining portions of the system would, in certain instances, contribute more complexity and less desirable characteristics than the original conventional circuits. In these cases, an adaptive interconnect approach[1] using uncommitted silicon wafers obtained from major integrated circuits and manufacturers is being applied.

The doppler radar system, with its standard MICs, thin-film adaptive networks, and MICs with special interconnects—will be test flown in mid-1964. Even as the flight test program is underway, a continuing product improvement program will reduce discrete component use by increasing use of special interconnect MICs.

Future areospace navigation systems will be required for a wide variety of missions and aircraft, including VTOLs, helicopters, advanced manned penetrator strike systems (AMPSS), as well as conventional high performance vehicles. While initial hardware developments have been concentrated on

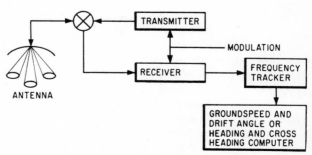

Self-contained doppler navigation system consists of four principal electronic blocks—transmitter, receiver, frequency tracker and computer

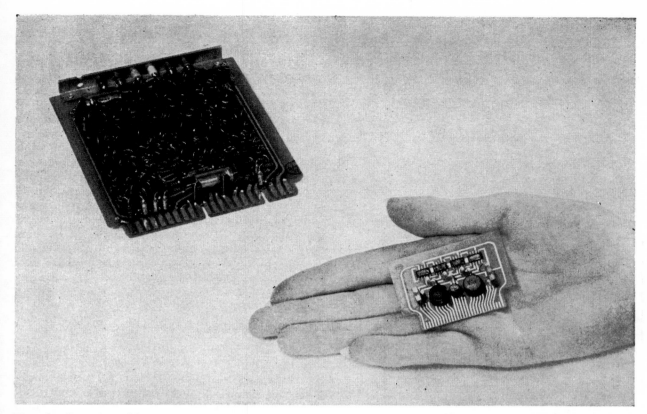

Microcircuit version of frequency tracker audio circuit replaces printed board version that uses discrete components

helicopter and VTOL applications, the new doppler navigation system design promises a universal navigation system for virtually all tactical, strategic and aerospace radar navigation requirements, at unmatched reliability and economy.

Doppler radar equipment measures the velocity of an aircraft with respect to the earth by measuring the doppler frequency shift returned from three or four beams of microwave energy aimed at the ground and reflected back to the vehicle. The measured doppler frequency is proportional to the component of velocity in the direction of the beam; beam velocities are processed to provide outputs of aircraft ground speed and drift angle and/or aircraft heading and cross heading velocities. Doppler systems can be completely self-contained within an aircraft operating without reference to external aids such as ground beacons.

Analog versus digital approaches

MICs, designed for digital applications, can be used repetitively in great quantities, the high volume requirements leading to low unit cost. Since digital circuits indicate one or the other of two states, power dissipation is low and tolerances can be loose. All these factors make digital MICs attractive, low in cost and readily available. On the other hand, analog type circuits have none of these advantages, and applicability of MICs to this type of circuit is not obvious. Thus it is desirable to use

digital techniques wherever possible to accomplish a function, and it is often advisable to employ digital circuits even at the cost of additional complexity. On the other hand, trade-offs have to be carefully investigated to avoid digitalizing "at all cost".

A study was made of a doppler radar frequency tracker in an attempt to convert it to digital circuits. The function of a frequency tracker is to measure the doppler shifted frequency of ground returns consisting of a Gaussian frequency distribution superimposed on varying amounts of background noise. Measuring the frequency of this type of signal is incompatible with pure digital techniques, so the digital approach had to be supplemented by analog circuits. This led to a small reduction in total number of analog circuits, but added the complexity of a great number of digital circuits. In this case, the total function is better performed using analog type MICs. The function of computing velocity outputs from the frequency signals was also investigated. Here it was found that frequency-to-current converters and servo loops could easily be replaced by digital computations, with an improvement in accuracy.

Designing analog portions of a radar system in microcircuit form can be accomplished in several ways: the application of thin-film, custom MIC, semi-custom MIC, or off-the-shelf hybrid approaches.

With a minimum of redesign, existing circuits can

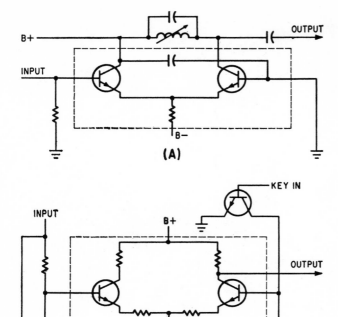

Receiver requires external adaptive circuits (A) for the 30-Mc amplifier stage. The suppressed carrier double-balanced modulator (B) has achieved a carrier rejection of 40 db. MICs are outlined by dashes.

be replaced by thin-film networks where active components were added in discrete form. Each circuit requires its own thin-film mask, increasing the expense with little reliability improvement. Size may be greatly reduced, but reliability is only improved by reduction in the number of interconnections.

At the present state-of-the-art, special MICs can be designed and built in single or multichip form to accomplish most analog circuit functions. This is an extremely expensive undertaking, not only in the design effort, but in ultimate high production costs. With little redundancy required in such circuit functions, small quantity requirements of any single MIC lead to excessive cost. In addition, proof of reliability is almost impossible since samples large enough for statistical validity would not be available.

To overcome most of the undesirable features of custom MICs, a semi-custom approach appears to be an attractive alternative. A recent development[1] consists of purchasing from major MIC vendors silicon wafers upon which both active and passive elements exist but without deposited interconnects between elements. These uncommitted wafers can be adapted to a wide variety of circuits by simply depositing the appropriate interconnect pattern.

Current development in this area has been quite encouraging and work is continuing to further advance the capability.

Each of the above approaches used independently falls far short of all the objectives sought. In the development of the helicopter doppler radar system, the necessity to minimize the transition time from laboratory to production hardware resulted in an off-the-shelf hybrid approach. In essence, this approach consists of purchasing only those MICs, both analog and digital, which are being offered as standard catalog items and then combining them where necessary with external adaptive networks made up of thin-film and/or discrete components. Actual implementation of this method demonstrates improved reliability, performance, and maintainability, and considerable reductions in weight and size. A slight cost disadvantage now exists but all predictions prevalent in the microcircuits industry are quite optimistic and anticipate a rapid downtrend during 1964.

Design procedures

Although microminiaturization techniques are far from being amenable to "cook-book" design procedures at this time, an orderly succession of design and evaluation steps speeded development of the helicopter doppler radar system. The main steps:

1) The areas most adaptable to the use of MICs are determined on a system-wide basis. Decisions are based primarily on whether analog and/or digital circuits are required to perform the overall functions.

2) Major system functions so chosen are carefully subdivided into their detailed sub-functions.

3) Each sub-function is analyzed separately to obtain required performance parameters and then related to the preceding and following sub-functions. Tentative decisions as to the choice of available MICs and adaptive networks are made.

4) Based on the choices made above, discrete component circuits are designed, bread-boarded, and evaluated. In some instances, this intermediate step can be by-passed in favor of going directly to the ultimate microcircuit version.

5) Regardless of which version is adopted first, the designer must evaluate each circuit on the basis of insuring compatibility with adaptive network requirements. Specifically, all external passive elements are scrutinized to determine whether they can be easily converted to thin-film devices on a practical basis. Circuit redesign may be necessary at this stage to reduce resistor and capacitor values and to lower voltage and dissipation in order to realize compatibility with present state-of-the-art.

6) To avoid the use of an excessive number of different MICs, the designer examines the available devices carefully to decide which units are most universally applicable to a variety of circuits. As an example, the Fairchild MIC differential amplifier type DA10111 has been made to function in a-c and

d-c amplifiers (both single and double ended), modulators, phase splitters, d-c controlled astable multivibrators, crystal controlled oscillators, sum-difference amplifiers, and a d-c inverter, using simple adoptive networks.

7) Design field-effect transistors (FETS) into circuits wherever they may be used to advantage. The trend in microcircuits, and this includes both MIC and thin film, appears to point markedly toward increased use of FETS as integral portions of these devices.

Here is how this system worked during the design and development of the doppler radar system. A completely self-contained doppler navigation system (below) consists of four principal electronic building blocks—transmitter, receiver, frequency tracker, and computers.

High power and high frequency (gigacycle) requirements in the transmitter are not now compatible with microcircuit techniques. But, in keeping with microminiaturization and the use of all-solid-state hardware, conventional magnetrons or klystrons commonly used in a radar system are being replaced by varactor multipliers. Advanced development is also underway to replace microwave plumbing with stripline.

Most adaptable for integrated circuit use are the timing frequency generating circuits required for the transmitter. Low-frequency beam switching is usually accomplished with crystal switches. A large signal is required to drive these switches in their best operating range. This restriction dictates a discrete transistor driver, but MICs may be used in all frequency dividers and gates.

To preserve coherence, and to avoid a multiplicity of oscillator instabilities, all modulation and reference frequencies are derived from a single, high-frequency oscillator. This frequency is divided down in a chain of countdown circuits. Motorola's MECL logic circuits have been found suitable to perform the countdown operation in the megacycle range, and Texas Instruments' Series 53 units are used in the low frequency counters. A single type, low-cost logic circuit, covering the entire frequency range, should be available in the future.

All 30-Mc circuits in the received employ Motorola MC-1110 emitter-coupled MIC amplifiers. These amplifiers require external adaptive circuits for a typical 30-Mc amplifier stage (see A). Here the advantages achieved are not so much in the reduction of numbers of components, as in greatly improved performance. The noise figure for an MIC is similar to that of its discrete component counterpart but the variation from unit to unit is considerably less. Due to greater uniformity obtained using MICs, the need for adjustments to counteract circuit nonuniformities is minimized or completely eliminated. Resultant designs are amenable to volume production with savings in handling, quality control, and eventual repair costs.

Most doppler systems require multiple i-f stages where much of the necessary gain is in the vicinity of 100 kc. Texas Instruments' SN-522 operational amplifiers will supply this gain if negative feedback is used to broaden the frequency response. The open loop gain of these operational amplifiers is 60 db. If only 20 db of closed loop gain is utilized, a bandwidth of 150 kc is available and the resulting gain stability is very high. Similar performance in conventional transistor circuits would require more complexity and many more components.

After amplification, detection, and frequency translation in the receiver, the frequency shift of the doppler returns is measured in the frequency tracker. Circuits, operating in the audio and sub-audio ranges, are required and analog type MICs can be used extensively. Some of the specific functions that have been successfully instrumented using MICs are modulators, integrators, filters, and audio amplifiers.

A suppressed carrier double-balanced modulator is shown in (B). Without balance adjustments, a carrier rejection of 40 db has been achieved. Double-balanced operation is obtained without necessity of using push-pull carrier and signal inputs. The MIC package used is a Fairchild 10111 differential amplifier. This eliminates added circuits to obtain the push-pull signals, such as transformers or transistor phase splitters. The modulator also provides 20 db of gain.

The figure (p 92) compares a conventional integrator (A) with the MIC version (B). Since high gain and low drift are essential, a chopper stabilized integrator is mandatory. To obtain low drift characteristics, minimum offset in the chopper is essential. With conventional circuits, the chopper transistors must be used in matched pairs.

Use of a field-effect transistor (FET) in this application has the advantage of zero offset as an inherent device characteristic. Only one FET is neces-

The authors

Emilio M. Pacifico joined GPL Division in 1954 and has been active in developing advanced semiconductor circuits for GPL's line of doppler navigation systems. He obtained his BEE at New York University in 1951.

Stanley King has been with GPL since 1956 and is responsible for circuit design for advanced doppler navigation radars. He obtained a BS in Physics from Technische Hochschule, Vienna, Austria in 1938 and a MS in Electrical Engineering from Columbia University in 1952

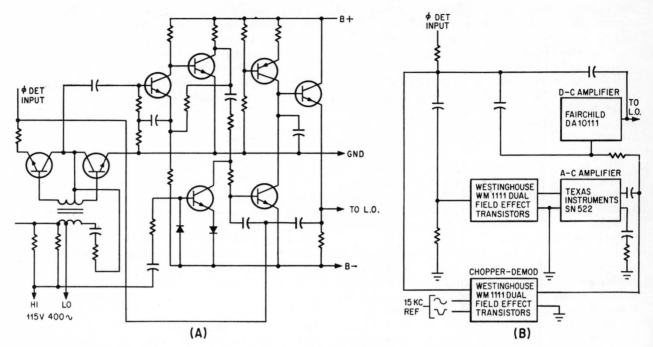

Integrator's conventional circuit (A) uses chopper transistors in pairs while the MIC version (B) uses field-effect transistors to handle chopping and demodulation

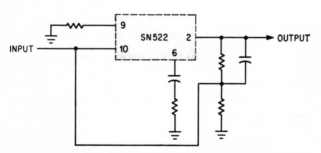

1.5 kc single section low-pass filter uses the practical approach of combining MICs and thin-film passive components

sary. Referring to (B), the chopping and demodulation are easily handled with a Westinghouse Electric double Unifet WM1111, housed in a ¼ x ¼ inch flat pack. In addition, an identical unit is used as a high impedance buffer between the chopper and the a-c amplifier. One of the FETs in the package is used in the constant current high-impedance region of its characteristic as a load for the other FET. Essentially, this connection is the source follower circuit. Impedance transformation is needed since resistance of an FET chopper in its "on" state is in the order of 2000 ohms resulting in large loss of gain unless the amplifier input impedance is large. Impedance transformation makes it possible to use smaller values of coupling capacitors, simplifying conversion of external resistors and capacitors from discrete to thin film components.

The Texas Instruments SN-522 operational amplifier is used in an open loop mode to provide 60 db of a-c gain. The signal is then demodulated in one half of the WM1111 as described above. Additional d-c gain which is now considerably less sensitive to drift is supplied by a Fairchild differential amplifier. External capacitive feedback completes the integrator.

R-C high- and low-pass filters with cutoffs in the low audio or subaudio ranges are required in this application. Active filters are used to avoid the use of large value capacitors and resistors combining the inevitable amplifier stage with the filter. Complete filters therefore may be practically fabricated within MICs without using external adaptive networks.

A current approach consists of combining MICs and thin-film passive components. The circuit diagram shows a 1.5 kc single section low pass filter. Due to high gain in the operational amplifier, external resistor and capacitor values have been greatly reduced compared to those required in an equivalent passive filter. Multiple section filters and filters with a twin-T circuit in the feedback loop are practical when this technique of combination is used. The cutoff frequency of these filters will not be consistent from unit to unit, or over a large temperature range. Stabilization of cutoff frequency may be effected by reduction of the operational amplifier gain using negative feedback, but only at the cost of requiring larger resistors and capacitors, and reduced overall gain.

Both the operational and differential MIC amplifiers may be used for audio amplification. As in the applications described above, high gain of the operational amplifier makes it possible to use a great amount of feedback, resulting in excellent gain stability. The differential amplifier is only useful in applications where larger gain variation can be tolerated. Use of active filters and modulators eliminates the need for audio amplifiers since the modulators and filters already have built-in gain.

The outputs of the frequency tracker are frequency analogs of velocities along the beams. To produce the final system outputs, a computation of groundspeed and drift angle or heading and cross heading velocities must be performed. This function is implemented by digital MICs, using mostly counters, registers, and various gating circuits. These circuits represent little that is new in design techniques. Reference to current literature will provide the reader with sufficient background.

The overall benefits to be achieved in using MICs have been repeatedly emphasized. However most comparisons with conventional circuits and other microcircuit techniques have been general, quite philosophic and organized to demonstrate the advantages on a broad system basis. A departure from this viewpoint will be presented here in that only the common system function of amplification will be considered.

Assume that a choice must be made between an operational amplifier such as Texas Instruments' SN-522 MIC or its equivalent in discrete component form. Which factor or factors would determine the final choice—size, weight, cost, power dissipation, performance, reliability, or maintainability?

Conventional circuits vs. MICs—table

	SN-522 MIC	Conventional circuit
Volume per unit gain	0.003	1
Weight per unit gain	0.03	1
Cost per unit gain	1.7	1
Power dissipation per unit gain	0.12	1

Of the many possible figures of merit which may be used for comparison, a useful combination consists of evaluation of the applicable factors noted above on per unit gain basis. Such a comparison normalized for conventional circuits is shown in the table. The conventional circuit referred to is one in which the input-output characteristics are equivalent to that of the MIC. In this case, it is a transistorized operational amplifier typical of those used repeatedly in a dopplar radar system. From the table, the cost based on December, 1963 prices favors the conventional approach. Forecasts point toward at least an equalization in cost by the end of 1964, and a rapidly lowering cost after that.

Performance, reliability and maintainability factors can be evaluated as follows:

Performance: In general, the gains presently available with analog MICs exceed those required for most applications. This excess gain can be used to improve the performance of the circuit. The equivalent gain in conventional circuits could only be obtained with a great number of components and therefore would not be economically feasible. Better linearity, temperature stability and reduced distortion are also possible with much less circuit complexity and cost. Such improvements have been demonstrated in GPL doppler equipment currently under development, particularly in the application of Texas Instruments' SN-522 amplifiers.

Reliability: It is almost an order of magnitude better than that obtained using discrete components of standard military quality. For the conventional circuit operational amplifier used in the comparison (Standard Military Quality components), the failure rate per million operating hours (F_m) is 3.8 while the MIC equivalent is 0.47. The latter figure is based on Texas Instruments, Inc., published data in combination with a GPL reliability study estimate. If the use of high-reliability discrete components of the Minuteman class is considered for the conventional circuit, then the F_m is 0.564. Therefore, it is evident that the MIC approach has some advantage over the use of high reliability components. All industry observations point toward even better reliability figures for MICs as more test data become available.

Maintainability: Fault isolation is greatly simplified if MICs are used. One or more MICs with their external components are combined in a throwaway module. Isolation of a failure to this type of functional module is easily and quickly accomplished. Though the replacement cost is bound to be higher than in conventional circuits, it is justified by fewer repairs and savings in downtime of the equipment.

Future development

From our experience with MICs it is evident that many functions must be implemented in a complex manner because available building blocks must be adapted to uses for which they were never intended. Although the advantage of a minimal number of different MICs is apparent, development of a few more building blocks (mixers, level detectors, universal logic circuits) by MIC manufacturers will help simplify designs.

Major breakthrough[1] in thin-film techniques are being made by several companies where work is in progress leading to deposition of active devices on an inactive subtrate. Also, deposition of thin-film resistors and capacitors directly on an integrated circuit subtrate will further extend the MIC capability. Characteristics of deposited resistors and capacitors can then be better controlled and larger value capacitors, will be available. These techniques will permit further reduction in the number of external discrete components and will broaden the applicability of these circuits to functions not feasible at this time.

Reference

1 Electronics, p 48, Jan. 24, 1964

Microcircuit Doppler Radar

In-house facility to build smallest, most accurate and reliable system from standard integrated chips

By **SAMUEL WEBER**
Senior Editor

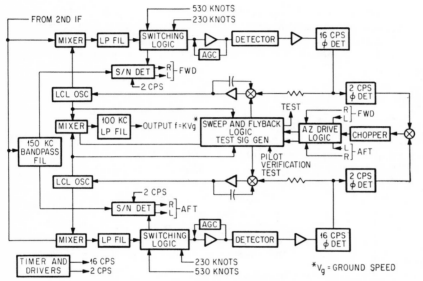

MORE THAN 70 percent of the frequency tracker portion of the high-performance Doppler navigational radar shown here will be implemented with presently available standard integrated circuit packages—Fig. 1

PLEASANTVILLE, N.Y. — Radical new systems designs based on integrated circuit techniques will be incorporated in a series of Doppler radar navigational equipments by General Precision Inc., resulting in systems with ten times the reliability of current in-production systems (about 1,000 hours MTBF), total weight less than 25 pounds, and a substantially lower cost.

According to J.C. Forrest, Director of Engineering at General Precision's GPL Division, the new molecularized Dopplers will make Doppler navigational radar practical for virtually any aircraft, including new supersonic transports,

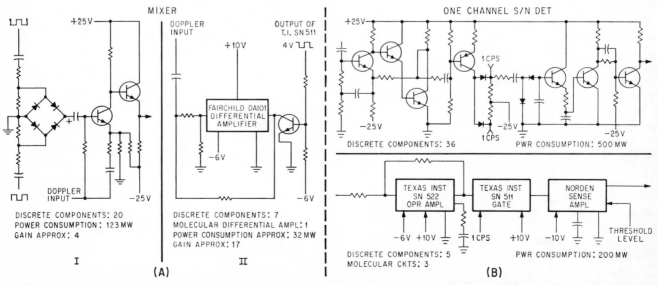

COMPARISON of discrete and integrated versions of mixer (A) and S/N detector (B) reveals distinct advantages in power dissipation, gain—Fig. 2

VSTOLS and advanced manned penetrators (AMP). One of the systems under development is a molecular version of a transistorized high performance equipment produced for use in an advanced Bomb/Nav system. GPL claims that when completed, the miniature pulsed coherent system will be the smallest, most reliable and—like its counterpart—the most accurate system available.

The company-funded microelectronics program also includes the development of a helicopter Doppler-Altimeter (Helipath), using integrated circuits and solid state transmitter, which is well along in the breadboard stage.

Figure 1 shows a block diagram of the frequency tracker section of the high-performance Doppler navigator. The tracker configuration is essentially the same in the Helipath system. Both systems will be implemented by a combination of standard integrated circuit packages, GPL-modified standard chips and discrete components. With the present availability of integrated analog circuits, GPL engineers estimate that 70 percent of the frequency tracker, and more than 50 percent of the overall system can be integrated now, with a view to replacement of the discrete components as integrated equivalents become available.

Implementation of the mixer (Fig. 2A) and S/N detector (Fig. 2B) with standard circuits clearly shows the advantages obtained in terms of power consumption and component reduction. Though the numbers are totaled for discrete components used with the molecular circuits, the resistors and capacitors will be combined into thin-film packages for a compatible form factor. Other components, such as resistors and transistors for use in feedback loops, will be produced by modification of standard chips.

The new Doppler systems are the fruit of careful planning on the part of GPL to retain the organization's identity as a systems developer and manufacturer, and at the same time utilize the advantages inherent in integrated circuits. Thus, GPL has recently completed an in-house microelectronics facility capable of implementing non-standard circuitry with standard chips, using what is called an "adaptive interconnect approach". Here's how it works:

Adaptive approach—The technique is based on securing from the major integrated circuit vendors, standard silicon wafers on which the resistors, capacitors, transistors or diodes have been placed in a particular pattern, but not interconnected to form a circuit. As GPL engineers design circuits of a non-standard nature for a system, they are guided toward the use of elements available on the uncommitted wafers.

In the microelectronics facility, which is established in the engineering department and not as an R&D function, the circuit requirement is analyzed and selection made of particular integrated circuit chips. The number and variety of circuit elements dictate the need for one, two or three chips each, with a maximum area of 0.01 sq. in. All chips for a particular circuit will be in a single case ranging from $\frac{1}{8} \times \frac{1}{4}$ to $\frac{3}{8} \times \frac{3}{8}$ by 0.06 in. thick, or a standard TO-5 case. Chips will be interconnected with 0.5 or 1-mil gold wire, and the circuit intraconnections on each of the chips are accomplished using an aluminum thin film technique applied directly to the silicon chip surface.

Thus the use of advanced semiconductor techniques and large equipment investment has been avoided through the purchase of standard circuit wafers from the major vendors. By performing the engineering function of committing the wafers to circuit patterns, GPL retains approximately 60 to 75 percent of the total direct labor involved in fabricating devices, yet can produce circuit designs based on industry-proven semiconductor technology. The majority of processing masks are standard vendor items permitting a low cost end product for ultimate production procurement.

According to Forrest, the alternative method of obtaining prototype non-standard integrated circuits from vendors would have been prohibitive from a cost or delivery point of view. "The need to take our turn at the vendor's facility would create an almost impossible scheduling problem during the relatively routine development phases, and a truly impossible and costly one during periods of development difficulty," he told ELECTRONICS.

Chapter 7

LINEAR INTEGRATED CIRCUITS

Latest Approach to Integrated

First a closed loop response satisfying circuit specifications is selected, then the open loop response is calculated and errors are considered

By F. D. Waldhauer, Bell Telephone Laboratories, Inc., Murray Hill, N.J.

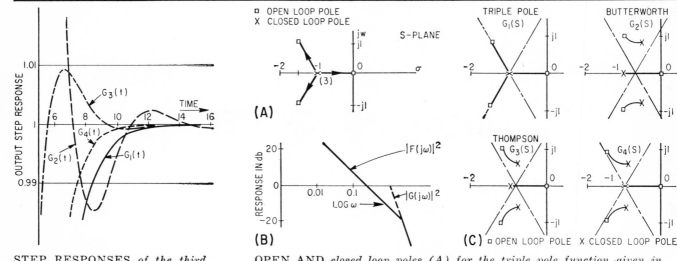

STEP RESPONSES *of the third order functions given in the table —Fig. 1*

OPEN AND *closed loop poles (A) for the triple pole function ·given in the table and its Bode plot (B). Root loci (curved lines) for functions in the table (C)—Fig. 2*

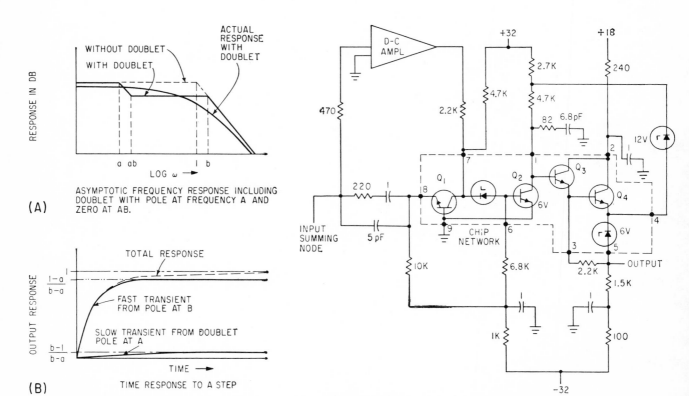

SPURIOUS *pole-zero pairs, or doublets, affect amplifier frequency (A) and transient (B) responses—Fig. 3*

ALL TRANSISTORS *of the wideband amplifier are in the integrated circuit package, thereby reducing the signal path and signal delay and improving response—Fig. 4*

Amplifier Design

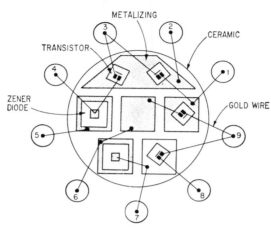

LAYOUT *of TO-5 header showing interconnections—Fig. 5*

TO-5 header holds four transistors and two zener diodes

IN THE ANALOG portion of analog digital systems, amplification with critical tolerances on time domain performance is often required. The requirements can sometimes be reduced to stating maximum output error for a step input after a stated settling time. For accuracy of 0.1 to 0.01 percent, feedback techniques are mandatory. But to obtain these accuracies in tens of nanoseconds, the bandwidth of the feedback amplifier must be large, which can produce loop delay and parasitics with conventional assemblies. By integrating the circuit using separate chips[1], critical signal paths are made small compared with a wavelength and parasitics and delay are greatly reduced.

But the amplifier must be designed to realize the potentials of circuit integration. Ordinary design using pole-zero cancellation introduces pole-zero pairs or doublets, which cause transients in the response. The new procedure avoids this to a great degree, thereby achieving accurate step and unusually flat frequency response.

First the step responses of various well-known filter functions are examined and a suitable closed-loop pole configuration is selected. From this closed loop function, an open loop function is derived. Allowable error in the open loop in terms of spurious pole-zero pairs due to either parasitics or faulty design is

then considered. Then the circuit is put together by integrated circuit techniques.

CLOSED LOOP RESPONSE—To determine the closed loop response necessary to realize time domain specifications, the time response of several common filter functions having the same final (normalized) asymptotic frequency response are compared. Step responses of four such functions in the region of one percent accuracy are shown in Fig. 1. The order has been chosen as three, corresponding to three transistor stages of comparable final asymptotic response.

The table gives the pole locations and settling times for each of the functions of Fig. 1, and shows that the exact function is not particularly critical, as long as the poles maintain sufficient distance ($\frac{1}{2}$ or 1) from the $j\omega$ axis.

The problem therefore is to synthesize an amplifier having the pole configuration of one of these functions for its closed loop gain. Exact pole locations are not important but for accurate response there must be no other spurious poles in the s plane nearer to the origin than the main cutoff poles.

OPEN LOOP RESPONSE — The function having the selected pole configuration represents the closed loop gain $G(s)$ of the equivalent unity gain amplifier; the feedback network is included in the open loop gain function $F(s)$. Thus, $G(0)$ is equal to unity. Open loop gain in terms of the closed loop is given by

$$F(s) = \frac{G(s)}{1 - G(s)} \qquad (1)$$

When $G(s)$ includes no zeros (as in the functions in the table)

WHY USE INTEGRATEDS?

Now that integrated circuits are starting to come on strong, circuit designers have to learn how to take advantage of the opportunities they present. By keeping the signal path in a feedback amplifier short, for example, propagation delay is minimized and bandwidth is increased. F. D. Waldhauer points out that each linear inch of signal path contributes about 0.1 nanosecond delay. By keeping most of the amplifier's signal path inside the TO-5 header package, he keeps loop delay to a little less than 0.1 nanosecond

---

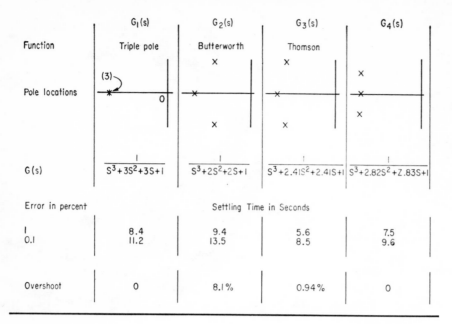

Table – Step input setting times for four third-order functions

Function	$G_1(s)$ Triple pole	$G_2(s)$ Butterworth	$G_3(s)$ Thomson	$G_4(s)$
Pole locations	(3)	× ×	× ×	× ×
$G(s)$	$\dfrac{1}{S^3+3S^2+3S+1}$	$\dfrac{1}{S^3+2S^2+2S+1}$	$\dfrac{1}{S^3+2.41S^2+2.41S+1}$	$\dfrac{1}{S^3+2.82S^2+2.83S+1}$
Error in percent		Settling Time in Seconds		
1	8.4	9.4	5.6	7.5
0.1	11.2	13.5	8.5	9.6
Overshoot	0	8.1 %	0.94 %	0

$$G(s) = \frac{1}{s^n+\alpha_{n-1}s^{n-1}+\cdots+\alpha_1 s+1} \quad (2)$$

and

$$F(s) = \frac{1}{s(s^{n-1}+\alpha_{n-1}s^{n-2}+\cdots+\alpha_1)} \quad (3)$$

Equation 3 reduces to $1/s$ over most of its range as a result of the restriction on closed loop gain that the poles maintain a sufficient distance from the $j\omega$ axis.

Thus, $F(s)$ has a pole at the origin and $|F(j\omega)|^2$ has a unit (6 db per octave) cutoff slope over its entire range from frequencies near 0 to a frequency near the final asymptote cutoff, considering the restrictions on the closed loop gain.

As an example, consider the closed-loop response

$$G(s) = \frac{1}{(s+1)^3} \quad (4)$$

The closed-loop poles are all at $s = -1 + j0$, as shown in Fig. 2A. The open loop poles can be found by following along the root loci; one pole moves into the origin, supplying the unit cutoff slope, while the other two become complex, as shown. The corresponding Bode plot is shown in Fig. 2B. The root loci for the other functions in the Table are shown in Fig. 2C. All have a single open loop pole at $s = 0$.

OTHER ERRORS — The finite speed of the transistors produces

an error in step response which is minimized by the selection of the cutoff shape for the closed loop response, which is then translated into open-loop gain requirements. Errors due to the finite transistor speed are not the only ones. Inaccuracy of the feedback resistor will produce a gain error, and drift, in a d-c amplifier, will produce an offset error, but these will not be discussed further here.

Another step response error of importance arises from transients produced by spurious pole-zero pairs, or doublets, which are caused by parasitic reactive elements or by incomplete pole-zero cancellation in pole-zero design. Doublets produce departures from exact flatness in the closed-loop frequency response, and relatively larger departures

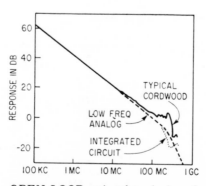

OPEN LOOP *gain of typical cordwood amplifier shows high frequency instability—Fig. 6*

from exact unit slope cutoff in the corresponding open-loop response.

The effect of a real doublet on the asymptotic frequency response and the time response is shown in Fig. 3. The error transient produced by the doublet will have an initial value equal to the variation in frequency response that it produces. Thus, for a step response accuracy of 0.1 percent, the net effect of all doublets must not vary the closed-loop response by more than 0.1 percent. At sufficiently high frequencies, the doublet transient will die out quickly, so larger doublets may be tolerated.

When feedback is removed, the open-loop response falls at 6 db per octave, and doublets express themselves as departures from this cutoff slope. Feedback reduces doublet size (that is, flattens the response) by roughly the magnitude of the return ratio, so open-loop doublets will be larger than their closed-loop counterparts. Thus, since the return ratio varies inversely with frequency, the allowable open-loop doublet size becomes relatively greater at low frequencies.

ACTUAL CIRCUITS — If frequency doublets are to be minimized, it is undesirable to use pole-zero cancellation techniques to synthesize the unit slope cutoff function. Of the four forward transfer functions of a common emitter transistor amplifier, one, namely the forward transimpedance, z_{21}, has a unit slope cutoff over a wide range of frequencies. The forward transimpedance may be made to control the response in the cutoff region by providing open circuit source and load impedances. This can be accomplished by providing a unity voltage gain amplifier at the output, such as one or several tandem common collector stages as shown in Fig. 4 (Q_3 and Q_4). Bootstrapping the d-c bias resistors of these stages keeps the input impedance high.

The basic unit slope cutoff comes about because the output voltage, V_o, appears (slightly increased) at the collector of Q_2, where it creates a base current $V_oC_{c2}s$ through the collector capacity of Q_2. This base current is the input current for the amplifier multiplied by the α of an input common base stage; this α is nearly unity.

This amplifier was designed as a

d-c operational amplifier. A parallel path arrangement was developed in which d-c signals at the input summing mode are amplified in a low drift· d-c amplifier and reinserted into the amplifier signal path at the input to the common emitter stage. The common base stage isolates the input from the output of the d-c amplifier and provides a high impedance source for the common emitter stage. A resistor in series with the input of the common base stage provides d-c signal voltage for the d-c amplifier and broadens the bandwidth of the common base stage so that it does not add significant slope to the final asymptote in the cutoff region.

The response of the d-c amplifier in parallel with the common base stage is complementary to the high frequency amplifier comprising Q_2, Q_3, and Q_4, and maintains the unit slope down to about one Kc, where the gain is over 100 db. The junction of the two responses produces a small frequency doublet but at a low enough frequency to avoid excessive time response errors.

FREQUENCY RESPONSE

— The transfer function of the whole amplifier is of eight order in the frequency variable, but a reasonably good approximation is obtained from

$$G(s) = \frac{1}{s^3 + a_2 s^2 + a_1 s + 1} \quad (5)$$

or

$$F(s) = \frac{1}{s(s^2 + a_2 s + a_1)} \quad (6)$$

The coefficient of the s^3 term, normalized to unity here, is set by the final asymptotic transistor response. Coefficients a_2 and a_1 establish how the unit slope cutoff joins the final asymptote (the smaller a_2 and a_1 the more lively the response). The last coefficient in the denominator of $G(s)$ (taken as unity) comes about from the feedback, and is accordingly absent from the open loop gain of Eq. 6.

Coefficient a_1 controls the magnitude of the unit slope cutoff. Its value may be increased by increasing the collector capacity of Q_2. Coefficient a_2 will also increase slightly when this is done, as will a_3. The effect on a_3 can be reduced by placing a resistor and perhaps inductance in series with the added ca-

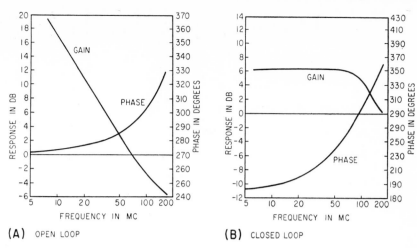

OPEN *and closed loop responses of the integrated amplifier—Fig. 7*

pacity. In the amplifiers which have been constructed, the collector capacity of Q_2 was adequate, so that none was added.

Coefficient a_2 may be increased without significant effect on a_1 by adding capacity from the base of Q_3 to ground, again through a resistor to avoid reducing the final asymptotic response. If a_2 is too small, the open-loop gain will have a peak at the asymptotic cutoff frequency.

With these two adjustments, the desired closed-loop filter function of the table can be approximated. Exact analysis is difficult because of both circuit complexity and propagation delay, so experimental work is important.

DELAY

— Propagation delay has an unstablizing effect on performance, and since it adds phase proportional to frequency, ultimately limits the bandwidth of the feedback amplifier. Delay comes from two sources: first is excess phase in the transistors (about 0.1 nanosecond in high frequency silicon transistors) and mainly comes about through the lattice-scattering limited drift velocity in the collector depletion region; the second is transport delay around the feedback loop. In a cordwood version in which particular attention was paid to minimizing the distance around the feedback loop, the loop distance measured three inches, representing roughly 0.3 nanosecond of delay. This was reduced to less than 0.1 nanosecond in the integrated circuit version.

Delay modifies the values of the

coefficients of s in the open-loop gain, but the general effects of increasing a_1 and a_2 remain.

EXPERIMENTAL WORK

—High-speed measurements in the time domain are difficult to perform with sufficient accuracy, so frequency domain measurements were performed on three different amplifiers. First, a low frequency analog was built and tested to check the theory without the complications caused by parasitic reactive elements; second, a full speed cordwood model was constructed, with signal path and ground lead lengths minimized; third, integrated circuit was built using separate chip mounting of the four transistors and three zener diodes.

The structure of the integrated circuit is a gold deposited ceramic substrate on a TO-5 header. Silicon planar transistors and diodes and bulk silicon resistors in chip form are bonded to the substrate, as shown in Fig. 5.

Open loop gain of the three amplifiers is shown in Fig. 6. The separate chip approach helps keep parasitic elements to a minimum. Open and closed-loop gain and phase are shown in Fig. 7.

The fabrication of the integrated circuit was performed by Richard Lindner and Karl Martersteck whose help, along with that of James Goldey, is gratefully acknowledged.

REFERENCES

(1) B. T. Howard and R. Lindner, "The Influence of Evolving Technology on Integrated Circuits," Report No. 8 on Transistors, Contract DA 360-39 SC-88931, Chapter 4, March 31, 1962.

Parasitics In Integrated Circuits:

*Design of fully integrated circuits is going to be more complex
than circuit design using conventional components. Isolation problems can
be solved by adding extra p-n junctions, but at the expense of
introducing extraneous diodes, capacitors and transistors*

By H. K. DICKEN

Motorola Semiconductor Products, Inc.,
Phoenix, Arizona

SPECIAL SYMBOLS FOR INTEGRATED CIRCUITS

One of the troubles with fully integrated circuits is that they are more complicated than circuits using discrete elements. A resistor no longer is a simple passive device—not even at d-c.

Accordingly, some engineers feel conventional circuit symbols do not lend themselves to integrated circuits because of the parasitic effects and the method of circuit construction. The symbols here are used at Motorola to show component function, construction, and parasitics.

Basic to the symbols is a third terminal on the passive devices and a fourth on the active devices that indicates each component has some parasitic action to a common substrate. The arrow indicates the direction of the diode action between the component and the substrate material in immediate contact, such as a **p**-type diffused resistor in an **n**-type isolated area. Here it is assumed the resistor has been designed such that there is no parasitic transistor action. It is also assumed that associated with each arrow is the parasitic capacitance inherent with every **p-n** junction.

The circuit example illustrates two possible advantages. First, the requirements for a fully integrated layout are apparent from the connections of the substrate terminals. Second, the effects of the parasitic capacitances on the circuit performance are apparent and an accurate picture of the final circuit is produced

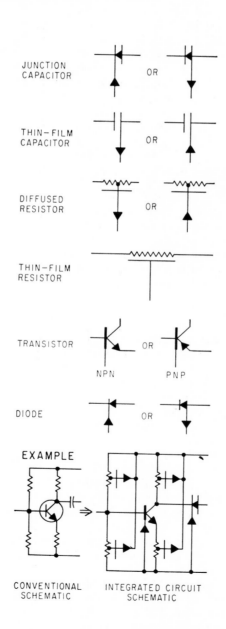

JUNCTION CAPACITOR — OR

THIN—FILM CAPACITOR — OR

DIFFUSED RESISTOR — OR

THIN—FILM RESISTOR

TRANSISTOR — OR — NPN — PNP

DIODE — OR

EXAMPLE

CONVENTIONAL SCHEMATIC — INTEGRATED CIRCUIT SCHEMATIC

IN A FULLY integrated circuit, both active and passive circuit elements are formed by diffusions into a single-crystal silicon substrate. Circuit elements, however, must still be isolated from each other, and this is now typically accomplished with diffused *p-n* junctions that form back-to-back diodes. Although adequate isolation is obtained, the structures have several inherent detrimental parasitic effects. These include substrate transistor action from diffused resistors, parasitic capacitance at each junction and higher series resistance in some conducting paths. These effects can completely degrade circuit performance.

Isolation by *p-n* back-to-back diodes is the basic technique of integrated circuit construction. In a typical structure, as shown in Fig. 1A, a 20-micron layer of 0.5 ohm-cm *n*-type silicon is grown epitaxially on a wafer of 5 ohm-cm *p*-type silicon. Channels are then selectively etched through the SiO_2 coating on the surface of the wafer for the *p*-type isolation diffusion. This diffusion forms the electrically isolated areas for each section of the circuit. Each *n*-type area then provides the basis for the remaining diffusions to form transistors, diodes, resistors, and capacitors—all isolated by the equivalent of the reverse characteristics of a diode. Normal leakage current of the reverse biased diodes is less than 1 microamp.

PARASITIC ELEMENTS — Each *p-n* junction of the resulting four-

More Trouble Than Meets The Eye

FULLY INTEGRATED *logic circuit has high reliability and small size*

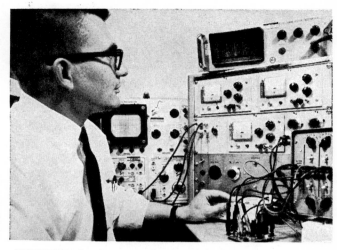

BEFORE *the integrated circuit is built, its design is checked out with circuit simulator for parasitics*

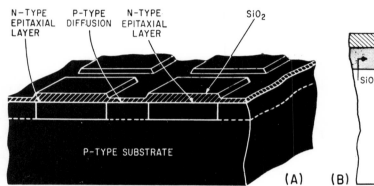

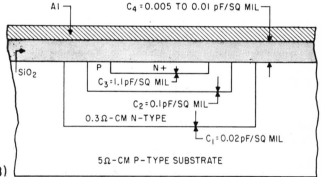

ISOLATION *of both active and passive circuit elements in a fully integrated circuit (A) is obtained by diffusion into etched channels. For each junction (B) there is an associated capacitance—Fig. 1*

layer structure (Fig. 1B) has a capacitance that is function of the impurity concentration of the more lightly doped layer. For a step junction, the capacitance per unit area is[1]

$$C = \sqrt{\frac{qK\epsilon_0 N}{2V}}$$

where q = electron charge (1.6 × 10^{-19} coulomb), k = dielectric constant of silicon (12), ϵ_o = permittivity of free space (8.85 × 10^{-14} farad/cm), N = impurity concentration of more lightly doped layer, and V = total junction potential.

Average valves for C_1, C_2 and C_3 are indicated in Fig. 1B at zero volts bias; C_4 is not affected by bias. Actual capacitance will depend on the impurity concentration.

In addition, the designer must consider emitter efficiency of each junction, base transport factor across each region, and collector multiplication factor of each junction. These factors all influence the gain of the parasitic transistors and thus determine if interaction between circuit elements will occur.

Resistors, capacitors, diodes and transistors have greatly changed equivalent circuits in fully integrated structures. The elements are now tied to a common p-type silicon substrate. The equivalent circuits following have been simplified to show only the critical elements. Actual equivalent circuits would be based on a model similar to a distributed four-layer active structure.

TRANSISTORS — The transistor structure is the fundamental four-

layer integrated circuit device. All other circuit elements, such as resistors, diodes and junction capacitors, may be derived from the transistor structure, which is shown in Fig. 2A.

In the equivalent circuit, Fig. 2B, an integrated circuit transistor is shown as a four-layer device. However, under normal bias conditions, parasitic action to the substrate is limited to a diode and distributed capacitance C_1, with C_1 approximately 0.02 pf per sq mil of collector area. For normal transistor geometries, this would give a total collector to ground capacitance of less than 10 pf. However, other detrimental effects are inherent in this structure. One of the primary disadvantages is the increase in the collector saturation resistance, R_c,

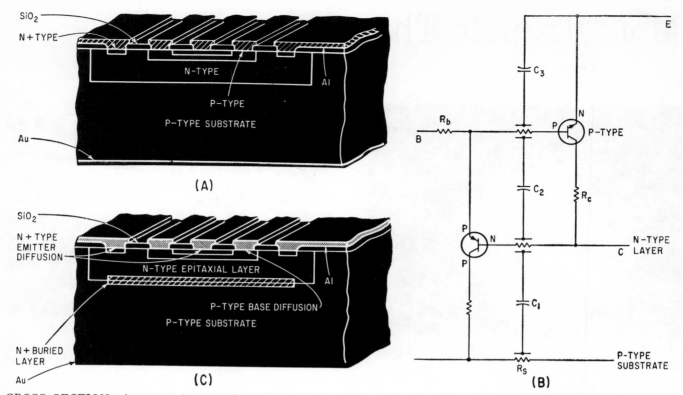

CROSS SECTION *of an npn integrated-circuit transistor (A) and its simplified equivalent circuit (B). Collector saturation resistance can be reduced by adding n-type buried layer (C)—Fig. 2*

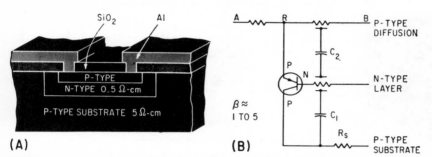

DIFFUSED *resistor (A) has an associated, built-in, distributed transistor, as indicated at (B)—Fig. 3*

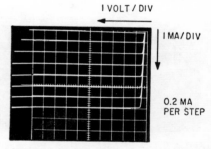

CHARACTERISTIC *of a substrate-type npn transistor—Fig. 4*

due to the collector being brought out to the surface of the wafer through a relatively high resistance material. The product of this resistance and collector capacitance limits high-frequency response.

The alpha-cutoff frequency f_{hfb} (gain is down 3 db) of any transistor is a function mainly of four terms: ω_e the emitter delay-time constant; ω_b the base-transit time; ω_d the collector depletion-layer transit time; and ω_c the collector delay time constant. This collector delay time constant is $\omega_c \approx R_c\,C_2$, where R_c is the series resistance of the collector region and C_2 is the collector capacitance. For an integrated circuit transistor, ω_c is the dominante time factor. For typical geometries, R_c is of the order of

50 to 100 ohms and C_2 is approximately 5 pf, thus resulting in f_{hfb} from 300 to 500 Mc. The high saturation resistance also causes large power losses in such applications as audio amplifiers.

The effects can be minimized by several methods. One technique is to sacrifice the breakdown voltage and lower the resistance of the collector material, thus decreasing r_c but increasing C_c. A second more promising method involves an epitaxial growth over a buried $n+$ layer under the transistor, as illustrated in Fig. 2C.

RESISTORS — The integrated resistor differs more than the other circuit elements from its conventional counterpart and illustrates

most of the parasitic *pnp* transistor effects. The elements are normally formed during the base diffusion cycle. Figure 3A is a cross-sectional view of an integrated circuit resistor. The *n*-type silicon layer is used for isolation while the *p*-type layer, approximately three microns deep, determines the resistance.

As shown in Fig. 3B, the final element has both a distributed capacitance and a distributed transistor effect. Thus the *n*-type layer, which is used for isolation, becomes the base of a low beta (h_{fe}) *pnp* transistor. The distributed transistor, which has a beta from 0.5 to 5, is a result of the relatively narrow (approximately 17 microns) *n*-type epitaxial layer between the *p*-type substrate and the *p*-type resistor diffusion.

The alpha (h_{fb}) of this pnp transistor is determined by the emitter efficiency of the normal base-collector junction, the base transport factor across the collector material, and the collector multiplication ratio of the collector-substrate junction. The overall alpha may be written as the product of these mechanisms.

$$a = \gamma \, \beta^* \, a^*$$

where γ = emitter efficiency, β^* = base transport factor, and a^* = collector multiplication ratio.

Emitter efficiency γ is defined as the ratio of the injected hole current to the total emitter current. The value of γ is a direct function of the ratio of emitter resistivity to base resistivity, or for this structure, the ratio of the base diffusion resistivity to the epitaxial layer resistivity, which is on the order of 1 to 5. This ratio gives a value for γ of 0.8 to 0.9.

For this structure, the base-transport factor β^* is defined as the probability that the hole carrier will cross the n-type epitaxial layer and reach the substrate. This is given by

$$\beta^* = \text{Sech} \; W/L_{pb}$$

where, in this structure, W is approximately 17 microns and L_{pb} is the hole diffusion length in the epitaxial layer. This gives a value for β^* of 0.6 to 0.8.

The collector multiplication ratio a^*, is related to the ratio of the minority carrier concentration to the majority carrier concentration in the substrate region. For integrated circuits, where the substrate resistance is from 5 to 10 ohm-cm, a^* may be equal to or greater than 1.

These factors result in an approximate over-all alpha of (0.85) (0.7) (1) or 0.6, thus giving a typical beta for the substrate pnp transistor of about 1.5. Figure 4 shows the V-I characteristics of a pnp transistor of this type.

Because the substrate is normally connected to the lowest potential of the circuit, conduction will occur when the p-n junction of the resistor and the epitaxial layer is forward biased due to junction leakage or other defect. As Fig. 3B shows, current leakage between the substrate and the n-type layer could be multiplied by the beta of the transistor and act as a shunt leakage between the resistor and the substrate. To prevent such effects, the n-type layer is connected to the highest circuit potential.

Other parasitic effects associated with diffused resistors are the distributed junction capacitances. Their values are a function of junction area and are as given in Fig. 1B for C_1 and C_2. The effects of these capacitances become significant at

high frequencies. The h_{21} transfer characteristic (i_2/i_1) decreases from unity in the range from 10 to 100 Mc because of the shunting effect of the distributed capacitance.

CAPACITORS—Integrated circuit capacitors are formed by two techniques: first, through the utilization of the capacitance inherent in a large area p-n junction; second, through the use of the thin film of silicon dioxide (SiO_2) between an n-type silicon layer and the aluminum metalization. For both types of capacitors there is a finite ratio of total to shunt capacitance. This ratio, which is on the order of 20 to 1, limits the usefulness of either type, particularly at high frequencies.

With the junction capacitor, a sandwich of two junctions can produce a higher ratio of total capacitance to shunt capacitance. As shown in Fig. 5A, a transistor structure is used with one contact to the p-type layer and the other shorting the two n-type layers. This structure has a relatively large capacitance per unit area — approximately 1.1 pf per sq mil.

Several factors should be considered when utilizing the junction capacitor, as the simplified equivalent circuit of Fig. 5B indicates. First, the total capacitance is a function of the applied voltage, decreasing

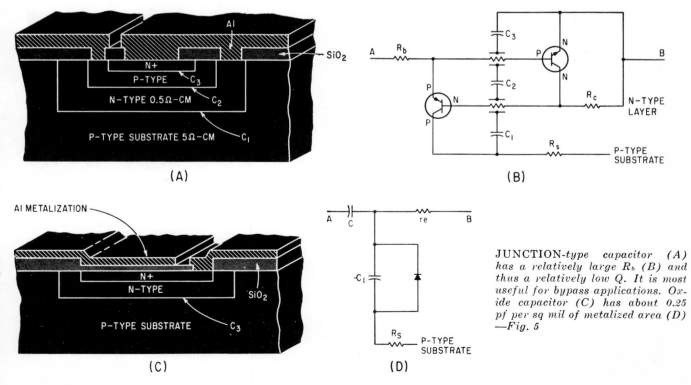

(A)

(B)

(C)

(D)

JUNCTION-*type capacitor (A) has a relatively large R_b (B) and thus a relatively low Q. It is most useful for bypass applications. Oxide capacitor (C) has about 0.25 pf per sq mil of metalized area (D)* —Fig. 5

with an increase in reverse bias. Thus in some circuits an unwanted voltage modulation would be present. Second, because it is a diode, the unit must be reverse biased. Third, series contact resistance R_b is relatively large, thus reducing the Q of the unit. R_b may be minimized by the same techniques used to reduce the r_b' of a transistor. Because of these factors, the junction capacitor is normally used for bypass.

The oxide-type capacitor, Fig. 5C, eliminates some of these effects. The structure is simply a dielectric (SiO_2) between the n+ silicon and the aluminum metalization on the surface. Again, the n-type layer is used for isolation from the substrate. As shown in the equivalent circuit, Fig. 5D, the parasitic effects consist of a small series resistance r_e, a diode and shunt capacitance C_1 to the substrate.

CIRCUIT SIMULATOR—The substrate *pnp* transistor action typically associated with a diffused resistor can completely change circuit performance. However, an integrated circuit simulator, shown schematically in Fig. 6, can be used with standard components to produce the same parasitic effects that occur with the diffused resistors of a fully integrated circuit. The simulator, Fig. 6, consists of low beta (h_{fe}) *pnp* transistors and capacitors to simulate the isolating junctions associated with integrated resistors.

The resistor terminals are connected across each resistor of the circuit breadboard. The substrate terminal is connected to the most negative potential of the circuit while the n-layer terminal is connected to the most positive. The switch associated with each grouping determines if the resistor is separately isolated. Switching characteristics of a standard component circuit with the simulator attached are shown in Fig. 6A and 6B. These characteristics reveal an improperly designed integrated layout. The corrected switching characteristics shown in Fig. 6C and 6D are obtained when the n-type layer for each resistor of the simulator is connected to the highest circuit potential, thus preventing transistor action.

Circuit design can eliminate some of the parasitic effects. The effect of a high series collector resistance can be reduced by a buried n+ layer. To eliminate the collector to substrate capacitance C_1, a resistive bar of silicon provides isolation between transistors, thus eliminating the capacitance associated with diode type isolation.[2]

Much of the work reported here was done under Air Force Contract #AF33(616)8276 on Compatible Techniques for Integrated Circuits.

REFERENCES

(1) A. B. Phillips, "Transistor Engineering," McGraw-Hill Book Company, Inc., New York, N. Y., 1962.
(2) G. R. Madland, *Design of Integrated Radio Frequency Amplifiers*, National Electronics Conference, Chicago, Ill., Oct., 1962.

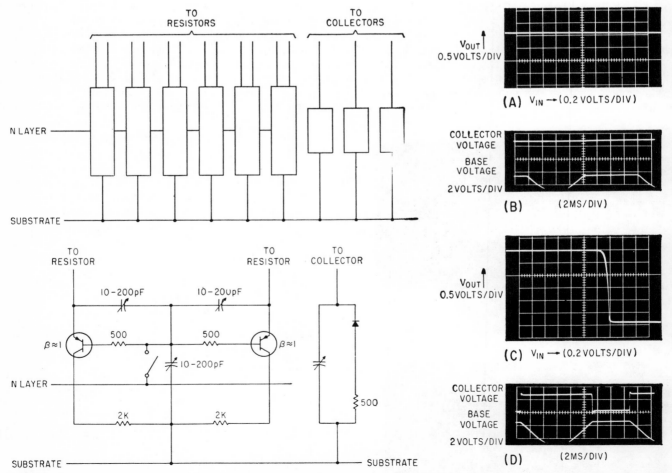

INTEGRATED CIRCUIT *simulator (sketch) can show circuit operation with parasitics present, (A) and (B), and corrected (C) and (D)*—Fig. 6

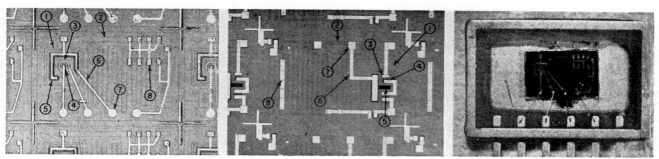

TWO BLOCKS, *common emitter (left) and Darlington Circuit (center) illustrate construction. Photo (right) shows a packaged common-emitter functional block with leads*

Latest Design Techniques
For Linear Microcircuits

By L. POLLOCK and R. GUTTERIDGE, Westinghouse Electric Corp., Youngwood, **Pa.**

Linear functional electronic blocks are produced through solid-state diffusion and photoengraving techniques. Here the process is described in detail, illustrated with two examples

MOLECULAR ELECTRONICS seeks to use a single piece of material with predetermined electronic properties to synthesize circuit functions conventionally requiring many separate active and passive components. A monolithic structure

---

MORE MICROELECTRONICS

A few years ago, when engineers discovered that complete circuit functions could be developed on and within a single block of silicon, the art of microelectronics was hailed as a great new revolution. But claims and counterclaims often tended to outrun performance.

Meanwhile, the industry has settled down to hard-core development work and recently more concrete results have appeared—a wider choice of circuits, reliability figures, even production contracts.

This story follows up one in our Sept. 21 issue that discussed the overall problem of translating systems requirements into an array of functional electronic blocks

---

of this type is known as a functional electronic block.

THE PROCESS—The method of producing functional blocks can be understood by considering a typical double-diffused, silicon planar *npn* transistor structure as shown in Fig. 1. The dimensions are typical of a high-frequency, small-signal transistor with a gain-bandwidth product of 300-500 Mc.

Topographic dimensions are an order of magnitude greater than the depth dimensions. It would be of no value to be able to reduce one without reducing the other to the same extent, since dimensions in the range shown will result in a device whose R-C time constants, determined by area, are approximately equal to the transit time of minority carriers across the base region, determined by depth. Two processes have been developed to achieve control of both area and depth dimensions in these ranges: selective solid-state diffusion introduces the correct impurities to the desired depth, and photoengravings

select the areas to be diffused.

Selective solid-state diffusion of impurity atoms into the silicon crystal lattice is achieved by heating the material to approximately 1,200 deg C in an atmosphere containing the doping impurity. Diffusion of the elements boron and phosphorus is inhibited by a surface layer of silicon dioxide, and this property is exploited when localized *p* or *n* type regions are required. The introduction of a *p*-type region into an *n*-type substrate follows a simple sequence.

A layer of silicon dioxide is first grown over the entire surface, then removed from the areas to be diffused. Impurities are then diffused into these areas. The SiO_2 prevents their entry into other regions of the surface. During diffusion a new layer of oxide is grown over the exposed areas to be used in subsequent selective diffusions. The depth of penetration and impurity distribution within the diffused region are determined by the time and temperature of the diffusion and by the nature and concentra-

Table I—PERFORMANCE DATA ON AMPLIFIERS

Common Emitter	Conventional Circuit	Functional Block
Supply.....................	22.5 v	22.5 v
Total Current.................	2 ma	2 ma
Input Impedance..............	750 ohms	750 ohms
Output Impedance...........	3,000 ohms	3,000 ohms
Power Gain..................	30 db	30 db
Band Pass....................	2.5 Mc	2.5 Mc

Darlington	Conventional Circuit	Functional Block
Supply.....................	22.5 v	22.5 v
Total Current.................	7 ma	7 ma
Input Impedance..............	26,000 ohms	21,000 ohms
Output Impedance...........	1,500 ohms	1,000 ohms
Power Gain..................	38 db	36 db
Current Gain.................	1,200	850
Max. Output Current...........	4.5 ma	4 ma
Harmonic Distortion at 3 ma out.	<1%	<1%

Table II—PERFORMANCE DATA ON AN/ARC-63 RECEIVER

	Specification	Molecular Receiver
Frequency...........	238–248 Mc	238–248 Mc
1st i-f.............	28 Mc	28 Mc
2nd i-f.............	3 Mc	3 Mc
Sensitivity...........	7 μv	3–5 μv
Bandwidth...........	−6 db at 60 Kc	−6 db at 40 Kc
	−60 db at 180 Kc	−60 db at 110 Kc
Spurious Response		
Adjacent Channel...	−80 db	−80 db
Image and Harmonic	−65 db	−50 db
AGC..............	±10 db for 7–500,000 μv	+6 db
Squelch Level........	variable	0–100 v adjustable
Audio Power at 150 ohms...........	200 mw	250 mw
Response.........	300–6,000 cps	300–6,000 cps
Distortion........	10%	8%
Input Power........	24.5 w	2.6 w
Volume...........	148 in³	9 in³
Weight...........	5.2 lb	0.46 lb
No. of Components...	219	82

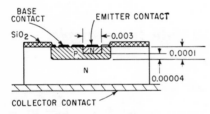

DOUBLE DIFFUSED *silicon planar npn transistor structure—Fig. 1*

tion of the source of the impurity.

Photoengraving is ideally suited to fabrication since it is capable of reproducing fine detail while avoiding undue mechanical strain on the sample. Applications of the process to the selective removal of oxide allows precise geometric control over the diffused areas. Here the oxidized silicon is coated with a thin film of photosensitive resist, and exposed to ultraviolet light through a high resolution photographic plate bearing an image. Where the uv is able to pass through the plate, the resist is polymerized and rendered insoluble. The portion not exposed remains in monomeric form and can be removed by a solvent. The residual coating then protects against the oxide etching solution. Thus small, intricate patterns can be etched with a high degree of reproducibility from one sample to the next. This plays a large part in determining the tolerance of circuit components.

Photographic plates are prepared by reducing the original art work 100 times on micromodular cameras. The final reduction is carried out on a step-and-repeat camera to give an array of accurately indexed images. Linear dimensions on the plates are held to 1 micron to minimize the accumulative misalignment error between successive masking steps. With these multiple image plates, many devices can be fabricated on a single slice of silicon.

MAKING ELEMENTS — Through photoengraving and selective diffusion, a number of active and passive elements can be built directly on a silicon wafer (see Fig. 2).

In Fig. 2A, a resistor is formed by a single diffusion with a contact at either end. Practical values of resistors run from about 4 to 400,-000 ohms and can be made with ten percent tolerances. The simple diode of Fig. 2B can perform as a rectifier, as a controlled voltage supply in the avalanche region, as a variable or fixed capacitor in the reverse bias condition and as a zener coupling element. A second diffusion is all that is necessary to make the conventional transistor of Fig. 2C or the field-effect transistor of Fig. 2D. Where it is desired, component isolation may be obtained as in Fig. 2E, which shows a transistor and a resistor formed in two regions separated by a deep diffusion. Because of the insulating oxide over the surface it is possible to interconnect contacts on the block using an evaporated film of aluminum directly on the oxide as in Fig. 2F without danger of shorting the junctions.

The elements described are sufficient to build a variety of linear circuits directly in a single chip of silicon without any external components. These circuits may be direct analogs of those made with conventional components; however, limitations on the component values or properties may require a circuit modification or a new approach to the circuit function. This is true in bias networks for small signal circuits where, because of small currents, high-value resistors are required. Since the area required for the resistance is directly proportional to the resistance, the practical upper limit on the total amount

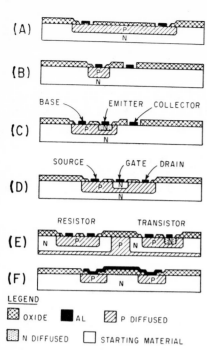

(A)

(B)

BASE EMITTER COLLECTOR

(C)

SOURCE GATE DRAIN

(D)

RESISTOR TRANSISTOR

(E)

(F)

LEGEND

▨ OXIDE ■ AL ▨ P DIFFUSED

⠿ N DIFFUSED ▢ STARTING MATERIAL

BOTH ACTIVE AND PASSIVE
elements are built directly on a silicon wafer through photoengraving and selective diffusion techniques—Fig. 2

of linear resistance in a circuit is about 300,000 ohms. Where the linear resistance required is in excess of this, the same function can often be performed by either a network of two or more resistors, a nonlinear circuit element such as a diode or field-effect transistor, or some combination of resistors and nonlinear elements, with a saving in total area. Significantly the cost of a functional block bears little relation to the number of separate components in the circuit, but is almost directly proportional to the area they require.

TWO BLOCKS—The first is the general-purpose single-stage common-emitter amplifier of Fig. 3A. This simple and versatile circuit can be used as a voltage or power amplifier for frequencies ranging from d-c to a few megacycles. The component values are such that the circuit can be made directly on silicon with special consideration only to active element design, isolation and stray impedance. The more specialized Darlington circuit of Fig. 3B is useful over a frequency range up to about 100 Kc, but has features such as high input impedance desirable in audio-preamplifier applications. More important,

it has the gain of two stages with the dissipation of only one. Although isolation and stray impedance are not important, the bias network normally used with separate components would consume a prohibitively large area on a functional block. The circuit of Fig. 3C uses a voltage divider to reduce the bias voltage and therefore the resistance. Collector bias is used for the block circuit to gain the added voltage and thermal stability and better reproducibility. Load impedance is usually low so that little gain is lost.

The photographs show the common-emitter (at left) and Darlington (center) functional blocks. The individual operations used in constructing the finished blocks can be interpreted by studying the surface. The square path (1) is a deep *p*-type diffusion isolating the region within the square, where the transistor is formed, from the rest of the block. The darker areas, which are the resistor paths (2) and the transistor base region (3) are formed simultaneously by the diffusion of boron. The darkest areas are the emitters (4) and the collector contact area (5), which are formed simultaneously by a phosphorus diffusion. The white paths are evaporated aluminum lead-outs and interconnections (6) and lead bond terminals (7). The outlines of the contacts, which are alloyed to the silicon prior to the final evaporation, are visible under the interconnections (8).

The third photograph at the right shows a packaged common-emitter functional block with the leads attached.

Table I compares the performance of typical functional blocks with that of conventional circuits.

OTHER FACTORS — Functional

blocks can be designed to operate to at least the temperature normally specified for a transistor. However, this can be achieved only if the design of the entire circuit is considered, since silicon properties exhibit high temperature sensitivity and vary with impurity concentration. However, temperature properties can be accurately predicted and, due to the intimate thermal contact of components, the temperature of the entire circuit will be uniform. Thus, the temperature characteristics of silicon resistors, diodes, and field-effect transistors can be used to improve the temperature characteristics of circuits.

Reactances pose the biggest single limitation on achieving an integrated circuit. The maximum capacitance of a reverse-biased silicon junction of practical dimensions is in the range of 100 pf and pure inductance in silicon as yet has been obtained only on a laboratory scale. Where inductors or larger capacitors are needed it is still necessary to use separate components. However, solid tuned and tunable circuits are now available as piezo-electric crystals and notch filters.

To demonstrate the mutual compatibility of a wide variety of functional blocks, a molecularized version of the AN/ARC-63 emergency communications receiver was developed. This is a 243-Mc receiver using conversions to 28 and to 3 Mc. The molecular version of the receiver uses miniature circuits for the r-f amplifier and first conversion and 9 functional blocks for the remainder. These include a 25-Mc oscillator-mixer block, 3 i-f amplifiers, a detector, a Darlington audio amplifier, a power amplifier, agc and squelch amplifiers. Table II compares the performance of the molecular receiver with the AN/ARC-63 specification.

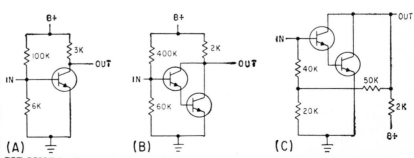

CIRCUITS *for functional blocks. Common emitter (A), conventional Darlington (B) and functional block Darlington (C)—Fig. 3*

Molecular Blocks Simplify Microcircuits

Double-base diodes, tunnel diodes and surface-controlled devices

in single-chip form increase reliability and reduce size and cost

By **VASIL UZUNOGLU** and **MARVIN H. WHITE**
Aerospace Division, Westinghouse Electric Corporation, Baltimore, Maryland

ALTHOUGH integrated circuits are beginning to be accepted widely, it has been pointed out that making use of some properties of semiconductor devices to realize some of the required functions of a microcircuit may prove more advantageous than transferring each element of a circuit to an integrated block.[1,2] This paper deals with this approach and shows how to use double-base diodes, tunnel diodes and oxide-coated devices to perform useful functions in microcircuits.

Analog-digital conversion can be achieved by using the double-base diode structure shown in Fig. 1A.

The V-I characteristic of each n-region with respect to common point is shown in Fig. 1B. Proper signal levels and the negative resistance region of each section are used to switch the operating point from H to L. The load lines can be adjusted to any operating point on the high positive resistance region depending on the required sensitivity. The number of junctions can be increased to a desired number depending on the conversion efficiency.

By adjusting the input biases and the load lines, it is possible to actuate each section with a different voltage level. For example, unit 1 may be turned on to its L level with lowest information available, whereas unit 3 requires the highest actuat-

ing signal. Thus, depending upon the amplitude of the information, a certain number of sections can be actuated. If all the sections are at high current level, the information has reached its peak. The information across R_1, R_2 and R_3 is recovered by feeding it to flip-flop stages. Such a structure can be used also as a voltage comparator. For example, if unit 2 is turned on, the signal is less than ΔV_3 but higher than ΔV_2. Improved performance can be obtained by isolating each diode section by a diffusion layer as shown by dotted lines in Fig. 1A.

Tunnel Diodes—A circuit that can be used as an analog-digital converter or as a voltage comparator is shown in Fig. 2A. The number of tunnel diodes connected in series depends on the required conversion efficiency.

The combined V-I characteristics of the tunnel diodes is shown in Fig. 2B. Initially, the load line rests on point A. A pulse applied to point S (Fig. 2A) assuming it is high enough, will shift the load line parallel to itself up to point D' because the apparent supply voltage across the tunnel diodes has increased. As soon as the pulse dies out, the load line has to return to its initial position A. In returning to its original state the load line follows

the path shown in Fig. 2B and the output voltage at point N_1 (Fig. 2A) has the shape shown in Fig. 2C.

Once the load line arrives at point D' it may shift the first flip-flop stage. The voltage drop at point N_2 is less by the amount of drop across T_1(T = tunnel diode). Thus the second flip-flop stage may be adjusted to change state once the second tunnel diode is actuated. Following the same reasoning the voltage at point N_3 is less by the amount of drops across T_1 and T_2. Thus the third flip-flop stage may be adjusted so that it flips when the load line arrives at point C'. For the largest signal available, all tunnel diodes are actuated so all flip-flop stages are in their high voltage states. The capacitors provide d-c isolation of the tunnel diodes from the flip-flop stages.[1] Such a circuit can be used also as a voltage comparator.

Surface-Controlled Devices — With the introduction of the planar diffused structures, the SiO_2 layer on these devices gained considerable importance. In his articles[3,4] Sah introduced the idea of utilizing such devices and explained the basic theory underlying the operation of such structures. For example, an oxide layer on top of the emitter-base junction of a transistor may be used as a fourth terminal to control some important properties of the transistor. This control terminal has a high input impedance, the resistance being in the order of 10^{14} ohms, and a shunting capacitance of around 10 $\mu\mu$f. The oxide layer introduces an inversion layer on the structure between emitter and base. Normally the emitter extends into the base re-

---

MOLECULAR BLOCKS

The concept of transferring circuit elements to an integrated block is not always the best method of approach. On the other hand, the utilization of unique semiconductor properties to realize required functions potentially simplifies design, increases reliability and reduces the size and cost of such blocks

---

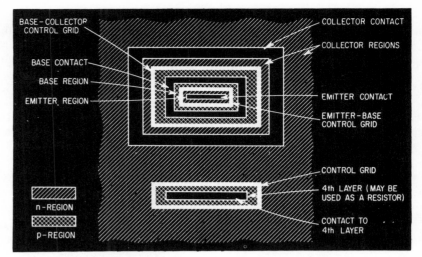

OXIDE-COATED DEVICE may be used as a three terminal device with associated resistor or as a four-layer diode

gion as seen in Fig. 3A. Use of this oxide layer improves the gain-bandwith ($\omega_\beta \beta_0$) of the transistor.

Operation—By applying a fixed bias between the oxide layer and the emitter in the polarity shown in Fig. 1A, two basic improvements are introduced in the transistor operation. The transport factor is improved and the surface defects are reduced. Improvement of the transport factor leads to high β_0 and the reduction of surface defects improves the leakage as well as the current gain at low levels.

An attenuation versus frequency plot has been run on a typical transistor with the result of over 20 percent improvement in the $\omega_\beta \beta_0$ value, with an application of six volts between the control grid and the emitter. Higher improvements can be achieved by optimizing the operating bias voltage.

Memory Device—This structure has a long storage time and is shown in Fig. 4A. The device works as follows. The transistor, without any control bias, operates under its normal mode with a given voltage gain and current gain. If a pulse of the polarity shown in Fig. 4A is applied between the grid and the emitter, the current gain of the stage increases, increasing the output voltage at point A, as shown in Fig. 4B.

The oxide layer is composed of a capacitance shunted by a high resistance, so it has a high time constant. The resistances measured were higher than 10^{14} ohms. Owing to this high time constant, the charge created on this oxide remains for a long time, keeping the gain high. Measurements were made using a typical structure with a time constant of over 40 minutes. The increase of gain, at 2 μamp base current, with an application of 6 volts, was over 22 percent. The advantages of such a device are: (1), the device itself has gain so that information recovery is easy. Thus the variation can be amplified without necessitating any high quality low level amplifier; (2), the change in the output level is pro-

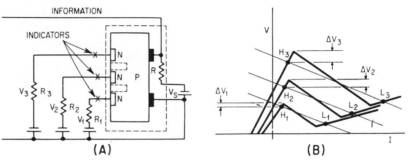

DOUBLE BASE DIODE used for a-d conversion (A) with voltage-current characteristics (B). Dashed lines connote single-chip device—Fig. 1

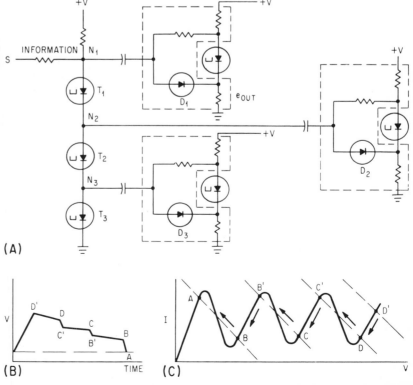

TUNNEL DIODES used for a-d conversion (A) with shape of output voltage at point N_1 (B) as load line returns to its original state (C)—Fig. 2

portional to the pulse level so information on the magnitude of the applied signal is present; (3), if power fails the information is stored; (4), the input impedance is high so it does not load the source; (5), it can be used as a polarity sensing element since reverse polarity across points *G-E* reduces gain. Thus the polarity of the signal applied to the gate can be determined from the variation of gain.

Multistable Device—The oxide controlled device can be used also as a multistable device. This device is unique in its performance since no other single active element exists that has more than two stable states. Moreover, it is as unilateral as any other two-stage device that performs bistable operation. From the point of stability and transient considerations, it offers a great advantage as there is no negative resistance region. Such a device operates as follows. Suppose the device rests on its high-voltage state *R* as shown in Fig. 4B. If a pulse of the polarity shown in Fig. 4A is applied between emitter and the oxide layer, the gain of the transistor increases as explained for the memory device. Thus the operating point rests on *M*. If another pulse of the same polarity is applied to the terminals and the gain is high enough ($i_b \beta R_L > V_{cs}$) the transistor will be shifted to its saturation state *S*.

To bring the device back to its original state *R*, it is necessary to apply a pulse of the opposite polarity between the terminals. For such an operation the driving source must have a high impedance so each time the pulse is applied more charge is stored on the oxide layer. A capacitor can be inserted between the gate and the source to drive the device with a narrow pulse. Thus the discharge path is blocked and the driving source resistance is not critical. The time constants are expected to be in the same order as for the memory device. By proper adjustment of the oxide thicknesses, the time constants can be increased to over an hour.

Transducer—The operation of such a device can be explained using the circuit shown in Fig. 5A. If a capacitance is connected between the grid and the emitter and a voltage is applied across the capacitance, there will be a charge distribution across the capacitance and the oxide layer. Changing the value of *C* will result in the variation of the applied voltage across the oxide layer or grid. For effective operation the circuit shown in Fig. 5B must be used.

Any change in the transducer state, such as a piezoelectric or capacitive effect, will change the potential applied across the grid and emitter resulting in the change of gain. Also, if reasonable transconductance can be achieved between

SURFACE-CONTROLLED DEVICE shows oxide inversion layer (A) used in a circuit (B) to improve $\omega_\beta \beta_0$ (C) with I_C-I_B characteristics (D)—Fig. 3

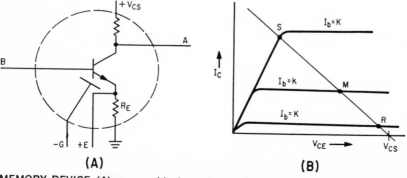

MEMORY DEVICE (A) uses oxide layer to provide long storage time with **V-I** characteristics (B)—Fig. 4.

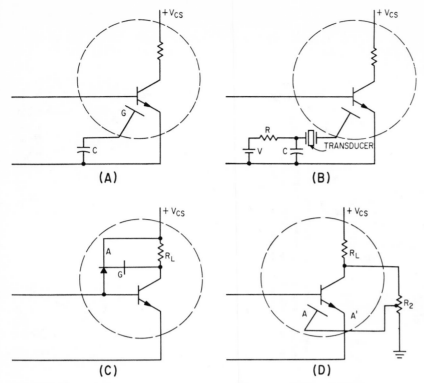

THE SIMPLE TRANSDUCER circuit (A) must be connected (B) for effective operation. The surface-biased controlled diode (C) stabilizes the transistor (D)—Fig. 5

THE FOUR-LAYER DIODE (A) uses the oxide layer to control V-I characteristics (B)—Fig. 6

the grid and the output, the same structure can be used as a frequency discriminator at low frequencies.

Grid-controlled Diode—A simple junction with a control grid on it may be used effectively in biasing and temperature stabilizing transistor stages. Figure 5C shows a transistor stage with a surface-biased controlled diode connected between the power supply, base and collector of a *npn* transistor.

The diode with a given inversion layer and polarity will supply a biasing current to the transistor. A change in the direct voltage across R_L owing to the change in temperature will change the voltage across the grid and point A accordingly. If the right inversion layer is formed and the voltage across R_L is in proper level, an increase of voltage across R_L will cause a decrease in the inversion layer voltage and thus, a decrease in the biasing current. This is an effective means of stabilizing the transistor against collector current (I_c) variations.

A diode with the right transconductance must be used to compen-

sate in the required level for I_c variations. The circuit shown in Fig. 5C suggests a means of adjusting the impedance level of a transistor stage. For example, if the grid is returned to a variable voltage source, it is possible to operate the transistor at desired impedance level by varying the voltage across the grid and one layer of the diode. This procedure offers the useful advantage of not degrading the input impedance of the transistor by external biasing elements. A transistor and a typical diode with a control element has been used for this purpose. Application of 6 volts across the grid and one layer of the diode increased the impedance level from 10,000 to 90,000 ohms.

Temperature Stabilization — The control oxide on a transistor can be used as a temperature compensating element (Fig. 5D), where the gate lead is tapped to the shunting load resistor R_2. An increase of temperature will increase β, the current gain of the transistor, and consequently the collector current. Thus the potential drop between points A-A' increases in the positive

polarity, tending to decrease the gain.

PNPN Switch—If a control grid, using an oxide layer, is introduced in the four layer diode shown in Fig. 6A, it is possible to have a control on the *V-I* characteristics of the device as shown in Fig. 6B.

This device has an apparent advantage over the normal *pnpn* controlled device, because it does not load the control source. Also, there is an isolation between the source and the load.

The author is grateful to P. Koenig for performing the experiments and offering suggestions during discussions, also, to R. P. Donovan for fabricating such devices and introducing information.

REFERENCES

(1) Vasil Uzunoglu, A new look at negative resistance devices, ELECTRONICS, p. 35, March 8, 1963.
(2) Vasil Uzunoglu, Circuits using tunnel diode flip-flops and *pnpn* diodes, IRE Trans. on Electronic Computers, Vol. EC-11, Dec. 1962.
(3) C. T. Sah, New semiconductor tetrode—the surface potential controlled transistor, Proc IRE, p 94, Jan. 1962.
(4) C. T. Sah, Effect of surface recombination and channel on *pn* junction and transistor characteristics, IRE Trans. on Electron Devices, p 94, Jan. 1962.

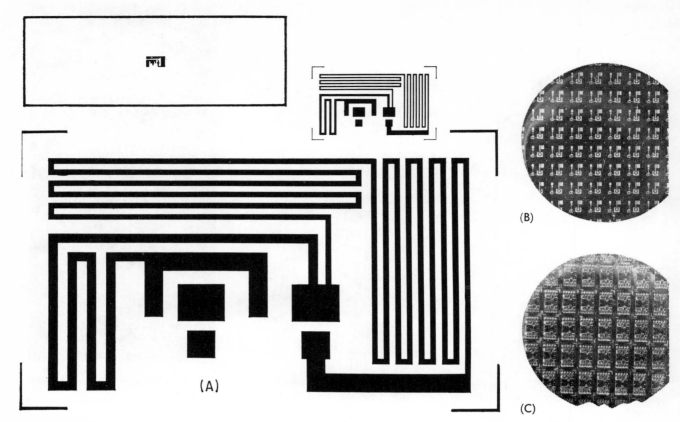

LARGE MASTER MASKS *are reduced in two steps to final size (upper left) appropriate for functional electronic blocks (A). On a large silicon slice, many blocks can be made simultaneously: shown here are three-stage amplifiers (B) and five-input double stroke gates (C)—Fig. 1*

Designing Molecular Circuits
For Use in Complex Systems

To use functional electronic blocks in a meaningful systems program, it is necessary to standardize basic system functions. Described here are new blocks under development whose functions are common to many electronic systems

By H. W. HENKELS,*

Molecular Electronics Dept.,
Semiconductor Div.,
Westinghouse Electric Corp.,
Youngwood, Pennsylvania

DESIGNING functional electronic blocks attention is directed towards obtaining a complete electrical function from a complete block of semiconductor material. Such designing does not involve a piecewise translation of a circuit diagram into the block, because the

* Deceased

relatively low resistivity of semiconductors prevents it and also because semiconductors exhibit special properties that might otherwise not be taken advantage of.

The feasibility of constructing functional electronic blocks has already been demonstrated. However, to develop such blocks in a meaningful systems program it is necessary to examine general system requirements. The approach to system design is to replace various parts or subsystems by functional blocks.

Selecting basic blocks that will adequately perform all or most required system functions presents difficult problems.

In one extreme, every block for every system would be custom made. Even when possible, this approach is prohibitively expensive except for some special systems. At the other extreme, a limited number of standard blocks would be produced. In some areas of the electronics business, in computers for example, a limited number of basic blocks

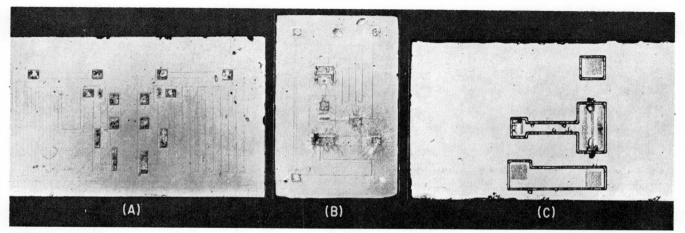

THESE BLOCK AMPLIFIERS *include a universal common emitter amplifier (A), a double Darlington amplifier (B) and a uniplaner bipolar amplifier (Unibi) (C)—Fig. 2*

can be specified. However, this is generally not possible when considering the entire field of electronics. Probably the most practical approach will involve the production of a considerable number of basic designs that are sufficiently flexible to permit reasonable parameter variation around design centers. An attempt has been made, therefore, to arrive at a limited number of subsystem functions common to a large fraction of military electronics systems.

MECHANICAL SPECS—In addition to electrical specifications, mechanical specifications such as size, weight and heat dissipation are needed. In complex systems consisting of a number of subsystems or functional electronic blocks, specifications describing block configuration and interconnection are required. While some aspects of block size, weight and configuration can be treated independently of the overall system by minimizing the former two and choosing the most simple form of the third, compatible with the semiconductor structure, a general knowledge of overall systems requirements is desirable.

Jedec Committee JS-15 recommended that packages should be flat, have external dimensions in multiples of one-eighth inch and lead centers on multiples of 25 mils.

DESIGN METHODS—One method of considering functional electronic block design is to use equivalent circuits. Alternately, the flow of field, displacement and diffusion currents in the semiconductor structure can be visualized, or the output

and input characteristics of sections of the structure can be integrated to develop a complete description. Many methods are useful and can produce semiquantitative results. Exact solutions involve complex equations in three dimensions that cannot be handled in reasonable periods of time. First approximations to exact solutions can be obtained using complicated analog systems such as compartmented electrolytic tanks or matrices of resistor-capacitor networks but the approximations are not good enough to justify the time required. In practice, the semiquantitive expressions are used with flexible trial fabrication techniques to obtain experimental solutions.

Different methods of expressing the configuration required are ap-

---

ABOUT THIS ARTICLE AND THIS AUTHOR

As *microminiaturization developments have moved along in the past few years, the problem of how to incorporate logically entire new sub-circuits into large electronic systems has come more and more to the forefront of attention. This paper, which describes some of the advanced functional electronic blocks under development, also discusses ideas on how to resolve the systems problem.*

Author Henkels, Engineering Manager of the Westinghouse Molecular Electronics Department, was well-known in microminiaturization circles for his work in this field. Mr. Henkels died late this spring. This is his last paper.

---

propriate with different types of functions. For example, in the design of linear amplifiers, equivalent circuits using lumped parameters are useful. On the other hand, with switch structures it is more appropriate to employ a technique of integration of input and output characteristics graphically expressed. With other complex structures, use simplified structural diagrams of the electronic energy levels and trace out field, displacement and diffusion currents.

Despite differences of approach there are no essential differences in the final structures designed. The only differences are in the degrees of sophistication in approach. Design of functional blocks is not accomplished by interconnecting discrete active and passive elements as in conventional circuits. There is, rather, a continuous spectrum of barely distinguishable active and passive regions, and the basic interest is to get a systems function in as direct a manner as possible.

SYNTHESIS METHODS—In using an equivalent circuit, the complexity of the circuit must be compatible with the state of the fabrication art. At the present time, feasibility of construction has been demonstrated for a variety of two and three-stage amplifier equivalents. The size of charge storage regions must be compatible with the rest of the block. Capacitances of approximately 0.01 μf can be readily handled. Polarization must be provided in *p-n* junction capacitances. Excessively large values of isolation resistance between regions of the block cannot be realized. In-

AUDIO AMPLIFIER *block operates between ½ and 2 w—Fig. 3*

TABLE I—SYSTEM REQUIREMENTS FOR FUNCTIONAL BLOCKS

Family (A) Amplification—Untuned

Internal Match		*Output Match (All Relatively Low Impedance 10–1,000 Ohms—Low Frequency)*	
Audio			
Video—4 Mc		*Power Paremeter*	
Video—10 Mc		½–1 w	
R-F—100 Mc		1–5 w	
Operational		5–20 w	
		10–50 w	
Sensor Match (All Low Power)		½ w phase inverter	
Impedance parameter		Push pull output 1—5 w	
<500 ohms		Push pull output > 5 w	
500–10,000 ohms			
5,000–50,000 ohms		(Freq to 30 Mc)	(Freq to 300 Mc)
50,000—1 megohm		½–1 w	½–1 w
50,000—1 meg (low noise)		1–5 w	1–5 w
50,000—5 megohms		> 5 w	

Family (A) Amplification—Tuned

Tunable Amplifiers (All Low Power)	*Tuned (All Low Power)*
455 Kc	*Frequency Parameter*
1.2 Mc	400–1,000 cycles
4.3 Mc	205 Kc
12.5 Mc-> 200 Mc	455 Kc
	1.2 Mc
Modulators	4.3 Mc
A-M, F-M, P-M (Adaption of	12.5 Mc
amplifiers and oscillators in the	30 Mc
same frequency range)	60 Mc
	120 Mc
Attenuators	160 Mc
Requirements not well defined	>200 Mc
(Distributed R-C networks)	

Family (B) Waveform Generators

Oscillators	*Square Wave*
<0.3 Kc	<10 Kc
0.3–3 Kc	10–100 Kc
3 Kc–30 Kc	100–1,000 Kc
30 Kc–300 Kc	1–10 Mc
300–3,000 Kc	
3–30 Mc	*Saw-Tooth Wave*
30–200 Mc	<10 Kc
> 200 Mc	10–100 Kc
	100–1,000 Kc
	Staircase Generator

ductors must be avoided, at least at low frequency. Inductor function can, however, be provided by R-C networks. Direct resistive coupling is desirable. It is estimated that about 200 milliwatts can be dissipated safely in load resistors without excessively heating the block.

With these ground rules, equivalent circuits can be constructed and electrical performance tested. Planar multiple diffusion methods employing oxide and photoresist masking have been adapted to the fabrication of functional electronic blocks. These methods are ideal for production of blocks with closely controlled properties and have been used in such a manner that no difficult registration steps are required even in complicated designs.

The structure to be fabricated is laid out on a one-and-a-half by two-foot master plate or series of plates. The master is then reduced in two steps to a final size appropriate for functional blocks, roughly one-eighth by one-quarter inch. The masks are shown in Fig. 1A. The large master is reduced to the final pattern (upper left). The starting material for a functional block is a piece of silicon 1/8 × 1/4 × 0.004 inch. In many designs the silicon is high resistivity n-type, and this will be assumed in the description of the processing of a transistor structure. A diffused region of p-type material is produced on the surfaces by conventional techniques. The wafer is then exposed to an oxidizing atmosphere in a high temperature furnace. The oxidation cycle produces a 4,000-A thick layer of silicon dioxide upon the surfaces.

Next, a thin layer of a photosensitive chemical is spun on the surfaces. The silicon wafer is then located under a microscope slide. There follows the usual series of operations employed in producing high-frequency transistor structures. However, for functional blocks, the photoresist masks are also used in defining resistive areas and in applying metallic contacts so that a series of slides is usually necessary to produce the three-dimensional printed pattern desired. Thus, there may be many masking, oxidation and diffusion steps. However, in all the processing, the silicon wafer is handled as a single piece. There are no delicate hand engraving operations. The complete patterns are produced on the original masters.

After the final diffusion operation and evaporation of contacts, units are tested. In some designs, various parts of the functional electronic block are interconnected by evaporated aluminum regions over the silicon-dioxide covering surfaces; in such cases another test is made after interconnection. Input and output and power supply leads are attached to the blocks by thermo-compression bonding. Units are encapsulated in hermetic flat ceramic or Kovar cases.

For production refinement, all designs have been modified, and made much smaller, for use with complete slices of silicon. The masks are replicated to provide patterns for complete slices. On a silicon slice about ½ inch in diameter, from 20 to 30 to 100 functional electronic blocks can be made at once. Figures 1B and 1C show three-stage amplifiers and five-input double-stroke gates, respectively. The processing is carried out on complete slices up to and including interconnection evaporation steps, which provide aluminum contacts.

BLOCK FEASIBILITY—To demonstrate technical feasibility of using functional blocks in information processing, many basic blocks have been studied. An important part of the systems program resides in the mutual compatibility of functional blocks to perform general subsystem requirements.

During the last year further analysis of general system requirements has shown the need for a number of additional basic types to

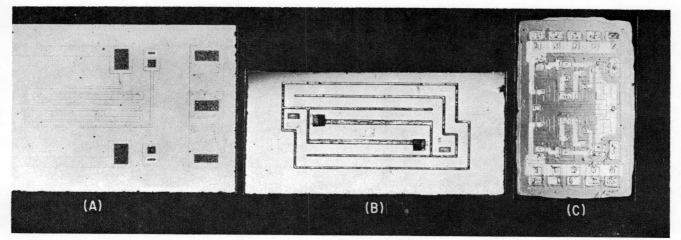

OSCILLATOR-MIXER *for 30-Mc range (A), a one-Mc multivibrator (B) and a double stroke logic block (C)—Fig. 4*

fill out a catalog of compatible blocks. Table I gives a summary of functions for which functional electronic blocks have been considered.

UNTUNED AMPLIFIERS—Internal Match: Common emitter amplifiers and two-stage Darlington amplifiers provide units for low level amplification in the frequency range from d-c to 2 Mc. Impedance levels are intermediate. Power dissipation is in the range of 100-200 milliwatts. Figures 2A and 2B present photographs of a universal common emitter amplifier and a Darlington amplifier, respectively. Structures are double planer diffused using oxide and photoresist masking techniques. Data on a typical Darlington amplifier are in Table II.

Sensor Match: Common emitter universal amplifiers and Darlington amplifiers match sensors of low or intermediate impedance. With sensors of high impedance, such as crystal phonograph pickups and infrared photoconductive cells, higher impedance blocks are required.

In the range to about one megohm, the Unibi (uniplanar bipolar amplifier) can be employed. Figure 2C shows a Unibi block. Data on typical amplifiers are found in Table III. The unipolar input structure of this block should operate at low noise levels. The block is designed to provide high input impedance at low noise with high gain.

At higher impedance levels, up to 5 megohms, three-stage Darlington structures can be used. They are designed to match a crystal pickup. The overall gain of typical units falls in the range of 45 db.

Output Match: Except in trans-

mitter applications, most output stages operate at audio frequencies. For example, audio amplifiers in communications, servoamplifiers in control systems, ultrasonic and relay drives operate in the frequency range < 100 Kc. There are other important exceptions, for example, writing heads on computers which must operate to 10 Mc. However, most effort has concentrated in the low-frequency range.

An audio amplifier, shown in Fig. 3, has been designed to operate in the range of one-half to 2 watts. Input and output impedances are respectively 100 and 200 ohms, and a power gain of 35 db is achieved at 200-mw output. For the range 5-20 watts, a split phase high level amplifier has been designed; typical data is given in Table IV.

In many applications of molecular electronics, phase inversion is necessary to avoid bulky transformers. A unit operating in the power range of one-half watt would be ideal as drive for high level two-phase amplifiers.

TUNED AMPLIFIERS—Table I shows complete coverage of requirements for tuned amplifiers in the range below 200 Mc. The range most adequately covered by meth-

ods compatible with the functional block approach lies between 455 Kc and 4.5 Mc, where tuning is effected by piezoelectric resonators operating in the radial mode. The frequency range between 4.5 and 30 Mc can be covered by thickness mode piezoelectric resonators and by overtone radial and thickness mode resonators. In the 100 to 200-Mc range, the Q's of conductive loops on silicon are high enough to permit considering their use.

Oscillators: Family (B) of Table I indicates that modifications of existing amplifiers can readily provide oscillators in the frequency range of 455 Kc to 30 Mc. This has been illustrated by the construction of the crystal controlled oscillator, which works at 30 Mc.

An oscillator-mixer functional block for the 30-Mc range is shown in Fig. 4A. A 30-Mc oscillator signal is mixed with an incoming signal to give a 3-Mc output.

Square-wave generators can be readily constructed from multivibrators operating in the appropriate frequency range. Several designs of a one-Mc multivibrator have been developed. One is shown in Fig. 4B. However, it is probably simpler to construct multivibrators from basic gating circuits.

TABLE II—AUDIO AMPLIFIERS

Unit	Operating Voltage (v)	Operating Current (ma)	Freq (Kc)	Voltage Gain	Current Gain	Power Gain (db)
VJF5	10	6	1–50	170	60	42
VLC4	12	15		130	90	37
VLH1	15	9		70	720	45
V1D5	10	12		55	620	46
VLE2	5	5		45	470	41
VMC1	10	9		200	70	47
VMC2	9	5		560	100	37

Mixers: Again, as in oscillators, mixers can readily be constructed by adaptation of basic amplifier blocks. For illustration, this has been done in producing a mixer designed for the 30-Mc range.

Demodulators: A detector has been designed with a built-in distributed filter for operation in the frequency range 100 Kc to 10 Mc. Discriminators can be produced by employing the notch filter.

Wave Shaping: Little direct attention has been given to the problem of wave shaping, since specific requirements have not been defined. However, a complete catalog of basic filters and structures exists to meet such requirements.

Short Time Storage: While requirements have not been well defined, a series of flip flops can meet such requirements. Some attention should be given to the construction of a typical storage system.

Logic Switches: Effort has concentrated upon the development of a universal logic block, the double five-input stroke. A diode transistor configuration has been used as shown in Fig. 4C. Five input channels have been provided for each stroke gate to give maximum flexibility in computer design with a minimum of parts. The fanout of each stroke element is five. Maximum propagation delay is 200 nanoseconds. The saturated diode transistor stroke can be improved to the point where operation beyond one megacycle is possible. As yet, saturated logic gates are being considered for operation above 10 Mc, but little work has been done.

Signal Sampling: The multiple *pnpn* switch provides a block for signal sampling which must have external provisions for commutation. A number of designs have been made. Some development work has been carried out on multiple switches with commutation provided by transverse base fields. There are other designs being considered that will provide the commutation without base fields.

STANDARDIZATION — Feasibility of construction of segments of electronic systems has been demonstrated by successful assembly of a number of these.

A variety of audio amplifier systems has been constructed. An experimental phonograph system requires high impedance matches to crystal pickups. Two different blocks have been employed for the high impedance match. The first of these is a Unibi amplifier consisting of a unipolar transistor structure coupled to a bipolar. The second is a three-stage common collector Darlington with feedback. Both have input impedances in the megohm range needed. The low level amplifiers are coupled to the power stages, consisting of two-phase high level amplifiers, by transformers or, more recently, by phase inverter blocks. Such systems are capable of operating to 30 or 40 watts.

The compatibility of a longer series of blocks is illustrated in radio applications. The Air Force ARC-63 communications receiver was built from functional electronic blocks. In addition, a number of radios operating in the citizen's band have been constructed from a series of blocks. Recently a FEB-PAK consisting of a number of compatible blocks which can be assembled to produce a radio operating in the citizen's band, has been made available.

In molecular electronics a great flexibility exists in the design of functional electronic blocks but this flexibility applies primarily to the block manufacturer. Design freedom could be extended to systems engineers provided a complete custom design basis for functional electronic blocks were reasonable. It is anticipated that this flexibility will in time be developed.

A standardization of functional blocks requires a logical subdivision of basic subsystem functions. This has been done to a large degree. Large numbers of basic subsystems are generally recognized in the industry.

Although it is technically feasible to produce blocks performing complex functions equivalent to several stages of transistor circuits, standardization at such complexity is not achievable without first standardizing more basic functions than have already been selected.

Of primary importance in standardizing is the question of mechanical compatibility. The Electronic Industries Association and the National Electrical Manufacturers Association have set up Jedec Subcommittee JS-15 concerned with integrated electronics. EIA has also set up two other committees. The Microminiaturization Advisory Committee is charged with determining user preferences in standardization. The EIA Parts Committee, P-9, is concerned with new approaches to micromodules and printed circuits. The three committees have acted in joint accord to assure general agreement.

While many obstructions lie in the road, the tremendous effect of standardization on electronic design could certainly make all efforts worthwhile. This is particularly true in military activities. New equipment designs could be much more rapidly translated into operating hardware. Replacement parts storage and servicing could be revolutionized.

Suitable manufacturing techniques for producing functional electronic blocks in large volume are in the process of development.

TABLE IV—CURRENT GAIN CHARACTERISTICS OF TWO PHASE AMPL

Unit	I_c →	500 ma ϕ_1	500 ma ϕ_2	1 amp ϕ_1	1 amp ϕ_2	2 amp ϕ_1	2 amp ϕ_2	V_{CEO} at 25 ma ϕ_1	V_{CEO} at 25 ma ϕ_2
1B	h_{fe}	7,500	2,400	5,600	4,000	4,000	2,750	84	160
	h_{FE}	3,333	1,666	4,400	2,700	5,000	3,000		
2B	h_{fe}	4,000	4,400	3,800	4,000	2,250	2,500	100	180
	h_{FE}	1,833	2,000	2,500	2,750	2,858	3,000		
5B	h_{fe}	4,000	3,200	4,200	3,300	2,750	2,375	124	148
	h_{FE}	1,666	1,715	2,500	2,350	3,440	2,500		
8B	h_{fe}	3,200	4,000	2,600	3,600	2,000	2,750	140	116
	h_{FE}	1,652	1,400	2,300	2,600	2,250	2,812		

TABLE III—UNIBI CHARACTERISTICS

B+ — 10 v
I_{total} — 1–3 ma (depending on bias)
Z_{in} — > 2 meg
Z_{out} — 100 ohms
A_i — 2,300
A_v — 10
A_p — 43 db
Distortion < 1 percent at 1 V_{rms} out
Device is self-stabilizing up to 100 C

The Frustrating Problem of Inductors in Integrated Circuits

Tuning integrated circuits is still an unsolved problem because inductors can't be made small enough. Here three different approaches are compared, pointing out the advantages and limitations of each. They are: active feedback, passive feedback and feed forward nets

By **W. E. NEWELL**
Fellow Engineer, Information Devices Dept., Westinghouse Research Laboratories, Pittsburgh, **Pa.**

INTEGRATED circuits are coming of age and are now capable of performing many of the digital and linear functions previously performed by conventional circuits using discrete components. However, one of the functions which has stubbornly resisted full integration is frequency-selective amplification. The source of the difficulty lies in the fact that it has not been possible to miniaturize high-Q inductors to the point where they are consistent in size with other integrated components. When a capacitor is miniaturized by scaling down all of its dimensions, the capacitance decreases proportionately but the quality factor remains constant at constant frequency. On the other hand, when an inductor[1] is similarly miniaturized, the Q decreases as the square of the scaling factor. Therefore major improvements in material properties are necessary before high-Q *LC* tuning networks can be integrated.

Many solutions to these tuning problems have been suggested. The purpose of this article is to show that each of these approaches falls into one of three categories. The advantages and disadvantages of each category are illustrated by typical examples. Elimination of the unpromising categories then points the way in which future work must be directed towards the solution of the tuning problem.

Passive Feedback—The well-known *LC* tank circuit will serve as a standard of comparison and is an example of the passive-feedback category of tuning networks. Although it is not ordinarily recognized that the selectivity of an *LC* network depends on feedback, a signal flow graph shows the similarity between these networks and other selective feedback networks. Such networks become frequency-selective when at some frequency the loop gain approaches unity. In the case of passive feedback networks, this requires the use of nearly lossless reactive elements. For example, passive *RC* networks can never have sharp selectivity.

Selective networks using passive feedback have two very important advantages. They are simple in that relatively few components are required and the component tolerances are relatively uncritical. A useful quantitative measure of how critical the tolerances are may be obtained from the sensitivities[2] of

---

COMPARISON OF NETWORK TUNERS

Active feedback does not provide an attractive solution to the problem of tuning integrated-circuits because of the tight component tolerances needed. Feedforward also is not attractive because of circuit complexity. The most promising tuners would be passive LC circuits and piezoelectric resonators which, although not necessarily integrated, are at least compatible in size with integrated networks

---

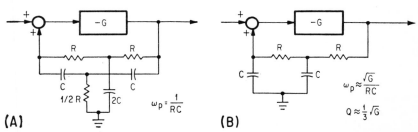

SELECTIVE tuners use parallel T feedback network (A) and reactance-tube circuit (B)—Fig. 1

Q with respect to the various components x_i, where

$$S_{x_i}{}^Q \equiv \frac{x_i}{Q} \qquad \frac{\partial Q}{\partial x_i} \approx -2Q \operatorname{Im} S_{x_i}{}^{,p}$$

Here s_p is the dominant pole causing selectivity, and the sensitivities S_{x_i} may be evaluated from the characteristic equation of the network. A total Q sensitivity for the network, Σ_Q, may then be defined by

$$\Sigma_Q \equiv \Sigma_i \left| S_{x_i}{}^Q \right| \approx 2Q \, \Sigma_i \left| \operatorname{Im} S_{x_i}{}^{,p} \right|$$

Σ_Q may be interpreted as follows. If every element in the network changes by 1 percent in a direction such that the effects are additive, the Q will change by Σ_Q percent. Conversely, if Q is to be held within a tolerance of $\pm \theta$ percent, component tolerances of the order of (θ / Σ_Q) percent are required.

When the sensitivities of Q with respect to the L, C, and R of a tank circuit are evaluated and summed, it is found that

$$\Sigma_Q = 2$$

Since it is impossible for a passive network to be self-oscillatory, this value of Σ_Q is relatively small and in particular it is independent of Q. Therefore *LC* tuning networks are well behaved and are the ideal tuning method wherever they can be used.

Active Feedback—Numerous circuits for obtaining frequency-selectivity without using inductance have been discussed in the literature[3] and are commonly used at low frequencies where the alternative is to use a bulky inductor. Most of these circuits use an *RC* feedback network around one or more active elements. As before, selectivity results when the loop gain approaches unity, but now the active elements are necessary to cancel most of the signal losses in the *RC* network. Because of the delicate balance which must be maintained, selective active feedback networks are inherently very sensitive to component tolerances. If a component drifts slightly in one direction, selectivity is lost, while a drift in the other direction

causes loss of the desired bandwidth and then self-oscillation.

A typical network of this type uses an *RC* null circuit in the feedback path, such as the parallel T, as shown in Fig. 1. The total sensitivity for this circuit is $\Sigma_Q = 2Q$, where the sensitivity of Q with respect to the amplifier gain, G, has not been included in the summation. The reason for this omission is that $S_G{}^Q$ may be made arbitrarily small if G is made large enough. However the total sensitivity cannot be reduced. Since Σ_Q is proportional to Q, the attainment of higher Q (with the same percentage tolerance on Q) always necessitates tighter tolerances on the components. For example, to achieve a Q of 50 within ± 10 percent, component tolerances of the order of 0.1 percent are required over the entire range of operating conditions. Such tolerances on integrated circuits are completely unreasonable in the foreseeable future.

Similar conclusions hold for all other networks using an active feedback loop to obtain selectivity (other null circuits and phase shifters,[3] negative impedance converters, negative resistance devices,[4]) with one notable exception. Second-order feedback networks, such as the bridged T or the two-section phase shifter shown in Fig. 2, are unconditionally stable if connected around an amplifier having no excess phase shift. Under these circumstances Σ_Q is again independent of Q as it is for an *LC* tank circuit. The circuit shown in Fig. 2 is that of the well known reactance tube, and gives $\Sigma_Q = 7/6$ where, in this case, $S_G{}^Q$ cannot be reduced and has been included in the summation. The disadvantage of these circuits is that very high gain is required for useful Q. For Fig. 2, $G \approx 9Q^2$ so that a

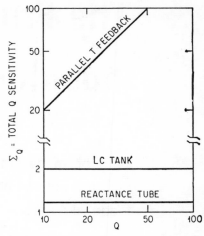

TYPICAL selective feedback networks illustrate the tolerance-sensitivity problem—Fig. 2

Q of 50 would require a gain of about 87 db. The high gain requirement, together with the low phase shift, have thus far made a transistorized reactance tube impractical for building an integrated tuning network. However, the development of high-gain, high-input-impedance field-effect transistors could change the future prospects of this circuit.

The seriousness of the tolerance sensitivity problem for most high-Q active feedback networks is shown in Fig. 3. in which the values of Σ_Q are plotted as functions of Q. The graph for parallel-T feedback, although not the minimum that is possible,[5] is representative since it is the slope which poses the major problem.

Feed-Forward Networks — The unique feature of a feedback network is that the same network is used to process the signal an infinite number of times. The price which is paid for this feature is the inherent possibility of self-oscillation. However, any feedback network may be

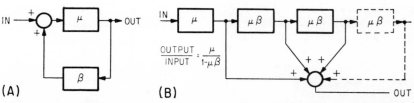

(A)   (B)

FEEDBACK network (A) and its equivalent feedforward network (B) present problems of complexity—Fig. 3

replaced by an equivalent feedforward network consisting of an infinite chain of identical stages, where the output is obtained by summing the outputs of the individual stages as shown in Fig. 4.

The question now arises: can a selective feedback network be satisfactorily approximated by a finite feedforward network, and if so, how many stages are required? The anticipated advantage is that a finite feedforward network cannot become self-oscillatory, and therefore the extreme tolerance sensitivity of a selective feedback network can be avoided.

As with the active feedback approach to tuning, there are many specific circuits which fall into the feedforward category. Some are ordinary linear networks or devices[6] while others use sampling techniques,[7, 8] and each differs from the others in details. The common disadvantage of these networks is not one of stability and tolerances but one of complexity. No high-Q feedforward network is known which promises to be economically feasible in integrated form.

As an example, consider the case where each stage consists of a lossless delay line. This network is the electrical analog of a diffraction-grating monochromator. Then $\mu(s) = e^{-\tau s}$ and $\beta = 1$ where τ is the delay in each section. The fundamental passband is centered at $1/\tau$ cycles per second, but other passbands occur at multiples of this frequency. It can be shown that the approximate Q for a large number of stages, N, is then given by $Q \approx 9N/8$. Therefore about 45 sections of delay line, together with the appropriate summing network, would be necessary for a Q of 50. Aside from the difficulty of trying to integrate a nearly lossless delay line, it is very unlikely that this much complexity can be justified in the accomplishment of such a simple function.

Looking Ahead—Assuming that an economically feasible solution to the integrated circuit tuning problem will eventually be found, it is unlikely that it will be either an active feedback network (because of the required tolerances) or a feedforward network (because of complexity). The remaining alternative is a passive tuning network, that is, a

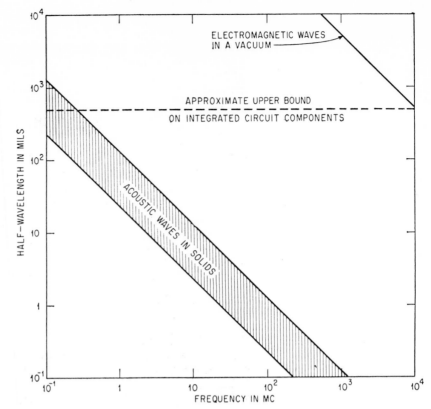

COMPARISON of half-wavelength of electromagnetic and acoustic waves favors the latter—Fig. 4

classical *LC* circuit or its electromechanical analog, an acoustic resonator. Although the investigation of integrated tuning networks over the past five years appears to have returned to its starting point, the present situation differs in at least two important respects. There is a fuller awareness that there is no mystical easy solution to the problem and the hard facts of life force the acceptance of a compromise solution as better than no solution. In this light, hybrid circuits that are not completely integrated become more attractive.

For frequencies of 50 Mc or more, relatively little inductance is required for tuning and it may yet be possible to develop a satisfactory inductor of compatible size. Piezoelectric devices also show great promise. These devices exhibit a resonance when the controlling dimension is of the order of an acoustic half-wavelength.

If 500 mils is taken as an upper limit for the size of an economical integrated circuit component, Fig. 5 shows that resonant acoustic devices lie below this limit for all frequencies greater than about 100 kc. The analogous electrically resonant traveling wave structure would be larger

by a factor of about 10^5. The necessity of special mountings for these devices to prevent acoustic coupling has been a serious disadvantage, but this difficulty may not be insurmountable. Therefore the solution to the tuning problem, although not attained, has at least been circumscribed.

REFERENCES

(1) A. Rand, Inductor Size vs. Q: A Dimensional Analysis, IEEE Trans. on Comp. Parts, Vol. 10, p 31, March 1963.
(2) W. E. Newell, Selectivity and Sensitivity in Functional Blocks, Proc. IRE, Vol. 50, p 2517; Dec. 1962.
(3) S. W. Punnett, Audio Frequency Selective Amplifiers, Jour. Brit. IRE, Vol. 10, p 39, Feb. 1950; T. E. Price, G. Bradshaw, C. H. Taylor, A Tunable Solid-Circuit Filter Suitable for an I.F. Amplifier, Electronic Engineering, Vol. 35, p 806, Dec. 1963; G. Herskowitz, R. Wydrum, Jr., Design of Distributed RC Feedback Networks for Bandpass Amplifiers, Semiconductor Products, Vol. 7, p 13, Jan. 1964.
(4) H. G. Dill, Inductive Semiconductor Elements and Their Application in Bandpass Amplifiers, IRE Trans. on Mil. Elect., Vol. 5, p 239, July 1961.
(5) W. E. Newell, A Frequency-Selective RC Feedback Network with Relatively Low Component Tolerance Sensitivity, to be published, Jour. of Electronics & Control.
(6) S. N. Levine and J. J. Sein, Semiconductor Bandpass Filters, 1961 IRE Intnl. Conv. Rec., pt. 6, p 133.
(7) W. R. LePage, C. R. Cahn, J. S. Brown, Analysis of a Comb Filter Using Synchronously Commutated Capacitors, Trans. AIEE, Vol. 72, pt. I, p 63, March 1953.
(8) A. Campora, B. Rabinovici, C. A. Renton, Generation of Band-Pass Filters by Switching Techniques, Proc. IEEE, Vol. 51, p 256, Jan. 1963.

Putting a Servo Amplifier on a Small Silicon Wafer

MOLECULAR SERVO *amplifier, on fingertip, packs enough power to drive a size 8 servo motor*

Inside-out transistors are key to high-power output of a molecular servo amplifier

By M. W. AARONS, Norden Division, United Aircraft Corp., Norwalk, Conn.

MOLECULAR SERVO amplifiers with enough power to drive a servomotor are diffused into a thin silicon wafer only ¾-inch diameter. These analog units are the result of several new molecular electronic techniques developed to simplify fabrication and to enable the output stage to deliver a sizable amount of power. An important result is the topological inversion of the transistor structure to achieve extremely low saturation resistance. The geometry of conventional transistor structures was altered by turning the transistor inside-out. It is difficult to use conventional geometry, with all contacts in the same plane and extract the power required.

The amplifier is direct-coupled, class A and contains almost four dozen components. Rated power output is 1.5 watts. All circuit connections are deposited on a passivated surface. The transistors can sustain 75 volts and deliver up to 200 ma into size 11 and size 8 servo motors.

CIRCUIT—In Fig. 1A, transistors Q_1 through Q_4 form a differential high impedance voltage preamplifier. Transistors Q_5 and Q_6 are emitter follower driver stages, which are zener diode coupled to the push-pull power output stages Q_7 and Q_8. Re-

NEW APPLICATION OF MOLECULAR ELECTRONICS

To date, most molecular electronic devices have been digital. And they handle relatively low power. This unit is an analog device and can provide enough power to drive standard size servo motors. In fact, the amplifier has driven 3-watt motors

sistors R_{11} and R_{12} provide thermal stabilization for the power stage and guarantee that the zeners are broken down.

Open-loop gain of the differential forward amplifier Q_1 through Q_8 is greater than 2,000. The closed-loop gain, however, is determined by resistor ratios in the differential feedback network: R_1 through R_4 and R_{13} through R_{20}. The overall gain is precisely specified to be 200 by this technique.

Direct-current operating points are stabilized by the common-mode feedback amplifier consisting of Q_9 and Q_{10} with resistors R_{21} through R_{26}. The signal across the output is differentially summed by R_{21} and R_{22} cancelling the a-c components. The d-c component is then amplified and applied to the emitters of the differential input Darlington pair.

The method of isolation, which consists of back-to-back junction surfaces, alters the actual circuit

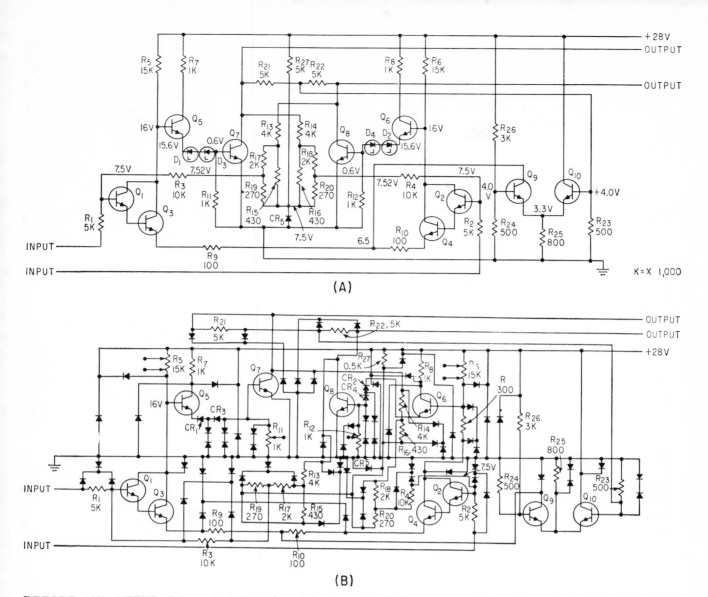

BEFORE AND AFTER. *Schematic (A) is the original circuit of the servo amplifier. When it is fabricated on the silicon wafer, circuit (B) results because of distributed diode planes introduced by the substrate—Fig. 1*

operation by inserting distributed diodes in a complicated manner within the circuit, Fig. 1B.

TRANSISTOR DESIGN — Since the circuit must deliver sizable amounts of power, the output stage received a great deal of attention. In conventional power transistors the bulk of the collector body is of low resistivity. Modern n on n^+ epitaxial planar diffused devices are examples of this geometry. In crystal circuits it is difficult to achieve this result and maintain a collector breakdown of 120 volts. The motor that the circuit drives requires 94 volts peak-to-peak and 120 milliamperes peak current.

To solve the problem of low collector resistivity, 200 to 1 scale models of planar power transistors were constructed. Emitters and collectors were made of aluminum foil using tape to mask surfaces between collector pads. Solutions of NaOH were mixed in different concentrations to simulate substrate material of 1, 2, 3 and 4 ohm-cm bulk resistivity. The depth of the solution was varied in 0.1-inch increments, simulating 0.5-mil variations in the depth of the collector region. The models were also modified to vary the length of emitter and collector junctions, and the separation of these junctions. A successful topological inversion of the power transistor structure was achieved as a result of data obtained from these models.

INTERCONNECTIONS — A set of rules was developed so that the complex circuit could be translated into the best arrangement of the elements within the crystal. These rules eliminate interconnection crossovers and require that elements with critical interconnection lengths be close together.

Because the program involved placing an entire electronic system in one crystal of silicon, it was necessary to determine whether process technology was sufficiently advanced to enable initial good yields. Therefore, a layout that dissected the amplifier by symmetry into four distinct circuits, Fig. 2, was chosen. An interconnection scheme was developed that allows a choice of assembly methods depending upon test results of the individual wafers.

The first choice was to interconnect within each independent circuit then dice the wafer to pick and choose the best circuit of each category, Fig. 3. The four 100-mil square chips are then mounted on the same header. Ball-bonded wire connections between chips complete the amplifier.

The second choice was to interconnect within and between four adjacent circuits by deposited aluminum and dice the wafer into complete amplifier chips, Fig. 4. The decision of which way to go is made by electrical tests after ohmic contacts are alloyed to the crystal.

FABRICATION—Circuits are produced from two types of material. The first type consists of a 20 ohm-cm p-type crystal upon which is grown a 1-mil 2.5-ohm-cm n-type epitaxial layer. The second type is a bulk 2.5-ohm-cm n wafer. Processing of the second type is described since the steps are typical of both.

The wafer is lapped and polished to a 4.5-mil thickness. Then a 25,000 angstrom thickness of steam oxide is grown and subsequently etched away. This step removes work damaged crystal layers and yields a smoother surface than mechanical polishing. A 10,000 angstrom thickness oxide is now grown and photoresisted to produce isolation moat contours. Boron from a tribromide source is deposited (C_o approximately 10^{21} atoms per cm³) and simultaneously diffused from top and bottom, thus creating n regions that are isolated by back-to-back junction planes. The bases of the transistors, the p part of diodes, and all resistor networks are diffused from a boric-acid source. The predeposition is controlled so that a sheet resistivity of 250 ohms per square is maintained. The next step is to diffuse all emitters, make n^+ contact areas in the collector regions, and complete the zeners. A phosphorus pentoxide process is employed for n^+ deposition.

Holes are then etched into the oxide where contact to the crystal is desired. Aluminum is evaporated over the entire wafer and subsequently etched completely off the oxide. The aluminum is spike-alloyed into the crystal. Regrowth of p material in the collector regions are prevented by the n^+ diffusion. Interconnection of elements is ac-complished by a similar procedure of deposition and removal. The aluminum leads are vacuum baked at 500 C to alloy the aluminum into the surface of the oxide layers.

Careful attention to the porosity of the photoresist is maintained throughout to prevent development of pinholes in the oxide. The KPR (Kodak photoresist) is monitored in a crossed Nicol prism arrangement, for small particles and filaments. Impurities reveal themselves by depolarizing light that they scatter. Oxides are routinely checked by exposure to chlorine gas at 950 C. Pinhole counts range between 0 and 10 per wafer.

After dicing, mounting and lead attachment, the circuit is electrically evaluated. The good units are cleaned in deionized water and vacuum baked for 1 hour at 300 C. Hermetic sealing is accomplished by electron-beam welding.

TESTING—To evaluate the servo amplifier functionally, a controlled 400-cps input signal is coupled to the amplifier through a ratio transformer. The input signal is measured both rms and peak to peak. Output of the amplifier is fed into a tuned servo motor, whose primary is open so that the load simulates stalled conditions. The rms output from either Q_7 or Q_8 to ground is then measured. Peak-to-peak output voltage is measured across the motor windings.

Transfer characteristics of the amplifier are determined by adjusting the ratio transformer and reading input and corresponding output voltages. The rms output is only read across half of the output; however, the two halves are 180 deg. out of phase so that they can be added linearly to obtain the total rms output. Quiescent current is approximately 60 ma per power transistor with an additional 10 ma in the B+ circuit. The current swings between 0 and 120 ma, while the rms into the motor winding is 36 volts for a 28-volt supply.

This paper represents the work of a team of scientists and engineers at Norden, who have been supported by United Aircraft Corp. and the Navy Bureau of Weapons. The work was sponsored by the Bureau of Naval Weapons under contract NOw-61-1053-C.

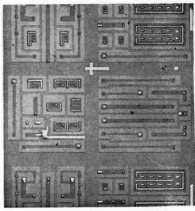

FOUR CIRCUITS *comprise the complete amplifier. Here they are shown without interconnections—Fig. 2*

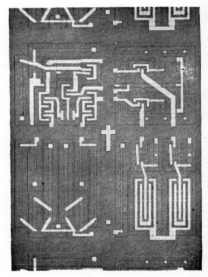

CONNECTIONS *within each individual circuit are made first. Then the circuits are tested to determine the next step in fabrication—Fig. 3*

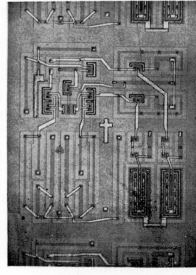

COMPLETED *servo amplifier with all interconnections—Fig. 4*

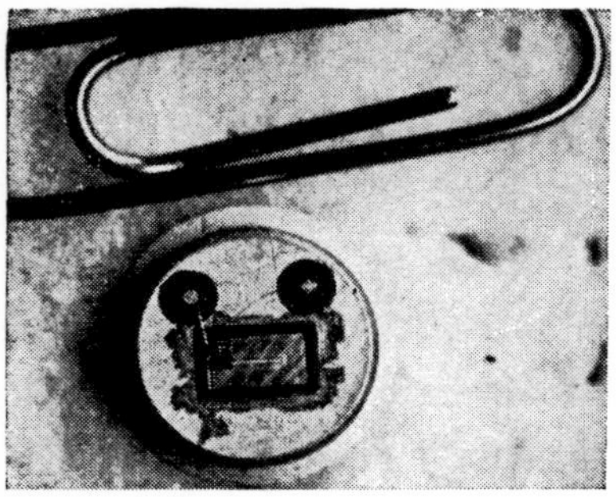

RC OSCILLATOR is constructed with integrated circuit techniques and mounts on a standard TO-5 header

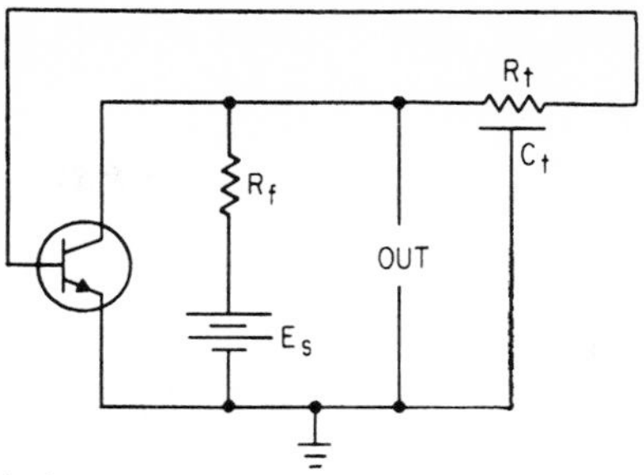

(A)

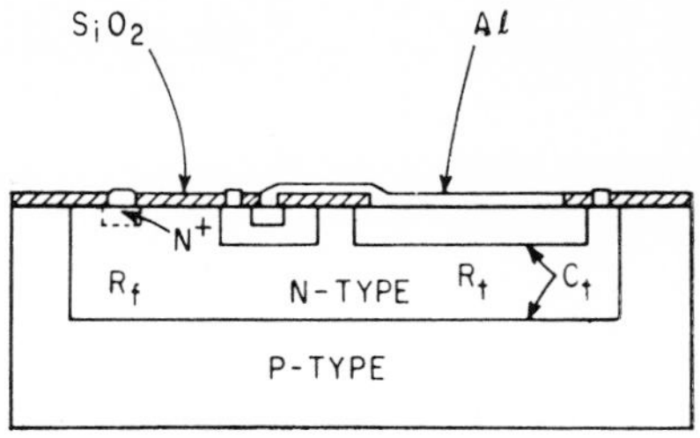

(B)

SCHEMATIC of the oscillator (A), and sectional view of the integrated circuit (B)

Integrated-Circuit Oscillator

REQUIRES FEW COMPONENTS

By **H. YANAI, T. SUGANO** and **M. YOSHIDA,** Tokyo University, and
T. KUROSAWA and **I. SASAKI,** Nippon Electric Company, Tokyo, Japan

OSCILLATOR shown in drawing A utilizes a distributed resistance-capacitance transmission line as a phase shifter and a transistor as an amplifier. Stable oscillation can be obtained when the sum of the phase shift due to the transistor and that from the RC line is an integral multiple of 2π. Oscillation is maintained as long as sufficient energy is supplied through the feed resistance.

Design—The monolithic integrated circuit of the oscillator is useful from viewpoints of size reduction, economy, and reliability. A sectional view of the integrated circuit appears in diagram B. This circuit is simple and requires a minimum number of components.

Resistors R_t and R_f are formed using the bulk resistance common to the transistor collector body, rather than by using a conventional *p*-type diffused layer. These resistors are convenient to use because they require no interconnection. If a spreading resistance is available for R_f, construction may be even simpler. However, it is difficult to use this resistance because of the resistivity of the wafer. Capacitor C_t is formed by *pn* junctions surrounding resistor R_t. Transistor characteristics are similar to those 2SC31. Ohmic contacts can be attached to the *n*-type region by evaporating aluminum after diffusing phosphorus into the contact areas.

Construction—Seven ohms-cm *n*-type silicon is employed as a starting material. After polishing and oxidation, windows are selectively etched on the top surface and boron is diffused in from both the upper and lower surfaces. This process yields *n*-type islands that form the transistor collector and resistors R_t and R_f. The depth of the *n*-region is 55 μ. Two boron diffused *p*-type layers are produced in the *n*-region; one serves as the transistor base and the other as the anode of capacitor C_t together with *p*-type bottom. The *n*-region between the upper and lower *p*-regions forms R_t.

After phosphorus diffusion for the emitter and contacts to the *n*-region, aluminum is evaporated and selectively etched to give a pattern for interconnections and other contacts.

Performance—The peak-to-peak oscillation voltage has a maximum value at $E_s = 14$ volts or $T = 25$ degrees. This is true because increasing either the supply voltage or temperature shifts the transistor bias point to saturation. Oscillation frequency varies linearly with temperature; it depends upon both the transistor and the transmission line.

The frequency distribution of the circuits fabricated was ±20 percent. Another experiment indicated that the oscillation frequency can be varied by applying reverse voltage to junction capacitor C_t. This suggests that the circuit is suitable for f-m use.

TRULY SIMPLE DEVICE

This oscillator represents an ultra-simple circuit that achieves small size through use of integrated-circuit techniques. It is versatile and offers economy and reliability at both high and low frequencies. Moreover, it is suitable for f-m applications if designed in a somewhat different form. This redesigning is necessary because the frequency-determining line and the collector portion of the transistor overlap so that a change in voltage on the line changes the collector voltage. For f-m use, the frequency determining line must be set off by diffusion isolation

New technology sparks an expansion for germanium

General-purpose germanium transistors can now be built with
a planar structure, possibly extending applications to phased
array radar, tv tuners and computer switching circuits.

By K.B. Landress

Senior project engineer, Semiconductor-Components Division,

Texas Instruments Incorporated, Dallas, Texas.

Although the first commercial semiconductor devices were made of germanium 15 years ago, silicon devices have outstripped them in the high quality device area, even though germanium has better high-frequency electrical characteristics. The reason is simple: Silicon transistors are easier to build to the tighter dimensions required for devices that operate at high frequency. In fact, commercially it has been impossible to build germanium transistors with good high-frequency characteristics beyond 5 gigacycles.

That's why the heterogeneous oxide technology developed at Texas Instruments Inc. looms so significantly. With it, the circuit designer can have general-purpose germanium transistors with excellent high-frequency characteristics at costs that compare favorably with present germanium mesa structures. The company can build germanium transistors to almost any dimensional tolerances. This development may mean an expansion for germanium as a semiconductor material even in such applications as L-band phased array radar, television tuners and computer switching circuits.

The single most significant feature of the germanium planar transistor—in itself a major development—is its structure. Now for the first time it is possible to manufacture the very small device structures required for outstanding performance in the 1 gigacycle to 5 gigacycle range.

In the past, the design engineer has been severely limited in the size of the active areas of the transistor because of the exponentially increasing difficulties of assembling smaller and smaller structures. This limitation has been overcome by the use of expanded contacts, which are described later.

The outstanding electrical performance in the 1 Gc to 5 Gc frequency range will be provided primarily through increased values of the maximum frequency of oscillation, much lower values of extrinsic base resistance, lower noise figure, significantly lower values of capacitance between the three terminals of the device, and improved gain-bandwidth product. In addition, higher production rates than with mesa transistors are achievable because the lead attachment problem has been lessened.

Planar technology

Development of the planar technology for silicon gave a boost to the use of silicon transistors because the planar process provides inherent surface passivation and also allows using photographic masking in the manufacturing process. Latter is particularly important for high-frequency transistors because photographic masks give higher resolution than metal masks and therefore allow making small, closely controlled junction areas. This small size and close spacing between collector and emitter results in lower junction capacitance and smaller base resistance than in mesa transistors with resulting higher frequency operation and lower noise figures.

The present standard technology for germanium has been limited to the mesa type of device shown in the illustration. A key reason for the interest in germanium is that it has higher hole and electron mobilities than silicon, and is therefore inherently capable of operating at higher frequency. Germanium also lends itself to automation more readily than does silicon.

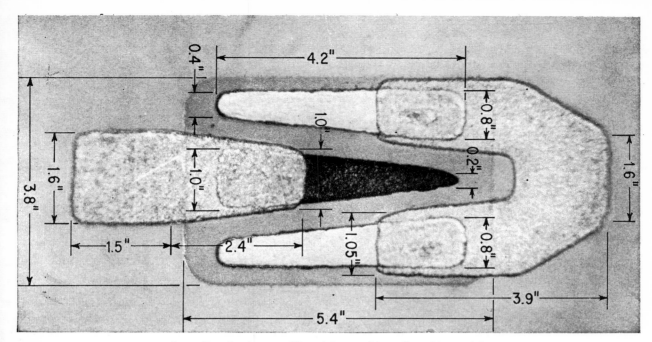

Planar germanium transistor has alloyed p-type emitter stripe and two alloyed base stripes.

Thus, a germanium planar transistor should be useful wherever high frequency (1 to 10 Gc) transistors are desired at operating temperatures below 100°C. This would include consumer electronics and computer switching, for example.

Fabrication of silicon planar transistors involves growing a passivating layer of silicon monoxide thermally on the surface of the silicon substrate and then etching through this oxide layer. This technique cannot be used with germanium because germanium monoxide has a high vapor pressure and would simply evaporate. However, a technology has been developed that combines the inherent high-frequency capabilities of the germanium mesa structure with the high mechanical resolution techniques used in manufacturing silicon planar transistors. This technology shows promise of providing devices with excellent high-frequency characteristics in the 5 to 10 Gc range, and also devices with low noise figures in the 1 Gc to 3 Gc range.

Successful mating of the two technologies meant solving several basic problems. One was to discover a material suitable for diffusion masking and insulating the contacts. This was accomplished by a technique in which an amorphous film of silicon dioxide is deposited at high temperatures on ger-

manium. This method, which requires careful control of impurities and of film deposition to avoid pinholes, can be used to produce a planar collector-base junction with extremely sharp breakdown characteristics at the knee of the reverse voltage-current curve. Typical reverse characteristics are shown in the oscilloscope trace.

Glass masks

In the production of the typical germanium mesa transistor, the geometric patterns of the alloyed emitter and the base contact are produced by vacuum evaporation of the desired materials through metal masks. The definition of the resulting patterns is naturally limited by the definition of the metal mask patterns. In addition, the minimum linear-device dimension that can be obtained is controlled by that obtainable in metal mask fabrication. The present state of the art in metal mask fabrication limits the minimum linear dimension to approximately 0.0005 inch with a definition permitting adjacent metal areas to be separated by 0.0005 inch. These values can only be obtained if the geometric pattern is limited to a relatively simple shape. By way of contrast, the glass photographic masks employed in production of silicon planar structures

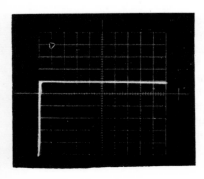

Reverse collector-base characteristics. Vertical scale is 5 v/div. horizontal is 10 microamp/div.

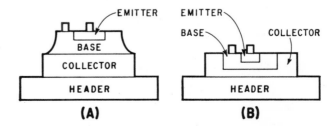

Basic structure of mesa transistor (A) and planar transistor (B).

are limited to a minimum linear dimension of approximately 0.0001 inch with a definition adequate to permit separation of distinct areas by 0.0001 inch.

Early in the development program, it was recognized that for the germanium planar transistor to reach full potential, the use of metal evaporation masks would have to be discontinued. Consequently, a technology based on glass photographic masks was developed to provide formation of the geometric metalized device areas. The decision to continue the alloyed emitter structure of the germanium mesa devices, rather than pursue the diffused emitter structure of the silicon planar devices was made because of the theoretical advantages of the alloyed emitter structure. As a result of the development activities, well-defined metalized areas with a minimum linear dimension of 0.0003 inch are being produced routinely. The processing steps that were finally developed are outlined below.

1) Slice preparation

The basic substrate material (see diagram p 65) is obtained from a gallium-doped, germanium, single-crystal of 0.002 ohm-centimeter resistivity, oriented in the 110 plane. The sliced crystal is chemically polished to provide a smooth surface. A vapor deposited epitaxial layer of 1 ohm-centimeter resistivity is grown on the lapped and polished substrate. The thickness of the slice is approximately 5 mils.

The completed epitaxial material is placed in a specially designed SiO_2 reactor where a 2,000 angstrom SiO_2 film is deposited onto the epitaxial layer by the pyrolytic decomposition of tetroethoxysilane. Through the use of photolithographic techniques, windows are etched out of the SiO_2 film in preparation for the base diffusion.

2) Base diffusion

The slice is then placed into a diffusion chamber at elevated temperatures and arsenic is allowed to diffuse for a specified length of time into the epitaxial layer through base windows etched out of the SiO_2 film in step 1. Arsenic is vaporized at an elevated temperature and is transported across the slice using a constant flow of gas consisting of a mixture of hydrogen and nitrogen.

The author

K.B. Landress is a senior project engineer in the Semiconductor Research and Development Laboratories, responsible for design of planar germanium very-high-frequency amplifier transistors and management of the germanium passivation development project. He was a member of the International Operations Department from 1958 to 1961. Before coming to TI, Landress was employed as an engineer by the firm of A. Earl Cullum, Jr., Consulting Radio Engineers.

3) Emitter stripe deposition

A continuous film of Kodak metal etch resist (KMER) is placed on the entire surface of the base-diffused side of the slice. With the use of a glass photomask, the emitter stripe design is etched into the thin film of KMER. A continuous film of emitter material is then vacuum deposited on top of the KMER film. A second KMER film in the outline of the emitter, on registry with the original emitter windows, is placed onto this film of emitter material. After etching away the exposed emitter material, the "top-hat" KMER film is removed, leaving a well defined, desired emitter pattern. The emitter stripe is alloyed at elevated temperatures.

4) Base stripe deposition

The ohmic-base contact is fabricated by the same techniques employed for fabricating the emitter. Highly conductive materials such as gold and silver are used in conjunction with the appropriate impurity to provide ohmic contact to the base. The base stripes are then alloyed at elevated temperatures to insure ohmic contact to the base.

5) Fabrication of expanded contacts

A continuous film of SiO_2 approximately 3,000 angstroms thick is deposited onto the slice (this is the second pyrolitic deposition). KMER techniques are employed to cut a window through the SiO_2 film to the emitter and base alloyed stripes.

A relatively thick, continuous film of aluminum is vacuum-deposited on top of the SiO_2 film. KMER patterns in the outline of the desired expanded contact area are placed on the thin film. After the etching of exposed aluminum film and removal of the KMER "top-hat", the expanded contact appears well defined and of the desired shape. These expanded contacts provide large metalized areas for attaching the lead wires, the size of the lead wires no longer being limited by the minimum dimension of the emitter stripe.

The remaining device assembly steps are consistent with those normally used in fabricating germanium mesa devices except that no etching or wet processing is employed.

Design

The capability of fabricating very small active regions in a device with relatively complex geometric shapes permits the design engineer to exploit more fully the capabilities of the basic germanium semiconductor material. The most obvious approaches in improving the electrical device characteristics by geometry are the reduction in emitter area and the use of the interdigitated geometry. The theoretical advantages of even the simple interdigitated geometric pattern of one emitter stripe and two base stripes in comparison to the usual mesa pattern of one emitter stripe and one base stripe has long been understood.

The difficulties associated with providing lead attachment to three rather than two distinct areas, however, have relegated this structure to small quantity, high cost, experimental laboratory devices. The use of expanded contacts to parallel the individual areas while providing a large region for lead attachment should result in the use of the interdigitated structure in future production device designs.

Prototype unit

A prototype pnp germanium planar epitaxial transistor was designed to demonstrate the capabilities of this type of structure and to evaluate further its production aspects. The designed active areas of the germanium planar device were selected to approximate those of the small germanium mesa device in high volume production. A photograph of the geometric structure is shown on p 63. As seen, the geometric design is an interdigitated structure of comparatively complex active device areas paralleled by means of expanded contacts.

This prototype germanium planar epitaxial transistor was announced by Texas Instruments Inc. at the IEEE meeting in New York last month. The transistor is designated as the TI X-3032 and characterized as a general purpose 1 Gc amplifier/oscillator. The typical high-frequency device parameters obtained in the laboratory are in the table.

The TI X-3032 was not specifically designed to meet the requirements of any particular application. To repeat, the purpose of design was to demonstrate the capabilities and applicability of the basic structure to the 100 Mc to 10 Gc frequency range. It is quite possible, however, that the specific design will find general acceptance in several areas of application. It is considered a general-purpose transistor that can be used in the same circuits as the germanium mesa transistor.

Transistor characteristics

f_t	——	750 Mc
f_{max}	——	3,000 Mc
r_b'	——	15 ohms
$r_b'C_c$	——	3.0 p sec
CTc	——	3.0 pF
Noise fig.	——	2.5 db @ 200 Mc

Sufficient time has not elapsed to permit any extensive high temperature storage or operating life test data to be accumulated. Early indications are, however, that the reliability is consistent with that expected from silicon dioxide surface passivated structures. The mechanical reliability and the moisture resistance of the planar structure have been proven superior to the mesa structure as had been anticipated. No concrete statement of the device failure rate can be made until sufficient data on all reliability tests is available, however.

The mechanical structure of the device should be greatly enhanced because the expanded contacts permit using large diameter wires for leads. Moisture resistance data shows that the planar structure is exceptionally superior to the ordinary mesa structure where no surface protection is used, such as the silicon dioxide on the planar structure.

Reverse leakage currents are comparable to those found in germanium mesa transistors. Well constructed and carefully assembled mesa devices have reverse leakage currents equal to the theoretical minimum obtainable for a given device area and material resistivity.

The typical mesa structure, however carefully constructed, normally exhibits a certain degree of rounding at the breakdown voltage knee. It has been established that this rounding is caused by surface effects of the unprotected mesa structure. The planar structure, because of its surface passivation from the silicon dioxide film, exhibits extremely sharp breakdown characteristics at the knee (see oscillogram). The breakdown voltages of the planar structure equal or exceed those obtained by the mesa structure for equal values of starting resistivity and the same primary diffusion.

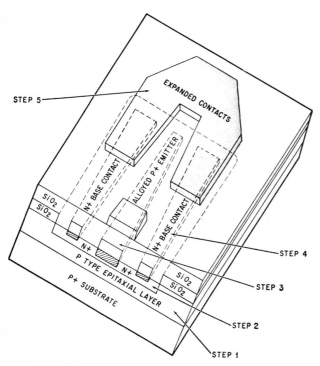

Structure of pnp germanium planar transistor.

Engineers improve on the computer's topological diagram, using a light-pen

Computer in the microcircuit design room

Engineer's mechanical aide indicates ability to
speed the layout and manufacture of integrated circuits

By Michael F. Wolff

Senior Associate Editor

In designing an integrated circuit, many an engineer has spent days positioning areas of different kinds of semiconductor materials. Now there are signs that computers can speed the process, thereby cutting costs of producing complex microcircuits.

If scientists of the Norden division of the United Aircraft Corp. are correct, the circuit designer may one day have a fast, accurate mechanical aide — one that can obey specific rules for locating all the p-n junctions and interconnections, display the resulting design on a cathode-ray tube, and follow designer's subsequent suggestions for improving the circuit.

The engineer's role may evolve toward that of a computer supervisor.

In the Air Force-sponsored program in Norwalk, Conn., which began only seven months ago, the Norden researchers successfully applied computer techniques to the two most time-consuming phases of linear microcircuit production: design analysis and mask layout.

The major part of the cost of a nonstandard microcircuit, such as a 100-component, six-watt servo amplifier, is in preparing a design capable of good integration and transferring this design to the best possible topological layout in a silicon chip. "Topological" refers here to the arrangement of p-n junctions, which define the active and passive zones of the crystal, and to the interconnections on the oxide surface, which complete the electrical network.

The missing breadboard — The flow diagram (bottom, page 131) shows how the computer is used in the Norden program.

When an engineering problem arrives, a designer prepares a preliminary basic circuit. The design is then fed into the computer, which makes a complete electrical analysis of the design and equivalent circuit, thereby eliminating the need for breadboarding. Norden has developed programs permitting a-c, d-c and transient analyses in 28 minutes that would normally take several man-months.

The next step is mask layout— deciding where the components should be placed on the crystal, how they should be connected, and what fabrication processes should be used. The goal is maximum yield and performance using a minimum area of crystal and as few interconnections and crossovers as possible.

In the past the mask designer was guided by an informal set of topological rules accumulated from previous experience. Now these rules have been expanded and organized so that design criteria, constraints and degrees of freedom can be specified in a language that can be handled by a digital computer.

For design by computer, the leads from every element are tabulated, as are the external points and the nodes connecting three or more points of the circuit. The computer searches this list for the reference cycle—the closed loop containing the largest number of circuit elements. The computer then constructs an initial topological layout by arranging the components of the reference cycle into a rectangle and distributing the various component appendages along the rectangle according to previously programed rules governing the spacing of circuit elements and interconnections.

Commands for the computer — Several hundred instructions have already been developed for the computer. Eventually there will be thousands to cover all possible manufacturing processes. Typical instructions are:

"Break the circuit at the most negative potential and tie into the isolation moat."

"Find a line or point of sym-

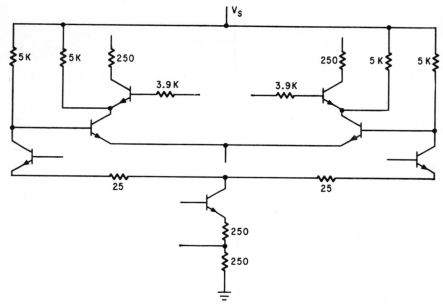

Two-strobe sense amplifier, designed with computer techniques into a single silicon chip

Two-stage differential amplifier was designed with computer techniques. Note the arrangement of circuit elements about a vertical line of symmetry

metry and place symmetrical circuit elements around it."

"Keep sensitive elements away from regions of power dissipation."

When the computer finishes its calculations, the resulting topological diagram is displayed on a cathode-ray tube. From the display, it may be evident to the mask designer that some space has been wasted or that other elements should have been added. He can reshape and reposition the elements in any way with a light pen —a small photocell. The technique is similar to that used in the Sketch-pad program at the Lincoln Laboratory of the Massachusetts Institute of Technology (Electronics, May 17, 1963, p. 16). The computer will display the consequences of the changes, as determined by the design rules built into the computer's program.

Broader role for automation — Ultimately, Norden expects automation to play a role not only in mask-cutting and manufacture, but also in complete circuit synthesis and analysis from a transfer function. Because it would depend on geometric considerations rather than on particular manufacturing processes, such a system also would have great flexibility, and ability to quickly reproduce existing circuits that might have been lost or destroyed. Such a system might only be 3 to 5 years off.

Norden scientists have used their design instructions to build a basic integrated circuit that could be either a two-strobe sense amplifier or a two-stage differential amplifier, depending on the final interconnection pattern. The differen-

tial amplifier (see photo) has an internal common-mode feedback rejection of about 100 db and a power-supply rejection of about 40 db. Depending on external resistor ratios, signal gain can be adjusted from one to 1,000. The stabilized feedback amplifier is flat to about 20 Mc and rolls off 12 db per octave.

The sense amplifier (see circuit diagram) has an over-all gain of 200. Both amplifiers use aluminum interconnections and leads, and consequently have shelf storage in excess of 350°C.

These amplifiers were built according to the flow chart accompanying this article. Circuit analysis was done by the computer, but the topological rules were applied manually. However, other amplifier mask designs have been carried out on the computer. One design cut the size of a 61-by-70-mil sense amplifier to 35 by 51 mils.

Norden believes it has shown that automated design for the manufacture of microcircuits is practical. Future work will be aimed at applying these concepts more fully. The project is conducted in Eugene Tatom's solid-state engineering section. Dr. Melvin W. Aarons, chief of the research and development branch of solid-state engineering, is project engineer. The study is sponsored by the Manufacturing Technology Division of the Materials Laboratory at Wright-Patterson Air Force Base, Ohio.

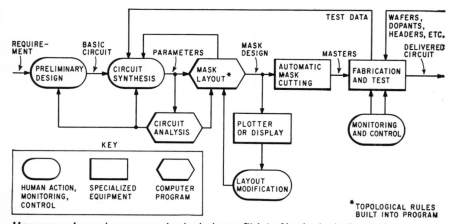

Hexagons show where computer techniques fit into Norden's design and manufacture of microcircuits

EVALUATING
Integrated-Circuit Performance

By PETER SCHINK, Fairchild Semiconductor, Mountain View, California

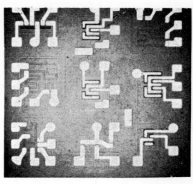

ASSORTMENT *of integrated circuits, also shown on the cover, including resistors, transistors and diodes*

Plan functional circuits with available parts, save time and money

INTEGRATED circuits, or circuits existing in a single substrate, offer possibilities of remarkable increase in reliability at circuit cost approaching that of a single transistor.

Integrated-circuit parts are now available to facilitate breadboarding a custom circuit and determine its adequacy. Offered by Fairchild Semiconductor, these functional parts provide circuit designers with a degree of freedom in obtaining a custom-designed integrated circuit without undergoing unnecessary and expensive tooling costs.

Cover photograph shows integrated parts offered initially to custom designers. Two 15K resistors are shown top right and left center. A 6K resistor is shown at bottom left; two medium geometry transistors, top center and right center; a small geometry transistor, bottom right; a large geometry transistor, right center; a common anode diode array, bottom center; and a common cathode diode array, top left. These parts represent an initial offering to fill particular needs. Future parts will include field-effect transistors, large-valued resistors, and capacitors.

The objective will be to provide further versatility in using integrated circuits, to obtain electronic functions with the ultimate in reliability at minimal cost.

TYPICAL CHARACTERISTICS

—A high speed *npn* switching transistor is available with these typical parameters: $LV_{CEO} = 10$ v, $C_{ob} = 5$ pf at $V_{CB} = 5$ v, $f_t = 400$ Mc at $I_c = 3$ ma, V_{CE} (sat) $= 0.25$ v at $IC = 3$ ma. and $\tau_s = 20$ nsec at $I_c = I_{B1} = I_{B2} = 10$ ma. The total power of a circuit incorporating this transistor should not exceed 500 mw.

The diffused *p*-type 6K resistor is available with taps at 100, 200, 500 ohms, 1K, 2K, and 6K. Resistor breakdown voltage $= 20$ v at 10 μa, and temperature coefficient from $+25$ C to $+125$ C is $+2,000$ ppm per deg C.

Three high speed silicon diodes are available in the common-anode configuration, with these typical characteristics: $BV = 30$ v at 10 ma, $V_F = 0.8$ v at 3 ma, $C_o = 4.0$ pf at $V_R = 0$, and ΔV_F (voltage match between diodes) $= 15$ mv max. at 3.0 ma.

These integrated parts, packaged in standard TO-5 cans, provide a breadboard circuit with characteristics similar to those of the final single-substrate circuit. Each device encounters a *p*-type diffusion to isolate it from the substrate, and therefore has the inherent capacitances and leakage currents of the eventual device. Geometry of diffused areas of the elements remain constant when integrated into the circuit, so parameters will not vary between breadboard and final circuit. Temperature coefficients of resistors in an integrated circuit are taken into account by providing diffused resistors.

DESIGN ADVANTAGES—Relia-

bility of integrated circuits is enhanced by the fact that both passive and active elements are in effect placed in the circuit, using proven, silicon planar transistor diffusion techniques. These elements are then connected into a circuit by evaporating interconnecting metal in a single step.

As in the case of transistors, integrated circuits are manufactured in large numbers on silicon wafers which, following diffusions and evaporative metal interconnections, are scribed into individual circuits and packaged. The cost of circuits per wafer is inversely proportional to yield, and can approach transistor costs, because manufacturing techniques are similar to those used on transistors, and the number of circuits per wafer can approach the number of transistors per wafer.

As an additional cost factor, the circuit must meet necessary blackbox conditions, regardless of the numerous device parameters required of a single transistor in the circuit. It therefore becomes meaningless to subject various transistors within the integrated circuit to individual parameter requirements which do not influence circuit operation. Circuit yields per wafer thus can be theoretically better than transistors per wafer.

DESIGN DRAWBACKS—An apparent, but possibly surmountable, drawback of integrated circuits is lack of flexibility in circuit configuration. Microelectronic approach doesn't adapt itself to last-minute circuit change, because of the relatively expensive and time-consuming art of making high resolution and accurately-registered masks for each diffusion step in the process. An answer to this problem is simply a thorough, exact worst-case design, using rules of design pertinent to integrated circuits.

To make a valid worst-case design, however, certain peculiarities of integrated circuits must be taken into account. To obtain electrical isolation between adjacent active devices in the substrate, an isolation diffusion is required to form compartments of n-type or collector material in the substrate. The isolation diffusion is p-type, forming a wall around and a floor under the n-type starting material. By virtue of a back-biased pn junction, isolation between collector regions is obtained. Associated with the p isolation region is the parasitic junction capacitance and leakage current associated with a junction area of this size.

Diffused resistors are normally made during the p-type base diffusion of the transistors, and they have temperature coefficients of approximately $+2,000$ ppm/deg. C. Since a diffused resistor uses the bulk resistivity of a p region floating on n material, a distributed capacitance is associated with the resistor in an amount determined by the voltage gradient along the resistor.

These factors discourage worst-case design, unless they may be taken into account with a bread-board that accurately simulates operation as it would be in the final integrated circuit. It is obvious that a valid simulation of the leakages, temperature coefficients and capacitances would be difficult when using standard individual components.

USE OF KIT—This is the way the integrated parts enable manufacture of a custom integrated circuit:

Designer is provided with integrated parts, data sheets, circuit boards, and an application handbook.

Designer develops his circuits, using the data sheets and breadboards, designates parts of the circuits he wants integrated. Breadboard is returned to the maker, accompanied with black box parameters.

The maker lays out the masks necessary to make the circuit, and constructs test equipment to insure circuit performance within specifications. These are the expensive steps in the process which will be minimized by this approach.

Circuits are then diffused, packaged, and tested to specification as they come off the production line. Some of the design rules that have to be followed in using the integrated units are described below:

A point-count system is used to determine area consumption of the final circuit. Each device is assigned a point-count value, and the total for the circuit should not exceed a prescribed figure. This corelates with the maximum possible amount of circuitry permitted per chip, before yield becomes markedly affected.

The isolation diffusion region should always be committed in the circuit. This reduces undesirable collector-to-collector capacitive coupling effects, and facilitates layout of the evaporative metal interconnections over the silicon dioxide on the top surface of the substrate.

Resistors designed into the circuit may be expected to vary ± 20 percent from the desired absolute value, but if absolute values can be discarded as a criterion, like resistors in the same substrate will be matched within ± 1 percent.

New Field Effect Device May Aid Integrated Circuit Design

High-field triode has single junction, output resistance exceeds 1 megohm

By **MICHAEL F. WOLFF**
Senior Associate Editor

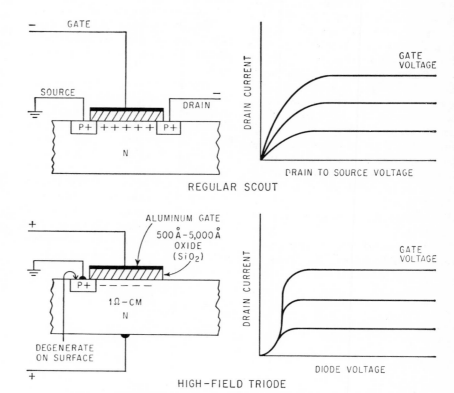

COMPARISON OF regular Westinghouse surface-controlled oxide unipolar transistor (SCOUT) and high-field triode

HIGH-FIELD TRIODE reported at the IEEE Electron Devices Meeting (p 10, Nov. 8) may add a new degree of flexibility to integrated circuit design. The experimental device is a planar silicon triode that resembles the metal-oxide-semiconductor (MOS) transistor yet differs in several respects: It has only one junction, it operates on positive gate voltage, and pinch-off doesn't obey the ordinary field-effect device relationships.

This was described by H. C. Nathanson, J. R. Szedon and N. A. Jordan, of Westinghouse Research Labs, Pittsburgh.

The high-field triode and the regular surface-controlled oxide unipolar transistor (a name Westinghouse Electric prefers for MOS transistors) are shown in the illustration. In operation, the p^+n junction of the high-field triode is reverse biased and an electric field of the order of 10^6 volts per cm is applied to the gate. The gate voltage, which is positive with respect to ground, serves to pull electrostatically large numbers of electrons to the surface of the n region. The resulting current flow is tentatively believed due to tunneling through the raised barrier at the p^+n junction. This differs from the SCOUT, where the junction barrier is lowered and holes are drawn to the surface.

Several factors point toward internal field emission, or tunneling, as the mechanism of current flow: 1) gate control is not observed if the p-region is nondegenerate, 2) fields in the oxide necessary to initiate current in the diode exceed 10^6 volts per cm, 3) the current is essentially temperature-insensitive, exhibiting a slight negative temperature coefficient, and 4) an exponential rise of diode current with oxide voltage is observed.

Characteristic — When potentials of a few volts are applied across the junction, a V-I characteristic similar to that of a reverse-biased tunnel diode is observed. At higher voltages the diode current saturates much more sharply than in the SCOUT, yielding a pentode-like characteristic. This apparent "pinch-off" is not well understood at present. For a periphery of 10 mils, typical output resistances exceed 10 megohms, open-circuit voltage gains exceed 200 and g_m's are 80-100 μmhos. Larger devices have been made with g_m of 5,000 μmhos and voltage gains greater than 300.

Since gate current is negligible (less than 10^{-12} ampere), the high field triode may be promising for integrated nanowatt logic circuits.

As indicated in the illustration, changes in gate voltages in the SCOUT produce equivalent changes in the pinch-off voltage. In the high-field triode, however, changes in gate voltages are reflected only slightly in pinch-off voltage changes. Because of this, more of the device characteristic is available for linear amplifier design and it may allow using lower-voltage power supplies.

Present understanding of the operating mechanism indicates the active area of the high-field triode is small, probably of the order of a depletion width of the diode, and typically ½ micron or less. Thus, low input capacitances should be possible. At present non-optimized geometries have yielded rise times of about 100 nsec.

Because the high-field triode is a single-junction triode while the regular SCOUT requires both a source and drain junction, simpler integration of semiconductor blocks may be possible. Also, the gate area can theoretically be made small since there is no source-to-drain distance to control.

While the device is still experimental, fabrication involves the same steps as in ordinary planar transistor production and high yields have been observed. Although gate voltages are as high as 60 v, a new fabrication technique is being developed that allows operating at less than 14 v. There are still reproducibility problems associated with this technique, however.

Squeeze in more components by adding a micro amplifier

Designers of military equipment usually cite reduced size and weight and increased reliability as their reasons for going to microelectronics. But designers of consumer items may find microcircuits advantageous for other reasons.

Bill Greenbaum, director of hearing aid engineering at Zenith, designed a Texas Instruments monolithic silicon microcircuit into his latest eyeglass hearing aid to permit adding extra features to the product. For the first time it became possible to build a magnetic pick-up coil into a small-size hearing aid. The coil couples the hearing aid's input directly to the receiving coil of the telephone handset and thus bypasses both the hearing-aid microphone and telephone earphone to achieve less noisy reception. There is also a special telephone switch that has both spring-return and lock modes of operation with a tap return in the lock mode. These features could be added because microminiaturization cut the size of the printed-circuit board in half.

The new amplifier delivers 75 decibels of power gain (transducers account for the 22-db loss). Distortion from 300 to 5,000 cps is less than two percent. This is as good or better than the performance of an equivalent amplifier using discrete components. The integrated amplifier is a triple-diffused, four-layer module that measures only 0.065 by 0.150 by 0.007 inch and occupies only $\frac{1}{16}$ of the volume of its flat pack.

The first stage is an npn common-emitter amplifier with an unbypassed emitter resistor that contributes negative feedback.

The second stage is an npn common-emitter with a grounded emitter. It is directly coupled to the first stage. The top of the volume-control potentiometer is connected to the second-stage collector while the tap on the voltage-control potentiometer feeds the base of the third stage. The third stage is a common-emitter npn transistor. Its emitter resistor is unbypassed and is shared with the fifth stage.

The third, fourth and fifth stages replace a single output stage in the discrete-component amplifier and eliminate the problem of the tight electrical tolerances on this part. The sixth transistor stabilizes the fifth stage against increased current drain when temperature rises.

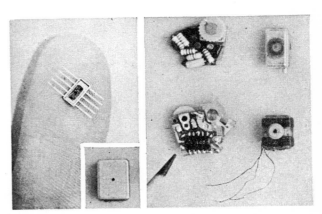

Monolithic amplifier, old circuit and earphone (top); microphone, new circuit and telephone coil (bottom)

Chapter 8

ACTIVE THIN-FILM DEVICES

THE FUTURE OF THIN-FILM ACTIVE DEVICES

Survey of potential applications of thin-film field-effect devices as amplifiers, varistors and current limiters

By CHARLES FELDMAN, Melpar, Inc., Falls Church, Va.

FREQUENCY MODULATED oscillator, slightly less than an inch wide—Fig. 1

AT PRESENT, the principal value of thin-film electronics appears to lie where environment conditions preclude the use of conventional electronics. Recent radiation tests have indicated that thin-film active devices, as well as thin-film passive devices, offer considerably more resistance to gamma rays than conventional components.[1] There is little question that thin-film devices, which are composed of polycrystalline material and operate on majority-charge-carrier concepts, will be generally more radiation resistant than conventional single-crystal devices. It is becoming increasingly clear, however, that present thin-film devices represent merely a beginning of thin-film electronic technology.[2] Under study at various laboratories throughout the world are numerous types of physical effects, many of which will lead to practical film devices in the ensuing years. Some of these possible devices are listed in the table, which is by no means complete, but illustrates the large variety of materials and effects under various stages of development. The physical effects leading to the listed devices, of course, already exist. It is only a matter of time before all or most of the devices in the list are developed into useful devices.

The transformation of the effects and materials under study into practical components must, however, be considered only a prelude to the thin-film electronics of the future. Materials listed in the table will be combined in various sophisticated geometries to produce complete electronic functions. The ability to form complete electronic functions through geometry may be considered as the key to advanced electronics. The use of this key in two thin-film devices, a field-effect transistor and a varistor, will be discussed.

Field-Effect Devices — Field effect, or the variation of current in a material by the application of a transverse electric field, may be used as a variable resistor, a variable capacitor or a purely amplifying device depending on the configuration of the layers. An excellent example of the use of a field-effect as a variable resistor is shown by the application of distributed parameter concepts in an f-m oscillator. The circuit was designed to use a commercial transistor as the amplifying device. The essential element in this circuit consisted of successive layers of germanium, silicon monoxide and aluminum forming a distributed capacitor. The germanium plate was shaped, in the plane of the substrate, in a logarithmic taper to achieve an impedance match to the amplifying transistor. The resistance of this germanium film could be modulated by an electric field applied between it and the top aluminum plate. Other semiconducting materials, such as CdS and CdSe,

AUTHOR'S PREDICTION

Systems containing the film device concepts discussed here will probably be in operation within three to five years. This in itself is remarkable, considering that a few years ago it was believed impossible to form useful thin-film active devices. This viewpoint has gradually changed through the efforts of numerous people in various laboratories. Many effects suitable for film devices are being explored. Effects such as tunneling and hot-electron emission hold promise, as well as other phenomena listed in the table. It thus appears that thin-film electronics will soon outgrow the laboratory and take its place in the electronics industry

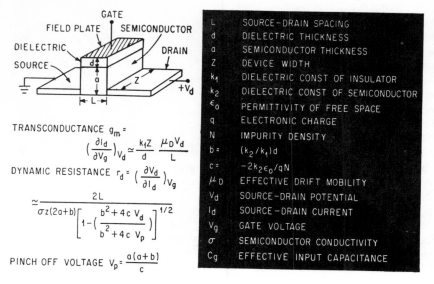

TRANSCONDUCTANCE $g_m = \left(\dfrac{\partial I_d}{\partial V_g}\right)_{V_d} \simeq \dfrac{k_1 Z}{d} \dfrac{\mu_D V_d}{L}$

DYNAMIC RESISTANCE $r_d = \left(\dfrac{\partial V_d}{\partial I_d}\right)_{V_g}$

$\simeq \dfrac{2L}{\sigma z(2a+b)\left[1-\left(\dfrac{b^2+4c\,V_d}{b^2+4c\,V_p}\right)\right]^{1/2}}$

PINCH OFF VOLTAGE $V_p = \dfrac{a(a+b)}{c}$

AMPLIFICATION FACTOR $\mu = \left(\dfrac{\partial V_d}{\partial V_g}\right)_{I_d} = g_m r_d$

GAIN BANDWIDTH PRODUCT $GBW = \dfrac{g_m}{2\pi C_g}$

L	SOURCE-DRAIN SPACING
d	DIELECTRIC THICKNESS
a	SEMICONDUCTOR THICKNESS
Z	DEVICE WIDTH
k_1	DIELECTRIC CONST OF INSULATOR
k_2	DIELECTRIC CONST OF SEMICONDUCTOR
ϵ_0	PERMITTIVITY OF FREE SPACE
q	ELECTRONIC CHARGE
N	IMPURITY DENSITY
b =	$(k_2/k_1)d$
c =	$-2k_2\epsilon_0/qN$
μ_D	EFFECTIVE DRIFT MOBILITY
V_d	SOURCE-DRAIN POTENTIAL
I_d	SOURCE-DRAIN CURRENT
V_g	GATE VOLTAGE
σ	SEMICONDUCTOR CONDUCTIVITY
C_g	EFFECTIVE INPUT CAPACITANCE

DEFINITIONS of thin-film transistor parameters—Fig. 2

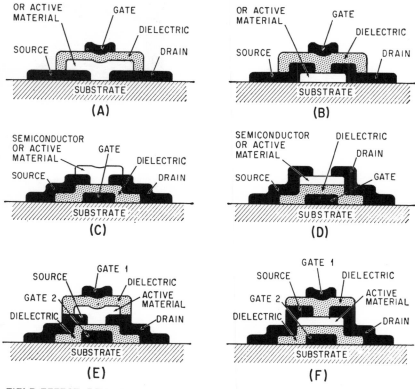

(A) (B) (C) (D) (E) (F)

FIELD-EFFECT DEVICE structures: simplest structure for automatic deposition (A), most frequently used at Melpar; structure (B) is used when semiconductor layer is to be treated prior to device completion; (C), reverse deposition order of (A) with exception of source-drain electrodes, used as first step of structure (E); (D), exact reverse deposition order of (A), no particular advantage except when forming double gates as in (F); (E and F), same as structures (C) and (D) respectively, with addition of dielectric and second gate. The second gate increases the overall gain of the device, but is more difficult to fabricate—Fig. 3

may also be used in place of this germanium film. This circuit (Fig. 1) has been described in detail elsewhere.[3] The use of active film layers combined with distributed parameter networks will reduce the number of individual circuit components, thus resulting in greater circuit reliability.

The influence of geometry on an amplifying field-effect element is shown in Fig. 2, and other variations of the device structure in Fig. 3. An enlarged photograph of the front and back view of an array with 81 devices per square inch is shown in Fig. 4. Note that the gate electrodes (small circles) as well as the source and drain electrodes may be connected by a straight line. Figure 2 shows how electrical parameters such as transconductance, dynamic resistance and gain-bandwidth are related to sample geometry. The behavior of input capacitance and resistance on the thickness of the dielectric layer is shown in Fig. 5A and 5B. The frequency response of the device is determined through the gain-bandwith product. The ratio of channel spacing to charge carrier mobility (L/μ), which determines the transit time of the carriers, in addition to the total capacitance of the sample, limit the frequency response. It is believed that, with the presently attainable film mobilities and channel spaces, frequencies of over 100 Mc can be achieved.

Performance—As shown in Fig. 2, transconductance (g_m) is directly proportional to the width of the source-drain electrodes (Z) and inversely proportional to the channel spacing (L). The electron mobility (μ_0), which appears in the expression for g_m, is also dependent on the thickness of the semiconductor layer. Thus, any desired transconductance can be achieved with proper geometry and available space. Recently, tests have been made in this laboratory in which five similar devices were connected together simulating a width, Z, five times larger. The resulting characteristics are shown in Fig. 5C. The individual units had nearly identical characteristics. Transconductance values of each sample was in the vicinity of 1,500 μmhos, and the parallel arrangement, yielded a transconductance of 8,000 μmhos. Similar high transconductance values were also obtained by forming a single unit with a source-drain width of 500 mm, five times the single units described above, and a 0.013-mm channel spacing. Values of transconductance up to 20,000 μmhos were achieved in this manner; however, appreciable hysteresis was noted in the oscilloscope displays for devices with transconductance greater than 10,000 μmhos.

The ability to choose the desired electrical properties through the choice of geometry enables one to simplify electronic circuits. One example of this simplification (Fig. 5D) illustrates the reduction in numbers of devices, components and connections in a resistance coupled amplifier, achieved by making the device width (Z) three times larger. Device characteristics can, of course, be altered in crystalline transistors as well as electron tubes; however, nowhere is the ability to alter easier than in vacuum-deposited film circuits where a change in masks during deposition will result in the required modified device parameters.

The amplifier in Fig. 5D was built, and had a flat response to 100 kc. The voltage gain was about 1,000; however, no degenerative feedback was used as is commonly done with direct-coupled amplifiers.

An attractive application of field-effect devices is their use as current limiters.[4] In a current limiter, the source and gate are connected making the device into a two-terminal one as in Fig. 5E. The effect of connecting the source and gate together is to essentially reverse-bias the device, which causes a depletion layer to be created in the semiconductor film. As the applied voltage increases, the effective conducting path decreases (depletion layer increase) until "pinch-off" is reached and the constant-current condition is attained. The ultimate value of the current depends on the device with (Z).

It is easy to imagine many other variations in geometries that illustrate the versatility of field-effect phenomena in electronic circuitry. The examples given, however, illustrate the potentials of the device and the versatility of thin-film techniques. As fabrication techniques and material knowledge improves, device parameters will improve and applications will become more numerous. Device cost, even in laboratory quantities, looks extremely promising.

Thin-Film Varistors—Varistors or nonohmic, two-terminal, solid-state devices (diodes) have been under exploration for many years.[5] Layered or film varistors, such as selenium and copper-oxide rectifiers,

were among the first solid-state components commercially available. As indicated in the table, both symmetrical and nonsymmetrical varistors are being studied in thin-film form. Research is being emphasized on phenomena such as tunnel effects, field effects and barrier effects. Thin-film varistors using each of these phenomena have been fabricated in this and other laboratories. There is no question that each effect and corresponding device will play its role in the thin-film electronics of the future.

Varistors can be tailored to meet specific electronic requirements in precisely the same manner as the field-effect devices described above. An example is easily found in a new type of symmetrical varistor being

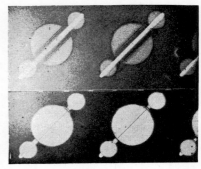

FRONT AND BACK views of array with 81 devices per sq cm—Fig. 4

explored in this laboratory. This varistor consists of deposited layers of metal, boron, and metal respectively. The metal-film electrodes are usually formed of aluminum; however, other metals such as gold

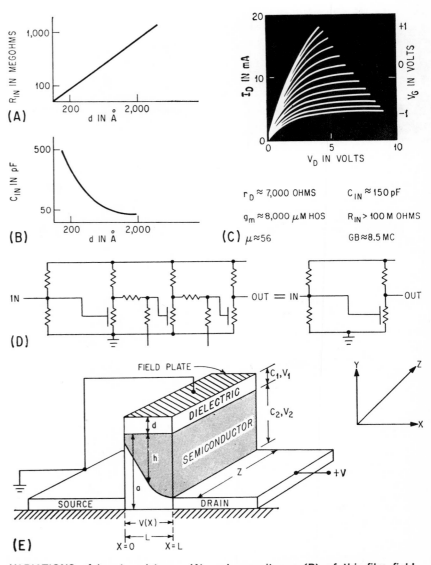

$r_D \approx$ 7,000 OHMS $C_{IN} \approx$ 150 pF

$g_m \approx$ 8,000 μMHOS $R_{IN} >$ 100 M OHMS

$\mu \approx$ 56   GB $\approx$ 8.5 MC

VARIATIONS of input resistance (A) and capacitance (B) of thin-film field-effect triodes with dielectric thickness; current-voltage characteristics (C) of five CdSe field-effect devices in parallel; resistance-coupled amplifier (D), reduced from three devices and nine resistors to one device and three resistors; self-biased field-effect device (E), a current limiter—Fig. 5

TYPE	MATERIALS UNDER STUDY	APPROX. HIGHEST STATUS	TYPE	MATERIALS UNDER STUDY	APPROX. HIGHEST STATUS
VARISTORS (Diodes)			**MEMORIES**		
Symmetrical	B, SiC, Al_2O_3, TiO_2, Si	Research	Magnetic	Fe, Ni, alloys	Commercial
Unsymmetrical	Cu_2O, Se, TiO_2, CdS	Development & Commercial	Ferroelectric	$BaTiO_3$	Research
Tunnel Diode	Si, Al_2O_3, Ge	Research	Fonic	PbCl, AgCl	Research
AMPLIFIERS (Triodes)			**PHOTODEVICES**		
Field Effect	CdS, CdSe, Ge, Si	Research & Development	Solar Cells	CdS, Si	Commercial
Hot Electron	Al_2O_3, TiO_2	Research	Photoconductors	Se, CdS, PbS, Ge	Commercial
Minority Carrier	Ge, Si, CdS	Research			

appear to give equal results. The boron deposition is carried out by an electron beam. The properties of a typical sample are shown in Fig. 6A and 6B. The device has characteristics similar to silicon carbide bulk varistors and may consequently be used in similar fashions.[6] The physical explanation of such non-linear current-voltage curves is, at the moment, not clear. It appears from experimental work that an extremely pure, amorphous, boron film is necessary. Considerably more research in the physics involved will be required to completely explain the nonlinear characteristics of the device. Obviously, the electrical properties of this varistor can be controlled by geometry. The area of the plates determines the total current flow, while the boron thickness controls the voltage operating point.

Distributed parameter techniques may be employed to advantage in thin-film varistors. If a resistive layer is substituted for one of the metal plates or electrodes, a three-terminal device is obtained. Such a device may be used as a clipping circuit, as in Fig. 6C to 6E. In this clipping network, the three-terminal device parameters are controlled by the thickness and area of the metal resistive layer as well as the area and thickness of the boron layer. A design engineer must thus specify, length to width ratio, ohms per square, area and device thickness to obtain "clipping" at the required voltage.

Conclusions—Circuits using thin-film active devices are currently being evaluated in the laboratory. These circuits will be fabricated on automatic deposition equipment, which uses a phonograph record changer concept for mask and substrate pallets and an electron beam source for deposition. Initial tests with this equipment have proven the feasibility of automatically depositing complete circuits on a production basis.

The author acknowledges the efforts of all the members of the Physical Electronics Laboratory. The work of Herbert Wilson and William Gutierrez on active devices and Charles Gane on device circuits is particularly appreciated. The support of the Bureau of Naval Weapons on all phases of this work is gratefully acknowledged.

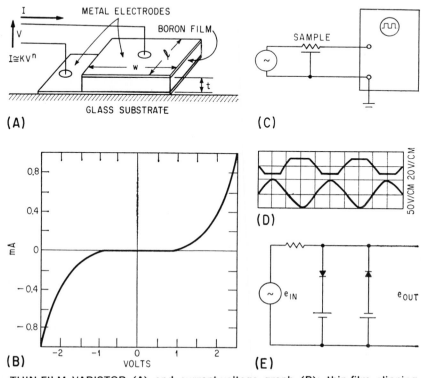

THIN-FILM VARISTOR (A) and current-voltage graph (B); thin-film clipping circuit (C), waveforms (D) and equivalent lumped-parameter clipping circuit (E)—Fig. 6

REFERENCES

(1) R. W. Marshall, Microelectronic Devices for Application in Application in Transient Nuclear Radiation Environments, Proceedings of East Coast Conference on Aerospace & Navigational Electronics, IEEE, Baltimore, Oct. 22, 1963. See also: Aviation Week and Space Technology, p 93, Aug. 17, 1963.

(2) For a state-of-the-art review see: "Integrated Circuits, Technical Review & Business Analysis," by Graduate Students of the Harvard Business School. Integrated Circuits Associates, P. O. Box 131, Cambridge, Mass., 1963.

(3) H. E. Culver and C. E. Gane, *Proc IEEE*, **51**, p 1,034, 1963. See also: ELECTRONICS, p 24, Oct. 12, 1962.

(4) W. A. Gutierrez, H. L. Wilson, "An Analysis of the CdSe Thin-Film Triode as a Current Limiter," to be published.

(5) F. R. Stansel, "The Characteristics and Some Applications of Varistors," *Proc IRE*, **39**, p 342, 1951.

(6) See for example, L. D. Kovack and W. Comley, *IRE Trans. on Electronic Computers*, EC-9, p 496, Dec. 1960.

POLYMERIZA-TION *of silicon oil, used as an insulator for grid of hot-electron triode, is observed by author Tantraporn*

HOW GOOD ARE
THIN-FILM TRIODES?

Impact of active thin-film devices can be gaged from current progress. Comparisons are made of performance capabilities and of problems in fabrication and use

By W. TANTRAPORN
Electronics Laboratory, General Electric Company, Syracuse, New York

THIN-FILM TRIODES may ultimately provide a variety of performance characteristics for use in microminiature electronic circuits. For example, the space-charge-limited type should provide the highest operating frequencies and be the least noisy of these devices. Comparable performance can be expected from field-effect triodes in thin-film form, and they should be the easiest to fabricate and the most versatile. Although the hot-electron triode will be limited to operation at lower frequencies and will probably be the most temperature-dependent, it is expected to be better able to withstand radiation.

Much theoretical and experimental work with new triodes has been reported during the past two years.[1-8] Many of these triodes contain semiconductor single crystals and are not amenable to present thin-film techniques. If those triodes that can be fabricated in thin-film form are logically classified, their expected performance capabilities can be compared.

Basically, a thin-film triode consists of three electrode terminals that are separated from each other by semi-insulating materials. Insulation requirements are dependent on the operating mechanisms. The mechanism by which the control electrode influences current between the other two electrodes can be used to classify thin-film triodes. On this basis, thin-film triodes can be placed in any of three classes: the space-charge-limited or analog triode and the hot-electron triode and field-effect triodes.

SCL TRIODE—A field must be established in the space-charge-limited triode between two electrodes in such a way that space-charge neutrality does not hold. This condition is possible in a wide band-gap insulator with the emitter electrode forming a low contact barrier against the insulator. Such a space charge in the solid is thus similar to the space charge in the vacuum tube except for the different nature of the mobilities.

If a metallic line grid is then inserted between the two electrodes to form a blocking contact with the insulator, the grid will function similarly to the grid in a vacuum tube. Since the spacing of the electrodes needed to achieve the space-charge condition is in the micron range, thin-film techniques can be used to fabricate the device. Grid fabrication is difficult, however, since the grid must be in the form of thin lines spaced about 1 micron apart within the insulator film and forming blocking contacts against the insulator.

A single-crystal type space-charge-limited triode[2] is shown in Fig. 1A. A space-charge-limited triode with single edge grid was demonstrated as early as 1959.[1] A present-day thin-film adaptation of the triode is shown in Fig. 1B with insulating layers replacing the blocking contacts. A blocking contact is difficult to achieve between a thin line and the semi-insulator, which is CdS.

Theoretically, the triode characteristic is expected to be similar to that shown in Fig. 1C. However, the parameters used are optimistic even for the single crystal CdS. The more critical parameters are the mobility of 500 cm² per volt-second and the trap density of less than $10^{15}/$cm³, which cannot be obtained in the polycrystalline state. However, the space-charge condition can be established at small mobility and large trap density by increasing the electric field. Thus it should also be obtainable by decreasing the distance between the electrodes. Space-charge-limited current has been observed in some carefully prepared CdS thin films a few microns thick.

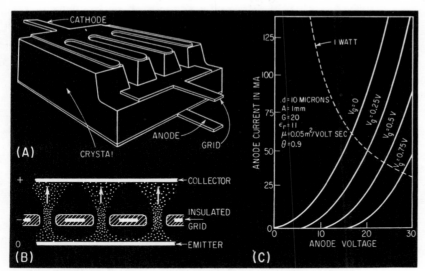

SINGLE-CRYSTAL *type space-charge-limited triode (A) has been adapted to thin-film form (B). Triode characteristics (C) have been predicted theoretically—Fig. 1*

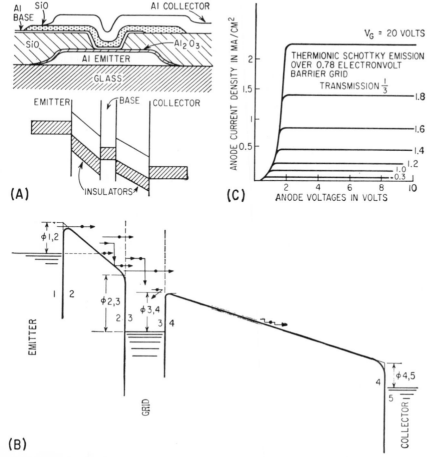

HOT-ELECTRON *triode (A) is shown as originally conceived. Energy diagram (B) is for hot-electron triode for which theoretical characteristics (C) are expected—Fig. 2*

SCL PERFORMANCE—Although the space-charge effect cannot be easily calculated, it is regarded as beneficial in reducing noise within the device compared with other devices operating at the same temperature.[9] Since it is a majority-carrier device, temperature dependence should be small.[10]

Voltage gain in a thin-film SCL triode will probably be about 10. Current gain should be large because of the small grid current. Power gain of about 10^6 is not unlikely, although actual power level may be small if trap density of the material (CdS) is large. For high density of shallow traps, however, the SCL triode is expected to have better frequency characteristics. Triode performance is limited by trapping relaxation time at lower frequencies but becomes better at higher frequencies as the signal modulates only the untrapped charges. Finally, frequency is limited by transition time. Gain-bandwidth product is thus given by the reciprocal of transition time and is about 10^9 cps if anode voltage is 100 volts, spacing is 5 microns and mobility is 3 cm^2 per volt-second.

HOT ELECTRON TRIODE—Considerable interest was first aroused by the hot-electron triode, followed by confusion and finally disappointment. The device as originally proposed[3] is shown in Fig. 2A. It was first assumed that electrons left the emitter and entered the grid by a quantum tunneling mechanism.

Another hot-electron triode was reported[4] that was assumed to work on the same emission mechanism but with the collector portion replaced by a germanium single crystal and an ohmic electrode. It was later pointed out[6] that current emission was more likely the result of the Schottky thermionic process than of quantum tunneling. Finally it was proved that operation of the triode must depend on another mechanism that is facilitated by the presence of pinholes. This mechanism is now being investigated by the originators of the triode, which is now called the metal interface amplifier. This triode, which is not a hot-electron triode but a field-effect triode, does not fit into the classifications established in this article. It uses a semiconductor single crystal and is not a thin-film device as it is here defined.

An energy diagram of the hot-electron triode is shown in Fig. 2B, which also shows relevant processes. Best operation of this device is achieved under the following conditions: For high emission and to reduce temperature dependence, $\phi_{1,2}$ should be approximately equal to zero. For hot electron transfer through the grid layer, $\phi_{2,3}$ should be about 1 electron volt and should be greater than $\phi_{3,4}$. Thickness of layer 3 should be about 100 angstroms (continuous film). Finally, $\phi_{3,4}$ should be greater than $\phi_{4,5}$,

which should be approximately zero for best collector efficiency.

Experimental evidence was recently reported[7] of hot-electron transfer across a thin metal film. Unfortunately, a semiconductor (germanium) collector was used in these experiments, although the same function could be accomplished in principle with a thin insulator layer with a strong bias. The state of the art of the hot-electron triode is thus represented by hot-electron transfer into the semiconductor crystal, and the problem in the future will be to fabri-

STATE OF THE ART IN THIN-FILM TRIODES—TABLE I

Triodes	Field Effect	Space-Charge Limited	Hot Electron
Structures	Semiconductor film of micron thickness. Electrodes on semiconductor surfaces	Semiconductor film of micron thickness between anode and cathode. Fine-line grid embedded in space between	Consecutive layers of emitter metal, emitter insulator, grid metal, collector insulator, collector metal. First two, last two or both may be replaced by semiconductor and ohmic contact
Feasibility	Proven experimentally	Predicted theoretically with preliminary experimental support	Predicted theoretically with experimental proofs for some triode parts
Achievement Dates	1961	1962–63	Late 1963
Anticipated Problems	Optimizing dimensions, developmental improvements	Isolated fine-line grid with spacings about 1 micron	Electron transfer across grid layer difficult in complete structure

EXPECTED THIN-FILM TRIODE PERFORMANCE—TABLE II

Triode	Field Effect	Space-Charge Limited	Hot Electron
Mode of Operation	Voltage controlled, best with positive grid bias. Input resistance 10^6 ohms	Voltage controlled, best with negative grid bias. Input resistance 10^6 ohms	Current controlled, positive grid bias required. Input resistance 1–100 ohms
Frequency Limit	About 10^8 cps (limited by transition time)	10^8–10^9 cps (optimized capacitance versus transition time)	10^6–10^7 cps (limited by input shunt capacitance)
Main Features	Ease of fabrication, high gain-bandwidth product, versatility (− or + gate)	High gain-bandwidth product, temperature insensitivity, low noise	High tolerance to radiation
Limitations	Reproducibility difficult because of critically small spacings	Grid structure fabrication difficult	Operation limited to low frequencies, temperature dependent, noisy (noise figure about 15 db)

cate a thin-film structure that has and can maintain the barrier heights prescribed.

CHARACTERISTICS

Operation of hot-electron triodes having insulator films of 20 to 1,000 angstroms will necessarily be near the

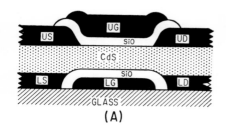

(A)

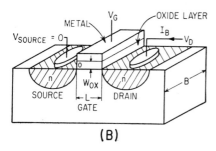

(B)

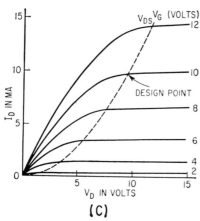

(C)

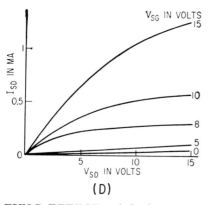

(D)

FIELD-EFFECT *triode has general configuration at (A). Charge redistribution process was assumed for suggested triode (B) with predicted performance (C), which is similar to results (D) at this laboratory—Fig. 3*

breakdown condition and will have to be current-controlled. Current gain is less than unity because of absorption of the hot electrons by the grid layer. The power gain that is possible is therefore the result of voltage gain, which is not expected to be large. Power gain of about 100 is considered high if transfer of hot electrons is about 10^{-1}. Theoretical characteristics for likely parameters are shown in Fig. 2C.

Because of the extreme nonlinearity in the current-voltage relationship of the emitter-grid section, input resistance at the operating point will probably be about 100 ohms or an order of magnitude either way and will be shunted by the input capacitance. For an alumina film 20 angstroms thick, capacitance is about 10^{-8} farad per mm^2. The input section thus limits operation to an upper frequency limit of about 10^6 to 10^7 cps. Although frequency capabilities are lower in the hot-electron triode, this limitation is compensated by its greater resistance to radiation. The thin film becomes essentially a massless absorber of radiation. Tests indicated that thin films are not affected by radiation corresponding to the stronger Van Allen belt.

Temperature dependence of the hot-electron triode will be dominated by emission $e \exp (-\phi_{1,2}/ kT)$. Noise figure is expected to be high, represented by a hot-electron equivalent temperature about 40 times room temperature. These disadvantages of the hot-electron triode contrast with the SCL triode.

FIELD-EFFECT TRIODE

The only thin-film triode in the three classes that is presently operational is the field-effect triode.[8] In this device, the control electrode affects the number of free carriers in the space between the other two electrodes. The predominant mechanism operating in this type triode is not presently clear. The effect may be on emission efficiency, the relocation of free charges from an irrelevant to the relevant region or the freeing of trapped charges in the semi-insulator thin film. The mechanism is now being studied in experiments at this laboratory with the aim of controlling or improving it.

The general configuration of the

field-effect triode is shown in Fig. 3A. The charge-redistribution process was assumed for one triode having the suggested configuration shown in Fig. 3B and the predicted performance shown in Fig. 3C. In the Weimer triode, the gate electrode was on the opposite surface from the source and drain electrode.

The results of one phase of the work at this laboratory is shown in Fig. 3D, which indicates the close similarity to the reported results of Weimer and the predicted curve of Ihantola. The results also indicate a trap-emptying mechanism.

Without a definite model, the limits of field-effect triode performance cannot be predicted. However, anticipated performance capabilities based on the reported experimental results should be comparable to those of the SCL triode.

Fabrication is relatively simple. However, producing identical samples may be difficult because of the critically small spacings (microns).

An attractive feature of the field-effect triode is its flexibility. It lends itself to various combinations of electrode positions, dimensions, electrode materials and large ranges of current and voltage, and various electrical configurations.

The state of the art in thin-film triodes is summarized in Table I. Expected performance is provided in Table II.

REFERENCES

(1) W. Ruppel and R. W. Smith, A CdS Analog Diode and Triode, *RCA Rev,* 20, p 702, Dec. 1959.
(2) G. T. Wright, A Proposed Space Charge Limited Dielectric Triode, *J Brit IRE,* 20, p 337, May 1960. See also *Solid State Electronics,* 2, p 165, March 1961.
(3) C. A. Mead, The Tunnel Emission Amplifier, *Proc IRE,* 48, p 359, March 1960. See also *J Appl Phys,* 32, p 646, 1961.
(4) J. F. Spratt, et al, Hot Electrons in Metal Films: Injection and Collection, *Phys Rev Let,* 6, p 341, 1961.
(5) J. M. Lavine and A. A. Iannini, Current Gain in the Metal Interface Amplifier, *Proc IRE,* 50, p 1688, July 1962. See also R. N. Hall, Current Gain in Metal-Insulator Triodes, *Solid State Electronics,* 3, p 320, 1961.
(6) P. R. Entage and W. Tantraporn, Schottky Emission Through Thin Insulating Films, *Phys Rev Let,* 8, p 267, 1962.
(7) D. Kahng, A Hot Electron Transistor, *Proc IRE,* 50, p 1534, June 1962. See also D. V. Geppert, A Metal-Base Transistor, *Proc IRE,* 50, p 1527, June 1962.
(8) P. K. Weimer, The TFT—A New Thin-Film Transistor, *Proc IRE,* 50, p 1462, June 1962.
(9) S. Seely, "Radio Electronics," McGraw-Hill Book Company, New York, p 146, 1956. See also ref 2.
(10) A. M. Conning, A. A. Kayali and G. T. Wright, Space-Charge-Limited Dielectric Diodes, *J Inst EE,* 5, p 595, 1959.
(11) W. Tantraporn, Non-Tunneling Hot Electron Triode, 1962 IRE-AIEE Solid State Device Research Conference (abstract in Trans PGED).
(12) H. K. J. Ihanatola, Tech Rep 1661-1, Solid State Electronics Laboratory, Stanford Univ, August 17, 1961.

Depositing active and passive thin-film elements on one chip

A thin-film transistor offers hope of removing the last obstacle to a long-time goal in microcircuitry

By Harold Borkan

RCA Laboratories, Princeton, N.J.

Thin-film transistors offer hope of clearing the last obstacle to attaining a long-time goal of microelectronics. They could allow all-thin-film circuits containing both active and passive components to be deposited on a single substrate in large volume and at low cost. One device being studied is the insulated-gate thin-film transistor (TFT).

Although the device is still in the laboratory stage of development, the life and stability observed in many of the versions have been encouraging. TFTs have operated many months after fabrication, and continuously for many weeks. They have been used experimentally in digital as well as linear circuits, and will eventually provide the circuit designer with the building blocks for integrating many different kinds of circuits.

Development is far enough along so that it is possible to relate electrical characteristics to physical parameters, describe operating characteristics and indicate circuits where the TFT may be particularly useful.

Many advantages

The TFT is well suited as the active element in a completely integrated circuit. It is small, has the desirable electrical characteristics of high input impedance, high transconductance and large gain-bandwidth product, and can be deposited upon an insulating substrate.

Thin-film resistors and capacitors can also be formed easily on the same substrate, with the important advantage that their electrical characteristics are similar to their conventional-component counterparts. In contrast, passive components that are prepared on semiconducting or other noninsulating substrates are not usually equivalent to conventional ones. Diffused resistors have lower tolerances and the capacitors have smaller values

because of present limitations in semiconductor technology.

The TFT is a field-effect transistor that consists of a metal gate electrode separated by a thin insulating film from a semiconductor layer that is usually cadmium sulfide. Construction details are given in the panel on p. 147. Current flows through a channel in the semiconductor between two electrodes called the source and drain. Conductivity of this channel is controlled by the voltage applied to the insulated gate.

TFTs can also be used as diodes by connecting the gate and drain. Besides being entirely compatible with passive components, the triodes and diodes can be interconnected into large arrays of complicated circuits, possibly through automated deposition techniques. Thus the TFT should be of great interest to circuit designers.

Operating characteristics

The TFT is characterized by a plot of drain current as a function of drain voltage with the gate voltage as a parameter. Typical drain characteristics are shown in the oscillograms on p. 149 and, like those for conventional field-effect transistors, can be seen to resemble the characteristics of a pentode vacuum tube.

Due to the presence of the insulating layer, the TFT gate may be biased either positively or negatively with respect to the source without drawing appreciable gate current. At zero gate voltage, no appreciable current flows between source and drain. But when the gate voltage is made positive, this small current is enhanced by several orders of magnitude because a conducting channel is formed in the cadmium sulfide just under the insulator. In some units this current may be less than one microampere and increase to 5- or 10-milliamperes with positive bias, limited only by the power-handling capability of the TFT.

This type is called an enhancement TFT. The oscillogram on top is that of an enhancement TFT where the gate voltage required for onset of drain current (V_o) is about one volt. Only negligible current flows for gate voltage less than $+1$ volt.

The other kind of TFT operation, called the depletion mode, is similar to the mode of operation in a conventional field-effect transistor having a p-n junction at the gate. A depletion TFT has sizable drain current flowing at zero gate bias because of an initial built-in conductivity in the semiconductor. This drain current may be depleted by applying negative gate voltage or enhanced by positive gate voltage. The characteristics on the bottom

oscillogram are of a depletion unit with V_o of about —1 volt and about 1 milliampere drain current flowing at zero gate bias.

Both types desirable

It is especially desirable to have both enhancement and depletion TFTs. Enhancement units are useful for direct-coupled applications since the quiescent d-c voltage of the output of one stage can match the quiescent voltage of the input to the succeeding stage. Depletion-type units are useful for input stages, detector stages and other applications where zero gate bias operation is desirable.

The TFTs whose oscillograms are shown are typical. Both units have transconductances (g_m) of about 4,000 micromhos and have similar character-

---

Insulated-gate TFT: how it's made, how it works

The insulated-gate thin-film transistor (TFT) is one of a variety of devices being examined by researchers looking for an active component for thin-film integrated circuits.

The devices under study fall into two categories—thin-film versions of conventional bipolar transistors, where both electrons and holes enter into the conduction process, and so-called majority-carrier devices where conduction is primarily by means of either hole or electron movement through the material.

Majority-carrier devices include the TFT and metal-base triodes. In the latter, "hot" carriers having relatively high energies are injected in either of two ways: by emission over a potential barrier that exists at a metal-semiconductor junction, or by tunneling through an extremely thin insulating layer.

All these devices are beset by fabrication problems of varying degrees, but the TFT appears to be furthest ahead in development.

Field effect

The TFT is a field-effect transistor. An early form of the field-effect transistor was described by Julius E. Lilienfeld in 1933.[1] In this device the conductivity between two electrodes was modulated by the potential applied to a third electrode—close to, yet insulated from, a semiconductor layer.

In 1952 Shockley described a "unipolar" field-effect transistor[2] in which the control electrode, the gate, consisted of a reverse-biased p-n junction in a semiconductor substrate. Many such field-effect transistors are now available commercially.

The insulated-gate field-effect transistor was first reported by P. K. Weimer,[3,4] and its characteristics were described by Borkan and Weimer.[5,6] The TFT is deposited upon an insulating substrate, usually glass, and is made entirely by evaporation techniques. Cadmium sulfide is usually used for the semiconductor substrate, but thin films of cadmium selenide have also been successful.[7-9]

S.R. Hofstein and F.P. Heiman [10] have described another insulated-gate field-effect transistor. This device is formed in the surface of a single crystal of silicon. Although some of its physical mechanisms are similar to those in the TFT, differences in the nature of the semiconductor and structure produce some differences in characteristics and their utilization.

Construction technique

Two forms of TFTs that differ in evaporation sequence and electrode materials are shown at the left. The TFT on top shows a staggered-electrode arrangement, with the source and drain on the opposite side of the semiconductor from the gate electrode. The one on the bottom is the more recent coplanar-electrode structure [11] where all three electrodes are on the same side of the semiconductor.

In both structures the semiconductor consists of an evaporated layer of a substrate such as polycrystalline n-type cadmium sulfide less than one micron thick. The two insulator materials used most frequently are silicon monoxide and calcium fluoride. The insulator is quite thin, usually less than 0.1 micron. The gate electrode is deposited through a mask and centered over the source-drain gap. Gold or aluminum is satisfactory for the gate material in either structure.

The source and drain electrodes must make low-impedance, or ohmic, contacts to the cadmium sulfide. Evaporated gold underlying the sulfide and evaporated aluminum overlying the sulfide have been found to be satisfactory for these contacts.

In the typical experimental units the electrodes are 100 mils long. The source and drain electrodes are separated by a gap of 0.4 mil or 10 microns. The thickness of the layers have been exaggerated in the figure; the gap width is about 20 times the thickness of the sulfide.

To obtain the required high-resistivity semiconductor, the sulfide is deposited on a heated substrate and later baked in air. The sulfide is deposited in one vacuum system; and all the other fine-pattern evaporation takes place in another system equipped for precision-masking.

The staggered structure requires a reregistration of the pattern with the masks after the sulfide is deposited. The coplanar structure is easier to fabricate because it does

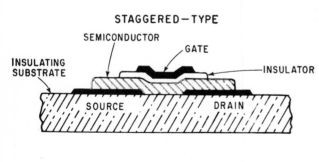

STAGGERED—TYPE

SEMICONDUCTOR
GATE
INSULATING SUBSTRATE
INSULATOR
SOURCE
DRAIN

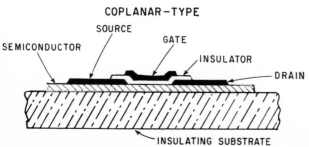

COPLANAR—TYPE

SOURCE
GATE
SEMICONDUCTOR
INSULATOR
DRAIN
INSULATING SUBSTRATE

istics except for the value of V_o. TFTs have been made with transconductances as high as 25,000 micromhos, comparable to the best vacuum tube. (Currently available field-effect transistors generally have transconductances under 3,000 micromhos.) As shown in the panel, g_m is a function of drift mobility, capacitance, source-drain spacing and drain current. Once the device is fabricated, g_m can be varied only by changing drain current through variations in gate voltage within the power handling capability of the structure.

The dynamic output resistance, r_d, of each of these units is about 40,000 ohms and the voltage amplification factor, mu, is about 160. The drain characteristics intersect at the origin with negligible voltage offset, indicating that the source and drain contacts are ohmic.

The gate current is very small in both depletion and enhancement TFTs because the gate electrode is insulated from the semiconductor. Typical d-c input resistance is high, usually greater than 10 megohms. The maximum safe drain voltage of the experimental TFTs is about 10 volts and maximum power dissipation is about 20 milliwatts.

Equivalent circuit

The small-signal equivalent circuit of a TFT is shown in (A) on p.150. The gate, drain and source electrodes are represented as the nodal points G, D and S. The impedances between gate-source and gate-drain electrodes are represented by parallel R-C circuits. The magnitude of these impedances is

not require the realignment procedure and the additional vacuum pumpdown. Another advantage of the coplanar structure is that the heat treatment needed to produce the high resistivity sulfide may be applied without damage to underlying electrodes.

Theoretical analysis

An analysis of the TFT has been made, which predicts the drain characteristic solely from the effect of the electric field produced by the potentials applied to the electrodes.[6] In this analysis it is assumed that the semiconductor layer is thin and homogeneous, and that the source and drain make ohmic contacts to the semiconductor. Only majority carriers are assumed to exist in the semiconductor and it is assumed that their mobility is constant. The drain current, I_d, as a function of gate voltage and drain voltage, V_g and V_d, relative to the source is

$$I_d = \frac{\mu\,C_g}{L^2}\left[(V_g - V_o)\,V_d - \frac{V_d^2}{2} \right] \qquad (1)$$

where μ is the drift mobility in units of cm²/volt-sec, C_g is the capacitance across the insulator layer in farads, L is the length of gap between the source and drain electrodes in centimeters and V_o is the gate voltage required for the onset of drain current.

Equation 1 is a method of calculating the drain characteristics, I_d and V_d, from the physical device parameters for positive drain voltages up to the knee of the I_d-V_d characteristic. Shockley[2] has shown that an "extrapolated pinch-off point" region occurs above the knee where the drain current is constant, independent of V_d. The normalized drain characteristics predicted by Eq. 1 are shown, where the parameter (V_g-V_o) is the effective gate bias.

As will be shown transconductance (g_m) and the TFT operating points can be obtained from these curves. The area plotted is divided into two regions by the dashed curve, 2, representing the locus of the knees of all the characteristics. In region 1, at low drain voltages well below the onset of current saturation, the output conductivity, G_d, is linear with (V_g-V_o):

$$G_d = (\mu\,C_g/L^2)\,(V_g - V_o)$$

The drain voltage at the knee, line 2, is equal to (V_g-V_o). In the high-drain-voltage, current-saturation region, 3, there is a square-law dependence of drain current on (V_g-V_o):

$$I_d = (\mu\,C_g/2L^2)\,(V_g - V_o)^2$$

A consequence of this is that the transconductance, g_m, is proportional to the square root of the drain current:

$$g_m = \frac{1}{L}\,\sqrt{2\mu\,C_g\,I_d}$$

With this square-law dependence, the TFT might become

an excellent r-f detector. Voltage V_o represents the gate voltage required for the onset of drain current. If surface states or traps (regions that can capture and immobilize electrons) are present in the semiconductor V_o is positive and TFT is of the enhancement-type. If V_o is negative, the unit has an initial source-drain conductivity at zero gate bias and is termed a depletion TFT.

A figure of merit that characterizes the high-frequency performance of a three-terminal active device is the gain-bandwidth product (GBW). For the TFT it can be shown

$$GBW \approx g_m/2\pi C_g \qquad (2)$$

The analysis predicts

$$GBW = \mu\,(V_g - V_o)/2\pi L^2 \qquad (3)$$

Equations 2 and 3 relate the electrical characteristics, transconductance and capacitance, with the physical parameters: mobility, L and V_o. The equations show that gain-bandwidth product can be increased by finding higher-mobility semiconductors and by decreasing the source-drain gap, L. However, the drain current will be limited by the power handling capability of the TFT. Present 100-mil-long TFTs are capable of dissipating approximately 10 to 20 milliwatts, giving GBW up to 25 megacycles.

Experimental measurements of TFT drain characteristics show excellent agreement with the analytically predicted parameters G_d, I_d and g_m. This is convincing evidence that the primary operating mechanism in the TFT is the conductivity modulation of the semiconductor channel by field effect.

DRAIN CHARACTERISTICS

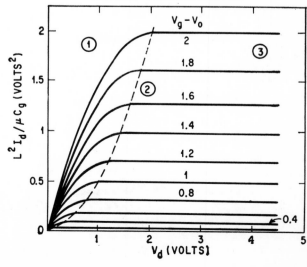

dependent upon the d-c operating point and also upon the frequency. The output circuit consists of the dynamic output resistance, r_d, driven by a current generator, $g_m e_{gs}$. Drain-source capacitance is small and can be neglected.

The impedances between the elements in a TFT have been measured by several different techniques with consistent results. The total gate capacitance, C_g, as measured between the gate and both the source and drain electrodes is shown in (B). The data were obtained from a staggered TFT (see panel) but the variations and magnitudes are typical of coplanar units.

Capacitance C_g is plotted as a function of gate-to-source voltage with drain-to-source voltage as a parameter. The transfer characteristic at the bottom of (B) shows that the unit is of the depletion type.

Approximately one milliampere of drain current

flows during the zero-bias condition. With zero drain volts applied, the capacitance increases and tends to level off as the gate voltage increases in the positive direction. This shows that the width of the space-charge region in the semiconductor adjacent to the insulator is being reduced as the gate voltage is increased. The asymptotic value of capacitance approaches the capacitance across the insulator layer.

Gate capacitance

At the higher drain voltages, it is found that the total gate capacitance increases, reaches a maximum, and then decreases with gate voltage. This has been observed in both enhancement and depletion TFTs, the peak in capacitance being shifted toward positive gate biases for the enhancement units. The capacitance data presented were taken at 100 kilocycles using a Boonton Electronics capacitance bridge. Other measurements, taken at frequencies between 2 kc and 200 kc, have shown similar results except that the measured capacitance decreases slightly at the higher frequencies. The percentage change in capacitance is quite small (roughly 20%). However, as described below, the important point about capacitance is that most of it exists in the gate-source circuit.

Three-terminal capacitance measurements have been made to determine the isolated capacitances and shunt resistances that exist between the three terminals of the TFT. The results of such measurements are shown in (C)p.150 where the black curves correspond to zero drain voltage and the colored curves are for five volts applied to the drain.

The total gate capacitance, C_g, is separated into two components: C_{gs}, the capacitance between gate and source, and C_{gd}, the capacitance between gate and drain. It can be seen that C_{gs} can be 25 picofarads, which is comparable to commercially available field-effect transistors having transconductances of about 1,000 micromhos.

With both source and drain electrodes grounded, the total gate capacitance divides about equally between the gate-source and the gate-drain regions. However, at drain voltage in the saturation region, the major portion of gate capacitance exists in the gate-source circuit, and only a relatively small amount is in the gate-drain circuit. It is fortunate that C_{gd} is relatively small since it is magnified by feedback in TFT amplifier circuits, as described later. If C_{gd} were large to begin with, it would be very difficult to use TFTs in cascaded wideband amplifiers.

The shunt resistances from the gate to the source electrode and to the drain electrode also vary with operating voltages. At zero drain voltage, the gate-drain and gate-source resistances are about equal and are not sensitive to gate voltage. But the gate-drain resistance increases and the gate-source resistance decreases as the drain voltage is increased. It has been found that these shunt resistances, measured at 100 kilocycles, are usually greater than about one megohm. In the operating range the gate

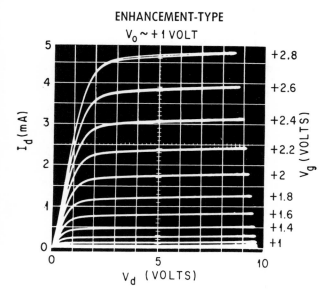

ENHANCEMENT-TYPE
$V_0 \sim +1$ VOLT

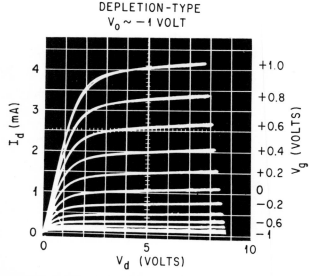

DEPLETION-TYPE
$V_0 \sim -1$ VOLT

Oscillographs of drain characteristics are shown for an enhancement TFT and a depletion TFT.

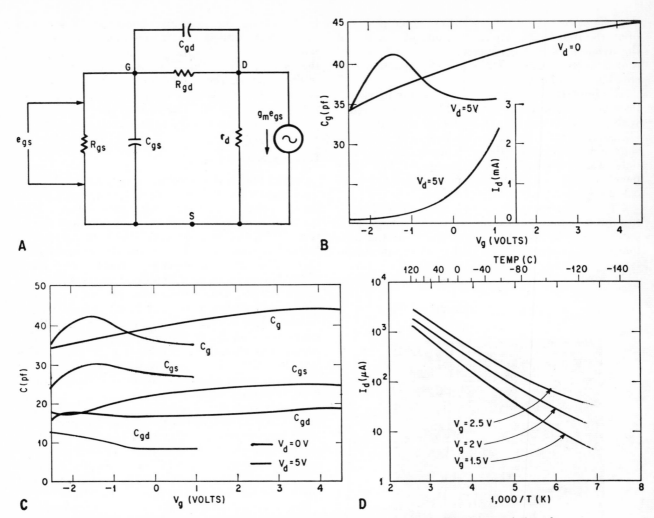

Small-signal TFT has an equivalent circuit (A). Total gate capacitances and transfer characteristics of a staggered-electrode depletion TFT (B). The total gate capacitance, C_g, is distributed between gate-source, C_{gs} and gate-drain, C_{gd}, regions (C). Temperature dependence of drain current (D).

is effectively tied to the source through a lower impedance than to the drain, even though the structure is symmetrical.

The measured capacitances and transconductances of experimental TFTs have indicated gain-bandwidth products of up to about 25 megacycles, which is sufficient for many wideband amplifier applications. Some TFTs with a gain of two have operated at 60 megacycles.

The temperature dependence of an experimental TFT is evident from (D). This shows the drain current plotted as a function of the reciprocal of the absolute temperature for a constant drain potential of four volts and various gate voltages. The drain current decreases to about 1/100 of its original value when the temperature is decreased from +120° to —130° centigrade.

TFT amplifier circuits

An understanding of the electrical characteristics of the thin-film transistor allows this use in designing both conventional and integrated circuits. The design of a single-stage linear amplifier is appropriate for beginning a discussion of circuit design.

As might be expected, a TFT amplifier can be made with either the source, gate or drain grounded. As shown in the table on p.151, the grounded-source TFT has high input impedance and is capable of voltage gain. The grounded-gate TFT has low impedance and it, too, is capable of voltage gain. The grounded-drain or source-follower amplifier has high input impedance, low output impedance and gain less than unity.

The measured performance on a typical TFT grounded-source amplifier is shown on p.152 where voltage gain of a low-pass and several band-pass amplifiers are plotted as functions of frequency. The low-pass amplifier produced a voltage gain of 8.5 from d-c up to 2.6 megacycles, and thereafter fell at six decibels per octave. The measured gain-bandwidth product is 22 megacycles.

These measurements were made using a low-impedance signal source while the output was loaded with additional capacitance simulating a subsequent TFT. Of course, in using three-terminal active devices, one may exchange gain for bandwidth if the inherent voltage amplification factor is not exceeded. For the characteristics of the three

TFT AMPLIFIER		R_{IN}	C_{IN}	VOLTAGE GAIN: A	R_{OUT}
GROUNDED SOURCE		HIGH	$C_{gs}+(1-A)C_{gd}$	$\dfrac{-\mu R_L}{r_d+R_L}$	$R_L \,\|\, r_d$
GROUNDED GATE		$\dfrac{r_d+R_L}{1+\mu}$	C_{gs}	$\dfrac{(1+\mu)R_L}{r_d+R_L}$	$R_L \,\|\, r_d$
GROUNDED DRAIN		HIGH	$C_{gd}+(1-A)C_{gs}$	$\dfrac{\mu R_L}{r_d+(1+\mu)R_L}$	$R_L \,\|\, \dfrac{r_d}{1+\mu}$

Impedance and gain characteristics are for the three amplifier connections of a TFT. Mu, g_m and r_d are the TFT amplification factor, transconductance and dynamic output resistance, respectively.

bandpass amplifiers that are shown, the output circuits were resonant at 25, 36, and 60 megacycles. At 60 megacycles the gain was 2.5 and the measured gain-bandwidth product was 17 megacycles.

A photomicrograph of an integrated all-evaporated three-stage amplifier shows the TFTs spaced two mils apart and directly coupled together[12]. The input, output, ground and drain-supply voltage connecting points, as well as the three load resistors, are shown in the photo on p. 152.

This circuit performed as a cascaded three-stage amplifier having a voltage gain of nearly 100. While this is a simple example of a TFT integrated circuit, much more sophisticated integrated circuits have since been built. For example, a completely integrated thin-film scan generator has been built (see photo) that has more than 100 TFTs in an area of 0.15 square inch[13, 14].

The author

Harold Borkan received a degree in electrical engineering from Rutgers University in 1950 and at that time joined the technical staff of RCA Laboratories at Princeton, N.J. He did graduate work at Rutgers on a part-time basis and received the MS degree in Electrical Engineering in 1954. Since 1952 he has been engaged in research on television camera tubes and associated circuits. He is more recently concerned with the measurement, analysis and utilization of developmental thin-film semiconductor devices. Mr. Borkan is a Senior Member of the Institute of Electrical and Electronics Engineers, a member of Eta Kappa Nu and the recipient of two RCA Achievement Awards.

Cascading

In the design of cascaded TFT amplifiers, the gate-drain capacitance restricts the bandwidth even though the capacitance is smaller than the gate-source capacitance. This feedback capacitance is usually about 10 picofarads, but appears to be magnified at the input of a grounded-source amplifier due to the Miller effect, in which an impedance between input and output appears as a reduced impedance at the input. The gain-bandwidth product that was described earlier is an optimum figure that is applied to TFTs unburdened by the Miller capacitance term, $(1-A)C_{gd}$ (see table). Cascaded grounded-source stages yield much poorer over-all performance than is expected from the individual gain-bandwidth products.

Some solutions

Many solutions to this Miller-effect problem are possible but most have severe limitations. The grounded-gate amplifier, for example, is capable of voltage gain but cannot be cascaded without introducing a poor impedance match that cuts the voltage gain. This situation may be improved by alternating source-follower and grounded-gate stages, a solution adequate for lumped-parameter circuits but very difficult to integrate. Another solution that suffers from the same difficulty is the cascode connection—a grounded-source amplifier driving a grounded-gate stage.

The most promising solution is to use a source-follower amplifier, direct-coupled to a grounded-source stage as shown in (A) on p. 153. The input capacitance is very low, approximately equal to C_{gd}, since degeneration reduces the effect of C_{gs}. At

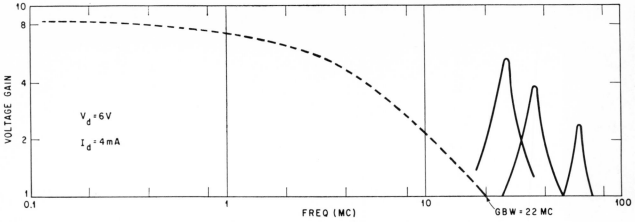

Gain vs. frequency data are for a low-pass amplifier (dashed line) and three band-pass amplifiers.

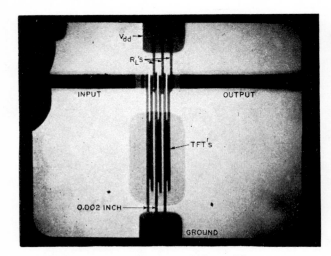

Cascaded three stage direct-coupled amplifier.

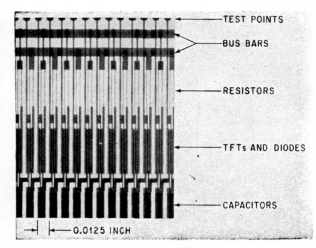

Enlarged portion of thin-film scan generator.

the output of the source follower, the large Miller capacitance of the gain stage is driven by the low output impedance of the source follower and, therefore, does not restrict the bandwidth. The output capacitance of this combination is low.

An essential feature of cascaded direct-coupled amplifiers is that the quiescent d-c voltage be the same at the output as at the input of each stage. Otherwise the d-c operating point would progress out of the useful operating range of the drain characteristics.

In the circuit illustrated, the drain supply voltage is 3V volts, with 2V volts existing across the TFT and V volts across the resistor. The TFTs required are enhancement types with bias of V volts on their gates. With this configuration the input and output are both at 2V volts. It is difficult to match input and output voltages with the arrangements mentioned earlier.

A layout for the integrated circuit of each amplifier stage is also shown in (A). The input and output electrodes are in line and the circuit may be cascaded simply by adding on to the array. Only two bus-bars, one for ground and the other for the drain supply voltage, are needed in this arrangement. The resistors can be made of evaporated Nichrome and are aligned with the length of the

TFTs to conserve space.

It is possible to fabricate this composite circuit in an area 10 mils by 100 mils, corresponding to a density of 1,000 stages per square inch. The composite electrical characteristics of this stage are much better than those of the individual TFTs. The resultant gain-bandwidth product approximates the optimum figure derived in Eq. 2 of the panel. This composite amplifier stage can also be considered for a building block in switching applications where high speed is important.

Bistable multivibrator

The simple bistable multivibrator (B) on p.153 uses direct-coupled enhancement TFTs. Only two resistors, two TFTs and the triggering circuit are needed. The graph at the right has been obtained from an actual TFT drain characteristic load line. Voltage V_1, the output voltage of TFT-1 (and also the input voltage of TFT-2), is plotted against voltage V_2, the output of TFT-2 (and also the input of TFT-1).

Since the input voltage of one TFT is the output of the other, the only possible operating points are the three intersections of these curves. The criteria for circuit stability are that the voltage gain of the TFTs be less than unity at the two outer points and greater than unity at the center. The two outer points represent the cutoff and full-on conditions, while the central point is the mid-range of the drain characteristic. These stability criteria are easily satisfied with TFTs.

Switching

The TFT is useful in switching applications, since negligible power is consumed in the off state and only moderate power (about a milliwatt) in the on state. The switching waveforms observed for a typical TFT show two 2-milliampere drain-current transitions: X-X is a transition from low to high drain current while Y-Y is the reverse, from high to low drain current. The transient of opposite polarity that is observed on the waveform represents direct feedthrough of signal via the gate-drain capacitance. These results were obtained using a pulsed source having 50 ohms impedance.

TFTs are ideally suited for switching circuits in digital computers; in fact, computer applications offer probably the greatest potential use for TFTs.

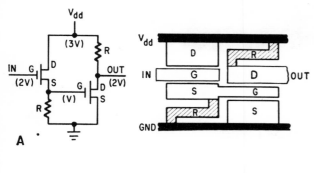

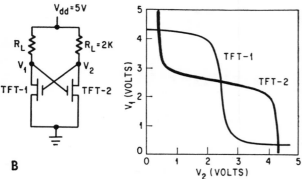

Direct-coupled composite amplifier stage consists of a source follower driving a grounded-source stage (A). The layout of the integrated pattern is at right. The possible operating points of multivibrator (B) are indicated by the intersections of the two load lines.

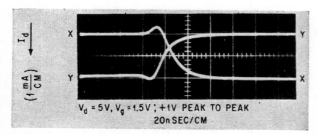

Typical drain current transitions occur in about 30 nsec.

This is because complete logic systems of AND gates, OR gates and inverter circuits can be fabricated in large arrays easily and economically. The circuit design would be the same as for conventional logic circuits—the main point to remember is that parallel logic, where all drains are connected together and all sources are connected together, is a better choice with TFTs than the series system where the drain of each TFT is connected to the source of the next. The reason is that when a TFT is conducting, its source-drain voltage drop is about one volt. In parallel logic these voltages do not add as they do with series logic.

Shift registers can be assembled by directly coupling multivibrators of the type described previously. The necessary triggering would be accomplished with conventional techniques.

The thin-film transistor can be made to function as a diode by connecting the gate and drain electrodes. The best diode characteristics occur when V_o equals zero. An example of a circuit employing diode and triode TFTs is provided by the scan generator referred to previously. This generator, which demonstrates the possibility of using TFTs in X-Y addressing circuits, has 30 clock-driven stages that transfer binary inputs in a manner similar to a shift register. Each stage consists of two TFTs two load resistors and a diode and capacitor.

The research reported in this article was sponsored by the Air Force Cambridge Research Laboratories, Office of Aerospace Research, under contract number AF19 (628)-1617 and RCA Laboratories, Princeton, N. J.

The author thanks H. Johnson, P.K. Weimer, W.S. Homa, V.L. Frantz, H.P. Lambert and R.G. Pugliesi.

References

1. J.E. Lilienfeld, "Device for Controlling Electric Current," U.S. Patent 1,900,018, March 7, 1933.
2. W. Shockley, "A Unipolar 'Field-Effect' Transistor," Proc IRE, Vol 40, p 1,365, Nov. 1952.
3. P.K. Weimer, "An Evaporated Thin Film Triode," presented at Solid State Device Research Conference, Stanford University, California, June 1961.
4. P.K. Weimer, "The TFT—A New Thin-Film Transistor," Proc IRE, Vol 50, p 1,462, June 1962.
5. H. Borkan and P.K. Weimer, "Characteristics of the Insulated-Gate Thin-Film Transistor," Northeast Electronics Research and Engineering Meeting, IRE NEREM Record, Nov. 1962.
6. H. Borkan and P.K. Weimer, "An Analysis of the Characteristics of Insulated-Gate Thin-Film Transistors," RCA Review, Vol 24, p 153, June 1963.
7. F.V. Shallcross, "Cadmium Selenide Thin-Film Transistors," Proc IEEE, Vol 51, p 851, May 1963.
8. F.V. Shallcross, "Evaluation of Cadmium Selenide Films for Use in Thin-Film Transistors," RCA Review, Vol 24, p 676, Dec. 1963.
9. H.L. Wilson and W.A. Gutierrez, "Cadmium Selenide Thin-Film Field Effect Transistors," presented at the Electrochemical Society Meeting, Pittsburgh, Pa., April 1963.
10. S.R. Hofstein and F.P. Heiman, "The Silicon Insulated-Gate Field-Effect Transistor," Proc IEEE, Vol 51, p 1,160, Sept. 1963.
11. P.K. Weimer, F.V. Shallcross, and H. Borkan, "Coplanar-Electrode Insulated-Gate Thin-Film Transistors," RCA Review, Vol 24, p 661, Dec. 1963.
12. P.K. Weimer, "Evaporated Circuits Incorporating Thin-Film Transistors," Presented at the International Solid-State Circuits Conference, Philadelphia, Pennsylvania, February 1962.
13. P.K. Weimer, H. Borkan, L. Meray-Horvath, and F.V. Shallcross, "An Integrated Thin-Film Image Scanner," presented at the International Solid State Circuits Conference, Philadelphia, Pa., Feb. 20, 1964.
14. M.F. Wolff, Thin-Film Transistors Form Scanning Generator, Electronics, Feb. 21, 1964.

SCAN-GENERATOR
using thin-film transistors
is viewed by engineer
at RCA Laboratories
(See the front cover)

By **MICHAEL F. WOLFF**
Senior Associate Editor

FORWARD STEP IN MICROCIRCUITS:

Thin-Film Transistors Form Scanning Generator

Use of TFT in experimental circuit points toward feasibility
of applying device to all-thin-film integrated circuits

ACHIEVEMENT OF an operating integrated-circuit scan generator using cadmium sulfide thin-film transistors (TFTs) was reported this week by researchers at RCA Laboratories. The development is considered an important step in the evolution of all-thin-film integrated circuits because it demonstrates the feasibility of using the TFT in them.

Announced at the IEEE International Solid State Circuits Conference by P. K. Weimer, H. Borkan, L. Meray-Horvath and F. V. Shallcross, the scan generator uses more than 100 TFTs deposited over an area of 0.15 square inch. Large-scale deposition of TFTs has hitherto been a stumbling block to their utilization in circuits.

The TFT is a field-effect transistor in which majority carriers are injected from a source electrode into a channel whose conductivity is controlled by the voltage applied to an insulated gate. The device is generally operated with the gate biased positively with respect to the source. In this mode drain current can be enhanced by several orders of magnitude without drawing appreciable gate current.

Although still in the research stage, the TFT has generally been considered to be further ahead in development than other active thin-film devices such as the experimental hot-electron tunnel triodes. Even so, this is believed to be the

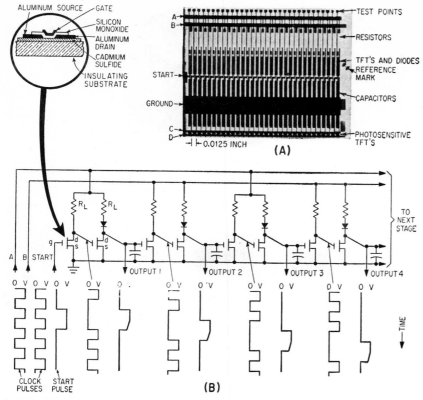

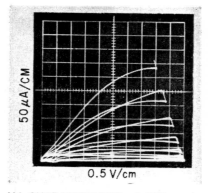

30-STAGE THIN-FILM scan generator (A) employs circuit (B)—Fig. 1

as a television picture tube.

Thin-film integrated circuits are considered a natural for such an application since both the photosensitive matrix and the scan generators could be made by evaporation, using cadmium sulfide in both. Work on a complete 30-by-30 element array is in progress.

For regular tv scanning, 4-Mc rates and approximately 500 stages are needed. This would require TFTs with higher g_m's and capacitors with smaller capacitance values than those used in the present experimental model. This is not considered to be a major problem, however, since the required g_m of about 10,000 micromhos is found in present optimum TFTs. Thus, while RCA feels it is not clear what the place is for the TFT as a single device, it does feel that for a period not less than five years off it could be very important to integrated circuitry in such areas as digital scanning of displays, and content-addressable memories.

Present Research—At the present time much work is required in processing to obtain stability and lifetimes that match those of present commercial transistors. For example, some unencapsulated TFTs deteriorate overnight while others remain stable for a year. RCA is devoting considerable effort to understanding the physical and chemical properties of the TFT that determine the sensitivity of the field effect properties to surface conditions and, hence, affect stability.

Two other aspects of RCA's thin-film program aim at increasing the utility of the TFT. One program, which has just begun, is to develop a process of laying down single-crystal silicon TFTs. This could lead to an improved TFT because of the higher carrier mobility in silicon. It would combine the processing advantages of the all-thin-film device with the improved performance of present metal-oxide-semiconductor transistors. These insulated-gate field-effect devices are constructed by diffusion into silicon and are already being used in a microcircuit ssb transceiver (ELECTRONICS, p 75, Oct. 25, 1963).

A second program is directed at perfecting the hole-conduction equivalent of the cadmium sulfide TFT. This would allow designing

first report of using so many TFTs in an integrated circuit application.

Scan Generator—The scan generator is shown in Fig. 1. Thirty stages have been constructed in integrated form, each stage consisting of 2 TFTs, 2 load resistors, and a diode and capacitor. The diodes are TFTs with the gates connected to the drains, the load resistors are nickel-chromium, and the capacitors consist of aluminum electrodes separated by silicon monoxide. The TFT gates are 1 mil wide, and 3 TFTs are deposited in an area 12 mils wide.

The generator is fabricated in essentially two steps — first polycrystalline cadmium sulfide is deposited on a glass substrate to serve as the semiconductor for the TFTs and the diodes, as well as the photosensitive elements on the image matrix. Next step is precision evaporation of capacitors, resistors and insulators through movable masks.

RCA has demonstrated it can pick up images from single lines; in the single-scan generator 30 consecutive stages have been operated at 100-kc clock rates and output pulses have been found to progress at a uniform rate (see Fig. 2).

Image Sensing Panel—It is anticipated that two such generators could be used as x-y addressing circuits for a completely solid-state image sensing panel—in fact this is the long-range goal of this Air Force sponsored program. The generators would be deposited along the periphery of a photosensitive matrix upon which the image is projected. Voltage pulses from the generator scan the matrix in an operation similar to that of a shift register, and the resulting outputs are intensity modulated signals that could be fed to any reproducing system such

V-I CHARACTERISTIC of TFT made at U. of California, Berkeley. Voltage is applied to gate in 0.2-v steps

nanowatt logic circuits with complementary pairs of TFTs. Already RCA has succeeded in making a hole-conduction TFT out of tellurium, a naturally *p*-type material. Transistor action has also been shown in organic semiconductors.

Other Work—Several other companies are investigating insulated-gate field-effect TFTs. Melpar is concentrating on cadmium selenide devices because they can be formed entirely in vacuum. These devices have shown very good stability, according to Charles Feldman, manager of the physical electronics laboratory. As of mid-January, two devices had been running continuously for approximately 2,000 hours without any changes in characteristics being observed, Feldman said. One is a kilocycle-range oscillator using one TFT, the other is a single TFT connected to a curve tracer. Both TFTs are unprotected except for the SiO coating. Aluminum rather than gold gates are used because aluminum adheres better to the SiO and is also a more stable film. Melpar plans a concentrated radiation effects study this year and is also looking for materials that can operate at 500 deg C. Work is supported by the Bureau of Naval Weapons.

Emphasis at Hughes Semiconductor division is also on the study of other materials. While the application of CdS films has yielded 2- and 3-terminal devices with good electrical characteristics, in order for the TFT to be a real asset to all-thin-film microelectronics it is important to have thin-film materials with higher mobilities and insulators with lower trap densities and greater temperature stability than SiO, according to Rainer Zuleeg, senior staff physicist. Present r and d at Hughes is aimed at obtaining mobilities greater than 200 cm²/vsec and fabricating better quality insulators by using new techniques.

Research on thin-film transistors is underway at the University of California, Berkeley, as part of an overall study of problems in microelectronic circuits. The Air Force-sponsored work has established the role of Schottky thermionic emission in the breakdown of rectifying contacts made to the CdS films, according to R. S. Muller, who is directing the research. TFTs have been made

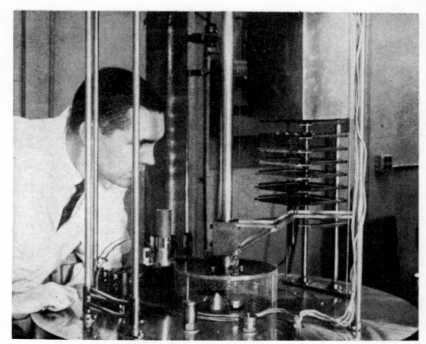

AUTOMATIC DEPOSITION equipment is used to fabricate thin-film circuits at Melpar

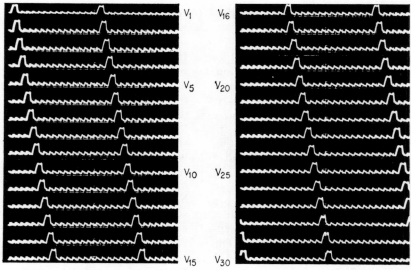

PULSE WAVEFORMS at each scan-generator output. Vertical scale is 3v/div, horizontal is 30 μsec/div; clock is 100 kc, 3 v peak-to-peak—Fig. 2

with g_m's up to 2 ma/v and source-drain voltage breakdowns of more than 10v.

Bipolar Transistors—Another approach to thin-film transistors involves growing device-quality semiconductors onto glazed ceramic substrates. It is expected that if one is able to grow an optimum minority carrier transistor in thin-film form it would be faster than the unipolar transistor. However, it might not be as easy to fabricate because more fabrication steps are required.

Sylvania is studying electron-beam vacuum deposition of silicon transistors directly onto glazed ceramic substrates (ELECTRONICS, p 14, November 1, 1963). Feasibility of the technique has been demonstrated by the deposition of simple logic circuits using both *p*- and *n*-type evaporated silicon films.

Individual transistors have been made with alpha cutoffs greater than 50 Mc. Sylvania is investigating an OR gate with 7 resistors, 5 diodes and 1 transistor. Project is headed by Egon Rasmanis.

METAL BASE TRANSISTOR
Pushes Back the Frequency Barrier

A transistor made of a metal film sandwich looks promising in amplifier and oscillator designs for microwave applications. It has better frequency characteristics, up to 100 Gc, and even interesting resistance to radiation

By **DONOVAN V. GEPPERT** and **ROBERT A. MUELLER**
Physical Electronics Laboratory, Stanford Research Institute, Menlo Park, Calif.

LIMITATIONS on high-frequency transistor performance (assuming optimum design for microwave units), include the effective transit time of minority carriers, base resistance, and collector capacitance. A useful figure of merit for a h-f transistor is the maximum frequency of oscillation, f_{max}. This is the frequency at which the gain drops to unity, and is given by $f_{max} \cong$ $1/4\pi(a_o/r'_b \, C_c \, \tau_{ec})^{\frac{1}{2}}$, where a_o is common-base current gain, r'_b is base resistance, C_c is collector capacitance, and τ_{ec} is the effective emitter-to-collector transit time. The latter is given by $\tau_{ec} = \tau_e + \tau_b + \tau_c$, where τ_e is emitter charging time given by the product of emitter capacitance and emitter resistance, τ_b is base transit time, and τ_o is collector attenuation time. There are two conflicting terms in the first equation, since if the base is made thicker to reduce base resistance (r'_b), transit time (τ_{ec}) increases. Thus, there is an optimum base thickness for best high-frequency performance.

Several proposals have been made recently for new types of transistors to overcome some of the frequency limitations of conventional p-n junction bipolar devices. Moll[1] recently made a comparison of proposed structures and has shown that best high-frequency performance should be attainable with a metal-base transistor using a Schottky emitter and collector. This device was first described by Geppert[2], and subsequently by Atalla and Kahng[3].

Metal-Base Transistor — The new device consists of a thin metal film sandwiched between two n-type semiconductors as shown in Fig. 2A. It resembles a conventional npn transistor in many respects. The energy diagram for the metal-base transistor is compared with that for a conventional-npn unit in Fig. 2B and 2C, respectively. Both cases show zero bias voltage.

The comparison between the metal-base transistor and the conventional npn device should not, however, be carried too far, since the physics of the two differ. In the

---

SOLID-STATE FREQUENCY LIMITATIONS

While the maximum operating frequency of conventional bipolar junction transistors has been steadily increasing, the rate of improvement has steadily declined. Earliest devices were limited to a frequency in kilocycles and present transistors are capable of operation near or slightly above 1 Gc.

In grown-junction units, frequency limitations can be attributed to large junction capacitance and high base resistance. With alloy-junction techniques, junction capacitance and base resistance are reduced, but high-frequency performance is degraded due to the large phase shift associated with diffusion of the minority carriers across the relatively thick and nonplanar base region. The surface-barrier transistor, diffusion techniques, MADT designs and finally the development of epitaxial devices, all represent frequency improvements in the state of the art. Moreover, dimension reductions of unit active regions and packaging advances also raise maximum operating frequency.

Many researchers feel that even with the latest advances, we have reached a point where further improvement of junction transistors will diminish, even with improved materials and continued size reductions.

In this article, the author describes a technique for developing new metal-base transistors that are now being designed for 10 Gc, and eventually may reach 100 Gc. This suggests that present-day microwave devices may soon encounter stiff competition

---

HYBRID vapor-vacuum system used in the fabrication of the metal-base transistor

npn device, electrons are injected into the base from the emitter, and some hole injection from base to emitter also takes place. The ratio of electron to hole current is made high by doping the emitter more heavily than the base, and also by using a relatively thin base region to cause a large diffusion gradient for electrons in the base region.

In the metal-base transistor, electrons are injected from the emitter into the base, and some hole injection from base to emitter also occurs. However, in the latter case, the electron current is not diffusion limited as in the npn device, but rather obeys a thermionic-emission law. Consequently, emitter injection efficiency is independent of base thickness, and depends only upon emitter doping, barrier height, and the diffusion length for holes in the emitter region. Analysis of this situation shows that high injection

efficiencies can be achieved.

In the npn device, the electrons injected from emitter to base are minority carriers that diffuse to the collector because of a diffusion gradient in that direction. (In the drift transistor, the carriers are also assisted by the built-in electric field.) A few minority-carrier electrons recombine with holes in the body of the base region prior to reaching the collector; the number of these depends upon minority-carrier lifetime, or diffusion length. Surface recombination also can contribute significantly to minority-carrier loss. The mean kinetic energy of electrons injected into the base is low, since they are only slightly above the bottom of the conduction band.

In the metal-base transistor, electrons injected from the emitter into the base are very energetic. The mean kinetic energy of these hot

electrons is relatively large, being on the order of 6 to 10 electron volts. Through collisions with the lattice and other electrons, their en-

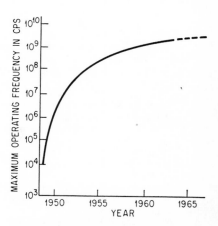

GRAPH showing the increase in transistor maximum-operating frequency vs time illustrates how the rate of improvement has been declining— Fig. 1

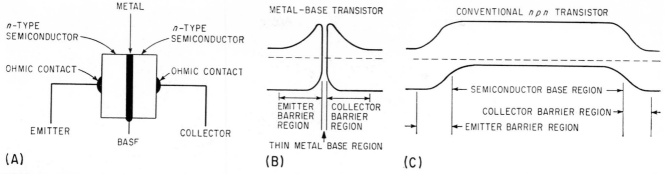

CONSTRUCTION of the metal-base transistor (A), comparison between energy diagrams of the new device (B) and a conventional **npn** structure (C)—Fig. 2

ergy is gradually decreased as they travel through the metal base. If the metal is not too thick, a large percentage arrive at the collector barrier with little or no energy loss, and fall into the collector-barrier region where they are swept into the collector-body area by the field. Electron-phonon losses are serious because they randomize the momentum of the electrons; to be collected, the hot electrons at the collector barrier must be incident almost perpendicularly.

Thus, the emitter-injection process and the base-transport mechanism are different for *npn* and metal-base transistors. In other respects, the two devices are similar.

Referring to the equations demonstrates why the Schottky-emitter metal-base transistor has good high-frequency performance. First, base transit time is negligibly small. For metal-base film thicknesses on the order of 100 angstrom units, τ_b is on the order of 10^{-14} second. Thus, τ_{ec} is reduced as compared to *npn* junction transistors (τ_e and τ_c being comparable for the metal-base and *npn* devices). Second, the base resistance of the metal-base transistor is about two orders of magnitude lower than values for optimum junction-transistor designs. Thus, f_{max} is about 10 times as high for the metal-base transistor as for a junction device, having comparable geometry and operating current density.

Noise—The noise figure is important because it is anticipated that a major application of metal-base transistors will be in the front end of microwave receivers where klystrons and travelling-wave tubes

are now used. At the present, there is little information on the subject, and further research is needed.

Other Advantages—In addition to considerably - improved frequency response, the metal-base transistor possesses other important advantages over conventional junction devices. One of these is anticipated radiation resistance. Whereas bipolar amplifiers require single-crystal material that has high crystalline perfection (particularly for the critical base region) the metal-base transistor can be fabricated from polycrystalline material, as described in the literature[4] and indicated by our own work. One approach[4] in use is directed towards an all-evaporated structure suitable for incorporation into integrated circuits, whereas our efforts are directed primarily towards high-frequency operation.

Research—Research and development have led to a metal-base transistor with several advantages over other known configurations.

Initial experimental devices used a copper base on germanium with a point-contact germanium emitter.[2] This configuration proved capable of a power gain of about 10 db, limited mainly by the high emitter resistance of the device. To overcome this, research has been directed towards a large-area emitter device. Gold was selected for the base film because the mean-free path of hot electrons in gold is higher than in any other metal tested.[5]

Gold-silicon diodes were fabricated and shown to be suitable for base-collector barriers. Emitters of

evaporated CdS were used to fabricate triode structures, but barrier and temperature considerations as well as the diffusion of gold into CdS fostered an investigation into higher-temperature fabrication techniques and more highly refractory materials.

Vapor plating of refractory metals is a standard method for depositing metal films, and since this was compatible with the epitaxial growth of silicon, it provided a reasonable approach to a metal-base transistor. Several metals were deposited on silicon with the greatest attention given to the refractory group. Of these, molybdenum looked most promising.[7,8] Work was undertaken to determine the mean free path of hot electrons in molybdenum, and because of the results, plus the compatibility of silicon and molybdenum, the silicon-molybdenum-silicon approach to the metal-base transistor was pursued.

There is essentially no diffusion of molybdenum into silicon below 800°C.[6] At higher temperatures, a compound forms that has been shown to be molybdenum-disilicide by electron diffraction.

This silicide formation limits the temperature of vapor phase reaction for the molybdenum chloride and silicon chlorides used for the base and emitter to approximately 750°C.

There may be other combinations of metals and semiconductors that have advantages over the silicon-molybdenum-silicon structure, such as silicon carbide for the emitter and possibly refractory metals other than molybdenum for the base region. For the present, however, the structure now used will continue to be optimized.

With the vapor-plated emitter approach, a selective etch is required that will etch Si but not Mo. Several etches that should fulfill this requirement are presently under investigation.

Another approach that shows promise utilizes an evaporated silicon-emitter region. The Si can be deposited only where desired by masking during the Si evaporation, thus obviating the necessity of selective etching.

The system in use was constructed to explore both these and other methods of fabricating a metal-base transistor.

The research models of the metal-base transistor produced so far have shown great promise. The base collector breakdown occurs at about 10 volts as shown in Fig. 3, but this and the low alpha are not serious detriments in low-level microwave amplifiers, which are the primary projected use of this device.

Design For 10 Gc—At present, efforts are directed at a broadband microwave amplifier utilizing a metal-base transistor in a grounded-base configuration, where the transistor has the following parameters: r_e is 2 ohms (achieved at a current density of about 3×10^3 amp/cm^2); r_b is 1 ohm; r_c is negligibly high; C_e is 1 pf (for an area of 0.5×10^{-5}/cm^2 and forward biased); C_c is 0.1 pf (for an area of 10^{-5} cm^2 and back bias of about 6 v); and a is 0.9 at 10 Gc. The collector load must be inductive to tune out the collector capacitance as shown in Fig. 4A.

At 10 Gc, the reactance of C_c is 159 ohms. To achieve the desired bandwidth of 1 Gc, the Q of the output circuit must be less than 10. Choose $R_L = 1{,}000$ ohms. An alternative equivalent of Fig. 4A is the series arrangement of Fig. 4B, wherein r_L is 25 ohms. This is a good characteristic impedance for a strip-line microwave circuit and suggests its use with a small inductance in series with the collector load.

The power gain of this amplifier is 25.2 db neglecting circuit losses. This calculation assumes negligible phase shift associated with a, permitting 5.2 db of circuit losses over

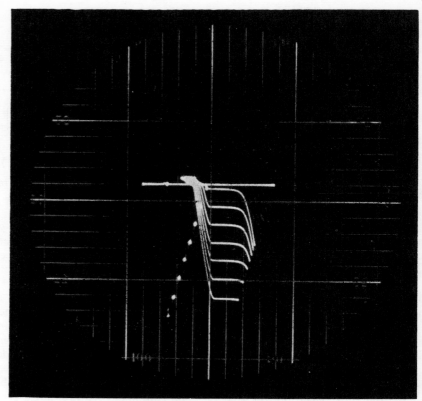

COMMON emitter characteristics of the MBT, where scales are 5 volts-per-division horizontal, and 2-ma-per-division vertical—Fig. 3

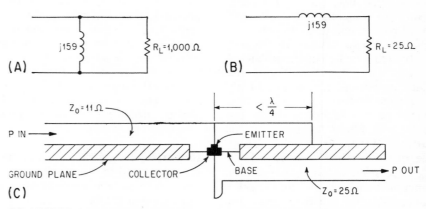

COLLECTOR load must be inductive to cancel capacitance at 10 Gc (A), alternative load circuit for a strip-line amplifier application (B), and actual strip-line circuit (C)—Fig. 4

and above the desired 20-db gain.

The grounded-base configuration is recommended because of the natural match achieved between the geometry of the device and the electromagnetic field pattern realized in a strip-line or waveguide circuit. Figure 7 illustrates a convenient arrangement and suggests the type of encapsulation required.

The input impedance of the transistor is $3.65 + j5.18$ ohms. By

shunting the input with a capacitive reactance of 7.75 ohms, a resistive input impedance of 11 ohms is achieved at a Q of about 2. The input circuit is very broadband under these conditions. Figure 4C shows a short-circuited line longer than $\lambda/4$ paralleling the emitter input; this length should be adjusted to present $-j7.75$ ohms to the input for tuning.

The small hairpin **loop in** series

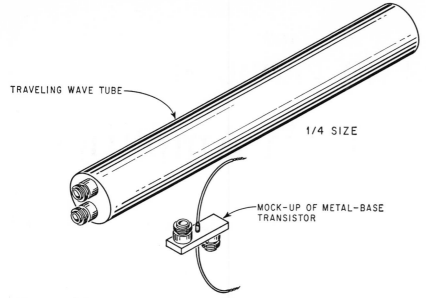

SIZE comparison between a metal-base transistor and a typical traveling-wave tube—Fig. 5

A base flange and a collector wire and pin are attached and the device is mounted in a strip-line circuit of the type shown in Fig. 4C, using the collector circuit of Fig. 4B. This technique is undoubtedly more expensive than the multiple-device technique on a single wafer generally employed for conventional devices. However, the metal-base transistor is designed to be competitive with other microwave amplifiers such as traveling wave tubes, rather than with low-frequency transistors of conventional design, and in the microwave area, the metal-base transistor should be highly competitive on a manufacturing cost basis. An artist's sketch of the complete metal-base transistor microwave amplifier package compared with a traveling-wave-tube package, both designed for broadband amplification at 10 Gc appears in Fig. 5. This design is nearing completion in the laboratory, and it is hoped that initial microwave-performance measurements can be made within two or three months.

At frequencies higher than about 10 Gc, the strip-line circuits become impractical, and it is necessary to use waveguides. Eventually, with good design, it should be possible to fabricate amplifiers and oscillators in the 50-to 100-Gc range. This will take more time however, just as the full frequency potentialities of conventional bipolar junction transistors required a reasonable development time.

Development work on the metal-base transistor performed at Stanford Research Institute has been partially sponsored by Sprague Electric Company, North Adams, Massachusetts.

The authors thank R. E. Parker for his assistance in the construction of equipment and devices.

with the collector lead as shown is a simple way to achieve the $j159$-ohm series inductive reactance required to tune out the collector capacitance. The d-c isolation and biasing provisions are not shown, but these should not present any serious problems.

The base connection should preferably be a flat, round metal plate contacting the hole in the ground plane. A good electrical and thermal connection is desirable. With this arrangement, the output circuit is completely electrically shielded from the input circuit, thereby preventing external feedback difficulties.

The 11-ohm input line can be readily matched to a 25-ohm line with a taper or a step transformer, thus making the over-all input and output impedances equal.

The same general design can be readily adapted to coaxial or waveguide circuits.

Fabrication—Reproducibility of the metal-base transistor is not known as yet because fabrication parameters are not yet fully optimized. This has prevented making many identical runs as required for a statistically meaningful reproducibility analysis.

Tests to date would indicate but not show conclusively that the stability and lifetime of the Si-Mo-Si structures equal or exceed those of conventional bipolar transistors.

Scores of devices have been fabricated simultaneously on large Si wafers, as in conventional technology. However, this technique does not lend itself well to a solution of the special connection and packaging problems inherent in microwave designs. We are currently fabricating six devices simultaneously, each device being deposited on the two-mil tip of a tapered metal pin shaped like an old-fashioned phonograph needle.

REFERENCES

(1) J. L. Moll, "Comparison of Hot Electron and Related Amplifiers," *IEEE Trans. on Elec. Devices*, ED-10, p. 299, September 1963.

(2) D. V. Geppert, "A Metal-Base Transistor," *Proc. IRE*, 50, p. 127, June 1962. Also, "The Metal-Base Transistor," presented at the Solid State Devices Research Conference, Durham, New Hampshire, July 9-11, 1962.

(3) M. M. Atalla and D. Kahng, "A New Hot Electron Triode Structure," presented at the Solid State Devices Research Conference, Durham, New Hampshire, July 9-11, 1962.

(4) J. P. Spratt, "Metal Oxide Amplifier," Final Report, Signal Corps Contract No. DA-36-039-SC-90715, 30 June 1963.

(5) C. R. Crowell, W. G. Spitzer, L. E. Howarth, and E. E. LaBate, "Attenuation Length Measurement of Hot Electrons in Metal Films," *Phys. Rev.* 127, p. 2006 (1962).

(6) G. V. Samsonov, Silicides and their Uses in Engineering, (English translation), Foreign Technology Div. AFSC, WPAFB, Dayton, Ohio, January 29, 1962.

(7) J. J. Casey, R. R. Garnache, J. Lindmayer, and J. L. Sprague, "Characteristics of Metal-Base Transistor Structures," presented at the Electrochemical Society Meeting, April, 1963 (Paper No. 100) (To be published).

(8) J. L. Sprague, J. Lindmayer, R. Garnache, and J. J. Casey, Rept. on 23rd Annual Conference Physical Electronics (MIT) March 20-22, 1963, pp. 210-219.

INDUCTORS NO PROBLEM

New Thin-Film Amplifier

By RICHARD LESLIE and THOMAS TOWNSEND, AIL Division, Cutler-Hammer, Inc. Deer Park, N. Y.

WHAT ABOUT THOSE BIG INDUCTORS?

Don't use them. That's how the authors solved the problem of making a thin-film amplifier. In addition, they solved a couple of other problems inherent with this type of device. They won't say what the amplifier is used for, except that it is in a classified space program and is working well

LOGARITHMIC i-f amplifiers, of tuned-stage design, do not lend themselves to microminiaturization. Inductors required are not compatible with size reductions possible with solid-circuit or thin-film techniques. A 60-mc log i-f amplifier with untuned stages has been specifically designed for microcircuit fabrication. Of modular construction, the amplifier occupies only 4 cubic inches, which is a reduction in volume of 20 to 1 over previous log i-f amplifiers.

Successive-detection log i-f amplifiers derive the log characteristic from the sum of the individual responses of each amplifier stage. These amplifiers have been designed using tuned common-emitter or common-base amplifiers. But there is a major problem of miniaturizing inductors. Also, a tedious alignment procedure is required because of reciprocal interaction of tuning and logging adjustments.

Investigation showed that RC-coupled amplifiers provide one solution to these problems. Untuned stages at 60 Mc are possible using one of the higher performance vhf planar transistors. To minimize the interaction of the i-f stages when driving a common video load, one video stage is included with each i-f amplifier.

The log i-f stage is shown in Fig. 1. Under small-signal conditions, video section Q_2 can be considered as a small shunt conductance. Its presence has only a second-order effect on the operation of i-f section Q_1. In this case, Q_1 acts as a linear r-c amplifier. Low-frequency cutoff is determined by the coupling capacitor and by the bypass circuits in the emitter. The upper-frequency cutoff is a function of the load resistance and the stray capacitances in the circuit. With the values shown, the i-f bandwidth extends from 20 Mc to 120 Mc (Fig. 2) Gain is about 10 db for good log operation.

As signal amplitude increases, rectification occurs in the emitter base diode of Q_1, causing the diode current and the emitter voltage of Q_1 to increase.

Since the base of Q_2 is held fixed, the collector current of Q_2 decreases. This action observed across R_L produces the sloped portion of the video transfer characteristic. The low-pass section between the emitters of Q_1 and Q_2 prevents the appearance of i-f at the emitter of Q_2. As the signal level increases further, transistor Q_2 cuts off completely so that any further increase in input-signal level does not appear in the video output. The power

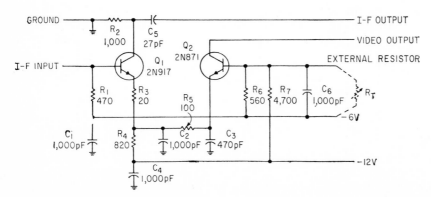

SINGLE *log i-f module*—Fig. 1

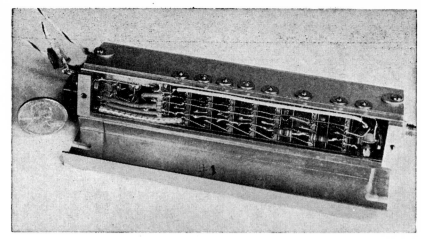

COMPLETE *log i-f amplifier showing module construction and relative size compared with a penny*

Solving the problem of inductor size in a thin-film amplifier design resulted in other plus features

range over which log action takes place is 10 db. By properly selecting the bias point, Q_2 can be made to cut off before the i-f output power of Q_1 saturates.

A thin-film technique of fabrication was chosen because of the design flexibility allowed. For a 0.5 by 0.5 inch wafer, the normal limits are: Resistors less than 100 kilohms and greater than 10 ohms; capacitors no greater than 1,000 pf; ratio of resistors within a module less than 1,000; and resistor tolerances greater than 5 percent. For unusual applications, the limits can be extended slightly at a greater cost.

FABRICATION—In thin-film circuit fabrication, Fig. 3, a substrate made of either glass or fired alumina ceramic is placed in a vacuum chamber. A mask containing the desired circuit pattern is interposed between the substrate and the material to be deposited, nichrome for resistors, beryllium copper for conductors, and silicon monoxide for dielectrics, is heated in a crucible. Vapor is driven off in all directions within the vacuum chamber. The evaporating material passes through the holes in the mask and condenses on the substrate. Several masks and deposition cycles are required to produce the finished circuit containing resistors and conductors. During deposition, the substrate is heated to provide a permanent molecular bond between the materials. Deposited silicon monoxide capacitors were not used in this amplifier because of a number of

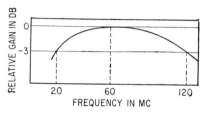

GAIN *characteristic of a single log i-f stage—Fig. 2*

associated problems—primarily dielectric breakdown due to minute pin holes. Standard techniques for eliminating pin holes result in too low an insulation resistance.

After the material has been deposited and removed from the vacuum chamber, chip transistors and capacitors are bonded to the substrate. These components are soldered to the appropriate deposited elements.

LAYOUT—After careful study, the complete layout of the log i-f stage including transistors was devised, Fig. 4. Environmental and electrical testing of this circuit shows that i-f circuit performance is not degraded when converting from conventional components to thin-film circuits. In many instances, circuit operation can be enhanced by microminiaturization because of the lowering of series lead inductances and stray shunt capacitances. The performance results for the thin-film stage are identical to those shown in Fig. 2 for the conventional stage.

After determining feasibility of the basic log stage, the require-

ments of the complete amplifier were considered. In general, for the successive-detection amplifier, the accuracy is limited to either input dynamic range divided by 100, or 0.5 db, whichever is greater. The number of stages, N, required to achieve this accuracy is

$$N = \frac{\text{Input Dynamic Range (db)}}{\text{Stage Gain (db)}} + 1$$

For this application, the input dynamic range can be considered to extend from -10 dbm to -70 dbm so that the maximum accuracy is 0.6 db, and $N \geq 7$. Choosing seven stages, a translation amplifier with a gain of 8 to 10 db is necessary to

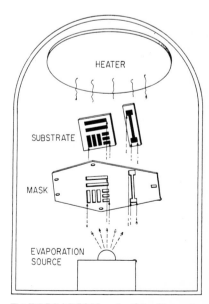

FABRICATION *of thin-film circuits is performed using a vacuum evaporation system—Fig. 3*

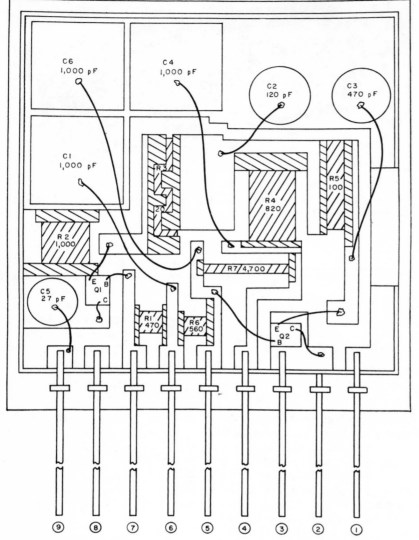

PHYSICAL LAYOUT *of a log i-f module with resistors, capacitors and transistors identified—Fig. 4*

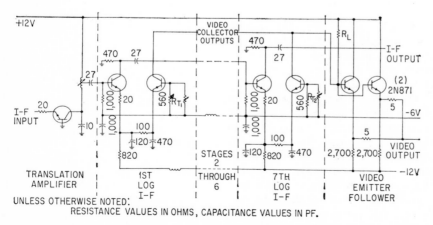

SEVEN-STAGE *log i-f requires a translation amplifier to limit bandwidth and a video emitter-follower to match the output to the load—Fig. 5*

ensure the start of the log curve at the lowest input power.

The overall log amplifier, Fig. 5, requires about 7 Mc of band-pass limiting so that a one-pole filter is included in the translation amplifier. However, the tuning inductor is placed outside the translation-amplifier module to permit substitution of other filters for other applications. The video emitter follower is required to match the available 10-volt video output to its load. Parallel emitter followers are required to produce the necessary video power to a 100-ohm cable and load.

Log operation by the successive-detection principle can be explained with the aid of the curves shown in Fig. 6. Under no-signal conditions, each video stage is adjusted to contribute 1.5 ma to the common load resistor R_L. At a particular low signal power level, stage 7 begins to detect causing the video current to decrease. As the power increases further, the video portion of stage 7 cuts off. Ideally, if the db gains of stages 5 and 6 are exactly equal to the range over which stage 7 contributes to the initial portion of the log response, stage 6 will start to detect at the point where the video portion of stage 7 cuts off. In this manner, for each 10-db increase in input power, 1.5-ma current increments are removed from the common load resistor producing the complete dashed curve of Fig. 6. After each stage has contributed its portion of the overall curve, its individual i-f output saturates thereby limiting the drive power to successive stages and minimizing recovery problems because of the unequal positive and negative conduction impedances.

A straight-line curve is not achieved in practice for several reasons. First, preceding stage gains are not absolutely equal or fixed producing variations in the point at which each stage starts detecting, when referenced to the input. Second, the absolute power level at which the emitter-base diode of each stage begins to detect is not accurately defined and the break point is not sharp. Third, the cut-off point of each video stage is rounded.

Seven log stages provide the required accuracy when taking into

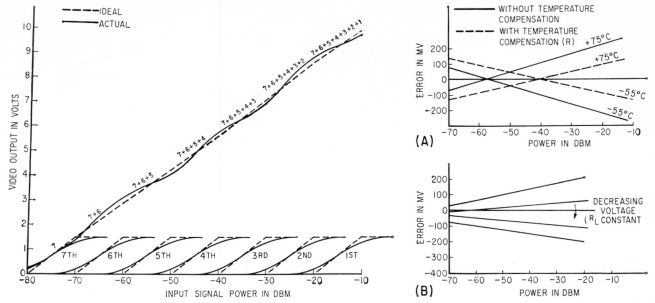

OVERALL PERFORMANCE *characteristics of the complete seven-stage amplifier—Fig. 6*

TEMPERATURE COMPENSATION *of the load resistor decreases error at the high power levels (A); further improvement may be had by using a temperature compensated —6 volt supply (B)—Fig. 7*

account gross deviations from the ideal curve due to the limited power range over which each stage adds to the overall curve. Other factors contributing to the inaccuracy cannot be remedied by using additional stages.

PROBLEMS—Size reduction introduced a number of problems. The greatest was that of stability. Because of the large gain of about 18 db per linear inch, oscillations were a constant problem. These oscillations can vary from 5 Mc (due to improper power-supply isolation) to 70 Mc (when interstage shielding is inadequate or poorly grounded).

By using toroidal choke power decoupling between the translation amplifier and the first log i-f, and between the first and second log i-f's, the low-frequency oscillation can be eliminated. Toroids are desirable since much of the field is contained within the iron core. Careful stage shielding and grounding can prevent feedback oscillations due to the proximity of the stages. However, it is necessary to maintain a center-to-center stage spacing of about 0.3 inch for the shielding to be successful.

Alignment of the stages to produce the overall log response can be accomplished by either of two meth-

ods. The first and simplest starts with the individual stages. As a part of the module test, the value of R_T (Fig. 1) that produces a known video stage current (I_{vc}) is determined. In this amplifier, it is chosen as 1.5 ma, which is a compromise between the size of R_L and the change in i-f stage current as detection takes eplace. With small initial values of I_{vc}, R_L must be large to produce the required video output voltage. Combined with the parallel output capacity of the seven stages, too large an R_L will limit the high-frequency video response. On the other hand, if I_{vc} is too large, the variation of i-f emitter current (I_{ie}) is too large over the detection range, thereby affecting the i-f gain during detection.

After the modules have been assembled in a complete amplifier, the nearest fixed resistor to the required value of R_T is added to each stage, and R_L chosen to be equal to $V/7_{Ivc}$, where V is the required maximum video output voltage. Experimental results show that an accuracy of ±200 mv with respect to the ideal curve can be obtained in this manner.

For greater accuracy, potentiometers can be substituted for the fixed resistors. The potentiometers of the subminiature square type can be inserted in the interstage space

required for stability. By this means, the overall inaccuracy can be reduced to ±50 mv with several points out only ±100 mv (0.67 db).

TEMPERATURE EFFECT—Average error from the ideal curve as a function of input power with temperature as a variable, Fig. 7A, demonstrates the effect of optimum temperature compensation of R_L. The result is to decrease the error at high power levels at the sacrifice of increasing the error at low power levels, although the overall maximum is decreased.

Although compensating R_L proved sufficient for the particular application, further improvement is possible by introducing a temperature-variable —6 volt power supply. The required variation is only of the order of tenths of a volt, but has the effect of changing the slope of the error-vs-power curve as a function of temperature, Fig. 7B, thereby providing complete compensation along with a variable R_L.

Acknowledgment is given for the assistance of William McCarthy and Joel Byer in developing the complete amplifier. The basic logarithmic stage is the work of Allan Brown. Layout and fabrication of the thin film modules was performed by Varo, Inc., Garland, Texas, under subcontract to AIL.

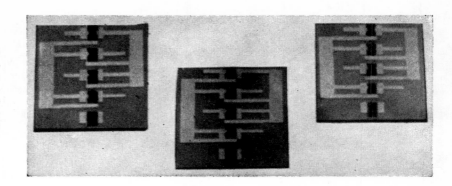

COMPLETELY DEPOSITED *multivibrators using thin-film, insulated gate, field effect devices formed on amorphous glass substrates. At least three semiconductors have been found suitable: cadmium selenide, cadmium sulfide and cadmium telluride*

Vacuum Deposited Circuits Use Field Effect

By CHARLES FELDMAN, HERBERT L. WILSON and WILLIAM A. GUTIERREZ

Melpar Research Laboratories, Falls Church, Va.

Active microcircuits studied at Melpar have thin-film construction

COMPLETELY DEPOSITED thin-film microcircuits containing both active and passive components are being formed and studied in the research laboratories of Melpar, Inc. The circuits make use of insulated-gate field-effect phenomena for the active elements, as described by Feldman[1], Weimer[2], and previously by Lilienfield[3], Heil[4] and Shockley[5] and others. The microcircuits are formed on amorphous substrates by a sequence of evaporations in vacuum, and require no intermediate or post-deposition treatment. Oscillators, multivibrators and various digital circuits are currently being studied. Passive circuit components consisting of rhenium film resistors (ELECTRONICS, May 11, 1962, p 69) and silicon dioxide dielectrics are combined with active thin-film devices.

Two types of field-effect modulation are under study. In one type, typefied by germanium films, conductivity modulation is controlled by surface states on the semiconductor (ELECTRONICS, Oct. 12, 1962, p 24). Such units show appreciable current and power gain. The second type of modulation involves voltage dependence of the semiconductor space charge region or majority carrier injection, or both. Devices formed with cadmium selenide, cadmium sulfide and cadmium telluride use this type of modulation. Appreciable voltage gains are achieved, as well as current and power gains.

MULTIVIBRATORS—The photograph shows three experimental multivibrators that were completely vacuum deposited. Each substrate contains five deposited cadmium selenide devices, four of which are used in the circuit. Evaporated gold films form the interconnections according to the schematic of Fig. 1. A cross-section of one of the active devices is shown in Fig. 1B. Devices are formed by subsequent evaporation of metals, source-drain electrodes, a semiconductor layer, a dielectric layer, and a metal gate electrode. Typical film thicknesses are 100 to 500 Å for the metallic electrodes, 200 to 500 Å for the semiconductor layer, and 300 to 1,200 Å for the dielectric layer.

Investigations at Melpar have shown that cadmium selenide and cadmium telluride, in addition to previously reported cadmium sulfide[2], are suitable for use in these devices. Cadmium selenide appears to be the most suitable material for completely deposited active devices. Thus far, the CdSe units have shown better reproducibility, stability, higher electron mobility, while

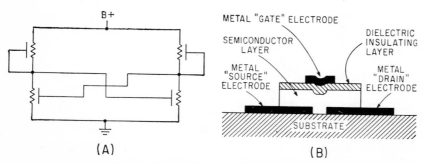

SCHEMATIC *of the experimental microcircuit, (A); cross-sectional view of a field-effect active device, (B)*—Fig. 1

their sensitivity, transconductance and voltage amplification factors are comparable to CdS devices. Characteristics of a CdSe thin-film transistor are shown in Fig. 2A.

SiO$_2$ is used as the insulating layer.

ARRAYS OF DEVICES—The circuits illustrated represent, of course, only a beginning in the development of sophisticated thin-film circuits. The ability to make large numbers, or arrays, of active devices simply and cheaply is a matter of masking techniques. The arrangement in Fig. 2B, under

study at Melpar, contains 81 isolated units on a one-inch substrate; interconnections and passive components may be added for computer and other applications. Further size reductions are possible.

The work is supported by the Bureau of Naval Weapons as part of a general program for development of temperature and radiation resistant circuits.

REFERENCES

(1) C. Feldman, Conference on Navy Lab. Microelectronics Program, Applied Physics Laboratory, The John Hopkins University, June 12-13, 1961, sponsored by Office of Naval Research (OTS No. PB-181314) p 53.
(2) P. K. Weimer, *Proc IRE* 50, p 1462 (1962).
(3) J. Lilienfield, U.S. Pat. 1,745,175 Jan 28, 1930 and U.S. Pat. 1,900,018 Mar 7, 1933.
(4) O. Heil, U.K. Pat. 439,457 Mar 4, 1935.
(5) W. Shockley and G. L. Pearson, *Phys Rev* 74, p 232 (1948).

New Vapor-Deposition Process Creates Tunnel Diodes

Program also establishes much higher inherent reliability of films

INCREASED emphasis is now being placed on new and improved vapor-deposition techniques for both active and passive devices, particularly for high temperature and radiation resistant circuits.

So far two approaches to vapor deposition of materials for active devices have been successful. One technique uses the properties of continuous thin films deposited on substrates, and encompasses field effect phenomena, field emission and tunneling. In a more recent approach, single crystallites of silicon are deposited on a substrate from the vapor.

The latter approach spots semiconductor crystals on a substrate by masking out definite areas, leaving free space on the substrate for fabrication of the other circuit elements.

Wire connections can be attached to crystallite facets, or leads can be made by evaporating connections to the active crystallite of silicon.

Diodes and tunnel diodes have been made at Melpar using the deposited crystal technique. Photo shows tunnel diodes formed on silicon film deposited pyrolytically on fused silica substrate. Characteristics of tunnel diodes formed in this manner are shown in Fig. 1.

FEASIBILITY—Ernest Bylander and Richard Murphey of Melpar say that formation of active devices in crystallites is basically no more difficult than forming active devices in bulk materials. However they use special techniques due to crystallite size, their adhering ability, and the nature of the insulating substrate.

The crystallites are deposited

TUNNEL *diode fabricated from pyrolytically-grown crystallites*

from the vapor by the reduction of silicon chlorine in hydrogen of fused substrate heated to 1,100 deg C. Doping is done with a phosphorus pentoxide emitter-type diffusion at 1,120 deg C for 24 hours using oxygen as a carrier. The phosphorus oxide layer is removed by hydrogen fluoride. Aluminumboron wire is alloyed to one facet and gold wire to an opposite facet. The peak to valley ratio of current-voltage curve is 2:1 in a typical unit. Future attempts to improve this ratio may center on increasing the n-doping level, and improving the alloying technique.

Tunneling has been observed in units formed in continuous pyrolytic films, however negative resistance was not observed even after etching. Imperfect nature of the junction may be responsible.

STABLE DIELECTRICS—Search for improved high-temperature di-

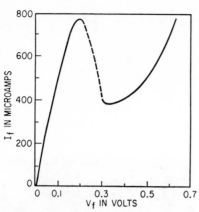

CRYSTAL-*grown tunnel diode characteristics—Fig. 1*

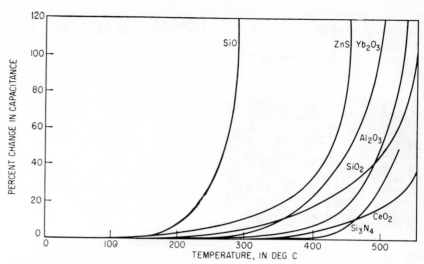

CAPACITANCE-*temperature characteristics of several dielectric films having thicknesses greater than one micron—Fig. 2*

electrics continues. Several films can go to 450 deg C with less than 10 percent change in capacitance (see Fig. 2). Melpar now has a special carbon crucible to contain the materials under study. This container has aided the study of the dielectrics.

Dielectric studies were conducted by Charles Feldman and Michael Hacskaylo of Melpar. Temperature of the crucible during deposition of the dielectrics was measured by an optical pyrometer. High substrate temperatures were controlled with a radiant heater.

A sharp peak in the dielectric constant of zinc sulfide at a particular thickness was studied rather extensively. A similar peak was observed in SiO_2 films. Anomalies may be connected with the piezoelectric nature of the materials, and due to stress on the deposited film. Annealing the film causes the anomaly to disappear.

Work on rhenium film resistors has been reported (see ELECTRONICS, May 11, 1962, pgs 69 and 70). Work since then confirms the fact that rhenium forms a suitable film resistor operating at 12 watts at a temperature of 850 deg C.

Vacuum-deposited germanium films with mobilities as high as 600 cm^2 per v-sec have been formed at 750 deg C. Increase in mobility is due to use of a substrate with an expansion coefficient similar to that of germanium.

Highest mobility observed for silicon films formed by vacuum deposition is 20 cm^2/v-sec on films deposited at 1,100 deg C.

Some success has been achieved with sputtered films of InSb and GaAs. C. W. Moulton reports that the sputtered films have the same conductivity type as the bulk material. Mobility of 2,400 cm^2/v-sec was obtained in InSb films.

PRACTICAL—Studies on materials and effects have been practically applied in the fabrication of a frequency modulated phase-shift oscillator (ELECTRONICS, Oct. 12, p 24). This circuit, composed of two functional blocks, lends verification to the predicted advantages gained in film circuits. Phase shift vs frequency characteristics have been improved, resulting in greater frequency stability. Network loss has been decreased .by a factor of three from a tapered lumped constant circuit, and by a factor of nine from an untapered lumped constant ladder. The entire feedback network consists of only three vacuum-deposited layers, having a much higher inherent reliability.

Chapter 9

PASSIVE THIN-FILM DEVICES

Photo-etching thin-film circuits

Selective chemical etching seems to be better, faster and cheaper than deposition through mechanical masks

By C.W. Skaggs

Bunker-Ramo Corp., Canoga Park, Calif.

A method of preparing thin-film circuits through photo-etching promises to achieve higher quality and yields at lower cost than conventional mechanical masking methods.

Instead of laying down thin-film patterns, one material at a time through expensive mechanical masks, on an insulating substrate, a layer of resistive material is first deposited over the entire substrate, then a layer of conducting material is deposited over the resistive layer. The conducting lands and resistive paths of the thin-film circuit pattern are made by selective chemical etching, using Kodak Photo-Resist and photographic techniques. Furthermore, large numbers of substrates can be prepared in each batch without breaking vacuum in the deposition apparatus.

Chromium or cermet is used as the resistive material, and compounds of chromium and gold, cermet and gold, chromium and copper, or cermet and copper are used as the conductive material. The cermet is—by volume—four parts 325-mesh electrolytic chromium powder and one part select-grade powdered silicon. The chromium is purified carbon-free metal; the gold is 40-mil wire that is 99.99% pure; and the copper is in shot form and also 99.99% pure.

So far, 0211 glass, 7059 glass, and glazed aluminum oxide (AL_2O_3) have been used as substrates. The substrates are prepared by an ultrasonic cleaning in a 40-60 mixture of alcohol and toluene, and then by a similar cleaning in a detergent bath. They are then rinsed, first in hot, running tap water and then ultrasonically three times in distilled water. They are finally dipped in alcohol and vapor-degreased. The substrates are stored in a vacuum dessicator until they are used.

Vacuum system

An oil-diffusion-pump vacuum system deposits the thin-film layers on the substrate. Initial pressure is 1×10^{-6} millimeters of mercury or lower. Substrates are mounted within a spherical dome that is radiantly heated to 120°C. While the thin-film layers are being deposited, the substrates are spun at 50 revolutions per minute, which insures even distribution of the thin-film material.

The cleaned substrates are loaded into the dome [photo] and the system is evacuated. The dome is spun. The substrates are heated to 120°C. The thin-film and conductive layers are deposited sequentially. A manually controlled mechanical feed-through positions any of six sources of thin-film material directly under the dome so the material can be deposited. The resistive and conductive materials are deposited until a precalibrated resistance monitor indicates that the desired values of resistance have been attained.

Chromium and cermet are evaporated from aluminum oxide crucibles with spiral stranded tungsten filaments used as radiant heaters. The gold and copper are evaporated from resistance-heated molybdenum boats.

The average rate of deposition of the resistive material is 12.5 ohms per square per second based on a deposition rate of 200 ohms per square. The conductor thickness is approximately 0.2 mil, having a resistance of 0.05 ohm per square or lower. The resistive material, besides being used to form the resistors, is also used to form a tenacious bond between the top conductor layer and the substrate.

After the materials are deposited in complete layers on the entire surface of the substrate, they are dip coated with undiluted Kodak Photo-Resist

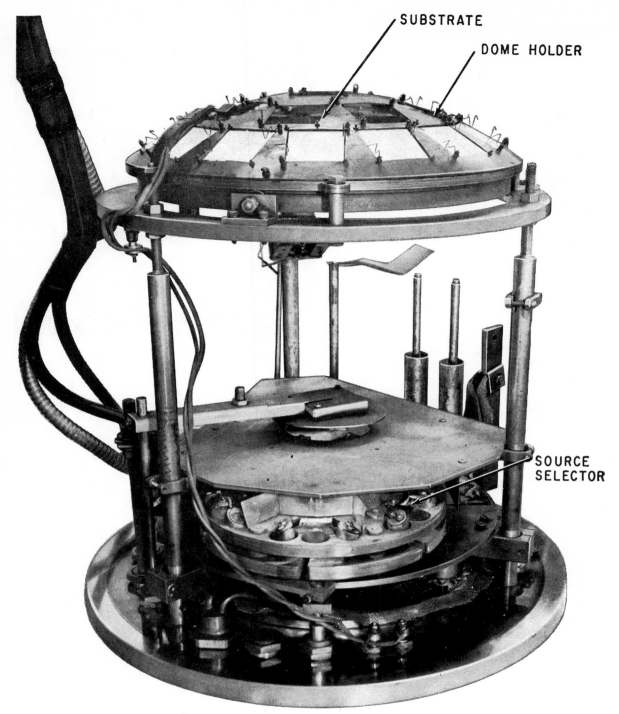

SUBSTRATE

DOME HOLDER

SOURCE
SELECTOR

Source selector permits selection of any one of six sources of thin-film material with a manually controlled mechanical feed-through. Substrates are rotated automatically at 50 revolutions a minute.

(KPR), air-dried for 15 minutes and oven-dried at 120°C for five minutes. Then these three steps are repeated.

Dipping and drying has to be done in a dust-free area using filtered KPR, since dust particles in or on the KPR can cause pinholes in resistors and conductors when the samples are later processed through the etchants. The care taken in the application of the KPR determines, to a great extent, the yield of acceptable units by the process.

The KPR-coated substrates are then exposed with an ultraviolet light through a sharp photographic negative of the complete circuit. The negatives are one-twentieth scale reductions of the original pressure-tape pasteups of the circuit. Any ultraviolet light source may be used with the appropriate distance and exposure time; 275-watt sun lamps at a distance of one foot and an exposure time of 3.5 minutes work satisfactorily.

In addition to the composite negative, a separate

Composite and conductor etching . . .

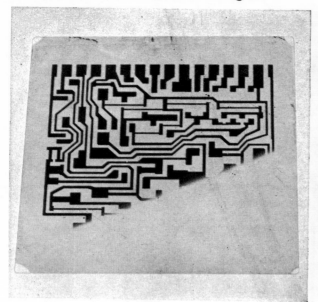

Substrate after first etching process. Under the dark areas, the resistive and conductive layers are unharmed.

Five-mil spread on conductive pattern is evident in close-up of substrate

negative showing only the conductive paths is prepared. It has a spread of five mils per edge. The spreading is accomplished by illuminating photographic film through the negative by means of a rotating collimated light through an appropriate angle and placing a transparent spacer of appropriate thickness between the negative and the photographic film. The speed positive obtained from this operation is then used to prepare the spread negative by contact printing.

Composite etching

First, the composite negative is used to expose the KPR-coated substrates. The exposed substrates are then developed in KPR developer for five minutes and rinsed in aerated running tap water for one minute.

After exposure and development, the samples are etched. Gold is removed with a commercial gold stripper, copper is removed with ferric chloride, and chromium or cermet is removed with hydrochloric acid. A temperature of 60° to 80° is maintained in the gold stripper and the ferric chloride solution. Chromium or cermet is etched with hydrochloric acid by placing the substrate into the acid

and introducing an aluminum wire. Since aluminum is above chromium in the electromotive series and both aluminum and chromium are soluble in hydrochloric acid, the aluminum ions replace the chromium ions in solution, stripping the chromium from the substrate in the unprotected areas.

The etching times are 15 seconds in the gold stripper, 20 seconds in the ferric chloride and 5 seconds in the hydrochloride acid. These times are for the material thickness described previously, and may vary if the thicknesses are different.

Following the etching process, the KPR is removed by a two-minute ultrasonic rinse in photoresist stripper, followed by a one-minute rinse in a strong spray of tap water. The substrates are then dipped in methyl alcohol (methanol) and degreased in trichlorethylene. The substrates are dipped in KPR a second time and dried as they were after the first application. This second coating of KPR is exposed to the ultraviolet light source through the five-mil spread conductor negative.

Conductor etching

The five-mil-per-edge spread is used to simplify alignment of the conductor negative and composite pattern, and protects the conductor lands while defining the resistor length. The specimens are developed and rinsed as before. The second resist pattern protects the conductors and defines the length of the resistors during the second etching.

In the second etching, only the gold- and copper-removing solutions—the gold stripper and ferric chloride—are used. The KPR is removed in the same manner as before, and the specimens are again dipped in methanol and degreased. The circuits are completed after the second etching and after the KPR is removed.

The author

Clyde W. Skaggs is a senior engineer at the Bunker-Ramo Corp., engaged in research and development of new processes for making thin-film components and circuits. Bunker-Ramo was owned jointly by the Martin-Marietta Corp. and Thompson Ramo Wooldridge, Inc. Last month, it was purchased by the Teleregister Corp.

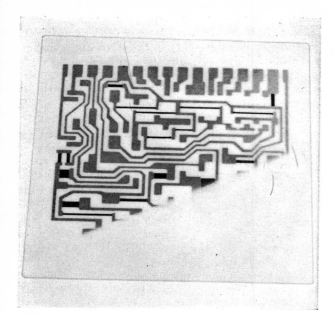

Completely etched substrate has been cleaned; darker areas are resistors and gray areas are conducting pads.

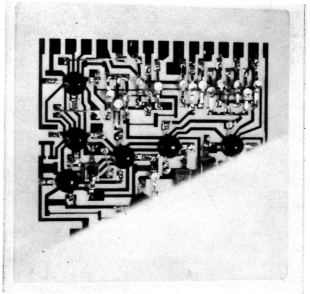

Completed circuit has transistors and chip-capacitors. These were soldered on, but could have been welded.

Bonding

Active components are subsequently attached by thermocompression bonding, chip bonding and soldering. This operation determines the choice of conductor materials. For thermocompression bonding or chip bonding, chromium-gold or cermet-gold conductors are used, depending on the type of resistive material. Chromium-copper-gold or cermet-copper-gold conductors are recommended for soldering, again depending on the type of resistor used. The gold is used over the copper to minimize oxidation of the copper.

Although active components initially were attached by hand, the photo etch process resulted in reduced costs and improved yields over conventional processes, and it became apparent that the attachment of semiconductors entirely by hand was not practical. To satisfy present demands and those of the immediate future, it was necessary to design an assembly system to meet the following conditions:

- Nonrecurring tooling must be low enough in cost so that it can be fully amortized on small production runs even when orders are for as few as 70 to 100 identical circuits.
- The assembly system must be operable by low to moderately skilled personnel.
- If possible, it is advantageous to do away with, or minimize, use of conventional assembly apparatus such as microscopes and micropositioners.

After analyzing several possible assembly systems and considering their costs, it seems that a system capable of assembling a circuit in five minutes would satisfy production requirements and cost considerations as well as the other conditions of manufacture.

Assembly

The resultant system is basically manual. However, when job requirements warrant, many functions can be automated.

The heart of the system is an aluminum die made in the image of the circuit to be assembled. The registration, which is critical, is achieved with a negative that is made from the master tapes. The negative is used to photocopy the circuit image onto a blank coated with photo resist. The die is then fabricated by a combination of chemical milling and drilling. This die accepts the transistors and diodes and—if applicable—capacitors into machined cavities that register them to the circuit and simultaneously provide a heat sink. When the transistors and diodes are placed into their respective cavities, their leads fall into recesses.

A device such as a transistor is held in the cavity by a vacuum. The lead is spring-loaded tightly to the interconnecting pad area as soon as the die is placed over the circuit substrate. Since all component leads are of standard geometry, it is possible to use tooling that crimps and cuts the leads to a standard configuration. The apex of the crimp bears tightly against the aluminum die, which effectively sinks the heat traveling from the end of the leads being soldered. In addition, the crimp in the lead applies spring pressure and provides relief from shear stresses on the solder joint. The solder joint is made by inserting a heated probe through the holes in the die at the extremities of the leads.

Sweating

To obtain uniform interconnections, an extension or modification of the system has been designed in which the die remains basically unchanged, but heated probes are not used to achieve the soldered interconnection. Instead, a solder ball is dropped into the hole at the end of each lead; then the entire assembly is heated to 250°C. To minimize oxidation of the conductors, and to keep the semiconductors at a safe temperature, the vacuum used during component insertion is relieved, and hydrogen is forced through the vacuum holes to act as a coolant and oxidation inhibitor.

Although most circuits made to date use chip capacitors soldered in place, this will not necessarily be the best approach in every instance. There are many situations where the capability of vacuum depositing the capacitors can cut costs even more. The major problem of combining vacuum-deposited capacitors with photo-etched conductors and resistors is maintaining continuity across the step that is created when the conductor pattern is etched. Unless the large step at the conductor edges is graded or rounded by chemical etching or some other process, it prevents deposition of capacitors after photo-etching of resistors and conductors.

One way to overcome this problem is to vacuum-deposit the capacitor first, then overcoat it with a layer of silicon monoxide 10,000 angstroms or more thick deposited through a second mask. The second mask is designed to leave a portion of the capacitor electrodes exposed. The substrates are then completely coated with the appropriate resistive and conductive materials, which make contact with the exposed portions of the capacitor electrodes where they should. The general conductor-resistor pattern can now be formed with the photo-etch process without affecting the capacitor, since the silicon oxide is impervious to the etchants.

The photo-etch process allows circuits to be made in which the resistors have tolerances of ±5% as they are removed from the vacuum system—that is, without further trimming. The temperature coefficients of resistance of the chromium resistors is —200 to 0 parts per million per degree centigrade for the pressure, at the substrate temperature and deposition rate cited above. Uncoated cermet resistors fabricated with this process exhibit temperature coefficients of —500 to —50 parts per million per degree centigrade.

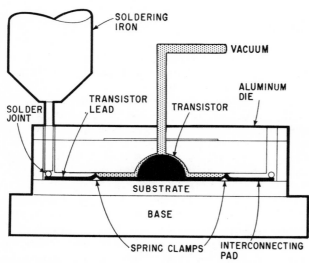

Vacuum (shaded) holds components, such as this transistor in the die until they are attached to the substrate.

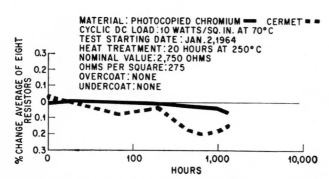

Typical load life data curves for eight 275-ohms-per-square chromium resistors and eight 275-ohms-per-square cermet resistors (dashed) made by this process. These resistors are uncoated and carry a power load of 10 watts/in² in an ambient temperature of 70°C. Neither type of resistor exhibits a very large change after 1,000 hours of cyclic dc loading.

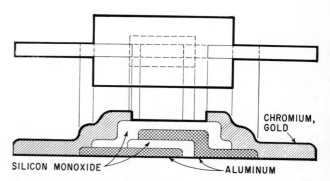

Capacitors can also be formed, as shown in cross-section.

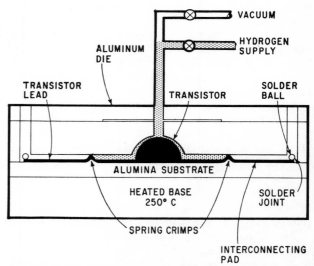

Advanced version of assembly apparatus uses a back fill of hydrogen (shaded) to keep the devices cool while the substrate temperature is raised to 250°C for soldering. Heat from the base melts solder and forms a joint.

THIN-FILM *thickness monitor deposition control equipment. Monitor oscillator is mounted below the vacuum-coater unit and thickness crystal is mounted within the vacuum system near the substrate*

LATEST THING IN THIN FILMS
Automatic Deposition Control

A known-frequency crystal is mounted in the same vacuum chamber as the substrate. Its frequency is mixed with a known standard. As deposition increases substrate thickness, the crystal also changes frequency. It then becomes an easy matter to relate beat frequency to deposited thickness

By STANLEY J. LINS and PAUL E OBERG
Univac Division of Sperry Rand Corp., St. Paul, Minnesota

DURING FABRICATION of electronic equipment, economies could be realized if a single process were able to produce and interconnect all active and passive components. Several techniques promise to satisfy these conditions. Of particular interest is the vacuum-deposited, thin-film process that presently can produce a wide variety of active and passive thin-film components.

The control of film thickness is essential to such a process. This article describes a compatible thickness monitoring instrument for the vacuum vapor-deposition process that can be included in a closed-loop control system. Since it has a nearly linear film thickness-signal output functional relationship, it is consistently accurate over its complete range. Furthermore, because of this linear behavior, it can be time-differentiated to allow film formation rate control.

OPERATION—The principal components of the film thickness monitor are a crystal-controlled monitor oscillator, an adjustable frequency standard, a mixer and a frequency counter. The monitor oscillator is mounted below the vacuum-coater unit and the quartz crystal that controls oscillator frequency is inside the vacuum system near the substrate.

One face of the thin rectangular crystal is exposed to the evaporant source. During operation of the vacuum coater, the substrate and the monitor crystal simultaneously receive a similar coating of material

---

MEASURING THIN FILMS

As there are 254,000,000 angstroms to the inch and some thin films are measured in hundreds of angstroms, determining their thickness can be a problem. The authors of this article use an approach based on superheterodyne theory in which an oscillator crystal whose frequency is changed by deposition thickness beats against a known standard frequency. The resultant beat note can be calibrated in deposition thickness

---

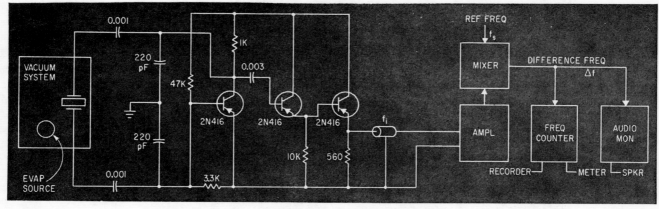

MONITOR *crystal, mounted in same vacuum system as components being made, changes frequency with deposition thickness. Difference frequency output of mixer changes as crystal thickness increases—Fig. 1*

gradually increasing in thickness. The increase in thickness results in a decrease of monitor-crystal resonant frequency. Monitor oscillator output is amplified and mixed with the output of a frequency standard. Before the evaporation process begins, the standard is adjusted to a frequency f_s equal to that of the monitor crystal f_t. Thus, the output of the mixer is a frequency equal to the difference of the two frequencies, and is initially zero. During evaporation, as the monitor crystal frequency decreases, audio difference frequency f will indicate the thin film thickness. This difference is converted to an analog signal and recorded on a moving-chart potentiometer to give a graphical record of thickness $\Delta d \propto \Delta f_i$ and the time rate of film growth (dd/dt).

CIRCUIT—The monitor oscillator is a transistor Colpitts oscillator (Fig. 1) operating as a parallel-resonant circuit. Oscillator output is amplified and matched to a coaxial cable through emitter followers. This enables one control chassis to operate any one of several monitor installations from a convenient remote location.

The signal is fed through tuned amplifiers thus blocking extraneous signals from entering the mixer. The audio output of the mixer (Δf_s) is amplified, clipped and converted to an analog signal by a passive counter operating on the nearly linear initial portion of the R-C charging curve. The output operates a linear-scale meter and a recording potentiometer, both calibrated directly in units of thickness. An audio monitor enables the operator to establish an accurate zero-beat.

PIEZOELECTRIC SENSOR—An ideal thickness-sensing element for this type of monitor must provide a continuous linear relationship between change of resonant frequency and increase of thickness of the condensed parasitic film and be insensitive to the elastic moduli of the parasitic film. Thus a thickness shear mode of vibration of a quartz crystal is used.

Crystals of this type are flat with the planar dimensions large with respect to thickness. An alternating electric field applied in the direction of the thickness, usually by sputtered or evaporated integral electrodes, causes the faces of the crystal to slide to and fro at the frequency of the electric field but in a

direction normal to the potential gradient. Because the faces slide in opposite directions, a nodal plane exists midway between the faces. The parasitic film condensing on one face decreases crystal resonant frequency. Such a situation under static conditions is shown in Fig. 2A.

A model (Fig. 2B) suggested in 1893 by Lord Kelvin, shows qualitatively why the direction of displacement can be normal to the direction of the applied field. The quartz (SiO_2) molecule comprises silicon atoms, which in the model are thought of as

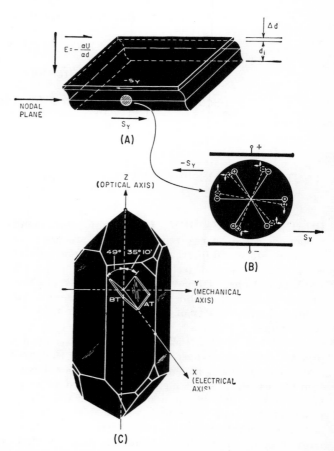

STRESS-STRAIN *condition of a crystal with a deposited layer (A) and a model of the stress-strain condition (B). The preferred cuts of a raw crystal are shown in (C)—Fig. 2*

being positively charged bodies, and double oxygen atoms, which are considered as having a net negative charge. They are arranged hexagonally, one axis being codirectional with the nodal plane of the crystal. When an electric field is applied across the crystal (normal to the nodal plane), the atoms are displaced because of the net charge so that on either side of the nodal plane there is a resultant strain S_Y and $-S_Y$. The collective result of this behavior of all the molecules is a thickness shear.

For crystals of this type there is a possibility of mechanically or electrically coupling to other modes of oscillation. For the AT cut and BT cut there is almost zero coupling to other oscillation modes. Lack of care in mounting and beveling can cause cross-coupling to other modes. For AT and BT crystals (Fig. 2C), if the ratio of planar dimensions to thickness is greater than 20:1, the crystal can be mounted by the corners with a negligible stress-strain relationship. The AT cut is preferred over the BT cut for this monitor system because of higher activity.

Once calibrated, it seems theoretically possible, using a knowledge of bulk density of any evaporant, to use the same calibration for a new evaporant. However, the same problem that makes x-ray fluorescence and colorimetric thickness determinations of evaporated thin films unreliable under certain conditions, also makes the vibrating crystal method inaccurate under the same conditions. The problem is that evaporated thin films do not always have densities equal to bulk densities. Since this instrument is calibrated with a multiple-beam interferometer, Δd is a metric thickness, not an effective or equivalent thickness.

The manner in which a thin film approaches bulk density will usually depend on the controlled conditions under which the deposition has taken place. Evaporated copper for example,[1] approaches to within 95 percent of bulk density at a thickness of 3,000 Å while silver achieves this value at about 1,000 Å. Unless density is considered to be variable—not constant and equal to bulk density, but a function of thickness—a significant error will be introduced for some evaporants.

As shown in the table, within error the empirical ratio of ρ_E/ρ_Q, (density of the film to the density of the quartz crystal) is always equal to or less than the bulk ratio of these materials.

Special consideration must be given to instrument calibration when interface effects are prominent.

Choice of f will depend on the characteristics of the installation. The resonant frequency of a crystal is inversely proportional to thickness and if a high-sensitivity S is required (large frequency shift per unit thickness), it will be desirable to use a high-frequency crystal, since sensitivity increases as the square of the frequency. However, a slight deviation from linearity occurs between the deposited mass and the frequency shift as crystal frequency increases. To keep error from this cause low, the resonant frequency of a high-frequency crystal must be taken into account, more so than for a l-f crystal.

CRYSTAL COOLING—All quartz crystals are temperature sensitive in at least one temperature range.

TABLE—DETERMINATION OF ρ_E/ρ_Q WITH CRYSTAL MONITOR

	EVAPORANT			
	Gold	Cobalt	Permalloy	Aluminum
Frequency Shift Δf(cps) ±20	1,550	1,320	1,650 1,900	1,640
Thickness (interferometric) Δd(A) ±25	515	750	980 1,190	2,300
Sensitivity $S = \Delta f/\Delta d$ (cps/A)	5.0 ± 0.3	3.0 ± 0.3	2.8 ± 0.3 2.7 ± 0.3	1.2 ± 0.2
Bulk Ratio of ρ_E/ρ_Q	7.50	3.36	3.25	1.02
Empirical Ratio of ρ_E/ρ_Q	6.3 ± 0.4	3.7 ± 0.4	3.5 ± 0.4 3.4 ± 0.4	0.8 ± 0.3

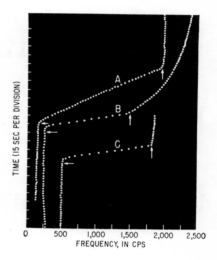

DIFFERENCE *between standard and monitor frequencies for evaporation with crucible (A) ring (B) and ring with water - cooled holder (C). Arrow defines evaporation period. Movement to right indicates drop in monitor frequency after evaporation while movement to left gives magnitude of thermal error— Fig. 3*

Although a properly-mounted, high-quality AT-cut crystal has a nearly zero temperature coefficient of frequency in the 0 to 20 C range, an unprotected crystal is usually driven beyond this range by radiation and energy of vaporization emitted by the evaporant source.

The behavior of an unprotected monitor crystal in a ring source system or an electron-bombardment source system is not so neat. The effect of heating on the resonant frequency of the crystal is apparent in curve B of Fig. 3 and the heating effect from a crucible source is shown in curve A. For the perfect crucible source, the ratio of evaporant area to thermally-radiating area is unity. For a ring source this can vary from unity to 10, therefore, a system using a ring source for high melting point evaporants or bakeout heaters may require crystal cooling. The success of a water-cooled crystal holder in remedying such situations is apparent in curve C of Fig. 3. This thickness determination was made under exactly the same conditions as curve B, except for cooling.

Work described in this article was performed under contract with the U. S. Navy, Bureau of Ships.

REFERENCE

(1) M. S. Blois, Jr., and L. M. Rieser, Jr., *Jour Applied Physics*, 25, p 338, March 1954.

ANOTHER NEW
COMPONENT

HOT CARRIER

DIODES Switch

in Picoseconds

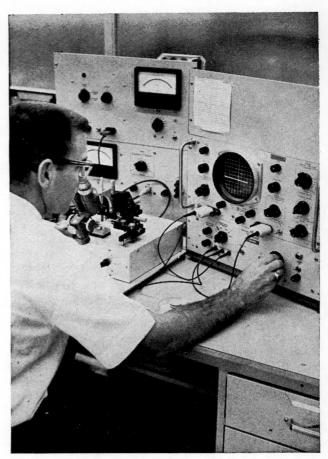

HOT CARRIER DIODE WAFER *undergoing evaluation of leakage current by project engineer Bill Baker*

Metal-semiconductor diodes increase switching speed now limited in **p-n** *junctions by minority-carrier storage. Devices need very pure materials and improved epitaxy*

By S. M. KRAKAUER, Applications Engineer
S. W. SOSHEA, Project Leader
HP Associates, Palo Alto, California

EPITAXIAL SILICON hot carrier diodes were introduced by HP Associates only recently, but many of the principles of rectifying metal contacts have been known for decades. The great advances in germanium and silicon *p-n* junction devices in the last 15 years have tended to obscure the potential of metal-semiconductor contacts. The *p-n* junction diodes are, however, approaching the limit of their high-frequency performance, because of storage of minority carriers. Since minority carrier storage is virtually eliminated, metal-semiconductor diodes show renewed usefulness. The development of the modern hot carrier diode was made possible by the availability of very pure semiconductors, by improved techniques of surface cleaning and passivation, and by the epitaxial construction method.

A hot carrier diode can be made in a variety of ways. A typical epitaxial type is shown in Fig. 1. Experimental models have been made on silicon using evaporated gold, platinum, palladium, silver and many other metals. Both hot electron (on *n*-type silicon) and hot hole (on *p*-type silicon) forms are possible, but the hot electron type is generally preferable because the higher electron mobility gives better high frequency performance.

OPERATION—Hot carrier diode operation and the distinction between it and a *p-n* junction can be understood most clearly by means of the appropriate electron energy diagrams. Figure 2A shows the electron energy diagram of a hot electron diode with a Schottky-type barrier, and Fig. 2B shows the corresponding diagram for an abrupt *p-n* junction diode with the *n*-type region more heavily doped than the *p*-type region. When the hot carrier diode is forward biased, the electrons in the *n*-type semiconductor

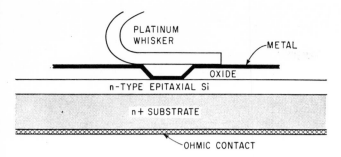

HOT ELECTRON DIODE *construction differs from that of hot hole where substrate would be* p-plus *material and epitaxial layer* p-type *silicon—Fig. 1*

	HPA-2001			HPA-2101		
	Min	Typ	Max	Min	Typ	Max
Forward Current I_F in ma	20	30		20	30	
(at $V_F = 1$ v)						
Forward Current I_F in μa	0.5	1.0		2,000	4,000	
(at $V_F = 0.4$ v)						
Capacitance C_o in pf		0.85	1.0		0.95	1.1
(at $V_B = 0$)						
Breakdown Voltage V_B in v	15	25		15	25	
(at $I_R = 10$ μa)						
Leakage Current I_s in na		1	10		30	100
(at $V_R = 3$ v)						

diffuse over the barrier and are injected into the metal.

The injected hot electrons interact with the lattice and the electrons of the metal and when the diode is reverse biased, these hot electrons are unable to surmount the barrier, so they do not contribute to the stored charge. When, however, the p-n junction is forward biased, the electrons diffuse into the p-type region and build up to a concentration that is limited by the rate of carrier recombination, as depicted in Fig. 2B. When the p-n junction is reverse biased, the stored electrons (minority carriers) flow back into the n-type region, thus lowering the rectification efficiency if the diode is used as a detector, or increasing the reverse recovery time if it is used as a switching diode.

The current-voltage characteristics of hot carrier diodes can be described very closely by the ideal diode equation

$$I_F = I_s \left[\exp(qV/kT) - 1 \right]$$

in which the saturation current I_s is proportional to $\exp(-qV_i/kT)$. The type of metal can be conveniently selected to have an internal barrier V_i from 0.3 to 0.8 volt, corresponding to a saturation current, for a typical diode size (about 6×10^{-6} cm²), from 10^{-11} to 10^{-3} amp. The junction capacitance of the hot carrier diode varies as the inverse square root of voltage and is only slightly dependent on V_i. This combination of characteristics is analogous to a family of p-n junctions of incrementally varying energy band gap and provides the circuit designer with an added degree of freedom that was not previously available. The reverse characteristics of hot carrier diodes appear very similar to those of p-n junction diodes. The

WHAT'S A HOT CARRIER?

Nothing radioactive! In rectifying metal-semiconductor contacts, current flow is predominantly by majority carriers. When such a diode is forward biased, these majority carriers are injected into the metal and have much greater velocity than the thermal electrons— hence the name hot-carrier diodes. With minority carrier storage virtually eliminated, these diodes surpass conventional p-n junction types at high frequencies

reverse leakage current increases with reverse voltage gradually, owing to the internal Schottky effect, until the avalanche multiplication voltage is reached.

Hot carrier diodes are similar in concept and in operation to the ideal point-contact diode in which the contact is neither formed, alloyed nor bonded. Both the hot carrier diode and the ideal point contact diode employ a Schottky barrier, but there are many notable differences. Being of much larger area, the hot carrier diode has larger capacitance than the point contact, but it can handle greater power and is less sensitive to current transients than is the ideal point contact. The hot carrier diode, furthermore, is more stable mechanically and has more nearly ideal and reproducible electrical characteristics.

PERFORMANCE—Recovery time as a function of minority carrier lifetime for these diodes is difficult to measure. The lifetime is so low that its influence is readily obscured by diode and circuit impedances and by transient response anomalies in the associated instrumentation. It has been found best to characterize the recovery time for these diodes relative to a sinusoidal excitation[1]. The circuit is shown in Fig. 3, the resulting oscilloscope patterns in Fig. 4.

The effective minority carrier storage can be related to the amplitude of the negative spike. Diode capacitance causes the baseline to tilt, and so capacitive conduction can be separated from storage conduction by measuring the spike amplitude from this tilted reference line, as shown in upper Fig. 4.

Measurement using this technique is not completely quantitative, but it gives a convenient index of the diode recovery that corresponds to most applications. If, for example, the signal generator and amplifier are adjusted to 53 mc with sufficient output to produce a peak forward current flow of 20 ma and scope gain set to give a 5-cm deflection for the positive peak, then the amplitude of the negative spike (read as shown) will be related to lifetime as $\tau = 500$ ps/per cm for deflections less than 1.5 cm. This value is an effective rather than a true minority carrier lifetime. It is essentially the product of true minority carrier lifetime by the ratio of minority to majority carriers that is associated with forward conduction. This ratio is made smaller with reduced barrier height and reduced substrate resistivity. Currently available diodes have effective lifetimes below the resolution capability of this measurement (<50

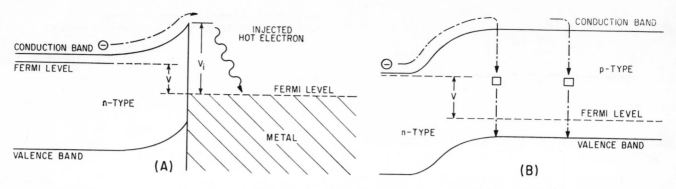

ENERGY LEVELS *in metal-semiconductor junction (A) and* p-n *junction of normal silicon diode (B)—Fig. 2*

ps). Sufficiently high values of forward current can cause minority carrier injection, and storage.

Hot carrier diodes now available are listed in the table. The static characteristics of these diodes, both in forward and reverse, are similar to conventional *p-n* junction diodes. The type 2001 resembles a conventional silicon *p-n* junction diode, and the type 2101 resembles germanium, as shown in Fig. 5.

To take full advantage of their fast response capability, care is necessary in mounting these diodes. Minimum possible lead length will reduce to a minimum performance degradation owing to shunt capacitance and series inductance. The self-inductance of the present package is approximately 3 nh. A lower inductance package is under development.

In general the same considerations that apply to the application of conventional *p-n* junction diodes will apply to the hot carrier diode. The differences between them is confined to the lower storage and wider choice of barrier height that is associated with the hot carrier diode. Accordingly, hot carrier diodes might be substituted in many existing circuits without design modifications being required, and with a substantial gain in performance.

NO DELAYS—Minority carrier storage in the hot carrier diode is so low that the turn-on and turn-off delays that are present in conventional *p-n* junction diodes will be essentially eliminated. Accordingly, hot carrier diodes can be used effectively in those pulse and high frequency applications where lag-free response is required, such as detection, mixing and limiting at microwave and high frequencies. Within fractional nanosecond limits they can be used for clamping and gating rapidly.

Freedom of choice in barrier height leads to applications that may or may not also require low storage. Low barrier, low storage diodes permit an approach to ideality for detection sensitivity, mixing efficiency, and harmonic generating capability because of the improved impedance matches. Also, tunnel diode logic circuits which require very low turn-on voltage for the associated diode may become possible.

REFERENCE

(1) S. M. Krakauer, Harmonic Generation, Rectification, and Lifetime Evaluation with the Step Recovery Diode, *Proc. IRE*, p 1665, July 1962.

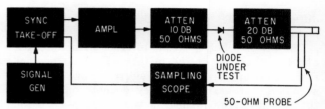

EFFECTIVE LIFETIME MEASUREMENT *of diode is made with this equipment setup—Fig. 3*

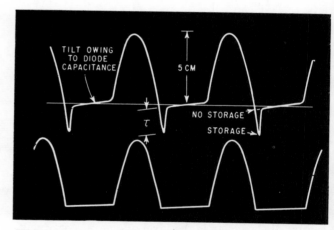

HIGH-SPEED SWITCHING DIODE *(top) compared with hot carrier diode. Sweep speed is 10 nsec per cm, vertical sensitivity is 20 ma per cm. Applied signal is a 30-Mc sine wave—Fig. 4*

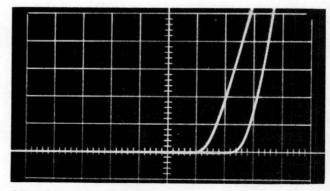

STATIC CHARACTERISTICS *of type 2101 (left) and type 2001 show that the former starts conduction at about 0.3 v and latter around 0.5 v. Vertical calibration is 2 ma per division and horizontal is 0.2 v per division—Fig. 5*

NEW CHARTS
Speed Thin-Film Resistor Design

Graphical method eliminates tedious calculations in finding thin-resistor dimensions for desired resistance and power rating

By HENRY L. COOK
Supervisor, Thin Film Laboratory
Martin Company, Orlando, Florida

GRAPHS and a chart have been developed that eliminate many tedious calculations from thin-film resistor design. This method, now in use at Martin-Orlando, has also improved overall reliability in thin-film operations.

The resistance of a thin-film resistor is determined by the dimensions of a resistive material deposited on a substrate. Many hours may be required to calculate the sizes required to obtain a large number of resistance values. Also, the calculated size is sometimes too small to manufacture, requiring additional calculations to obtain practical dimensions.

Thickness of a thin-film resistor, which is about 200 angstroms, is predetermined. A resistive constant is used in thin-film resistor design, which is the measured resistance of a geometric square (length equals width regardless of their actual dimensions) of a resistive material deposited at constant thickness. The resistive constant is commonly expressed in ohms per square. Since thickness is constant, a desired resistance is obtained by calculating the required length and width.

The ability of a thin-film resistor to dissipate power is governed by the substrate area occupied by the resistor. Power dissipation per unit area is an experimentally determined constant. At the present state of the art, redundant calculations are often required to obtain a desired resistance and power dissipation capability.

The length of a thin-film resistor required to obtain a desired resistance is determined from

$$L = (RP/K_r K_p)^{\frac{1}{2}} \quad (1)$$

where L is length in inches, R is required resistance in ohms, P is required power dissipation in milliwatts, K_r is resistive constant in ohms per square and K_p is power constant in milliwatts per square inch. Length is determined by Eq. 1 so that the resistor will be capable of the required heat dissipation.

Because of the direct relationship between length and width in establishing the resistance of a thin-film resistor, width can be found from

$$W = LK_r/R, \quad (2)$$

where W is width in inches.

When either calculated length or width is too small, additional calculations are required assuming a new length or width.

The table and graphs were constructed from the two equations. Length can be determined for numerous sets of constants from the graph at the top of the figure and from the table, and width can be found from the graph at the bottom of the figure. These graphs and the table are based on resistive constants from 125 to 4,000 ohms per square and power constants

TABLE—RESISTOR LENGTHS FOR GIVEN CONSTANTS

CONSTANTS		LENGTH IN INCHES									
OHMS PER SQUARE	MW PER SQUARE INCH	A	B	C	D	E	F	G	H	J	K
125	32,000	0.01	0.02	0.04	0.08	0.16	0.32	0.64	1.28	....	....
250	16,000	0.005	0.01	0.02	0.04	0.08	0.16	0.32	0.64	1.28	....
500	8,000	0.0025	0.005	0.01	0.02	0.04	0.08	0.16	0.32	0.64	1.28
1,000	4,000	0.00125	0.0025	0.005	0.01	0.02	0.04	0.08	0.16	0.32	0.64
2,000	2,000	....	0.00125	0.0025	0.005	0.01	0.02	0.04	0.08	0.16	0.32
4,000	1,000	....	....	0.00125	0.0025	0.005	0.01	0.02	0.04	0.08	0.16

from 1,000 to 32,000 milliwatts per square inch.

EXAMPLE — Determine the length and width of a 1,000-ohm thin-film resistor that can dissipate 5 milliwatts when the given resistive constant is 500 ohms per square and the given power constant is 8,000 milliwatts per square inch.

Using the graph at the top of the figure, locate the junction of 1,000 ohms and 5 milliwatts. If this point does not fall on a line length, continue upwards to the next line length (0.04 inch), which indicates the required length.

In the table, find the two constants 500 ohms per square and 8,000 milliwatts per square inch.

Horizontally along this line, find the line length (0.04). At the top of the column containing the line length, find the corresponding letter (E).

Using the graph at the bottom of the figure, find the intersection of line length E and 1,000 ohms. Moving horizontally from this point, the required width is indicated on the width axis.

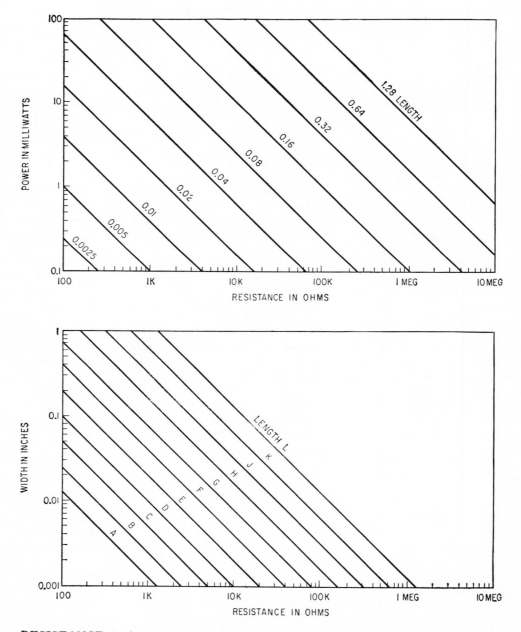

RESISTANCE *is shown as a function of power in upper graph and as a function of resistor width in lower graph*

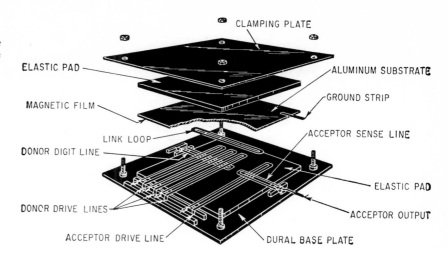

MAGNETIC FILM gate employs *magnetic-film conducting substrate and a floating planar linkage*

Labels on diagram:
CLAMPING PLATE
ELASTIC PAD
ALUMINUM SUBSTRATE
MAGNETIC FILM
GROUND STRIP
LINK LOOP
ACCEPTOR SENSE LINE
DONOR DIGIT LINE
DONOR DRIVE LINES
ELASTIC PAD
ACCEPTOR OUTPUT
ACCEPTOR DRIVE LINE
DURAL BASE PLATE

NEW DESIGN IDEA

Thin Magnetic Films Create Logic Circuits

By M. Williams The General Electric Co. Ltd., Central Research Labs, Wembley, England

A SIMPLE method of linking multi-element magnetic film memory cells has been used in the construction of a magnetic film gate. The method relies on the magnetic film having a conducting substrate. Linkages between cells are made by a floating planar conducting loop that transfers majority information by conservation of flux in the closed link. The exploded drawing of the gate and the accompanying general explication will make the method clear.

LINKAGE PROBLEMS—The idea of using the outputs of a group of magnetic film storage cells (using orthogonal fields) as the digit current for another cell is fairly obvious, but the realization of practical devices is difficult and descriptions have necessarily been speculative.[1]

One difficulty is that although the flux may be temporarily conserved in a short-circuit link, most of the flux change neutralizing the flux of one film cell may simply be an air flux change. This can be overcome, in principle, by a conducting substrate[2], which gives a low inductance to conductors close to the substrate.

A second difficulty is closing the link. Joining it to the substrate is not attractive for mass production and involves risks to the film. When links are superimposed, fixing becomes even more difficult.

A simple solution to these problems is afforded by symmetrical storage cells with two digit/sense lines[3]: these are joined to each other instead of to the ground plane, forming a floating, planar link. Such cells have these advantages:

• Very low writing threshold

• No electrostatic coupling between orthogonal sets of balanced conductor pairs

• Smaller dependence of output upon skew of easy axis than with single-element cells, important when cell outputs must balance one another in majority logic.

GATES—If four cells share a link, as in the figure, the majority output of three can set the fourth. If two cells store input information while the third stores a digit dictating the function, the unit forms an AND or OR gate, as in phase logic[4].

In experiments, the conductors were 40 mil × 1 mil aluminum, anodized for insulation. The 80Ni 17Fe3Go film[2], 1,500 Å thick, was on a polished Al substrate; it had H_k = 2.4 oersted and H_c = 3.4 oersted.

First trials involved activating a single cell and measuring the resulting link current. This involves measuring the area under the voltage waveform from a conductor having a mutual inductance with the link. Breaking the link, putting in a known current pulse, and repeating the observation makes it possible to calculate the original link current.

After insulation was adjusted to give over 50 ma link current, energy was successfully transferred from a cell into the link and back again (a form of nondestructive readout). However, during many repetitions the signal fell off. Transfer from one cell to another was tried, and was found possible. The gate shown in the figure was then tested: digits were written into the three donor cells, and majority information was transferred, although the magnitude of the flux set in the acceptor cell varied a little according to the order in which digits were written into donor cells.

REFERENCES

(1) W. E. Proebster and H. J. Oguey, High-Speed Magnetic-Film Logic, *Digest of 1960 International Solid-State Circuits Conf.*, p 22, Feb. 1960.
(2) E. M. Bradley, *J Appl Phys*, **33** Suppl., p 1051, 1962.
(3) M. Williams, *Proc Inst Elec Engrs*, London, **109 B**, Suppl. 21, p 186, 1962.
(4) R. L. Wigington, *Proc IRE*, **47**, p 517, 1959.

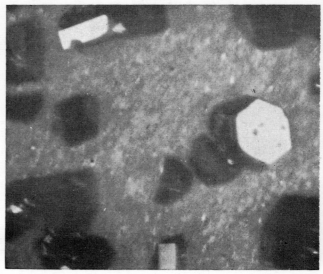

HEXAGONAL structure of photo-conductor material deposited on alumina. Cell contains cadmium, silicon carbide and sulphide compounds. Magnification is 1,800 times

Thin-Film

Photocells Get Brighter Faster

High density cells have

rise-decay under 50 µsec.

Deposits are uniform

IMPROVED light characteristics are claimed for photoconductive thin films, developed for optical displays.

The material and techniques for deposition on substrates were developed by Photometics Corporation, Walker Valley, New York. Performance and applications were described by Roland C. B. Beeh, company president.

The material will open up new avenues for optoelectronic devices and electroluminescent solid-state display panels, Beeh says.

A mosaic of photoconductive cells is formed on a substrate by vacuum deposition. Cells are said to exhibit fast recurrent or nonrecurrent illumination. Rise and decay time of less than 50 µsec is claimed. The photosensitive areas operate under light modulation up to 100 kc, according to reports.

Characteristics of the material can be applied to visual displays for command control centers, and large panel displays for air-traffic.

A high density of photoconductive regions can be attained. Performance is uniform and the material can be deposited over large areas with uniformity of deposition within 5 percent, Beeh added.

LATTICE—The photoconductor has a polycrystalline structure. Cadmium, silicon carbide and sulphide compounds are tightly bonded in a hexagonal lattice. Dimension of the lattice is given as less than 5 angstroms.

The materials are vacuum deposited, purified compounds are selected by molecular beam. Ion pumping is used, instead of oil diffusion, to avoid formation of hydrocarbons. Seven elements can be evaporated at the same time. Activators are introduced by ionization at high temperature, under high

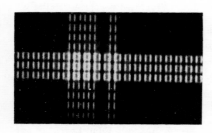

GHOST effect is shown on 100 element/inch solid-state electroluminescent panel. Approaches are now being considered to circumvent cross illumination

SPEED of response of material is shown in lower trace. Upper trace shows 10,000 cycle input. Material obtains full brightness within 2 cycles

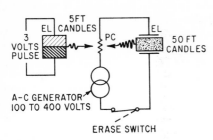

SINGLE element display with storage

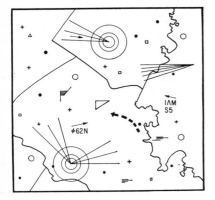

TYPICAL situation display shows coastline, radar stations, airfields, and armament centers. Vectors represent moving aircraft or missiles

picture elements and 40,000 photoconductors per sq in.

The sensitivity of the photoconductors averages 6,000 microamperes per foot-candle. Polarizing voltage of 50 v d-c with an illumination of 1 foot-candle from a tungsten filament source, operates at 2,853 deg K.

The photoconductors may also be photoetched directly on the substrate to provide isolated junctions. Once deposited, the cells are not hygroscopic, and are said to have good surface hardness. Protective envelopes are not needed. This cuts the cost of fabricating a mosiac of cells. There is no need for hermetically sealing feedthrough for the lead wires.

One method looks promising for el displays. A storage would be provided on the display panel itself. A mosaic of photoconductors on the back of the panel would provide an el-pc latch. The photoconductor lowers its internal resistance when the picture element is excited by the x and y voltages. Current flows through the picture element, even though the selected electrical pulses have been removed.

The dark current characteristic

of the cell is less than 0.0015 ma after removal, within 50 μsec, of an illumination of 100 foot candles. Dark noise is less than 10^{-11} amperes. Beeh says that this is important in making decoding circuits using many cells.

The photoconductors operate within a range between —60 C and 150 C. Dark resistance is in the order of 800 megohms. Resistance under illumination can be as low as 4,000 ohms, depending upon application and intensity of illumination.

GHOST EFFECT — Suppression of illumination between the x and y drive lines has been a problem in el displays. Six x drive lines and eight y drive lines were selected in a 100-element-per-inch panel to

show this effect, see photo. The ghost effect can be reduced using nonlinear resistive elements.

Layers of silicon carbide, cadmium sulphide, imbedded in epoxy, can be placed between the x and y electrodes. However, this approach increases voltage requirements. In higher-resolution panels, this can result in cross talk and uneven illumination.

Several other approaches are being considered at Photonetics to circumvent this problem.

The company is making available to industry, under development contracts, mosaics of photoconductors and electroluminescent panels. These are supplied with photoconductive wafers on isolated substrates to suit a variety of electrode geometrics.

Ferrites: Can They Be Deposited As Thin Films?

Deposition techniques are sought as part of inductor development

RESEARCHERS AT Motorola, Phoenix, have produced thin-film, flat-spiral inductors by depositing gold through nickel-on-copper masks onto ferrite substrates. A 21-turn configuration has yielded 1.6 microhenries when deposited on a nonmagnetic material and 3.3 microhenries when deposited on a ferrite substrate (ELECTRONICS, Jan. 31, 1964, p 19).

Goal of research program is to produce 30 to 1,000-microhenry devices with Q values of 100 or more at 1 Mc, according to a Motorola spokesman. As part of the program, thin-film ferrites were deposited on

ferrite substrates holding the gold flat-spiral inductors. The deposited ferrite acted as a ferrite core for the thin-film inductor. The ferrite overlay is expected to raise inductance.

Ferrite Thin Films—A technique has been developed for preparing ferrite thin films which possess properties that are compatible for use with thin spiral coils to provide increases in the air-core inductance of these coils. The films are ferrimagnetic, possess a detectable magnetic moment, are of the ferrite spinel structure, and are formed at temperatures compatible with gold coils.

Initial permeabilities have been measured and values as high as 90 attained. No measurement of film Q value has as yet been made but measurements could be made by actual construction of a device. These films have a density comparable to that of conventionally formed ferrite of similar composition. The

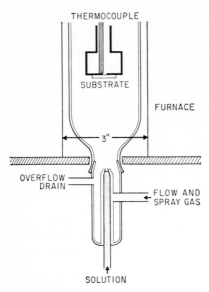

THERMOCOUPLE

SUBSTRATE

FURNACE

3"

OVERFLOW DRAIN

FLOW AND SPRAY GAS

SOLUTION

FILM DEPOSITION apparatus developed for ferrites. Above the thermocouple, and not shown in the illustration, is a vacuum system for evacuating the chamber

density would seem to indicate the useful Q values in film material could be obtained.

The composition used for the majority of the work is a nickel-zinc-cobalt ferrite. This composition —$Ni_{0.4}An_{.573}Co_{.027}Fe_2O_4$— in bulk form has the desired properties at 1 Mc. (i.e. high initial permeability and Q value).

The main problem in the ferrite film program has been controlling the composition of the film as compared to the starting solution composition. The most difficult element to control is the zinc, which has the undesired tendency to be preferentially volatalized in reference to the other constituents. Precise control of the process temperature seems to be the most important parameter in the control of the film composition.

Spiral Coil Fabrication—The formation of a conducting spiral pattern is a three-step process. First, the required material is deposited to thickness up to 1 mil. Second, a suitable photoresist is applied, exposed, and developed to give the required spiral pattern. And third, the pattern is etched to produce the desired spiral inductor. The use of specific materials depends upon the condition of the substrate surface, and the metal being used for the conducting path.

Deposition of Metal Films—The gold or copper sheet film from which the spiral pattern is etched is

deposited in two steps. Initially a thin conductive film a few thousand angstroms thick is vacuum deposited, preceded by thin nonconducting film of chromium to provide adhesion to the ferrite surface. The evaporated film is then built up to the required thickness by electroplating techniques. An alternate method for preparing the first deposit for the copper film was an electroless process using "Cuposit," (available from Shipley Company, Wellesley, Massachusetts). The process was used on ferrite surfaces which were excessively porous and not suitable for accepting a continuance evaporated film. As a third method, copper was electroplated from a copper fluoroborate solution using standard current densities. Periodic current reverse was used to obtain a smooth, pinhole-free film. Surfaces were then gold plated in a cyanide bath.

Kodak Photo-Resist (KPR) was used for the copper films and Kodak Metal Etch Resist (KMER) for gold films. Both resists were applied by spin techniques and exposed through a contact mask of the de-

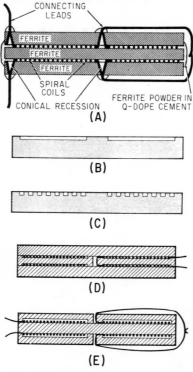

CONNECTING LEADS

FERRITE
FERRITE
FERRITE

SPIRAL COILS

CONICAL RECESSION

FERRITE POWDER IN Q-DOPE CEMENT

(A)

(B)

(C)

(D)

(E)

TYPICAL configurations of inductors and ferrite substrates. Typical ferrite inductor is shown in (A); ferrite substrate recessed for coil application (B); and with integral spiral pattern (C); configuration of inductor with coil formed in recess (D) and recessed ferrite used as an overlay (E)

sired spiral pattern by a strobeflash unit. Developing was done in trich-

lorethylene and a post-development bake was used to further set the resist. The copper spirals were etched in a heated 50-percent solution of ferric chloride, and gold patterns in aqua regia. On occasion, the cross section of the conducting path was increased with additional electroplating to lower the resistance and, therefore, increase the Q value of the coil.

Preliminary Results—A number of coils were fabricated on various bulk ferrite wafers. The majority used a 20-turn configuration on a Ceramag 9 wafer, 0.25-inch square. Total inductance values varied between 2.5 and 4 microhenries which is an increase over the air-core value by 20 to 30 times. Q values were between 10 and 20 as measured at 1 Mc.

Preparation of Recessed Ferrites—Two different approaches to the preparation of ferrite surfaces for reducing air-gap effects were evaluated. One approach was to form the desired spiral pattern directly in the ferrite, and the second was to shape a recession in the ferrite in which the coil would be fabricated by the conventional techniques.

Spiral patterns were formed in ferrite material by pressing the spiral shape in the ferrite surface prior to the final firing of the ferrite, and also by etching the ferrite surface using photo-resist.

In the latter method, a negative of the desired spiral image was prepared on the ferrite surface using KMER. The ferrite surface not protected by the exposed resist was etched using a stannous chloride, disodium ethylene diaminetetra-acetate, hydrochloride solution heated to 65 deg. C. This solution would satisfactorily etch the ferrite material; however, the etchant was absorbed under the KMER surface by the porous ferrite, resulting in uncontrollable pattern resolution.

Because of ferrite shrinkage during final firing, die dimensions were made about 30 percent larger than the desired pattern. To form the conducting path in the spiral recess, the entire surface was covered with the copper film and the film above the recess removed by lapping. Although this technique proved to be successful, it was not pursued beyond the feasibility stage as the ferrite material used did not possess the required permeability and Q value.

Chapter 10
MICROMODULES

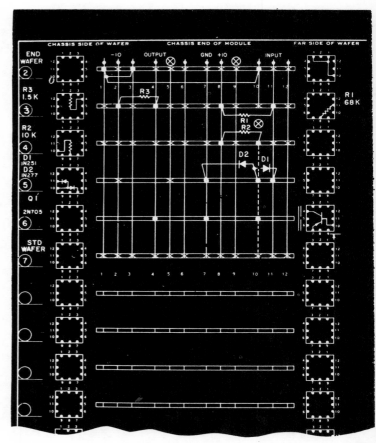

MICROMODULE ASSEMBLY *layout sheet shows component locations, jumpers, riser-wire lengths and solder points—Fig. 1*

How To Design Micromodules

By RENATO DiSTEFANO, JR.
Semiconductor and Materials Div
Radio Corporation of America
Somerville, N.J.

DESIGN METHODS for micromodule electronic or electromechanical systems can be applied to existing systems that require a minimum of redesign, as well as to developmental systems that consist of only a performance specification and a list of environmental requirements.

In either case, the design of the system begins with the breadboard construction of the entire system, or of that portion of the system to be redesigned in micromodule form. The completed breadboard is subjected to all specified operating and storage environmental test conditions, with the exception of such tests as shock, vibration or thermal dissipation, which yield no applicable information when conducted on a breadboard.

DESIGN CONSIDERATIONS — The present range of microelement capability is shown in Table I. When possible, a micromodule is designed to include the microelements required for a complete functional unit or stage, such as an amplifier stage, mixer, local oscillator, multivibrator, inverter or gate. This method of circuit division provides design simplicity and minimizes the number of connections between micromodules. In certain cases, such as cascaded intermediate-frequency stages, the requirement for isolation of signal leads strongly influences the manner in which the circuit is divided into micromodules.

The designer divides the circuits of the entire system or subsystems into sections, each of which represents a separate micromodule, and

KUDOS FOR MICROMODULES

Just two weeks ago, Major General E. F. Cooke, Chief Signal Officer, said that the Chief of Staff for Logistics has issued a directive to incorporate the micromodule concept in Army equipment where appropriate (ELECTRONICS, p 7, Sept 7). Meanwhile, six items considered highly suitable for micromodule application have been
funded for R&D by the Army in 1963-64. These include an airborne h-f ssb radio, a lightweight hand-held surveillance radar, a "flash ranging set" to detect gun flashes, an electronic teletypewriter, a tactical digital communications system and the production version of Micropac, small field computer to be delivered in November by RCA

TABLE I — PRESENT MICROELEMENT-CAPABILITY

RESISTORS

	Carbon	Cermet
Number of Resistors per Microelement	1 to 4	1 to 4
Value Range per Resistor (ohms)	10–150,000	10–150,000
Value Range per Microelement (ohms)	2.5–600,000	2.5–600,000
Maximum Dissipation per Resistor (watts)	⅛	⅛
Maximum Dissipation per Microelement (watts)	½	½
Maximum Micromodule Temperature for Rated Dissipation (degrees C)	70	70
Temperature Characteristic (ppm per degree C)	±1,300	±200

CAPACITORS

	Precision (T. C.)	General-Purpose	Electrolytic (Tantalum)
Number of Capacitors per Microelement	1	1	1
Value Range	5 pf to 3,000 pf	100 pf to 0.15 mf	1 to 47 mf
Tolerance (percent)	1 to 10	10 to 20	10 to 20
Temperature Range (degrees C)	−55 to +85	−55 to +85	−55 to +85
Temperature Characteristic	±30 ppm/°C (nominal)	+10%, −30%	±15%
Maximum Dissipation	0.001	0.015	0.06 at 120 cps
Maximum D-C Voltage	50–100	50–100	35 (470 mf-volt) max.

INDUCTORS

Maximum Inductance (millihenries) 1.5
Maximum Operating Frequency (megacycles) 50

DIODES

Most miniature diodes that are not larger than 0.2 inch may be mounted on a microelement wafer. From one to four diodes may be mounted on a microelement, depending upon dimensions and terminations. Diodes are now available in packages suitable for microelement mounting

TRANSISTORS

Any transistor that can be mounted on a microelement wafer so that its case does not short to the micromodule riser wires is suitable for use in micromodules

notes the occurrence of repetitive circuits that can utilize identical micromodules. Identical modules in repetitive circuits are especially desirable in systems to be produced in large volume, because they result in cost savings of materials and testing.

Micromodules can be constructed with external leads at both ends; however, interconnection considerations have made the single-ended micromodule definitely preferable for most systems. The single-ended micromodule normally has twelve external leads spaced on a 0.075-inch grid pattern at one end.

Although micromodules can be made in heights up to one inch, most units are between 0.4 and 0.8 inch high. Micromodule lengths within this range can accommodate many types of stages without exceeding the twelve-lead limit on external connections. Some of the more complicated amplifiers, multivibrators, and other types of stages are subdivided into two or more micromodules; similarly, some simple repetitive stages, such as gates, may be combined with one or more similar stages into a single micromodule. In some cases, the maximum height of one or more micromodules in a system is limited by the volume specifications for the complete system.

A rough estimate of the height of a micromodule may be made by adding the space requirements for each of the microelements, or wafers, of which it is composed. The space requirement for each wafer is determined by adding 0.01 inch to the maximum allowable thickness of each wafer. The 0.01 inch includes the height required by soluble spacers which are inserted between the wafers during the assembly process. Additional allowances of up to 0.02 inches may be required where riser wires are "cut," as explained below.

Since the maximum allowable thickness of standard resistor microelements is 0.02 inch, an allowance of 0.03 inch is made for each resistor in the micromodule. Because each resistor wafer has a maximum dissipation allowance of one-half watt, each wafer can accommodate either four one-eighth-watt elements, or two one-quarter-watt elements, one on each side of the wafer. When a resistor wafer has two resistors on one side, the ratio of the higher resistance value to the lower should be less than five, and the terminations of the two elements must be so arranged that the elements do not cross each other.

For microdiodes mounted in wafers, space allowance is 0.03 inch more than the maximum diode diameter, for each diode wafer used.

The space requirements for some of the other types of microelements are listed in Table II.

When the space requirements for all of the microelement wafers in the micromodule have been determined, they are added, and an additional 0.12 inch is added for encapsulation, end wafers, module pedestals, and building tolerance. The total is the maximum estimated height of the micromodule; the actual height may be as much as 25 percent less, depending on the actual microelement dimensions, number and location of riser-wire cuts, and similar considerations.

When the height of each micromodule has been estimated, the total height is compared with the system volume specifications to determine if the circuits to be included in each micromodule must be adjusted to fit the space available.

MODULE ASSEMBLY—Figure 1, a completed micromodule assembly layout, shows the method of numbering riser wires. Figure 2B shows the system of numbering notches on the microelement wafers. The uncircled numbers are the notch numbers; the circled numbers refer to the corresponding riser-wire numbers. On those wafers that are mounted in the normal, or *A1* position, the notch numbers coincide with the riser wire numbers. The rectangular index notch in the corner of the wafer is used for orientation during assembly. On the assembly drawing, notch numbers are not shown, but all notches not mounted in the normal or *A1* position with respect to the micromodule riser wires are indicated by three short vertical lines adjacent to the drawing of the far side of the wafer. The mounting position of all wafers not mounted in the normal position is indicated by an

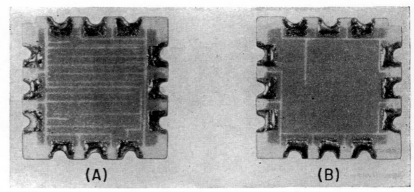

RESISTOR *wafer, showing first side (A) and reverse side (B)*

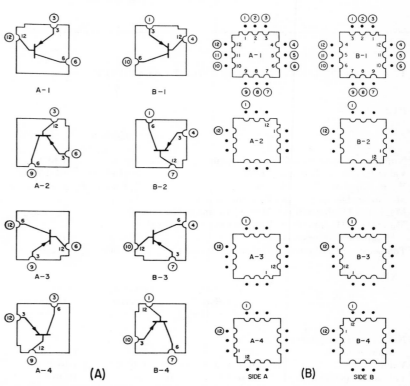

POSSIBLE MOUNTING POSITIONS *for a transistor microelement (A); for a microelement wafer (B)—Fig. 2*

MICROMODULES *mounted on a printed-wiring board—Fig. 3*

TABLE II — MICROELEMENT DIMENSIONS

Element	Value Range	Dimension Requirements* (Inches)
Capacitor (T.C.)................	to 250 pf	0.03
" "	250 to 1,000 pf	0.04
" "	1,000 to 2,200 pf	0.065
Capacitor, Gen. Purp............	0.003 to 0.022 μf	0.04
" "	0.022 to 0.1 μf	0.09
Capacitor. Electrolytic...........	1 to 3 μf	0.065
" "	4.7 to 22 μf	0.105
Diode, Microelement.............	——	0.08
Transistor, TO-46 Package Mounted on Wafer.....................	——	0.115
Transistor, Other Suitable Package Mounted on Wafer.............	——	Package height plus 0.035 inch

* Includes 0.01 inch allowance for spacers, etc.

arrow which points to the long side of the wafer index notch, as is the microlement Q_1 (item 6) shown in Fig. 1.

The various microelement wafers are connected by hard-drawn, solder-coated, tinned copper wires, which also form the external leads. These riser wires form the nodes of the module circuits. If thirteen nodes are required in one module, one of the riser wires is extended only far enough through the module to connect all the elements which meet at one of the nodes. An additional node is formed by placing a short section of a riser wire between those wafers, beyond the end of the shortened, or "cut" riser wire, which contain the elements to be connected to the thirteenth node. This procedure may be repeated with as many as seven additional riser wires to form additional nodes as required, but at least one riser wire on each of the four sides of the micromodule must extend along its entire length and form one of the external leads. Where the additional nodes formed by such segmented riser wires consist of connections between adjacent wafers having no more than 0.003 inch of build-up on each side of the substrate, the connection between the wafers is made by solder bridging during the dip-soldering process, and no riser-wire segment is required.

Transistor microelements and mounting wafers for transistors in TO-46 and similar types of cases are usually made so that the element is terminated to the wafer notches as shown in Fig. 2A, which also indicates the eight possible mounting positions for this wafer in the micromodule. When a micromodule is designed with two transistors connected in a common-emitter configuration, one unit can be mounted in the A1 position and the other in the B1 position, with a connection or jumper located on an end wafer between riser wires 1 and 3.

An end wafer is usually placed at each end of the module to protect the microelement wafers during manufacture, and to provide a mounting for jumpers between riser wires. When necessary, an end wafer may be eliminated if it contains no jumper and if the adjacent wafer does not contain an element on its outer face. Elimination of an end wafer will shorten the module height by about 0.015 inch.

Riser wires may also be shortened for additional isolation of a tuned circuit or other critical element located at the end of the module farthest from the chassis. The operation of such circuits may also be improved by locating input and output leads on opposite sides of the micromodule, and by designing the module so that the two riser wires on each side of a critical signal lead are grounded on the printed-circuit interconnecting board.

If less than twelve leads are required on a single micromodule for external connections, one or two of the riser wires on each side of the module may be cut off within 0.015 inch of the end wafer after the module is assembled to simplify the wiring on the printed-circuit interconnection board, as in the case of riser wires 5 and 9 in Fig. 1. However, in all such cases, at least one of the uncut external leads on each of the four micromodule sides must extend through the length of the micromodule. Printed-circuit interconnection board wiring may be further simplified, on occasion, by providing jumpers on micromodule end wafers between leads which do not connect to nodes within the micromodule, as shown for the end wafer at the chassis end of the micromodule in Fig. 1.

Unless element isolation requirements or cuts in riser wires dictate otherwise, resistors are usually located at the end of the module closest to the chassis, followed by capacitors, inductors, silicon semiconductors and germanium semiconductors, in that order, to ensure the most efficient transfer of heat from the micromodule. When one or more of the micromodule riser wires are shortened, the configuration of the various circuit nodes determines the order in which the wafers must be assembled. In Fig. 1, a cut is indicated on riser wire 10 inside the module, and the riser-wire segment used for the node identified as 10' on the schematic diagram is shown as a dashed line. In this case, the node cannot be formed by solder bridging because one of the wafers involved has more than 0.003 inch of build-up on both sides.

The first step in the design of a micromodule incorporating the circuit shown in Fig. 1 is the assignment of riser-wire numbers. For optimum micromodule system design, this assignment is made during the layout of the printed-circuit board on which the micromodules are to be mounted. Because it is preferable to use the standard transistor microelement wafer (Fig. 2A) when possible, the riser wires that connect to the emitter and collector of Q_1 are assigned first, and the printed-circuit mounting board is then laid out. Riser-wire numbers are then assigned to the remaining nodes of the micromodule.

The printed-circuit board layout usually determines the assignment of riser-wire numbers to the remaining circuit nodes which must connect to the board. As shown in Fig. 2A, the transistor base should connect to riser-wire 10; however because riser-wire 10 has already been assigned as one terminal of a jumper wire associated with the external circuits, the wire must be cut to form node 10′ for the transistor base.

With all the nodes of the circuit assigned, the microelement layouts can be completed. The jumpers required by the external circuits are placed on the end wafer, and R_1 and R_3 are placed on the adjacent wafer. Since R_2 connects to 10′ it is placed on the third wafer in order that riser wire 10 may be attached to the required minimum of two wafers before it is cut. The two diodes are mounted on the fourth wafer, followed by the transistor and the second end wafer.

Micromodules may be designed to include circuits tuned by trimmer capacitors with ranges up to sixteen picofarads. In such cases, the trimmer is mounted at the end of the module for access when tuning, and the transformer is mounted on the adjacent wafer, which may also include a larger fixed capacitor connected in parallel with the trimmer. This arrangement also provides some isolation from the remainder of the micromodule.

In the design of a micromodule system, it is often helpful to construct a breadboard of the micromodule by mounting hard-drawn wires about two inches long in each pin of a twelve-pin phenolic plug. The other ends of the wires are secured to a phenolic disk, which is similar to the base in diameter and separated from it by a small two-inch sleeve mounted at the axis of the connector. The twelve wires are numbered according to the numbers of the plug, and the circuit elements to be used in one micromodule may be connected between the riser wires. The resulting totem-pole arrangement is an electrical equivalent of the module in analogous physical form. An entire system may be made in this totem pole configuration, and the test circuits for the system may be mounted on a master board fitted

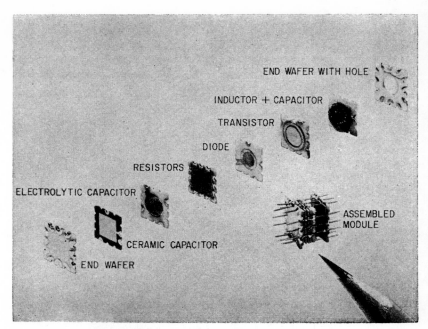

EXPLODED VIEW *of a typical micromodule*

with receptacles for the totem-pole plugs. This arrangement is often convenient for the tuning, testing, and adjustment of the prototype micromodules or systems of micromodules because, with an adapter socket, one or more micromodules may be substituted for the corresponding totem-pole units.

SYSTEM ASSEMBLY—After assembly, micromodules are tested and encapsulated in an epoxy resin. When the completed micromodules have been tested again for specification performance, they are ready for assembly in the system for which they were designed. Micromodules are usually interconnected on a printed-circuit board, as shown in Fig. 3.

The printed-circuit board is designed so that the micromodules are spaced 0.4 inch between centers, but, if room is available, this spacing may be increased to accommodate a complex printed-circuit-board wiring pattern on a single side of the printed-circuit board. If the spacing between the micromodules cannot be increased beyond 0.4 inch, a double-sided printed-circuit board may be used.

A micromodule may be enclosed in a shield covering all surfaces except the chassis end; the major part of the chassis end may be shielded by a portion of the ground plane on the printed-circuit board.

If the system being designed requires components which have not yet been adapted to the micromodule form, the components may be mounted directly on the printed-circuit interconnecting board near the micromodules to which they connect.

The foregoing is a general survey of micromodule system design procedure as it exists in March, 1962. As a result of extensive development work underway at the time of writing, it may be anticipated that the coming months will further improve on the already large range of component values and operating specifications of microelements which are now available, and that the constantly improving favorable situation of micromodules with respect to operating reliability will become an achievement goal for all future generations of microelectronic concepts.

The guidance and comments offered by the author's colleagues, particularly by R. Wilson, R. Pew, H. Keitelman and R. Samuel are gratefully acknowledged.

BIBLIOGRAPHY

D. T. Levy, A Packaged Micromodula Laboratory for Industry, *RCA Engineer*, Dec. 1960-Jan. 1961.
P. Schwartz and R. Stetson, Ceramics and Micromodule, *RCA Engineer*, Dec. 1959-Jan. 1960.
Micromodule Design Manual MDM 500 A. RCA Semiconductor and Materials Division, Somerville, New Jersey.

MICROPAC *weighs in at only 90 pounds, but is a complete digital computer for tactical applications*

Computers in the Front Lines:

Micromodules Make it Possible

Development of micromodules has significantly reduced the size and weight of electronic equipment. This computer has a wide range of uses. It takes advantage of micromodular construction

By **A. S. RETTIG,** Surface Communications Div.,
Defense Electronics Products,
Radio Corporation of America, Camden, N. J.

THIS GENERAL-PURPOSE military digital computer will be used in tactical applications where high reliability, small size and weight and low power requirements are primary considerations. The computer uses micromodular construction, providing high packaging density, excellent reliability and a predicted failure rate of 0.04-percent per 1,000 hours per two-circuit micromodule. The computer, as a whole, has a mean-time-before-fail-

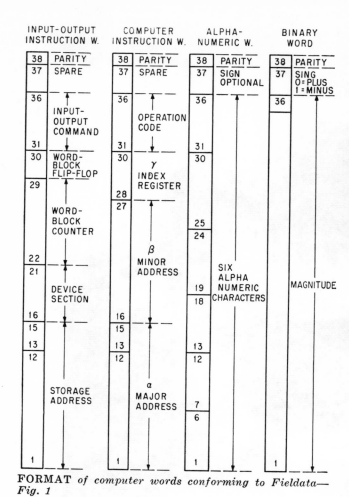

FORMAT *of computer words conforming to Fieldata—* Fig. 1

THE COMPUTER *is divided into five major subsections, all of which have micromodular features—Fig. 2*

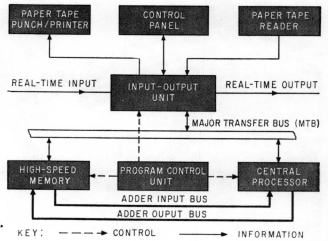

LOGIC RACK *(top), power supply and memory stack (right) of computer*

| PAPER TAPE PUNCH/PRINTER | CONTROL PANEL | PAPER TAPE READER |

REAL-TIME INPUT → INPUT-OUTPUT UNIT → REAL-TIME OUTPUT

MAJOR TRANSFER BUS (MTB)

| HIGH-SPEED MEMORY | PROGRAM CONTROL UNIT | CENTRAL PROCESSOR |

ADDER INPUT BUS
ADDER OUPUT BUS

KEY: - - - - → CONTROL ———— INFORMATION

ure of over 1,000 hours at a 60-percent confidence level.

Much of the equipment in the computer is time-shared to further reduce the required circuits. Developed under the Signal Corps micromodule program, its name MICRO-PAC, which stands for Micromodule Data Processor and Computer, was designed to be compatible with the U. S. Army's Fieldata automatic data-processing equipment.

The high packaging density gained with micromodules (about 150,000 components per cubic foot in the circuit section) permits the effective use of a single-case design of 2.7 cu ft that weighs 90 pounds. It requires 250 watts d-c power and 270 v-a generator power.

SYSTEM ORGANIZATION — The computer accommodates a wide variety of problems and has 21 mechanized instructions as shown in the table. It also has register provisions and is a binary synchro-

nous computer operating in a completely serial mode at a clock frequency of 1.6 Mc, permitting a reasonably short execution time per instruction.

The clock pulses drive a timing-level generator producing a sequence of gate levels of varying lengths within a 63-clock pulse period. This 63-clock pulse period of about 40 μsec is called a minor cycle, and is abbreviated during certain instructions to decrease operation time. An instruction is executed in one or more minor cycles plus a minor cycle for instruction access.

The various 38-bit word formats are provided. Figure 1 shows the format of a binary word, an alphanumeric word, a computer instruction word or an input-output instruction word. The basic random-access ferrite core memory of 2,048 word capacity is expandable in multiples of 2,048 to a maximum of 8,192 words.

The computer is divided into five major subsections as shown in Fig. 2. These include: high-speed memory, central processor, program control, input-output and major transfer bus.

HIGH-SPEED MEMORY — The high-speed memory unit contains the core-memory and registers for data storage, controls for reading, writing and word selection. The memory operates with coincident-current selection (destructive read-out with regeneration) having a duty cycle of 40 μsec between read interrogations.

The memory array consists of 20 double planes, each containing two 64 × 32 core matrices; also included in the stack are a diode board, heater assembly and header board containing plugs for external connection. This section appears in the lower right-hand corner of the photo. The 20 double planes provide two spare bits per word. These spares can be utilized by connecting the sense winding output to any input circuit and completing a circuit between the digit winding to the digit drive of the corresponding regenerative loop. The memory module bank is a completely self-contained plug-in unit. Four banks may be used with the computer.

A 13-bit address generated by the central processor determines which one of four memory banks and which of 8,192 words will be selected and sent to the two memory output registers. Register 1 is a temporary buffer for parallel data flow to and from the memory; register 2 is both a buffer effecting parallel-to-serial conversion of data and an operand register for several instructions.

CENTRAL PROCESSOR — The central processor performs internal data-processing functions. It has a one-bit adder, various shift registers that, among other functions are used with the adder to form the arithmetic unit, gates to transfer data between registers and adder, and control timing and logic.

All arithmetic operations are done in binary-serial form using a one-bit adder. Subtraction is accomplished by two's-complement addition. Multiplication is performed by successive addition of partial products, and division is executed by a nonrestoring algorithm. Computer operands are fixed-point, signed magnitude.

The accumulator, instruction and program-counter registers are contained within this section. The accumulator contains first the operand and then the result of the arithmetic instructions. In divide, the remainder is stored in the accumulator and the quotient in the Q-register (a register simulated in high-speed memory). In multiply, the high-order result is stored in the accumulator while the low-order result is in the Q-register. The instruction register holds the instruction during execution in the computer. The program counter stores the address of the next instruction to be executed in the program sequence. Other registers required for the central processing function are simulated in the memory.

PROGRAM CONTROL UNIT — The program control unit generates

the various controls required by the high-speed memory, central processor and input-output sections. It comprises the decoders, signal generators, and control flip-flops.

INPUT-OUTPUT DEVICES—The input-output section controls data exchange between the central processor and control panel, a paper-tape reader and printer-punch plus a real-time channel. The standard Fieldata intercommunication conventions, 8-bit characters, ready-busy line and strobe line, are used for all input-output operations. On-line insertion of information may be accomplished at 300-characters-per-second by a paper-tape reader or by a programmed instruction requesting operator input at the console. In the latter mode, the computer waits until a specified quantity of information has been inserted and then automatically continues program execution.

Similarly, on-line output of information may also be performed by a paper-tape punch-printer at 30 characters-per-second or through the control panel. In the last case, the computer waits until the operator has requested the display of the instruction-specified number of words and then automatically continues program execution.

The computer can communicate with other computers with real-time input and output channels on a computer-interrupt basis at a maximum rate of 300 characters-per-second.

The computer may concurrently perform real-time input, real-time output, and data-processing func-

---

HOW COMPACT CAN A COMPUTER GET?

This computer won't fit in a man's pocket, but it represents an achievement in size and weight reduction.

It is possible because of micromodules that permit a good deal of circuit to occupy a minimum of physical space. Groups of these tiny circuits make possible a design of high packaging density, excellent reliability and low power needs

---

INSTRUCTIONS AND TIMING

Instruction	Approximate Time μsec (including IAC)
Arithmetic:	
1 Add	80
2 Subtract	80
3 Multiply Fast (18 bits)	32°
4 Multiply	1035
5 Divide	1075
Transfer:	
6 Transfer Unconditional	40
7 Transfer and Load Pcs.	120
8 Transfer on Negative	40
9 Transfer on Zero	40
10 Transfer on Index	200
Logical	
11 Shift Right	280, max.
12 Shift Left	280, max.
13 Store	80
14 Logical Multiply	80
15 Load	120
16 Halt	40
Sense	
17 Sense	40
18 Sense and Set	40
19 Sense and Reset	40
Input-Output	
20 Read Alphanumeric	variable
21 Write Alphanumeric	variable

tions. When a character has been received from the real-time input unit or when the real-time output unit signifies that it is ready to accept a character, the computer temporarily interrupts its data-processing function, services the character and then resumes data processing from the point of interruption. One to seven-character storage or retrieval operations are implemented by computer interrupts until a complete data word or a single control character has been stored or retrieved. A program interrupt will then transfer the completed word to the message storage section of the high-speed memory, or retrieve a complete word from the message-storage section for output.

MAJOR TRANSFER BUS—Most transfers are accomplished by a major transfer bus; some transfers to and from the adder that occur concurrently with transfers of data through the major bus are executed by minor transfer buses.

CIRCUIT DESCRIPTION — Requirements of +90 C maximum internal ambient temperature to permit reliable circuit performance within the high-density micromodule packaging, made silicon semiconductor components mandatory. For the bulk of the micromodule logic circuits, the 2N914 switching transistor was selected for its relatively high-speed switching and good reliability record.

The basic circuit is the standard logic gate of Fig. 3A with the following characteristics: fan in—20 maximum; fan out—4; power dissipation—75 mw average; pair delay—60 nsec nominal, and rise time —30 nsec nominal.

This standard gate is the most frequently used micromodule in the computer. Low-power gates are provided when the speed and power capabilities of these standard gates are not required. Several micromodule configurations of the standard and low-power gates were designed. Gates are packaged two to a micromodule. Several gate micromodules were designed with different input-diode arrangements so that the module's 12 standard outputs could accommodate the input-terminal requirements of a number of different logical configurations. Diode-cluster micromodules are provided to handle unusual cases.

Although the gates make up the bulk of micromodules in the computer, many other special-purpose circuits are required. Figure 3B shows a shift register capable of shifting at a 1.6-Mc clock rate with an output drive of two standard gates and one steering resistor of another shift register stage.

A starting point for the design of the shift register was the standard gate. Two standard gates were interconnected in a flip-flop arrangement and capacitor-resistor-diode gates tied to the bases for the trigger input. This was satisfactory except for a worst-case condition at 125 C which had a turn-off time of 0.15 μsec instead of 0.13 μsec. The worst-case test included a maximum load of four standard gates and the steering resistor input of the shift register. The maximum output load was reduced to two standard gates, and the steering input and base drive loads were also reduced slightly. These modifications that permitted operation under worst-case temperature conditions were satisfactory and therefore consequently adopted.

The studies were continued to determine the requirements for even better operation. Inductors added in series with the steering input resistors permitted a sub-

stantial increase in operation speed and a reduction in trigger power.

The addition of the two inductors decouples the collector from the following trigger steering network during the time of the trigger pulse. After the trigger pulse, there is over 0.5 μsec for the capacitor to assume its new voltage state.

This circuit would be the most desirable one to use from an electrical viewpoint; however, the addition of the two inductors would require more than one micromodule for a shift-register stage and, in the interests of economy of volume, the design without the inductors was chosen.

All logic micromods are compatible and use common supply voltages and signal-voltage characteristics. Line receivers and drivers are provided for the transition from computer signal voltage to Fieldata operation.

All electronic components are operated well below rating to assure maximum reliability. Resistors are operated at a maximum of 20-percent of rating. Silicon transistors are junction-temperature limited to 100 C in operation, although circuits were designed and tested for 125 C operating temperatures.

POWER SUPPLY — The power supply is operationally typical of digital computers in that it furnishes a large number of well-regulated output voltages with low source impedance. However, it differs from most computer supplies in two major respects that complicate the design: the requirement for small overall size and poor regulation of the primary power source. A block diagram of this supply is shown in Fig. 4.

The input voltage source for the computer may range from a poorly regulated field-type to a well regulated commercial power line. The d-c power supply has been designed for the following input power conditions: voltage—120 v, 10 percent single phase; frequency—50 to 60 cps, 10 percent; transient voltage range—(5 sec) 31 to 86 cps.

The required d-c output of the supply with two memory packages (4,096 word capacity) is 250 watts, consisting of 13 different voltages. The wide range of input voltage and frequency coupled with the require-

ment of minimum size and weight, made unsatisfactory the conventional design approach using a power transformer with individual rectifiers and regulators for each voltage. Instead, a power supply incorporating the following features was designed: (1) controlled bridge rectifiers operating directly from the a-c line, to achieve rough regulation in the order of 15-percent; (2) single-section L-C-filter to reduce ripple to less than 10-percent after 60-cycle line input rectification; (3) Morgan regulator circuit, using a silicon-controlled rectifier and a square-loop core to achieve regulation in the order of 2-percent; (4) single-section L-C-filter to reduce ripple to less than 1-percent after high-frequency regulation; (5) silicon-controlled rectifier parallel inverter operating at 1,000 cycles, using a power transformer with separate windings for individual supplies; and (6) individual rectifiers and regulators for each output voltage, where required.

In the bridge rectifier and filter, silicon-controlled rectifiers are used as the primary type of rectification to provide lossless voltage regulation to the Morgan circuit. The regulation required is relatively crude with a large ripple voltage inasmuch as the Morgan circuit can operate with pure or pulsating dc-inputs. Severe voltage and frequency variations of the primary power source make the exclusive use of a Morgan circuit or controlled bridge awkward. If only a controlled bridge is used, the filter choke required is large and heavy, although the capacitor is reasonable. If a Morgan circuit is used exclusively with a conventional full-wave bridge input, the filter capacitor required on the bridge must have a high voltage rating, which represents height, weight, and volume, since physical size increases with voltage rating. In addition, the nearly 2:1 voltage variations from the bridge would make acceptable regulation difficult. The use of a combination of two circuits allows much smaller chokes and capacitors to achieve the same regulation and transient load response for the input to the inverter.

The Morgan regulator and filter circuit provides lossless, tighter regulation for the inverter input.

The circuit generates pulses of approximately constant width to the load, by virtue of the silicon-controlled rectifier acting as a switch in series with the load. The repetition rate of these pulses is controlled by a voltage-sensing feedback network that regulates average potential. The repetition rate ranges from 500 to 2,000 cps; thus, the filter choke and capacitor may be much smaller and lighter than those required if the controlled bridge were used to operate the inverter. The Morgan circuit regulation response is inherently faster than the controlled bridge since its repetition rate is so high. This is an advantage for transient load changes, because the controlled bridge response is always at least a half-cycle behind at line frequencies.

The parallel silicon inverter uses two silicon-controlled rectifiers in a parallel inverter to convert 50 volts d-c to 1,000 cycles a-c. Two additional silicon rectifiers are used for 400 cycles a-c. The scr requirements are 5 amperes average current and about 150 volts peak-inverse voltage to allow for switching transients. These are reasonable ratings, well within the range of available scr's. The rectifiers are triggered 180-degrees out of phase by a binary counter to insure symmetry of the applied square wave to the transformer.

Insuring symmetry of the 1,000-cycle square wave minimizes the 1,000-cycle ripple in the rectified outputs of the individual supplies and reduces the amount of regulation required.

The power transformer has eight output windings for the various voltage supplies. Bridge rectifiers are used on the higher-voltage windings to minimize winding space, while full-wave center-tapped windings are used for low voltage to minimize diode drops. Where voltages are close in value, or load currents are small, one winding is used for several voltage outputs.

The 128-v and 26-v fan-motor supplies are derived from taps on the primary winding of the 400-cycle auto-transformer.

The individual output regulators are of the series and shunt types. The series regulators are used for high-current supplies, with shunt

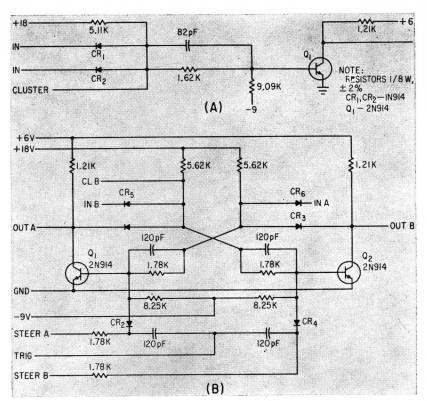

STANDARD GATE *circuit is the most frequently used micromodule in the computer (A); shift register operates at a 1.6-Mc clock rate (B)—Fig. 3*

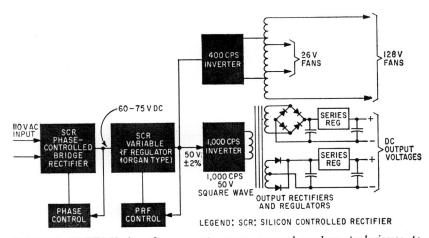

POWER SUPPLY *for the computer uses several modern techniques to achieve high regulation from a widely varying power source—Fig. 4*

zener-diode regulators for low-current supplies. These regulators are standard. Little regulation is required to compensate for input changes, because of good regulation preceding the inverter; hence, a minimum of power is wasted in series regulators, and power-supply efficiency and cooling are not problems.

CONTROL PANEL—The control panel provides for manual insertion of information into the computer and for monitoring and selecting the various operational modes.

Information may be entered manually by the keyboard on the control panel. Input or output data may be displayed in digital and binary forms by 10 Nixie tubes and 38 neons, respectively.

This work was a joint effort by the Tactical Data Processing activity of the Digital Data Communications Department of RCA Defense Electronic Products. The author thanks A. Coleman, E. Schlain, R. Torrey, W. Miller and H. Sauer for their work.

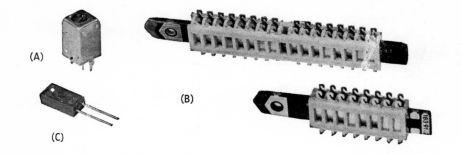

MINIATURE *coil (A), wavelength switch (B), and resistor (C), designed as family groups whose shape and dimensions are uniformly planned for complete system. Units, actual size, plug into circuit board which is considered as a multiple female connector* —Fig. 1

Ordered Geometry for Component Design

Aim is to attain greater flexibility and increased use of mechanization

By J. RODRIGUES de MIRANDA

N. V. Philips' Gloeilampenfabrieken, Radio Apparatus Laboratory, Eindhoven, Netherlands

INTEGRATED active and passive elements will eventually be applied to consumer electronics, and to the radio and television entertainment field. Although application is for several reasons far away, a design philosophy has been suggested so that if and when modules and molelectronics replace the present spatially-distributed lumped-circuit elements, these techniques can be introduced gradually.

The aim is to stimulate an international and frank cooperation between manufacturers of electronic equipments and components to create a logically consistent system of designing components, assembly systems and assembly methods thereby taking full advantage of the possibilities offered by the properties of solid-state components.

As a radio apparatus factory, Philips designs and manufactures practically all required components. Obviously, company seeks ways and means to shorten assembly time for consumer equipment produced in large quantities, such as radio and tv sets. This goal can be reached by bringing component structure and assembling techniques in harmony with each other.

FORM FACTORS—Search has been for design and assembly methods, not biased by the conventional shape of components. Components will be adopted to the requirements of the transistor circuits, to transistor dimensions, and to efficient assembly methods. Aim is for international standardization, improved reliability, better control of the manufacturing process.

Suggestions for a consistent system take the following important principles into consideration, and radio sets are now being designed to comply with these principles:

The circuit board is considered

FIVE PHASES OF EQUIPMENT DESIGN

PHASE	I	II	III	IV	V
chassis	metal	circuit board e = 2.54 mm	circuit board e = 0.635 mm		
active elements	tubes	tubes (transistors)	transistors	transistors	controlled growth of solid matter
components	conventional	conventional	conventional principles	united in building blocks	
design of components	conventional	conventional adapted	coherent system h = 10 mm, small tapered tags		
assembly	by hand	hand or cutting and bending mach. or insertion line	by hand or by insertion line		
soldering	iron	iron or dipsoldering	precision dipsoldering or small iron		
number of components per cub. inch	1–2	10	50	200	ꝑ
Introduction Philips	1925	1956	1961 "first steps"	1965–1970	2000ꝑ

WAVE RANGE *switch system in all-transistor four-band radio set is operated by pushbuttons. Some existing components had to be used, and Philips had to decide provisionally about dimensions of new components because international agreement is not yet feasible—Fig. 2*

as a multiple female connector. Components are to be pluggable and have contact points in the shape of stiff tapered legs, fitting tightly into the holes of the printed panel. This is advantageous for mechanized insertion as well as for assembly by hand.

To provide for optimal packing density, components will have a standard height, 10 mm is proposed, with the smallest projected surface possible. Standardization of the dimensions and the shape of the legs as well as their mutual distances and of the dimensions of components in general is necessary for the interchangeability of components made by various manufacturers.

Radio sets have been designed, complying as far as possible in this stage, with the above philosophy. Coils, see Fig. 1, are conceived as a family of coils. Dimensions chosen are $6 \times 6 \times 10$ mm³. They have five lugs, situated to fit the ϵ-grid. They can contain aerial or oscillator coils for all broadcast ranges, and i-f coils, or halfband filters for a-m or f-m. Obtainable Q is somewhere in the neighborhood of 140.

The wavelength switch used, see Fig. 1, is small and offers an enormous variety of possible applications, made possible by using two switching tracks on each side of the slider and correspondingly, two lengths of contact springs. Besides this, connections between the two sides of the slider are possible. Total height of the switch is 10 mm, terminals are situated to fit the grid pattern. Plug-in components, they can be dipsoldered after all components have been assembled.

STIFF LEGS—In the future, resistors, capacitors, transistors, and combination devices will all be produced in the shape of upright standing components with stiff legs, all having standard heights with configuration fitting the circuit board grid pattern. An example of a resistor, shown in Fig. 1, was designed by another component maker, not belonging to the Philips concern.

Modules and molelectronic devices can and should be made to fit the existing grid pattern. It is quite possible that these techniques can be applied to professional and industrial equipments, and military programs.

In general, the quality of transducers such as ferrite aerial, loudspeakers and batteries depends on their size. Space saving in the electronic part can thus be transformed in better quality by using this saving for increasing the size of one or more of these transducers.

BETTER MATERIALS—An interesting aspect of miniaturization is that because it leads to a reduced consumption of raw material, it offers the possibility of using better materials which are too expensive for larger constructions. Smaller components need not be more expensive, but will probably be cheaper than "standard" components.

Techniques developed tomorrow should be the runway from which future designs, not yet developed, can take off.

The borderline crossed when passing from phase II to phase III in Table p198 is important, because in phase III, for the first time, stringent demands are put on the mechanical configuration—shape and dimensions—of components.

Philips has designed a small radio set for long and medium wave as well as for f-m reception making use of ordered geometry techniques described.

INTERNATIONAL STANDARDS FOR COMPONENTS?

More demands are now put on the configuration of components in the development of consumer radio equipment. This observation leads to a more fundamental study of the direction consumer electronics will take based on modern design and assembly techniques. It is suggested that passive components to be used in these equipments be designed in accordance with transistor circuits, transistor dimensions, and efficient assembly methods.

Can such requirements be standardized internationally?

Electrical engineering evolved an international language of symbols for resistors, capacitors, batteries, transistors, tubes. The need for such a grammar was evident at the first international congress of electricians back in 1881. When the International Electrotechnical Commission met in Paris in 1912, it appointed a special advisory committee "to prepare a set of international graphical symbols for use in electrical diagrams and installation plans." Present committees are active to this day.

Can a similar advisory committee be formed to plan a set of international standards for the actual components?

One large firm that designs and manufactures practically all components it uses has proposed a logically consistent design system for components it uses in its own transistorized radio and tv sets aimed at the consumer market. They do not propose a plan for others, but suggest a philosophy they use for standardizing shape and dimensions of components on plug-in boards.

Now that we are at the crossroads of new directions in electronics, perhaps there will never be a better time than now to re-explore the entire subject of component standardization

Chapter 11

COMPOSITE
SEMICONDUCTOR COMPONENTS

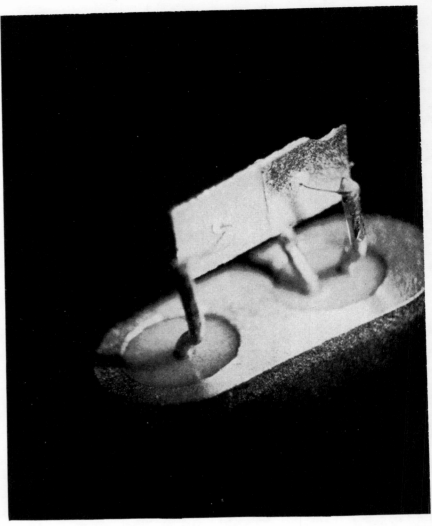

PHYSICAL *appearance and mounting of a four-layer structure as used in the circuits of this article*

Unique coupling and driver circuits are used with tunnel and four-layer diodes to develop simple counters and waveform generators. The circuits consist of semiconductors and resistors only, thus integrated circuits are easily realizable

A NEW LOOK AT
Negative-Resistance Devices

By VASIL UZUNOGLU, Solid-State Laboratory, Westinghouse Electric Corp., Baltimore, Maryland

NEGATIVE RESISTANCE is a phenomena controlled either by current or voltage but not both together.[1] Solid-state devices displaying a negative-resistance region such as the tunnel diode, *pnpn* four-layer diode, point-contact transistor, and the unijunction transistor are numerous. Electrically, such negative-resistance devices may be thought of as elements having some internal positive feedback.

Whatever the source and nature of the negative resistance, electrically they may be divided into voltage-stable devices such as the tunnel diode and current-stable devices such as the *pnpn* diode.

In voltage-stable devices, the control effect comes from the voltage source, and in the current-stable devices, control comes from the current source. A load line drawn perpendicular through the corresponding source should cut the *V-I* characteristic at one point only. Intersection at more than one point corresponds to an unstable condition as shown in Fig. 1A and 1B. The difference between the two

characteristics is that in the voltage-stable element, dI/dV goes negative passing through zero.

The two most familiar devices displaying negative resistance are the tunnel diode and the *pnpn* four-layer diode. The first displays the quantum-mechanical effect[2] and the second is due to a combination of avalanche multiplication and amplification resembling an arc or gas discharge with energy-storage. These are coming into greater use.

TUNNEL DIODE FLIP-FLOP—

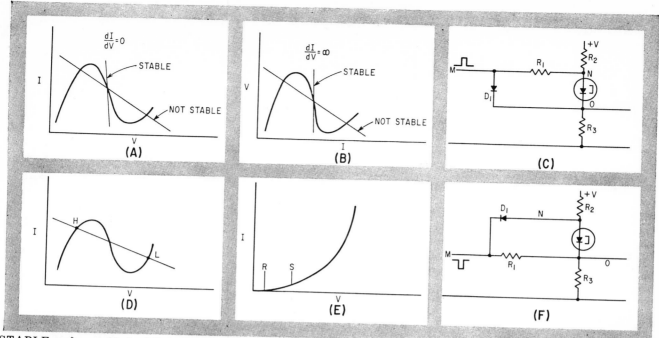

STABLE *and unstable load lines (A and B). Positive-pulse-triggered tunnel diode flip-flop (C) with V-I characteristics (D) and diode characteristics (E). Negative-pulse-triggered tunnel diode flip-flop shown at (F)—Fig. 1*

The circuit shown in Fig. 1C incorporates all necessary features of a bistable flip-flop driven by a positive pulse.[3] The speed-limiting element is diode D_1.

Using the V-I characteristic shown in Fig. 1D with the tunnel diode resting at high-current level H, and assuming that the driving source does not disturb the potential levels, the voltage across M-O (Fig. 1C) is equal to the voltage across N-O. As the tunnel diode is in low-voltage state H, voltage across D_1 is low. Under this condition, bias on D_1 is shown as point R in Fig. 1E.

Assume a positive pulse applied to M whose amplitude is not high enough to put D_1 in its low-impedance level (not exceeding S). The pulse appears at N but not at O because it is blocked by diode D_1. The pulse appearing at N will shift the operating point to L in Fig. 1D. As the tunnel diode changes state, bias across D_1 shifts to a point in the vicinity of S and normally does not exceed this point. A second pulse applied to M will appear at N as well as O as D_1 can conduct with the applied pulse.

The pulse appearing at N cannot change the operating level as the tunnel diode is already in high-voltage state L. The same pulse appears at O with a slight delay due to transit time of carriers across

D_1. This positive pulse is now able to shift the operating level back to H. Every pulse changes the state of the circuit and this is the necessary condition for bistable multivibrator action. Speed of such a flip-flop can be in the Gc range. Limitation is in D_1 that constitutes the circuit energy-storing element. Circuits of this type have been tested at 30 Mc and no attempt made to go to higher frequencies.

Circuit sensitivity depends on location of the load line on the characteristic curve. Location of points H and L closer to the negative-resistance region reduces stability. The effective load line is composed of R_2 and R_3 in series and the effective V-I characteristic is of the device across R_1 in series with D_1 when the diode is conducting. Both R_1 and D_1 across the tunnel diode are assumed to have small effect on the tunnel diode overall characteristic.

The principle of operation of a bistable flip-flop using a tunnel diode driven by a negative pulse is the same as the one explained for positive-pulse triggering. Such a circuit is shown in Fig. 1F and the V-I characteristic is shown in Fig. 1D. Assume the tunnel diode resting at point H. The voltage drop across the tunnel diode is low as is the forward bias across D_1. A negative pulse applied to M will not affect H as diode D_1 is not conducting. The pulse will appear at O and will shift the operating point to L. The voltage drop across the tunnel diode is high as is the bias across D_1. A second negative pulse applied to M will appear at O as well as N. The pulse appearing at O will not change the tunnel diode state, but the some pulse appearing at a slightly later time at N will shift the operating level back to H. The specifications and requirements for the positive-driven pulse

THE NEW LOOK

When designing circuits using negative-resistance devices, too many engineers use run-of-the-mill ideas. This article presents a new view of these circuits and covers both the voltage and current-controlled versions. If you are in the pulse-counting or waveshape-generating business, this is for you

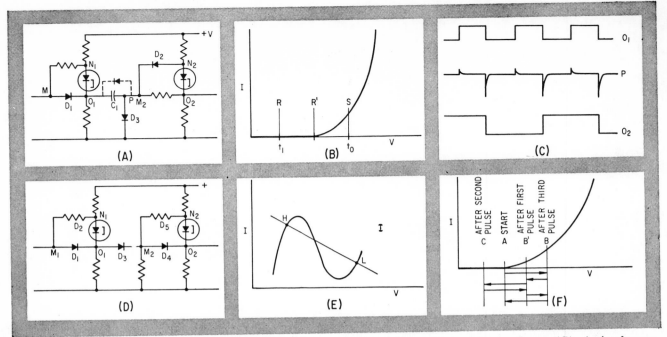

POSITIVE *and negative-pulse-driven flip-flop (A) with diode curve (B) and internal waveshapes (C). A simpler coupling (D) with tunnel-diode curve (E) and diode curve (F)—Fig. 2*

circuit also hold for this circuit.

COUPLING — In this approach, use is made of one positive driven and one negative driven bistable flip-flop as show in Fig. 2A. The function of coupling network C_1 (or a reverse-biased diode) and D_3 is to differentiate the waveform at O_1 and pass only the negative-going pulses that actuate the second stage. There may be low-level positive pulses at P but they are not large enough to trigger the second stage. To have the necessary waveshape at point P, the bias across D_3 has to be as shown in Fig. 2B so that at t_0, the diode has to be in high-conduction state S whenever the waveform at O_1 goes high. The bias at P is dependent on the operating level of the second stage. To accomplish the necessary condition, bias due to the second stage at point P must be kept between R and R' so that only positive-going

pulses at O_1 can make D_3 go to its high-conduction state.

Several stages of the negative-pulse type can be coupled to the 4:1 counter circuit to increase the counting level. Waveshapes of each stage are shown in Fig. 2C.

Three such stages have been coupled and operated at approximately 12 Mc although this is not the highest frequency of operation. Square wave rise and fall times are below 0.1 μsec. Lack of faster measuring equipment prevented more precise measurements.

A simpler coupling can be realized by adjustment of bias developed across D_3 as shown in Fig. 2D. Operation is explained with use of tunnel diode curve (Fig. 2E) and diode curve (Fig. 2F).

Assume D_2 at low-current level L, D_5 in high-current level H and the operating point of D_3 at point A. A positive pulse applied to M_1 will shift the operating point of D_2 to H.

The potential at O_1 starts rising, raising potential level across D_3 to point B that enables a positive potential to appear at point M_2 and shift the operating level of D_5 to L. As soon as stage 2 changes state, the potential across D_4 is at a new level B', lower than B. A second pulse applied to M_1 will make D_2 go to its low-current level L and the potential across D_3 goes to a new lower

level shown as point C.

As some negative pulse may appear at M_2, the load line of D_5 has to be adjusted so that a negative-going pulse cannot affect its state. A third positive pulse applied to M_1 will shift the operating level of D_2 to H and the potential across D_3 will be increased to point B'. A positive pulse appearing at M_2 shifts the operating point of D_5 to H. As soon as D_5 changes state, the operating point of D_3 shifts further to the right. A fourth pulse at M_1 shifts the operating point of D_2 but a negative pulse cannot affect D_5 because it is in high-current state H and needs a positive-going pulse to activate it. Three such counting stages have been coupled (8:1 count) with the overall frequency characteristics in the same order as the previous one. The action depends on the correct bias of D_3 and not on pulse differentiation. With adjustable parameters and potential levels, counting levels can be further increased. Output of the second and third stages of a three-stage counter are shown in the Fig. 3 oscilloscope photograph.

A third type of coupling is shown in Fig. 4A, based on principles mentioned in the two previous methods. The waveshapes shown on the circuit make operation self-explanatory. The coupling capacitor used to connect the two stages

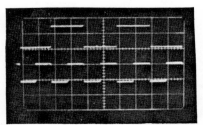

OUTPUT *of second and third stage of a three-stage counter—Fig. 3*

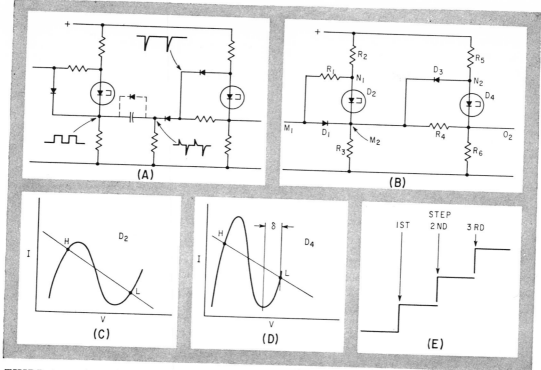

THIN *type of coupling is shown at (A). Staircase generator (B) with tunnel diode character-istics (C and D). Resultant output waveform is shown at (E)—Fig. 4*

can be replaced by a reverse-biased diode (shown dotted).

STAIRCASE GENERATOR

In this circuit, use is made of the four states of two cascaded flip-flops.[4] By arrangement of the operating points, a staircase generator can be realized as shown in Fig. 4B. The first stage is a positive driven flip-flop and the second stage is a negative-driven one. No delaying action is required through D_3.

Assume both stages are at low-current levels L as shown in Figs. 4C and 4D.

A positive pulse applied at M_1 will shift the operating point of D_2 to its H state. Operation of D_4 depends on operation of D_2 and is actuated only under certain conditions. When D_2 changes state from L to H, the increasing voltage across R_3 appears at O_2 and tends to shift the level of D_4. This is prevented by biasing D_4 further up the I-V characteristic, which necessitates a voltage of amplitude δ to actuate D_4. The effective voltage at O_2 has to be less than δ. A positive-going pulse decreases the potential across D_3 and no voltage appears at N_2. The first step in the output level shown in Fig. 4E, is produced as the current across R_6 is increased due to D_2.

A second pulse applied to M_1 shifts the level of D_2 to point L. In doing so, a decreasing voltage across R_3 will make D_3 conduct and shift the operating point of D_4 to H. An important consideration is that conductance of D_3 at this point has to be higher than that of R_4 to be able to actuate D_4. The second step in the output level (shown in Fig. 4E) is due to higher current level of D_4.

A third pulse applied to M_1 actuates D_2 but not D_4. When D_2 goes from state L to state H, an increasing voltage at M_2 will make D_3 further nonconductive and shift can only occur due to a pulse appearing at O_2. A negative pulse is necessary at O_2 to make D_4 change state, therefore D_4 does not change state.

To return both stages to their L level, a fourth pulse is applied to M_1

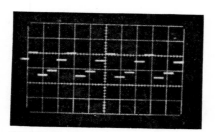

STAIRCASE *generator output waveform—Fig. 5*

that shifts D_2 to level L. In doing so, a negative-going voltage appears at M_2 and actuates D_4. A negative pulse will also appear at point N_2 and may shift D_4 back to the H state. To prevent this, the delay across D_3 has to be minimized then D_4 remains in the L state.

Better performance can be achieved by replacing D_3 by a zener diode in which case, almost no delay exists. This also meets the requirements of high conductance.

For proper operation, interaction of the stages is brought to a minimum by proper input circuits.

Typical waveshapes resulting from this circuit are shown in Fig. 5.

PNPN DIODES

The four-layer diode can be used to switch current levels in the order of amperes. The bistable flip-flop using four layer diodes[5] shown in Fig. 6A, is a basic building block for cascaded counter stages.

Assume the device resting on H (Fig. 6B). A positive pulse applied to point M will be differentiated at N-O. The positive-going portion of the pulse will shift the operating point to L' and as the pulse dies out, the load line tries to return to point L. Before there is any appreciable movement from point L'

to *L*, the negative-going portion appears at the device input terminals. This pulse is not high enough to shift the operating point back to *H* and the device rests at *L*. A second positive pulse applied to *M* will be differentiated but the positive pulse cannot make the device change state but pushes the operating point to the right. The load line moves slowly under high-current levels and before it moves, the negative-going portion of the pulse appears at *N* and shifts the operating point back to *H*. For proper operation, it is necessary that movement of the load line is slow under both operating conditions. Such devices have been operated in the 80 Kc range and if higher frequencies are to be realized, faster and narrower actuating pulses can be used with faster *pnpn* devices.

The five-layer structure shown in Fig. 6C, can use the entire fifth junction in connection with the bulk material as a differentiator.

The *p*-region with the n_2 region form the capacitance and the bulk material of the n_2 region forms the differentiator resistor. The equivalent circuit is shown in Fig. 6D with a small-value resistor connecting the differentiator and the device.

COUPLING PNPN DEVICES—

Coupling *pnpn* diodes for use as counters has been realized by the circuit shown in Fig. 6E. The coupling network uses two differentiating circuits with the second incorporated into the second device.

Diode D_3 bypasses the negative-going pulses of the first differentiating circuit incorporating D_1 and R_1. Fig. 6F shows the waveshapes appearing at each point within the circuit of Fig. 6E.

L-F ASTABLE MULTIVIBRATOR

—Here, use is made of the thermal effect associated with avalanche breakdown. Operation of the circuit shown in Fig. 6G can be explained by use of Fig. 6H. Assume operating point resting at point *L*. High current through the device causes heating and increases the avalanching point of the device. The new characteristic is shown as a dotted line in Fig. 6H. Under the new characteristic, the operating point at *L* is not stable enough and the characteristic is switched to

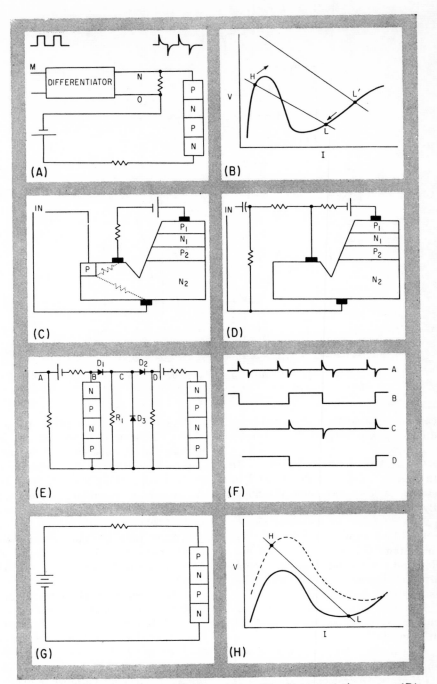

FOUR-LAYER *diode basic flip-flop (A) with characteristic curve (B). Typical four-layer structure (C) can be part of circuit (D). Coupling pnpn diodes (E) use two differentiating circuits and produce waveshapes shown in (F). A low-frequency astable multivibrator (G) with its associated waveshapes (H)—Fig. 6*

point *H*. At this level, current through the device is low and it starts cooling. It then returns to its original position. Point *H*, under this circumstance, does not exist and the operating point returns to *L*. This is a slow process and oscillations as low as 0.1 cps has been achieved using Ge four-layer diodes. Frequency variations for long periods of oscillation were within 3 percent.

REFERENCES

(1) W. Shockley and W. P. Mason, Dissected Amplifiers Using Negative Resistance, Jour of Applied Physics, 25, p 677.
C. Brunetti, The Clarification of Average Negative Resistance With Criterion of Its Use, Proc IRE, p 1,595, Dec 1937
E. W. Harold, Negative Resistance and Devices for Obtaining It, Proc IRE, p 1,201, Oct 1935.
(2) L. Esaki, Physical Review, 1958.
(3) V. Uzunoglu, A Bistable Flip-Flop Circuit Using Tunnel Diode, Proc IRE, p 1,440, Sept 1961.
(4) First observed by F. Shirk, Solid State Laboratory, Air Arm Division, Westinghouse Electric Corporation.
(5) First observed by E. Goins, Solid State Laboratory, Air Arm Division, Westinghouse Electric Corporation.

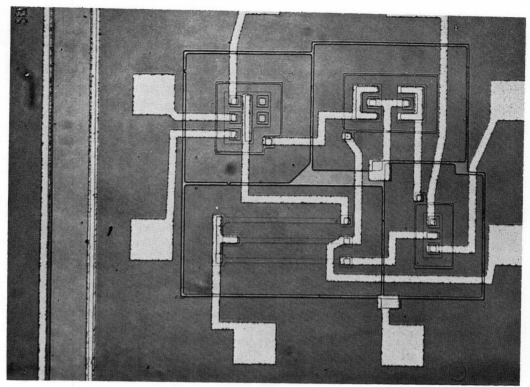

SOLID STATE logic block of the type diagrammed in Fig. 2C

LOGIC PRINCIPLES FOR

Multi-emitter Transistors

Devices with more than one emitter represent an
evolutionary step on the way to fully integrated circuits. Their
special qualities make some logic circuits simpler

By **P. M. THOMPSON,** The Plessy Co. (U.K.) Ltd., Ilford, Essex, England

SOLID-STATE circuits, with their sometimes unique solutions to the problems of element isolation and interconnections, have made semiconductor manufacturers aware of some new approaches to circuit design. A first step to take on the road to complete circuit integration is to add one or more extra emitters to basic transistors.

The resulting multiemitter transistors take the form shown on the cover of this issue; in this example five emitters are grouped around a single base, following the scheme shown in Fig. 1A. The emitters, in addition to being used in the normal forward conduction mode, can be used in the reverse conduction mode and also as capacitors.

Most of the applications are in logic circuits but multiemitter transistors can also be used in linear circuits. Figure 1B shows the conduction curve of a single emitter. If the emitter is biased negative with respect to its grounded base, it conducts in its normal forward mode; if it is biased positive, it conducts when its zener or avalanche voltage is reached. At voltages in between, the emitter can be used as a small capacitor.

If the transistor has several emitters, one emitter can be used in the forward mode with normal transistor action, another can be used in the avalanche mode and behaves as a zener diode connected to the base,

Still king of all semiconductor devices despite the growing threat of integrated circuits is the transistor. The diode has been around longer but nobody ever diodized a circuit.

But now we have the multiemitter transistor. It can act like a transistor with respect to one emitter, like a zener diode to another, and like a capacitor to still another. Is it still a transistor? Or is it an integrated circuit? Or is it something in between?

Maybe it's just a multiemitter transistor

---

while a third can be used as a small base input capacitance.

FORWARD MODE—Although the emitters of a transistor can be used in any of the three modes, in most circuits they are used in the forward conduction mode only. Since the reverse conduction mode is not used there is no need to control the breakdown voltage, and the conductivities of the base and emitter regions can be optimized without this additional limitation.

DIRECTLY COUPLED TTL — The application of multiemitter transistors as a replacement for a diode logic gate, illustrated in Fig. 2, occurred to several workers independently about two years ago.[1, 2, 3, 4] The multi-input gate using a multiemitter transistor has several features not found in the diode gate. These result from transistor action, and can be made clear by a comparison of the two circuits.

If a positive signal represents ONE in both Fig. 2A and 2B, transistors Q_2 and Q_3 represent a logical OR gate and inverter. Also, diodes D_1 to D_4 in Fig. 2A and multiemitter transistor Q_4 in Fig. 2B represent a logical AND gate. The fan-out of the circuit is from the collectors of Q_2 and Q_3, while the fan-in is to diodes D_1 and D_3, or the emitters of Q_4 respectively, and the collector of Q_1 represents the output of a previous stage driving the AND gate.

Circuit operation is as follows. If a collector of a transistor attached to any of the inputs of the AND gate is switched on (Fig. 2A and 2B) current in resistor R is diverted through it to ground. Point A will be approximately one-diode-forward-voltage drop positive with respect to ground and the base of transistor Q_2 will be at ground potential. Thus Q_2 will be switched off. If all the transistors connected to inputs

of the AND gate are switched off, the current in R flows through D_4 in Fig. 2A or the collector of Q_4 in Fig. 2B, and switches on Q_2. In Fig. 2A an extra resistor R from a negative supply to the base of Q_2 ensures that it switches off rapidly. An advantage of the multiemitter transistor is that this resistor and the negative supply can be eliminated, because current can flow from the collector of Q_4 to any of its emitters by normal transistor action. Thus, the output current of Q_1 is available to switch off Q_2 rapidly.

In addition to the multiemitter transistor having normal forward transistor action, it also has some transistor action in the reverse direction: the collector can act as an emitter and the emitters can collect the resulting carriers. Thus in the circuit of Fig. 2C when all the transistors connected to emitters of the multiemitter transistor are switched off, and the collector of Q_4 is conducting as a forward-biased diode, a current will flow into the emitters. This current would appear to other multiemitter gates connected to the collector of Q_1 as a collector current in Q_1, and it is desirable to place a resistor in the collector of Q_1 to supply this current. The maximum value of this current i_1 is

$$i_{1 \text{ max}} = i_2 \times (\text{fan-out}) \times (\text{max reverse } \beta)$$

Typically, with a maximum fanout of five, and a reverse β of 0.1, the circuit will be safe if i_1 is greater than $i_2/2$; there will be some extra current to charge the stray capacitances if $i_1 = i_2$. This type of circuit has proved useful for logic at high speeds (approximately 5 to 10 nanoseconds) and at medium speeds with low dissipation. A solid-circuit logic block based on this type of circuit is shown in the photograph.

EMITTER COUPLED — Although the directly coupled circuit is ade-

quate for small systems, designers of large systems frequently call for higher logic levels (2 volts or greater) to swamp out noise impulses induced in the interconnections. Another requirement in large systems is an accurately defined discrimination level set preferably half way between the ONE and ZERO voltages to obtain equal discrimination against interference for both states. For the emitter coupled OR gate shown in the photograph and diagramed in Fig. 3A, the discrimination level is defined accurately as ground potential and the outputs are +1.3 volts for ONE and −1.3 volts for ZERO. The ONE level is set by R_2 and R_3, and the emitter base voltage of Q_4, while the ZERO level is set by being the forward conduction voltage of a collector diode and an emitter diode in series. These circuits may be coupled either directly or by multiemitter transistor AND gates.

This emitter coupled OR gate is amenable to solid-circuit fabrication since only one transistor, Q_3, has a collector load, and only two isolated lands are required for the whole circuit. Much of the area in the photograph of the OR gate is taken not by the circuit elements but by the distance it is necessary to leave between the components and the edge of the isolated lands. Thus a circuit that needs only a few isolated lands occupies little space on a silicon chip. Furthermore, transistor Q_3 represents a single transistor on a land; since the land can be made small, the stray capacitance at the collector can be reduced to a minimum.

The operation of the circuit of Fig. 3A is as follows. If the base of either Q_1 or Q_2 is positive with respect to ground, the respective emitter supplies current to R_4 and turns off Q_3. The collector of Q_3 and the emitter of Q_4 then have the positive potentials shown on the diagram. However, if the bases of Q_1 and Q_2 are both negative with respect to ground, Q_3 will saturate and the collector of Q_3 and the emitter of Q_4 adopt the negative potentials shown. Transistor Q_3 switches rapidly, although it saturates, because its total emitter current is supplied or removed by the input circuit and no current gain is demanded.

This circuit, unlike most logic circuits, provides the output in the

ONE FORM of multiemitter transistor is shown at (A). Emitter-base circuit (B) shows the three ways the emitter can operate—Fig. 1

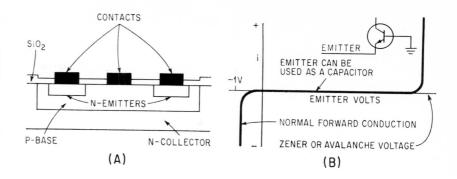

DIODE GATE (A) is transformed into a multiemitter gate (B). In (C), for a fan-out of five and reverse beta of 0.1 for Q_4, the circuit is safe if i_1 is greater than $i_2/2$—Fig. 2

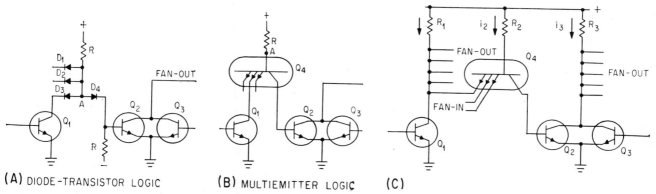

(A) DIODE-TRANSISTOR LOGIC   (B) MULTIEMITTER LOGIC   (C)

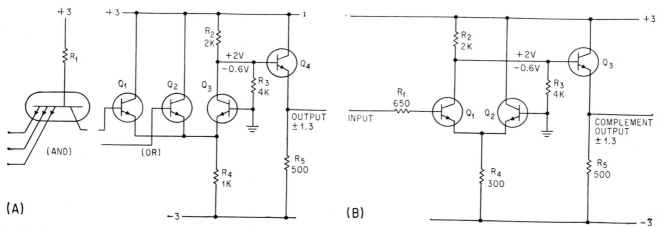

MULTIEMITTER and gate with emitter coupled OR gate (A). Circuit at (B) can be used with (A) to obtain a complement output—Fig. 3

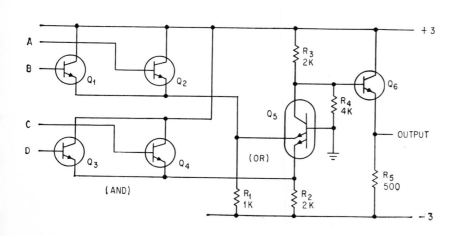

REPLACING Q_3 of Fig. 3A with multiemitter transistor allows an extra logic function without increasing the number of isolated lands—Fig. 4

same sense as the input, instead of inverting. If a complement output is required, the circuit of Fig. 3B will provide it. This circuit, in common with the circuit of Fig. 3A, has only one transistor that has an isolated collector, so if the circuits are combined only three isolated lands are needed. However, if this type of logic is used, it should be organized to use the minimum number of inversions.

The operation of the circuit in Fig. 3B is as follows. Transistor Q_1 is an inverting amplifier whose emitter is held one diode forward voltage negative of ground potential by Q_2 and R_4; R_4 is chosen so that Q_2 remains conducting at all times. Resistor R_1 is in series with the base of Q_1 to prevent the circuit that drives it from being overloaded; the remainder of the circuit is similar in operation to the output section of the circuit of Fig. 3A.

MULTIEMITTER COUPLED—If transistor Q_3 in Fig. 3A is replaced by a multiemitter transistor, an additional logic function can be performed without the addition of extra isolated lands. The modified circuit is shown in Fig. 4. It is convenient with this circuit to let a negative signal represent ONE, so that the circuit performs first the AND function, then the OR function. Operation is similar to the circuit of Fig. 3A, except that the collector circuit of multiemitter transistor Q_5 can be saturated by current at either emitter instead of only one. Also, in common with the circuit of Fig. 3A, the circuit requires an additional inverter if a complement output is required.

Multiemitter transistors, with the emitters in the forward conduction mode, are useful for low-level logic circuits. However, for logic circuits for applications where large noise voltages are introduced, as in many industrial environments, higher logic levels are desirable and can be obtained with reverse conduction.

REVERSE CONDUCTION — A convenient way to achieve high logic levels is to use the reverse breakdown voltage of emitter junctions. If one emitter of a multiemitter transistor is used in the reverse conduction mode, and another in the forward mode, the transistor performs as a conventional transistor with a

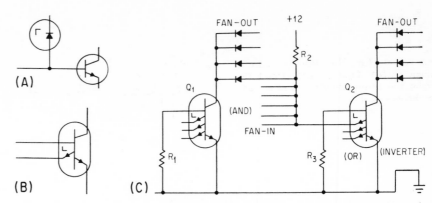

WHEN EXTRA emitter is used in breakdown mode, circuit is as at (A) and can be represented as at (B). High level saturating circuit using emitters at breakdown point (C)—Fig. 5

zener diode connected to the base; the configuration is useful for performing voltage translations in circuits where the collector voltage may be high. To aid in understanding the operation of the circuits where different emitters of the same transistor are used in different modes, the emitters are differentiated in the circuit symbols. Figure 5A shows the conventional circuit analog of a two-emitter transistor, with one emitter used in its breakdown mode; Fig. 5B shows proposed combined symbol. Emitters used as a base input connections are shown on the same side of the transistor as the normal base connection, and the breakdown symbol is drawn next to the emitter arrow. The symbol is in accord with IEEE standards for new semiconductor symbols.

HIGH LEVEL CIRCUIT—A simple high-level saturating circuit, where the levels for ONE and ZERO can be +12 and 0 volts and the discrimination level +6 volts, is shown in Fig. 5C. The major component in this circuit is a simple n-type silicon substrate on which is diffused a multiemitter npn transistor and several p-on-n diodes. The base region of the transistor is extended to form the base resistance (R_1 in Q_1) and connected to one of the emitters. The remaining emitters are used as an OR gate at the input, and the fan-out of diodes on the collector substrate is used as part of AND gates for the following stages. These major components can be connected as follows.

Each input terminal used is connected to the positive supply through a resistor (R_2 in Fig. 5C) and to the output diodes of other circuits.

Then, if all the circuits connected to an input are nonconducting, the current in R_2 can flow into the base circuit and switch on Q_2. If transistor Q_1 is conducting, the OR gate input terminal is held close to ground potential, the emitter cannot conduct in its reverse current mode, and Q_2 is switched off.

This type of circuit has good discrimination against noise and its speed is limited primarily by the total capacitance and the current available to charge it. If 1 ma is allowed at each input, the total delay can be about 0.5 microsecond.

CURRENT SWITCHING—Corresponding to the maximum switching speed for any type transistor is an optimum range of collector current and voltage. The current can be defined by resistors and the mean voltage by the reverse breakdown of emitters. In the circuit of Fig. 6A the collector potentials are clamped near ground and the base potentials are defined by the breakdown voltage of the input emitters.

The emitters of Q_2 and Q_3 are connected such that the current in R_5 will be conducted by one transistor or the other, depending on which base is more positive. If the transistors are fabricated at the same time on the same slice of silicon, the reverse breakdown voltage of the emitters can be closely matched. Thus, if the collector of Q_1 is positive with respect to ground, Q_2 conducts; if the collector is negative, Q_3 conducts; also, the discrimination level is close to ground potential.

Any conventional clamp technique can be used and the logic levels—negative and positive with

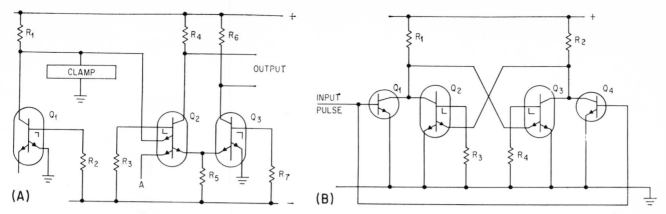

CURRENT switching circuit with collectors clamped near ground and base voltage defined by input emitter (A). Binary counter (B) uses cross-coupled emitters as capacitive inputs—Fig. 6

respect to ground—can be chosen as the best compromise between the requirements of speed and discrimination against noise. Point *A* in Fig. 6A represents a second input to Q_2, which conducts if either input is positive. There are many variations of current switching logic and the techniques illustrated in Fig. 6A are generally applicable.

EMITTER AS CAPACITOR — A large-area emitter performs as a satisfactory input capacitance to the base of a transistor. The addition of this large emitter results in an increase of collector area but the ratio of the emitter capacitance to the increase in collector capacitance is not unfavorable; the capacitance per unit area of an emitter junction can be approximately five times that of the collector. There are many circuits in which it is useful to connect a capacitance to a base of a transistor and a good example is the simple binary counter shown in Fig. 6B.

The bistable circuit consists of Q_2 and Q_3, which are triggered by Q_1 and Q_4 being switched on and saturated by a short pulse at their bases.

Circuit operation is as follows. Assume Q_2 is nonconducting. Then its collector will be positive and R_1 will supply current to the base of Q_3 through an emitter operating in its reverse conduction mode. Thus Q_3 will be saturated, holding its collector at ground potential. An input pulse causes the collectors of both Q_1 and Q_4 to be driven to ground potential. Thus at the input of Q_2 there will be no change of voltage, but at the input of Q_3 the voltage changes from the emitter breakdown potential to ground potential and the input emitter capacitance discharges

into the base. Some of this charge switches off the transistor and the excess causes it to become negative with respect to ground. If Q_1 and Q_4 switch off before this charge leaks away, Q_2 will switch on before Q_3 and thus hold off Q_3. The next input pulse switches Q_3 back into conduction and completes the cycle.

At the present state of the art it is not feasible to fabricate emitters with close capacitance tolerances. As with all *p-n* junctions the capacitance varies with voltage, but it is a useful capacitance when its value need not be precise or where the charge rather than the change of potential is defined.

LINEAR CIRCUITS — The multi-emitter transistor is generally more applicable to logic circuits than to linear amplifiers but it does have applications, one of the best known being as an integrated chopper in d-c amplifiers.[5] Here a two-emitter transistor is used as a switch and the off-set voltage between the two emitters is usually much lower than that between the emitter and collector of a conventional transistor chopper.

Another application of an extra emitter on a transistor is as a coupling element between a base and the collector of the previous stage, as in the counter circuit of Fig. 6A; as a coupling element an extra emitter can be used either in the reverse conduction mode or as a capacitor. As a capacitor it provides a low impedance to high frequencies between the collector of one stage and the base of the next; in its reverse conduction mode it provides a low impedance at all frequencies. Emitter-capacitance coupling is a useful technique in designing solid circuit

feedback amplifiers because it enables the output capacitance of one stage to be lumped with the input capacitance of the next and be treated as a single phase shift element, rather than as two separate elements with their attendant effects on high frequency stability.

INTEGRATED CIRCUITS—It is widely believed that solid state circuits, as we know them, where the separate elements can be related directly to components in a conventional circuit, are only a stage on the way to fully integrated circuits. It is not likely that this will happen immediately, because circuit engineers think in terms of components they know and device engineers rely on circuit engineers to design the circuits for fabrication in the solid form. The multiemitter transistor is thus a step towards integrating circuit several functions in a single part of a solid-state circuit.

The author thanks W. Holt and his staff for fabricating the devices discussed, and the Directors of the Semiconductors Ltd. for permission to publish the work.

REFERENCES

(1) P. M. Thompson, The Plessey Co. (U.K.) Ltd., British Patent application No. 24222/61.
(2) R. H. Beeson, H. W. Ruegg, New Forms of all Transistor Logic, Digest of technical papers, p 10, International Solid State Circuits Conference, Philadelphia 1962.
(3) B. A. Boulter, A New Active Device Suitable for use in Digital Circuits, *Electronic Engineering*, 35, No. 420, p 86, Feb. 1963.
(4) B. T. Murphy, High Speed Integrated Circuits with Load-Compensated Diode-Transistor Logic, ELECTRONICS, p 68, March 15, 1963.
(5) B. Mitchell, B. Bell, The Inch, Discussion and Applications, National Semiconductor Corp., General engineering memorandum No. 7, Jan. 6, 1962.

CIRCUIT *board for precision 12-volt regulated power supply is shown without rectifiers and filter capacitors*

New Device Simplifies Power Supply Design

Transistor and zener diode in integrated structure is both voltage reference and error voltage amplifier in highly stable regulated power supplies. New definition specifies integrated amplifier temperature coefficient throughout temperature range, and test circuits enable its measurement

By T. P. SYLVAN   General Electric Company Semiconductor Products Department, Syracuse, New York

INTEGRATED reference amplifier is comprised of a silicon *npn* transistor and a zener diode in a single pellet. The new device offers design simplification, low cost and high stability in regulated power supplies. The structure reduces the temperature differential between the zener diode and the transistors and also isolates critical regions of the device from the outside environment.

DESIGN REQUIREMENTS — A regulated power supply can be considered as being comprised of four functional blocks: power converter, reference element, error voltage amplifier and output power amplifier. The power converter might be a d-c to a-c converter, a d-c to d-c converter, an a-c to a-c converter (frequency changer) or an a-c to d-c converter. The most common type of power supply uses an a-c to d-c converter comprised of a transformer, rectifier and filter.

The reference element is generally one type of constant-voltage device, such a gas-tube regulator, zener diode, mercury cell or reach-through transistor. However, any device with a nonlinear characteristic, such as a tunnel diode, field-effect transistor, incandescent lamp or nonlinear resistor can also be used as a reference element. The zener diode has been widely ac-

---

EASIER CIRCUIT DESIGN

Design simplification is one of the primary objectives of engineering. Among the many benefits that can result from simplifying circuits are lower development and production costs, greater reliability, improved performance, weight and size reductions, and lower power consumption. This integrated zener diode-transistor unit permits regulated power supply design to be simplified with the consequent reward. Also, some additional benefits are inherent in structure of the device

---

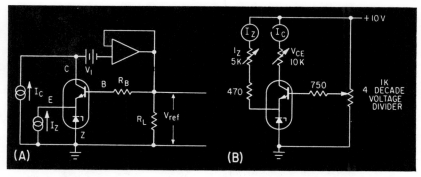

REFERENCE *amplifier can be tested using basic circuit (A) or alternate circuit (B)—Fig. 1*

cepted as a reference element because of its small size, low temperature coefficient, fast response and ability to withstand shock and vibration. Improvements in the structure and processing of zener diodes have made possible voltage stability better than 10 parts per million per year, which approaches a standard cell.

The error-voltage amplifier is used to compare output of the reference element with power supply output voltage, current or power and to provide an amplified error signal to the output amplifier.

Regulation, output impedance and ripple of a d-c regulated voltage supply depend primarily on the gains of the error-voltage amplifier and the output amplifier. Power supply temperature coefficient and long-term stability are set primarily by the temperature coefficient and stabilities of the reference element and the input stage of the error-voltage amplifier.

To achieve the best possible long and short-term stability in a power supply, temperature must be compensated individually in the reference element and the input stage of the error-voltage amplifier. If it is not, noncompensating voltage shifts can occur as a result of temperature differentials or changes in power dissipation. These requirements are generally met by using a temperature-compensated zener diode as the reference element and an integrated transistor differential amplifier or a chopper-stabilized amplifier as the input stage of the error-voltage amplifier.

INTEGRATED AMPLIFIER—The integrated reference amplifier is fabricated using a combination of grown-diffused and alloy techniques for optimum characteristics of both transistor and zener diode and post-passivation processes for long-term stability. A four-leaded TO-5 package is used. Electrical isolation from the case is achieved by mounting the pellet on a ceramic disk.

Temperature coefficient of the zener diode is a function of the zener voltage, becoming more positive as zener voltage increases. By controlling zener voltage in the reference amplifier, it is thus possible to achieve exact compensation for temperature variations in both base-emitter diode voltage and transistor current gain. At a collector current of 0.5 ma, compensation requires a zener temperature coefficient of about +2.5 mv per deg C, which in turn requires a zener voltage of about 6.3 volts.

A major advantage of the integrated structure is the reduction of the temperature differential between the zener diode and the transistor, with a consequent reduction in the long and short-term drift of the reference voltage. The estimated thermal resistance between the junction of the zener diode and the base-emitter junction of the transistor is 0.05 deg C per milliwatt, compared to a thermal resistance to air of 0.3 deg C per mw for each device. The overall structure thus provides an efficient thermal filter between the environment and the critical regions of the device, which minimizes the effects of sudden changes in ambient temperature on reference voltage.

TEST CIRCUITS—The most important characteristic of the reference amplifier is the temperature coefficient of the reference voltage. Temperature coefficient must be specified and measured with specific values of collector-to-base voltage, collector current, zener current and base source resistance.

A general test circuit is shown in Fig. 1A. Collector current and zener current are controlled by current generators I_c and I_z. Zener current is defined as the current flowing into the common terminal formed by the transistor emitter and the zener cathode, whereas the actual current flowing through the zener diode is the sum of I_z, I_c and transistor base current.

An operational amplifier used as a follower is connected between the collector of the reference amplifier

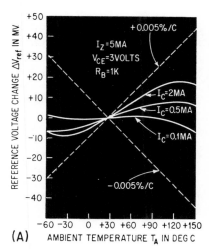

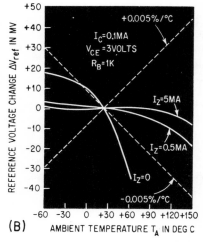

VARIATION *of reference voltage with temperature is shown for three values of collector current (A) and zener bias current (B)—Fig. 2*

and the output. Bias voltage V_1 provides a means for adjusting collector-to-base voltage of the transistor.

The circuit in Fig. 1A is in effect a regulated voltage supply that maintains constant bias on the reference amplifier. Reference voltage V_{ref} can be measured on an accurate differential voltmeter or digital voltmeter as temperature of the reference amplifier is varied. The percentage change in reference voltage for a given temperature change corresponds to the percentage change of output voltage that can be expected in a well designed power supply over the same temperature range.

Bias source resistance R_B is included in the specification of the reference voltage temperature coefficient to duplicate the effect of the resistance divider used in most power supplies to set output voltage. Divider resistance should be as low as possible for maximum gain of the reference amplifier and to reduce the effects of I_{co} and h_{FE} on reference voltage. However, such factors as power dissipation in the divider and current drain set a lower limit on divider resistance. Considering these requirements, a compromise value of 1,000 ohms was chosen for R_B.

An alternate test circuit that avoids use of differential voltmeters and operational amplifiers is shown in Fig. 1B. This circuit uses a 10-volt supply having a short-term stability of 2 millivolts or better and a four-decade voltage divider. The 5,000-ohm potentiometer is adjusted for desired zener bias current; the decade resistor is adjusted for collector current; and the 10,-000-ohm pot is adjusted for desired collector-to-base voltage.

The reference amplifier is then heated or cooled, and the voltage divider is adjusted to maintain the initial collector current. The variation in reference voltage can then be read to within 1 millivolt directly from the voltage divider. A 750-ohm resistor is added in series with the arm of the voltage divider to give a base source resistance of about 1,000 ohms.

TEMPERATURE COEFFICIENT
—Using the circuit in Fig. 1A, the

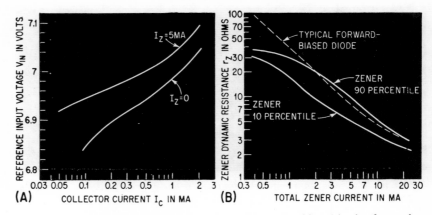

TYPICAL *transfer characteristic of reference amplifier (A) is shown for two values of zener bias current. Dynamic resistance of zener diode in reference amplifier (B) as a function of bias current is compared to dynamic resistance of forward-biased silicon diode—Fig. 3*

variation in reference voltage has been plotted against temperature on an x-y recorder using the base-emitter diode of the transistor as a thermometer. Voltage of the base-emitter diode is a linear function of temperature and is uniform among the devices. Because of the integrated structure of the reference amplifier, the device can be heated and cooled rapidly with no appreciable error in the voltage-temperature characteristic. Thus a complete x-y recording can be made over a temperature range of −55 to 150 deg C in less than 30 seconds with negligible hysteresis between the trace and retrace.

Curves obtained on an x-y recorder are shown in Fig. 2A for a typical unit operating at three different values of collector current. The upward bending of the curves at low temperatures results primarily from falloff of h_{FE} as is evident from the increased curvature at higher collector currents. The downward bending of the curve at high temperatures results primarily from the rapid increase of I_{co} and the resultant voltage drop across the base source resistor.

The curves for all reference amplifiers are similarly shaped. The curvature can be reduced by using transistors with higher values of h_{FE} and lower values of I_{co} or by decreasing the value of the base source resistor.

The similar set of curves in Fig. 2B were obtained on the same unit operating at three values of zener current. These curves show that it

is not advisable to operate with both low collector current and low zener current. Also, the temperature coefficient of the reference voltage becomes more positive as either zener current or collector current is increased, as shown in Fig. 2A and B. With some reference amplifiers, the temperature coefficient can be set exactly equal to zero at a specific temperature by adjusting the bias currents. Because of the relatively good linearity of the curves, extremely low temperature coefficients can be achieved over a moderate temperature range. For example, temperature coefficients as low as ±0.0001 percent per deg C or ±1 part per million per deg C have been observed over a temperature range from zero to 70 deg. C.

TRANSCONDUCTANCE
—The transfer characteristic of the reference amplifier, as shown in Fig. 3A, determines the change in collector current resulting from a small change in the reference voltage at the base. Circuit transconductance, defined as the ratio of collector current change to reference voltage change, is equivalent to the slope of the curve in Fig. 4 or

$$g_{mc} = dI_c/dV_{ref} \qquad (1)$$

where V_c and I_z are constant.

Circuit transconductance includes the effects of base source resistance and dynamic zener impedance. Hence, it is lower than the transconductance of a transistor common-emitter amplifier $(1/h_{ib})$. Cir-

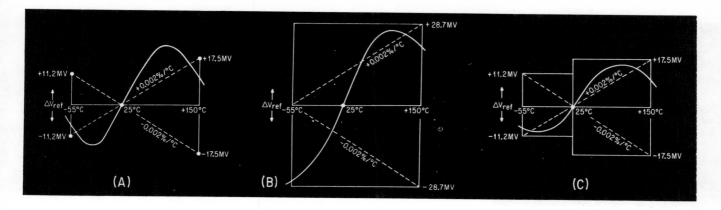

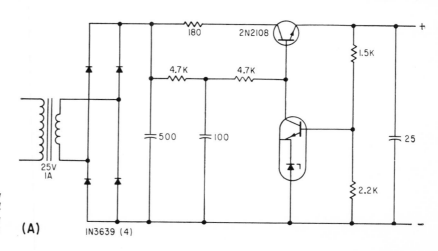

cuit transconductance is approximately

$$g_{mc} = 1/[h_{ib} + R_B/(1 + h_{fe}) + r_z], \quad (2)$$

where r_z is dynamic zener resistance and all parameters are measured at the specified bias conditions.

For maximum transconductance, a device should have high h_{fe} and low r_z and should operate at high collector current and zener current to minimize h_{ib} and r_z. In practice, an upper limit to collector current is determined by the linearity of the reference voltage curve at low temperatures, as indicated in Fig. 2A.

Dynamic resistance of the zener diode in the reference amplifier is relatively low, as indicated by Fig. 3B, which shows that at low current levels r_z is lower than dynamic resistance of a forward-biased silicon diode. The low value of r_z permits the reference amplifier to be operated at values of collector current as low as 0.5 ma without additional biasing current for the zener diode, permitting simplification in regulated power supply design without compromising performance.

Circuit transconductance can be conveniently measured using the circuit in Fig. 1B. After adjusting the circuit for nominal bias, the decade voltage divider is set 5 millivolts below the nominal value. The corresponding change in collector current is noted, and the value of g_{mc} is computed from Eq. 1.

SPECIFICATIONS—Three different methods are presently used for defining temperature coefficient of voltage reference devices. A particular device may have considerably different temperature coefficients, depending on which definition is used. Hence, in evaluating a specification, the exact definition of temperature coefficient must be known.

The methods of defining temperature coefficient are illustrated in Fig. 4 for a voltage reference device having a nominal voltage of 7 volts and a maximum temperature coefficient of ±0.002 percent per deg C over a temperature range of −55 to 150 deg C. The definition illustrated in Fig. 4A guarantees the variation in voltage at the temperature extremes but not at intermediate temperatures. The definition in Fig. 4B determines the allowable voltage variation on the basis of the total temperature range, whereas in Fig. 4C the allowable voltage variation is determined separately between 25 deg C and each temperature extreme. In both cases, a maximum voltage variation is guaranteed over the entire temperature range, but temperature coefficient over a smaller range can be considerably higher than the specified range.

A new and more exacting definition of temperature coefficient has been developed for the reference amplifier and is shown in Fig. 4D. This definition ensures that the temperature coefficient over any temperature range within the extreme limits will be less than the specified maximum temperature coefficient. An x-y recording of the voltage versus temperature characteristic can be provided with each unit to assure compliance with the specified temperature coefficient over the entire applicable temperature range.

Specifications for the reference amplifier include reference voltage, circuit transconductance and temperature coefficient. These parameters are generally all that are required to design a regulated power supply, although other parameters should also be specified for special applications.

Typical specifications for a reference amplifier were compiled under test conditions of 0.5 ma collector current, zero zener current, 3 volts collector-to-base voltage and 1,000 ohms base source resistance. The

SIMPLE *12-volt regulated supply (A) uses reference amplifier, and alternate precision 12-volt supply (B) uses current limiting—Fig. 5*

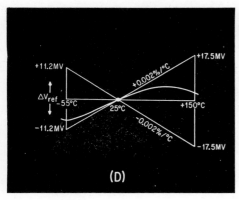

specifications are 7 volts ±5 percent reference voltage, 6,000 micromhos minimum circuit transconductance, ±0.002 percent per deg C temperature coefficient between −55 and 150 deg C, 40 to 120 current gain and 45 volts collector voltage rating.

POWER SUPPLIES—Two alternative power supply circuits are illustrated in Fig. 5: the simple 12-volt regulated supply that uses a reference amplifier, and an alternate power supply circuit of higher precision output voltage, using a current-limiting scheme. Both circuits can be easily laid out on a printed circuit board, as shown later. The simplest regulated power supply using the reference amplifier is shown in Fig. 5A. It is designed for an output of 12 volts at currents up to 100 ma. The 180-ohm resistor provides short circuit protection, limiting output current to less than 200 ma. The 100-microfarad capacitor and the 4,700-ohm resistors provide an effective filter for the base current of the 2N2108 transistor, reducing output voltage ripple to less than

80 microvolts under full load. Output impedance of the supply is about 0.65 ohms. For line voltage variations of ±10 percent, output voltage regulation is better than ±0.3 percent.

Use of the reference amplifier in a precision 12-volt, 50-ma regulated voltage supply is shown in Fig. 5B. The 2N1131 *pnp* silicon transistor is used to regulate collector current in the reference amplifier. Output current of the 2N1131 varies with line voltage because of the finite output resistance of the transistor and the voltage divider formed by R_2 and the dynamic resistance of D_1 and D_2. Resistor R_3, added to compensate these effects, makes output current of the 2N1131 almost completely independent of line voltage changes. For a line voltage change of ±10 percent, the variation in output voltage is typically less than ±0.001 percent and can be reduced to less than ±0.0001 percent by adjusting R_3.

Diode D_2 provides temperature compensation for the base-emitter diode of the 2N1131 transistor. This compensation is not critical, since, owing to the reference amplifier gain, a 1-percent change in the collector current of the 2N1131 has the effect of only a 0.01-percent change in reference voltage.

A 2N2785 Darlington transistor is used for the series regulator. Current gain of this transistor is typically 5,000 at 100 ma, so the normal variation of collector current

in the reference amplifier over the full range of output current is 20 microamperes or only 4 percent of nominal collector current.

In a constant-voltage power supply, regulation of collector current in the reference amplifier allows collector-to-base voltage to be adjusted to any desired operating value by adding a resistor between the base of the series regulator and the collector of the reference amplifier.

Sharp current limiting is provided in this circuit by R_1 and D_3. When the *IR* drop across R_1 exceeds 6 volts, diode D_3 conducts, decreasing emitter current to the 2N1131 transistor and thus reducing base current to the 2N2785. Dynamic resistance of the current-limiting characteristic is about 2,200 ohms.

Output impedance of the power supply is about 0.03 ohm, and output ripples and noise at full load is less than 10 microvolts. Output impedance can be reduced to about 1 millohm by adding another emitter follower stage to the series regulator and rearranging the circuit for voltage sensing across the load. Higher output current and power can be obtained by substituting a power transistor such as the 2N2197, mounted on an appropriate heat sink, for the series regulator. Temperature stability of the supply is mainly dependent on the temperature coefficient of the reference amplifier. An overall temperature coefficient of ±0.002 percent per deg C can easily be achieved.

The printed-circuit board layout of the power supply in Fig. 5B is shown in the photograph excluding the rectifiers and filter capacitors.

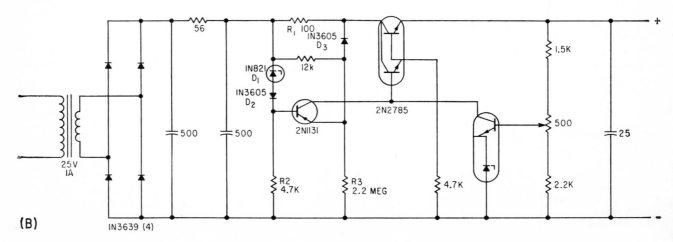

The Negative Resistance Element (NRE)

A New Circuit Component

FAMILY *of negative resistance elements are checked on a plotter to determine characteristic curves*

The family of electronics circuit components is continuing to grow as modern techniques generate new and versatile devices. This new series of components exhibits a-c negative resistance and has a variety of applications

By CARL D. TODD, Hughes Aircraft Co., Newport Beach, Calif.

INCREASE in voltage applied to the usual resistor will cause a proportional increase in the terminal current. Certain electronic devices have regions where an increase in applied voltage produces a decrease in terminal current. This represents an a-c negative resistance.

The four-layer diode, silicon-unijunction transistor and the gaseous discharge tube have a terminal characteristic curve of the general form shown in Fig. 1A. Here, a given value of terminal voltage between V_v and V_P may produce one of three possible terminal currents; however, any set current yields one and only one possible voltage. Thus, a device of this type is referred to as having a current-stable or N-type negative resistance.

The terminal characteristic curve shown in Fig. 1B is exhibited by devices like the tunnel diode, vacuum tube tetrode as used in the dynatron oscillator, and the common-emitter input of a point contact transistor. This characteristic is referred to as voltage-stable or S-type, since any one voltage will control the terminal current and any current between I_v and I_P may have three possible values of terminal voltage.

Negative resistance devices may be used to construct oscillators and Q-multipliers and perform many switching functions; their usefulness, however, is sometimes limited by nonlinearity or unpredictability of their electrical characteristics.

It is possible to design composite circuits with fairly linear negative resistances. Several configurations have been described,[1,2,3] but these have a certain amount of dependence on the device parameters of the semiconductors used, are temperature sensitive and lack carefully-controlled characteristics.

A patented[4] composite circuit is currently available tnat overcomes many of the previous limitations of negative resistance devices or circuits. Negative resistance elements (NRE) have predictability and

---

THE POSITIVE NEGATIVE

The high predictability of the negative resistance element (NRE) characteristic curve makes the device a natural as a d-c switch, circuit breaker, monostable multivibrator and a relaxation oscillator. It is also useful in threshold and comparator circuits.

In linear applications, the excellent linearity and temperature stability of the NRE gives the circuit designer a usable negative resistor for use in Q-multipliers, two-terminal oscillators and filters

---

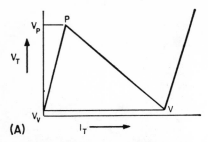 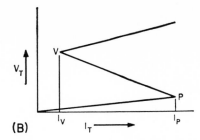 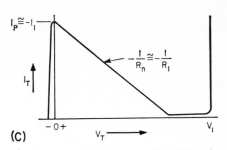

NEGATIVE *characteristics of N-type (A) and S-type (B) materials and the terminal characteristics produced by the* circuit *of Fig. 2B (C)—Fig. 1*

stability that yield performances and permit versatile applications not previously possible; thus, a new component is made available to the circuit designer.

BASIC OPERATION—The circuit arrangement shown in Fig. 2A, has two ideal power amplifiers connected together in a loop. Amplifier 1 is assumed to have unity voltage gain and infinite current gain; amplifier 2 assumes an infinite voltage gain and a current gain of minus one.

An a-c voltage, V_t, applied to the output terminals will produce a voltage at the output of amplifier 1 that is also equal to V_t. This will cause a current to flow in R_1 that is equal to V_t/R_1. This, in turn, is the input current of amplifier 2.

The output current of amplifier 2 will be equal then to $-V_t/R_1$. The terminal current, I_t, is also equal to $-V_t/R_1$ since the current supplied to the input of amplifier 1 is zero. The resulting terminal resistance R_t will be: $R_t = V_t/I_t = V_t/-V_t/ R_1 = -R_1$, or $V_t/(-V_t/R_1)$.

The amplifier circuit of Fig. 2A would yield a negative slope without any boundaries, thus implying an infinite power source. A modified equivalent circuit that is realized to a very close approximation in

the NRE is illustrated in Fig. 2B.

The resulting characteristic curve seen at the output terminals is shown in Fig. 1C. Boundaries on the negative resistance are established by clamping diodes D_1 and D_2. Voltage V_1 establishes the clamping level for higher values of V_T and D_2 prevents the terminal voltage from going appreciably negative.

The current bias source I_1 provides a terminal current for a zero value of V_T that will be approximately equal to $-I_1$. As V_T is increased in a positive direction, a current I_2, is produced that will add algebraically. For the actual case, the magnitudes will subtract, thus reducing the terminal current linearly and producing a negative terminal resistance.

Diode D_3 aids in simulating the actual input conditions to amplifier 2 as seen from the bias terminal. This indicates a slight temperature dependence of the input voltage of roughly 2 mv per-degree C, that must be considered in designing stable bias conditions.

Diode D_4 prevents a negative voltage from producing a current in R_1 and also compensates for the voltage drop across D_3. The magnitude of the a-c output resistance, R_n, in the negative resistance region, will

be somewhat different from that indicated by the first equation because of the finite dynamic resistance R_{d3} and R_{d4} of diodes D_3 and D_4 respectively as $R_n = R_1 + R_{d3} + R_{d4}$.

The values of R_{d3} and R_{d4} may roughly be approximated by the usual equation, $R_d = KT/qI_t = 0.026/I_F$ ohm at room temperature, where I_F is the value of forward current in the individual diode.

The equivalent circuit as shown, represents the NRE closely in most applications, although it is not an exact circuit.

GENERAL CHARACTERISTICS—Negative resistance elements are composite circuits similar to the equivalent circuit of Fig. 2B, and possess an S-type or voltage-stable output terminal characteristic curve. Two main families are available depending upon the polarity desired for the terminal voltage.

Typical output terminal characteristics for the family of NRE designed for use with negative terminal voltage supplies are given in Fig. 3A. Curves for an NRE with $R_n = 1,000$ ohms are shown for several different values of bias current I_1 and for two values of supply voltage V_1.

The magnitude of the peak current will be nearly equal to that of the bias current I_1, and the high-voltage clamping point is about 0.7 volt higher than V_1. By varying V_1 and I, the characteristic curve may be considerably modified.

Fig. 3B shows the many possible values of R_n represented as R_1, an

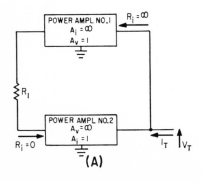

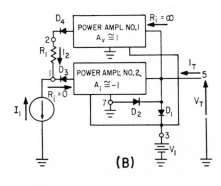

BASIC *method of producing a negative resistance (A) and equivalent circuit of an NRE (B)—* Fig. 2

external variable resistor connected across the terminals provided. For this curve, biases V_1 and I_1 were held constant at $-30V$ and 10 ma, respectively.

The excellent linearity of R_n for the NRE is illustrated by the typical performance curve shown in Fig. 3C. With the terminal voltage restricted between 1 and 30 volts, linearity is better than 2%. With V_T restricted to the 4.5 to 29.5 voltage range, the linearity is about 0.5 percent.

The temperature coefficient of R_n is a function of the value of R_n. It is possible to achieve a stability of 5 ppm per-degree C over a temperature range of -20 C to $+100$ C for values of R_n approximately equal to 700 ohms. For optimum temperature stability, wire-wound resistors must be used for the reference resistor R_1.

Maximum operating frequency is limited to around 1 Mc for the present negative supply NRE. Higher frequency devices will probably become available later.

The characteristic curves for NRE designed for positive terminal voltages are very similar to those given in Fig. 3 except that the polarities are all inverted; that is, V_T and V_1 will be positive, but I_1 will be negative. The maximum operating frequency for the positive supply NRE family is about 20 Mc.

In non-linear applications, the excellent predictability of the device's characteristic curve is excellent for an efficient d-c switch, a circuit breaker, monostable multivibrator or a relaxation oscillator. Moreover, the linearity and temperature stability of R_n gives the designer a usable negative resistor for use in Q-multipliers, two-terminal oscillators and filters. Some typical applications are shown in Fig. 4.

REFERENCES

(1) C. D. Todd, Transistor-Tunnel Diode Combination, Electronic Design, Vol. 9, pps. 48-51, April 26, 1961.
(2) C. D. Todd, Transistor-Tunnel Diode Produces an N-type Negative Resistance, AIEE Communication and Electronics, No. 26, pps. 284-290, Sept. 1962.
(3) C. D. Todd, A Composite Circuit Exhibiting S-type Negative Resistance, Semiconductor Products, Vol. 5, pps. 24-28, Oct. 1962.
(4) H. J. Pfiffner, U. S. Patent No. 2,943,282.

D-C SWITCH application of the NRE (A); the device applied to a Q-multiplier circuit (B) and monostable vibrator circuit and operating characteristics (C)—Fig. 4

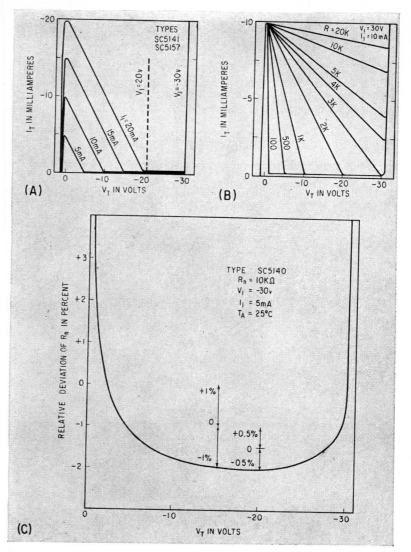

OUTPUT curves for Hughes SC5141 and SC5157 devices for $R_n = 1,000$ ohms (A); characteristics for SC5140 and SC5156 for several values of R_1 (B) and typical resistance linearity curves (C)—Fig. 3

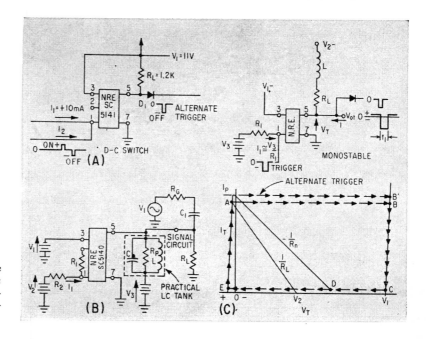

By CARL DAVID TODD

Head of Engineering, Modular Circuits,
Hughes Aircraft Co., Newport Beach, Calif.

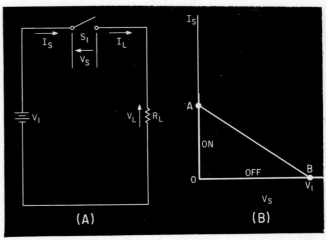

TYPICAL D-C SWITCHING *circuit (A); operating characteristics for a mechanical switch (B)*—Fig. 1

USING A NEW COMPONENT: Design of D-C Switches

Composite circuit recently made available, provides speed and freedom from contact bounce when used as an electronic switch. Design in switching applications is outlined step-by-step

A TYPICAL CIRCUIT for a mechanical switch is shown in Fig. 1A. Switch S_1, which connects source voltage V_1 to load resistor R_L, has two possible conditions: open or closed. In closed or ON, the full supply voltage is applied to R_L and the operating point on the load line is at A (Fig. 1B). When S_1 is open or OFF, the operating point must be at point B and little current can flow.

The ideal switch will have zero resistance, and thus zero voltage drop across it, when it is ON. It will have infinite resistance, so that load current will be zero, when S_1 is OFF. The ideal switch is approached even for practical switches of the mechanical form.

A characteristic known as toggle switching may be desired, where the switch remains in the position to which it is set until moved. Thus, it is not necessary to retain the control signal (force applied to the switch handle), to retain either the ON or OFF condition.

Although the mechanical switch approaches the ideal condition for ON and OFF resistance, it lacks the speed and freedom from bounce required for many applications. It is here that electronic switches prove valuable.

NEGATIVE—The Hughes family of negative resistance elements (NRE) (ELECTRONICS, p 21, May 31, 1963) are composite circuits having a voltage-stable or S-type negative resistance characteristic appearing at the output terminals. Figure 2A is a typical family of electrical characteristics for the SC5141 or SC5157 negative resistance elements.

The shape of the characteristic curve is clearly defined and is highly predictable. Peak current is a direct function of the magnitude of the bias current, I_1, and is almost equal to it. The polarity of I_P, however, is negative.

The slope of the characteristic curve in the region of negative resistance (region II), where an increase in terminal voltage produces a decrease in terminal current, is approximately $-1/1,000$ ohms or -1 milliohm.

The valley voltage, which represents the boundary between region II and the second positive resistance region, region III, is roughly equal to the product of I_P and R_n, the magnitude of the a-c negative resistance. For the SC5141 and the SC5157, V_V is given by:

$$V_V = I_P R_n = I_P (1,000) \qquad (1)$$

Therefore, if I_1 is made equal to 10ma, I_P will be nearly equal to -10ma and V_V will be -10 volts.

The current I_V that flows for a terminal voltage V_V is small. Typically the value of H, the ratio of I_P to I_V will be 50 or more. The slope of the characteristic curve for voltages just larger than V_V is positive, and is approximately 50,000 ohms. This

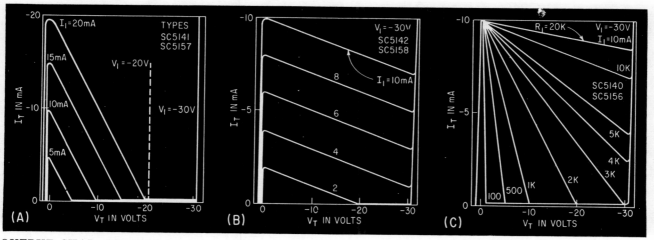

OUTPUT CHARACTERISTICS: *for negative resistance elements with $R_n = 1,000$ ohms (A); for an NRE with R_n of 10,000 ohms (B); for several values of R_1 (C)—Fig. 2*

With Negative Resistance Elements

value varies somewhat from unit to unit, depending upon the source resistance for I_1.

The terminal voltage, V_K, where the current rapidly increases with a small increase in the V_T, is approximately 0.7 volt larger than the bias voltage, V_1. The maximum allowable value of V_1 for the types of NRE shown is −30 volts. Should it be desirable to make the value of the knee voltage less than the value of V_1, a voltage regulator diode may be placed directly across the output terminals to modify the characteristic curve. If more convenient, a diode clamp may be used.

The electrical characteristics for the SC5142 and the SC5158 NRE are given in Fig. 2B; the value of R_n for these two types is 10,000 ohms and the valley voltage is:

$$V_V = I_P (10,000) \qquad (2)$$

Other characteristics of the curves will be similar to those of the SC5141 and the SC5158.

A third class of NRE, types SC5140 and SC5156, may be used to produce almost any negative resistance from −50 to −100,000 ohms. The value of R_n will be nearly equal to the value of an external resistor, R_1, placed across the input terminals provided. This approximation becomes less accurate for very low or very high values of R_1 or for very low values of I_1. A typical characteristic family is shown in Fig. 2C for several values of R_1 and for an I_1 of 10 ma.

BIASING—An NRE, operated under the load-line conditions of Fig. 3A will have two stable states, points A and B. At point A the voltage across the NRE is typically about 0.5 volt positive and the current through it is relatively high. This corresponds to operating point A in Fig. 1B for the closed or ON switch.

At operating point B the terminal current is much lower than it was at A and practically all of the supply voltage is dropped across the NRE. This condition corresponds to operation at point B in Fig. 1B for the open or OFF switch.

For the circuit of Fig. 3B, a voltage slightly larger than the supply voltage appears across the load when operation is at point A or the switch is ON. The load current when the switch is closed must be less than the peak current of the NRE, roughly equal to I_1 in magnitude.

When operation is at point B in Fig. 3A, most of the supply voltage appears across the NRE and little voltage is impressed across the load. The load current is thus small and corresponds to the condition of an open or OFF switch. Switching is not perfect since the current in the OFF condition is not zero, but this is not a problem in many applications. The value of the knee voltage, V_K, must be larger than the supply voltage. With the arrangement of Fig. 3B, this condition is automatically obtained, since V_K is about 0.7 volt higher than the applied voltage bias.

TRIGGERING—Consider the mechanism for switching from the closed or ON condition to the open or OFF condition and back again. Assume that the conditions are as illustrated by the solid characteristic curve of Fig. 3A and the operating point is at B.

As seen before, the switch is effectively open or OFF. A small trigger current, I_2, applied to terminal 1 will modify the d-c characteristic curve since it adds or subtracts from the value of I_1 depending upon the polarity of the trigger.

If I_2 is positive or in the direction shown in Fig. 3B, the characteristic curve becomes that illustrated by the dotted line. The load line now intersects the new characteristic curve at only one point, C, very

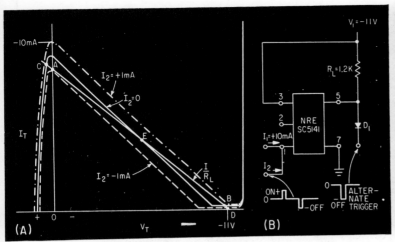

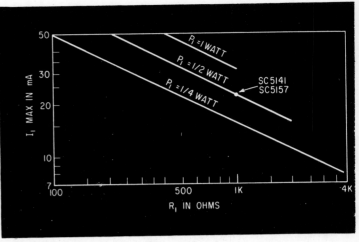

OPERATING CHARACTERISTICS (A) for switch circuit (B) using a negative-resistance element—Fig. 3

CURRENT LEVEL is limited by the power rating of R_1 for switching applications—Fig. 4

near to A and the operating condition must shift to this point. If I_2 is now reduced to zero, the characteristic curve of the NRE will assume its original form. The operating point, however, will remain at A. Thus, by the application of a positive trigger current applied to terminal 1, the switch is turned from OFF to ON.

Consider now what happens upon the application of a negative value of I_2, with the direction of I_2 being opposite to that indicated in Fig. 3B. The characteristic curve of the negative resistance element now takes the form of the dashed line of Fig. 3A. Again, the load line intersects the modified characteristic curve at only one point, but this time the only permissible condition is D, or a high-voltage state near B. As I_2 is again made zero, the operating point remains at B. Thus, a negative trigger current applied to terminal 1 will cause the switch to change from ON to OFF.

The switch is bistable and, once triggered, will remain in the demanded state until a trigger of the opposite polarity is applied. Thus, a memory function is provided similar to the mechanical toggle switch.

The circuit of Fig. 3B has considerable power gain both for the turn-off as well as for the turn-on conditions. The power required to turn the switch OFF is about 5 microwatts. For turning the switch ON, the required power is quite circuit-dependent, but may be held to around one milliwatt. The power switched in the load is 110 milliwatts.

The switch of Fig. 3B may be turned OFF by the application of a negative voltage pulse applied to the alternate trigger point. The amplitude must be greater than the terminal voltage corresponding to point E on the curve of Fig. 3A before switching takes place. The energy required is much greater than that required at terminal 1, but this method of triggering may be desirable in some applications. The trigger normally must be a pulse of short rise time for decisive triggering.

COMPENSATION—During normal operation of the switch of Fig. 3B, a voltage slightly larger than the

value of the supply voltage appears across the load resistor. This is due to the slightly positive voltage at point A and may be compensated for by the insertion of a small resistor R_c in series with load resistor, R_L. For perfect compensation, the voltage drop across R_c when the switch is ON must be exactly equal to the voltage V_A corresponding to point A in Fig. 3A,

$$R_C = \frac{V_A}{I_A} = \frac{V_A}{V_1/R_L} \qquad (3)$$

POWER DISSIPATION — The ideal mechanical switch of Fig. 1 dissipates no power since the voltage drop is zero when it is closed and the current through it is zero when it is open. The NRE switch of Fig. 3B approaches this state for most applications and therefore the power dissipation due to the ON voltage or the OFF current will be negligible, or at least within the $V_T I_T$ rating of 250 mw. There are other portions of the internal circuit of the NRE which do consume power that must be dissipated in the form of heat.

The area of major concern is the resistor that generates the effective negative resistance, R_n, whether the resistor is internal as in the SC5141, SC5142, SC5157, and SC5158, or external as with the SC5140 and the SC5156. The power dissipation in this resistor, R_1, is greater when the switch is OFF or operation is at point B in Fig. 3A. The maximum value of I_1 which may be permitted under the general circuit conditions of Fig. 3B may be determined from

$$I_{1max} = \sqrt{P_{1max}/R_1} \qquad (4)$$

where P_{1max} is the maximum power dissipation allowed in R_1.

Equation 4 is plotted in Fig. 4 for several possible resistor power ratings. This analysis is limited to the case where V_v of the NRE is less than V_1. It is not always possible to operate a given resistor up to its rated power because of voltage limitations. Only the switching case has been considered and it is assumed that power dissipation in switching from one state to the other is small.

DESIGN PROCEDURES—Consider the steps neces-

AUTHOR *measures the operating parameters of a bread-boarded d-c switch*

sary to arrive at a final design for a d-c switch circuit like that shown in Fig. 3B. Assume that it is desired to apply or disconnect a given supply voltage, V_1, to a given load resistor, R_L.

It is necessary that the peak current, I_p of the NRE be larger than the load current, I_L, when the switch is ON. This may be easily accomplished by making I_1, the applied bias current slightly greater than I_L. A 5 or 10-percent margin is normally adequate:

$$I_1 = I_L (1 + k) = \frac{- V_1}{R_L} (1 + k) \qquad (5)$$

where k represents the desired fractional margin.

For a bistable load line, the value of R_n, the magnitude of negative resistance developed by the NRE must be smaller than R_L. To reduce the trigger current required to turn the switch ON, R_n must be as large as practical and yet still be less than R_L. For the same relative stability as before, V_v should be made 5 or 10 percent lower than V_1. This demands that R_n be made 10 to 20 percent lower than R_L:

$$R_n = R_L (1 - k') \cong R_1 \qquad (6)$$

The next step is to determine the power requirements of the resistor R_1:

$$P_1 = I_1{}^2 R_1 \qquad (7)$$

where P_1 is the actual power dissipation in R_1 when the switch is in the OFF state. Should the switch remain ON most of the time and the duration of the OFF time be relatively short, it may be possible to use a resistor with a smaller power rating than that suggested by Eq. 7. If the switch is to remain OFF for rather long periods, the power rating should be somewhat higher than indicated by Eq. 7.

The NRE used must be rated for a voltage equal to V_1 or higher. In addition, it must be able to withstand the required value of I_1.

The required trigger current, I_2, to turn the switch ON or OFF may now be calculated:

$$I_{2\ ON} = \Delta I_P = - \frac{V_1}{R_n} - I_1 \qquad (8)$$

$$I_{2\ OFF} \cong - (I_1 - I_L) \qquad (9)$$

Thus, a positive current will turn the switch ON

if its value exceeds that indicated by Eq. 8, and a negative current will turn it OFF if its value exceeds that indicated by Eq. 9. Using the recommended margins given above, typical trigger currents will be 5 or 10 percent of the value of I_L.

Should it be desirable to compensate for the positive voltage drop when the switch is ON, the compensation resistor, R_c, may be calculated directly from Eq. 3, repeated here for convenience:

$$R_C = \frac{V_A}{I_A} = \frac{V_A}{V_1 / R_L} \qquad (3)$$

TYPICAL EXAMPLES—Suppose it is desired to design a switch that may be used to connect a power supply of −11 volts to a 1,200-ohm load resistor. The normal load current under the ON condition will be 9.2 ma. The required value of the bias current may be computed from Eq. 5:

$$I_1 = I_L (1 + k) = 9.2 \times 10^{-3} (1 + 0.1) = 10.1 \text{ ma} \qquad (10)$$

Here a margin of 10 percent has been used. A bias current of 10 ma will be assumed.

Next, it is necessary to calculate the required value of R_n. This may be done by using Eq. 6 and assuming the margin k' to be 15 percent:

$$R_n = R_L (1 - k') = 1,200 (1 - 0.15) = 1,020 \text{ ohms} \qquad (11)$$

An NRE with a negative resistance of 1,000 ohms may be used. The SC5140 may be used with an external R_1 connected between terminals 1 and 2, or an SC5141 may be used alone.

It is necessary to check that power ratings are not exceeded. Equation 7 gives a requirement of 0.1 watt, which is well within the rating of the SC5141.

Equations 8 and 9 yield the required trigger current level. Thus, a value of I_2 of +1 ma will turn the switch ON and a value of I_2 of −0.8 ma will turn it OFF.

For a second example, assume that it is required to switch a −28-volt power supply to a load resistance that varies from 1,000 to 3,000 ohms. The load current, therefore, varies from 28 to 9.3 ma.

When the load current varies, it is necessary to design for the maximum value of its range. Therefore, the design will be based on the limiting case where R_L is 1,000 ohms.

Equation 5 will indicate a required bias current, I_1, of 30 ma using a margin of about 7 percent. From Eq. 6 is determined a value of R_n of 820 ohms using a margin of about 18 percent.

Power in R_1 will be 0.74 watt, so a 1 or 2-watt resistor must be used between pins 1 and 2 on an SC5140 NRE.

The trigger current required to turn the switch ON will be about +3.4 ma. Because the load resistance varies, the trigger current required to turn the switch OFF also varies. As R_L is changed from 1,000 ohms to 3,000 ohms, I_{2OFF} varies from −2 ma to −2.7 ma.

The examples indicated are only representative of the many possible applications of the Negative Resistance Element family. The circuits shown are primarily for NRE types designed primarily for use with negative voltage supplies. Types are also available which will allow the use of positive voltage supplies.

USING A NEW COMPONENT—Raising

Semiconductor negative resistance elements can be paralleled with tank circuit to neutralize equivalent resistance and produce high Q's. Adjusting NRE for infinite Q leads to sinusoidal oscillations.

By **CARL DAVID TODD**
Hughes Aircraft Co.,
Newport Beach, California

WITCHCRAFT

Getting rid of resistance merely by introducing negative resistance to cancel it seems so obvious as to be unreal. Its like a science-fiction plot to use negative-gravity to hold the spaceship aloft. Yet for tank-circuits it works. The positive resistance disappears, near-infinite Q is left and the circuit becomes a sinusoidal oscillator

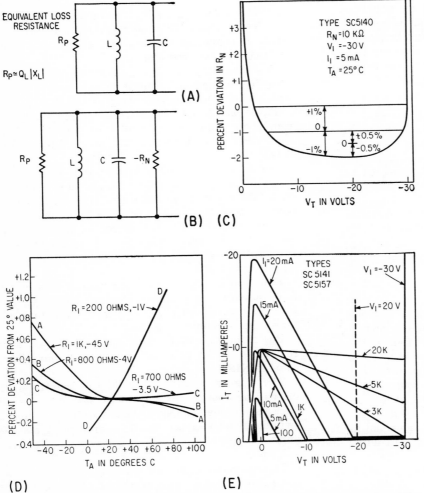

PARALLEL RESISTOR represents resonant circuit's equivalent resistance (A). Adding negative resistance neutralizes equivalent resistance, gives high Q (B). Voltage-stability of few tenths percent is possible with stable supplies (C), temperature stability to 0.1 percent can be achieved for 100 C temperature range (D). Negative resistance characteristics are drawn for $R_n = 1,000$ ohms, also for several values of R_1 (E)—Fig. 1

MANY RESONANT circuits require a higher Q than practical LC components can give. This is especially true for the lower frequencies where relatively large inductances are necessary and where a coil having sufficiently high Q is often too heavy.

The effective Q of practical LC resonant circuits can be increased by using negative resistances to compensate for losses within the resonant circuit. To achieve a stable Q yielding a constant bandwidth stable negative resistance is needed. Negative resistance elements (NRE) are now available giving excellent stability with time and for variations of supply voltage and temperature. If Q is infinite, the circuit becomes a simple two-terminal sine wave oscillator. Various formulae for design or analysis of Q-multipliers are presented using examples to illustrate practical design procedure.

Q Multiplier—In using a practical resonant circuit, losses may be considered as an equivalent resistor in shunt with pure reactive elements. Figure 1A illustrates the equivalent circuit for a practical parallel resonant LC tank circuit. Components L and C are assumed to be lossless and R_p represents all losses in the circuit at the frequency under consideration. The Q of the circuit is usually dependent on the losses within the inductor and may be expressed as

$$Q = Q_L = R_{p4}/\omega L \qquad (1)$$

Where R_{p1} represents the effective shunt resistance of the inductor at the frequency of interest. For a complete analysis or where the losses of the capacitor may be appreciable, an

Tank-Circuit Q With the NRE

effective loss resistance R_{pc} is associated with the capacitor. For this analysis, however, the term R_p will represent the total loss associated with the circuit.

Negative Shunts—Suppose that a negative resistance of magnitude R_n is placed across the tank circuit as shown in Fig. 1B. This combines with the positive resistance, R_p, to form a new equivalent resistance $R_{p'}$

$$R_{p'} = R_p (-R_n)/(R_p - R_n) \quad (2)$$

The magnitude of $R_{p'}$ changes rapidly as the value of R_n approaches R_p, but its sign remains positive as long as R_n is greater than R_p. At the point where R_n is exactly equal to R_p, the value of $R_{p'}$ becomes infinite and the circuit oscillates.

With a modified value of equivalent loss resistance, $R_{p'}$, has a new value Q' where

$$Q' = R_{p'}/\omega L = -R_p R_n/\omega L (R_p - R_n) \quad (3)$$

Taking the ratio of Q' to the original value Q, factor K indicates the increase in Q

$$K = Q'/Q = R_n/(R_n - R_p)$$

Stability—Equation 4 shows a graph of the sensitivity of K, and hence the sensitivity of Q' to changes in R_n with respect to R_p, This is especially pronounced as the value of K is increased by making R_n approximately equal to R_p. Thus, if K is made only 10, a one percent change in R_n will produce roughly a ten percent change in Q'.

If Q is to be held as high as possible, there will be limitations to the value of K since slight variations in R_n could produce unwanted oscillations. Variations of Q will also produce changes in the resultant bandwidth of the resonant circuit.

Assuming that R_p remains relatively constant with temperature, then negative resistance must remain stable. Figures 2C and 2D show that the desired stability is available from off-the-shelf negative-resistance elements.

Figure 1C shows that R_n varies less than ±1 percent for terminal

voltages from about 25 to 30 volts. Restricting the terminal voltage excursion will maintain a linearity or stability of R_n better than a few tenths of a percent.

Figure 1D illustrates the temperature stability of R_n for the SC-5140, using a wire-wound resistor for the reference. For R_n values around 700 ohms, stabilities in the order of 5 parts per million per degree centigrade are possible over a temperature range of −20 to +100 C. It is possible to produce negative resistances over a range of values which yield less than 0.1 percent change in value over a 100 degree centigrade temperature span. For values of R_n much above or below 700 ohms, it may be necessary to use a basic R_n of about 700 ohms and then use positive resistances to modify it.

Resistance Tracking—Although previously R_p was assumed to remain constant, in a practical case, this will not always hold. To demand a stable value of R_n would not help

much if R_p varies greatly. However, it is possible to produce relative tracking of R_p and R_n when using negative resistance elements.

The value of R_n approximates the value of a reference resistor R_1 connected across the input terminals. Hence, if R_1 varies in the same manner as R_p, then a tracking arrangement is possible in which variation in the difference between R_n and R_p is held to a minimum. The required variation in R_1 may usually be achieved by using a network of thermistors of positive and negative coefficients combined with normal resistors.

Load—While even the unloaded low frequency tank circuit may have an already inadequate Q, its Q-value may be reduced further by source or load resistances. All such losses, whether due to the capacitor, inductor, or source and load resistances, may be included in the one term R_p. Here again, for K or Q' to remain fairly constant, it is necessary for the total R_p to remain stable

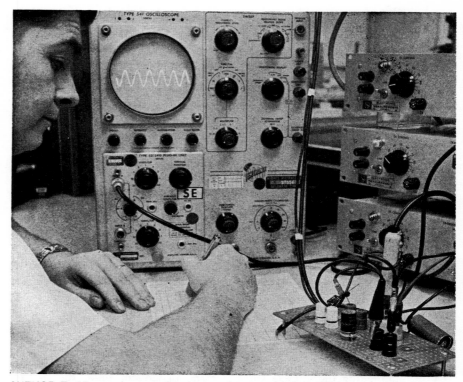

AUTHOR Todd measures performance of breadboard Q-multipler circuit

as well as R_n. If the load resistance has some variation, then a compensating variation may be induced in the value of the reference resistor R_1.

Biasing—The typical terminal characteristic curves are given in Fig. 1E for the SC5140 and SC5141. To bias the negative resistance element, a positive current bias, I_1, and a negative voltage bias V_1, must be applied. It is necessary, for linear applications, to bias the output terminals with a d-c load line that intersects the characteristic within the negative-resistance region. Circuits for the Q-multiplier and the two terminal oscillator will be the same. The only difference is in the choice of the value of Q.

Figure 2A illustrates the fundamental bias requirements for the NRE multiplier or oscillator. Positive voltage supply V_2 and series resistor R_2 comprise a d-c current source for current bias I_1. The magnitude of I_1 depends upon signal level requirements and other considerations.

A negative voltage supply, V_1 is applied to terminal 3. This determines the terminal voltage, V_T, at which the current rises sharply as indicated in Fig. 1E.

Finally, a second negative voltage supply, V_3, is applied through the inductor, L, to the output terminals of the NRE. For operation as a Q multiplier or oscillator, it is necessary that the d-c load line, fixed by the d-c resistance of the inductor and V_3, intersect the output terminal characteristic curve only within the negative resistance region.

For the normal case, where the d-c resistance of the coil is negligible, it is necessary only that V_3 be between zero and V_1. Signal requirements may impose other restrictions.

A reference resistor, R_1, must be connected between the terminals. Its value will be determined by circuit requirements. It should have the necessary stability with temperature or, if temperature tracking is desired, must have the appropriate temperature coefficient.

Two Bias Supplies—It is always possible to simplify the circuit of Fig. 2A by eliminating the voltage supply, V_3. This may be done by using a voltage divider from V_1 if the output resistance is held low enough to give a proper d-c load line. It will be necessary to bypass this point to an a-c ground.

A design approach which improves power-supply economy, yields considerable circuit simplification, and also improves bias point stability, is to derive the supply voltage V_3 from the V_1 source by using a series voltage regulator diode, as shown in Fig. 2B. Supply V_3 must always be less than V_1 and a current must always flow at the output terminal for linear signal operation. Hence, the voltage regulator diode will always be in the breakdown region and will present a low a-c impedance to ground.

Thus, no bypass capacitor will be required.

One Bias Supply—However, in some applications it may not be convenient to have both positive and negative supply voltages; however several possibilities exist for biasing the NRE Q-multiplier with a single source.

One possible circuit is given in Fig. 2C. This is a modified form of Fig. 2B, in which V_2, (I_1 supply), is generated with a second voltage regulator diode, D_2. To obtain the necessary polarity, it is necessary to lift the ground points of Fig. 2B to the voltage of D_2. Supply voltage V_1 must be increased by a voltage equal to that of D_2 to preserve the former bias condition of Fig. 2B. Should it be necessary to keep the tank circuit at d-c ground, configurations of Fig. 2D of Fig 2E may be used. In Fig. 2D a tapped supply provides both V_2 and V_1 bias voltages for the remaining circuit. A voltage regulator diode establishes the actual terminal bias voltage.

Fig. 2E illustrates a configuration in which a single supply may be used for holding the tank circuit at d-c ground. The value of I_1 will now be

$$I_1 = (V_1 - V_{B1})/R_2 \qquad (5)$$

Temperature compensation of I_1 in Fig. 2E circuit is possible if the temperature coefficient of D_1 is approximately 2 mv/degree C.

The operating characteristic curve of the basic circuit is shown in Fig. 2F. The d-c load line will have a slope dependent upon the d-c resistance of the coil, which for most cases is negligible. The d-c resistance load line produced by R_L will be the parallel equivalent of the source resistance, R_G, load resistance R_L, and the equivalent loss resistor, R_p.

The instantaneous output voltage swing must be between zero and V_1. Thus, for a maximum output capability, the voltage at the bias point Q must be half-way between zero and V_1. That is, at $V_1/2$.

Determination of R_n—The first design choice will be the determination of R_n. The value used for R_n will depend on the desired Q' plus loading and losses of the tank circuits, and may be expressed

$$R_n = R_L'/(1 - R_L'/LQ') = R_L'/(1 - Q/Q')$$
$$= R_L'/(1 - 1/K) \qquad (6)$$

Where R_L' is the total parallel equivalent loss resistance, consisting of the generator source resistance, load resistance, and the internal losses of the tank circuit; Q is the value of Q obtained before adding the multiplier circuit; and K is the ratio of multiplication.

The minimum allowable supply voltage for V_1 is equal to the maximum peak-to-peak output voltage and should be made slightly greater to allow for some component tolerance and rift. If low distortion is a severe requirement, it will be necessary to provide a guard band of two or three volts on both the high and low ends, and V_1 should be about four volts higher.

With V_1 and R_n chosen, the required value of bias current I_1 may be easily computed, as it is nearly equal to $-I_p$, the peak current of the NRE. With R_n fixed and V_1 chosen, an assumed arrangement shown in Fig. 2F yields a value for I_p

$$I_p = V_1/R_n = I_1 \qquad (7)$$

Thus I_1 is generated by a voltage source V_2 in series with resistor R_2'. Source V_2 should be large with respect to 0.8 v to reduce temperature dependence. Ideally, V_2 should decrease approximately 2 mv/degree C.

The remaining variable V_3, is chosen half-way between zero and V_1 and is

$$V_3 = V_1/2 \qquad (8)$$

Other Bias Schemes—These above design equations may be extended to other biasing schemes with some

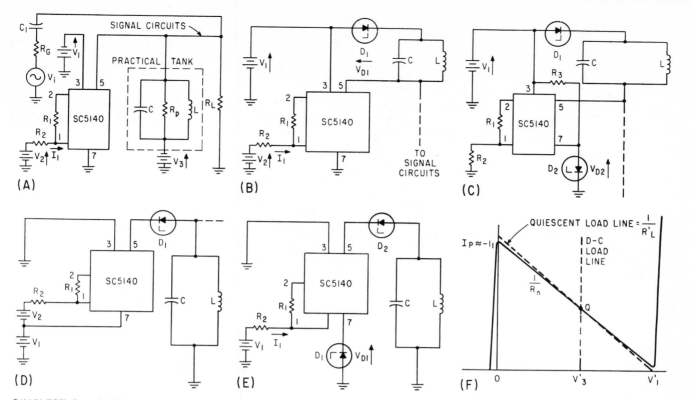

SIMPLEST Q-multiplier involves 3 voltage sources (A), improved circuit eliminates one supply with zener (B), two zeners permit operation on single supply (C). Tapped supply enables tank circuit to be grounded by (D), improved version has grounded tank and one supply (E). Characteristics refer to circuit 2A (F)—Fig. 2

modification. For example, consider the circuit of Fig. 2B. Here, the procedure is exactly the same as given above except a breakdown diode, D_1, is used to develop the value of V_3 indicated by Eq. 8.

$$V_{D1} = V_1 - V_3 = V_1/2 \qquad (9)$$

For Fig. 2C, the design procedure is as before, except V_1 must be increased by an amount equal to the breakdown voltage of D_2 which is usually made 5 volts or slightly less to obtain a slightly negative temperature coefficient for compensation. Also V_{D1} equals half the value of V_1, less the breakdown voltage of D_2.

$$V_{D1} = V_1 - V_{D2}$$

Figure 2D is just a minor rearrangement of Fig. 2B, hence, the same design procedures apply.

The circuit of Fig. 2E requires a slightly different procedure. Here V_{D1} must equal the voltage required for V_1 in the basic design. For temperature compensation, V_{D1} should have a temperature coefficient of about $+2$ mv/degree C; V_{D2} is then made equal to $V_{D1/2}$, and V_1 of Fig. 2E must equal V_{D1} plus an amount to produce the required value of I_1 through R_2. Thus

$$V_1 = V_{D1} + I_1 R_2$$

Design Example—Assume that a resonant tank circuit consisting of a 1- uf capacitor and a 1-henry inductor, resonating at 159 cps. The unloaded Q of the inductor is 10, and source and load resistances are each 10,000 ohms.

The value of the equivalent parallel resistance R_p may be calculated to be 10,000 ohms, then the net value of R_p including the source and load resistances would be 3,333 ohms for a loaded Q of 3. Shunting the tank circuit with a 3,600 ohm negative resistance gives a modified Q or Q^1 using Eq. 3 but including loading equal to

$$Q^1 = \frac{-(3,333)(3,600)}{2\pi(159)(3,333-3,600)} = 45$$

The loaded Q has thus been multiplied by 15. To achieve a higher multiplication factor it is necessary only to make the value of R_n a little smaller. Bias arrangements should be designed next, assuming separate power supplies for V_1, V_2 and V_3 in Fig. 2A.

For a single-supply arrangement such as shown in Fig. 10, operating from $+24$ v, V_{p1} is made equal to the desired value of V_1. To set up the same equivalent bias conditions as before, V_{D1} is set to 15 volts,

and V_{D2} is made equal to 7.5 volts. Resistor R_2 provides the bias current of 4.2 ma from the difference in V_1 and V_{D1}. R_2 should be

$$R_2 = (24 - 15)/4.2 \text{ ma} = 2,200 \text{ ohms}$$

To design an oscillator, it is necessary merely to reduce the value of R_n until it is slightly less than the total positive loss resistance. If low distortion is required, it may be necessary to make R_n adjustable. Otherwise, it should be some 10 percent lower than R_p.

If the peak to peak signal swing is 10 volts, then valley voltage for the NRE must be greater than 15 volts for the best linearity. Operating bias point is then chosen to be 7.5 volts, equal to V_3 if the d-c resistance of the coil is negligible.

The valley voltage is approximately equal to the product of R_n and the peak current, I_p. With R_n equal to 3,600 ohms and a valley voltage of -15 volts, I_p must be -4.2 ma. Current I_p is controlled by the value of bias current I_1, hence, if V_2 is 24 volts, R_2 must be approximately 5,600 ohms. The final voltage, V, must be between -15 volts and a maximum of -30 volts; the value of R_n is set by a resistor R_1 of 3,600 ohms. (Actually R_n will be slightly larger.)

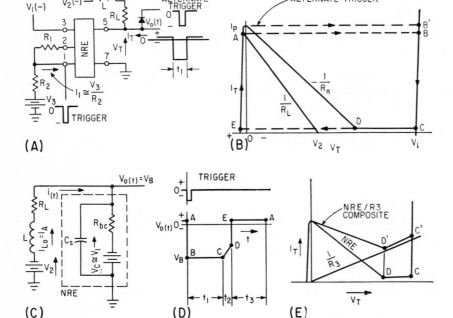

NRE in this monostable multivibrator breadboard is between the two sets of plug jacks

MONOSTABLE multivibrator circuit (A) requires three bias voltages. Rest position is point A in (B), and arrows indicate the switching path. Equivalent circuit (C) applies as point B is reached. Typical output waveform (D), with t_2 exaggerated. External loading produces a composite characteristic (E)—Fig. 1

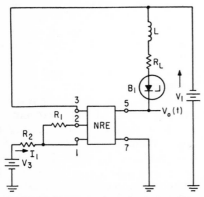

BREAKDOWN diode allows operation with two supplies—Fig. 2

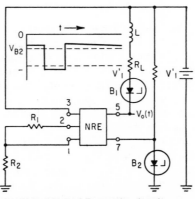

SINGLE VOLTAGE supply circuit uses two breakdown diodes—Fig. 3

USING A NEW
Designing

Basic circuit of the NRE

used to bring the supplies

NEGATIVE RESISTANCE elements (NRE) have a stable and predictable S-type or voltage controlled negative resistance characteristics. The stability of the characteristic is particularly useful for designing monostable multivibrators that are likewise stable and predictable. The design principles and equations should aid similar applications of the devices. Like all S-type or voltage-controlled negative-resistance devices, the NRE requires an inductor as the energy-storage element when used as a monostable. A typical circuit is shown in Fig. 1A.

Operating characteristics for the NRE monostable are given in Fig. 1B. Monostable operation requires that the d-c load line, determined by R_L, intersect the NRE characteristic curve at only one point and this point must lie within one of the positive resistance regions.

BIASING — Figure 1B illustrates the case where the load line intersects the characteristic curve in the low voltage positive resistance region. This can be assured by keeping V_2 less than the valley voltage, V_D, and keeping R_L greater than V_2/I_p. Since required trigger current is a function of the difference between I_p and the operating bias current (I_A, corresponding to point A in Fig. 1B), it is desirable to make the load line intersect the NRE characteristic just below the peak point.

Monostable operation can also be achieved by establishing an operating point within the high-voltage positive resistance region. In this case V_2 must be greater than V_D

COMPONENT

NRE Monostable Multivibrators

monostable requires three separate bias supplies. But breakdown diodes can be

down to one   By **CARL DAVID TODD,** Hughes Aircraft Co., Newport Beach, Calif.

and R_L must be less than R_n, the magnitude of negative resistance.

OPERATION—At rest, the d-c operating point will be at A in Fig. 1B. The output voltage is low and slightly positive (for the negative voltage family of NRE). A current I_A corresponding to point A flows through L, R_L, and the output terminal of the NRE. This current will be less than the normal peak current, I_p, as established by bias current I_2 and hence will not cause the NRE to switch.

A negative current pulse applied to the trigger input, terminal 1, will momentarily cause the peak current to drop below I_A. This will cause the NRE to switch along the line indicated to B and the output voltage to increase sharply. Inductor L will maintain the current during switching but as soon as B is reached the current will begin to fall at a rate determined by the L/R time constants of the circuit. As the operating point moves from B to C the output voltage remains relatively constant because of the steep slope of the characteristics in this region. After C is reached, the operating point moves along the curve at a faster rate due to the higher resistance of the character-

istic and hence lower L/R time constant. The output voltage will change appreciably in this region and will drop from approximately V_1 when the operating point is at C to valley voltage V_V when the operating point reaches D.

At D the energy conditions are still such that V_2 cannot increase the current in the load circuit. Hence the operating point must switch to E as the terminal current attempts to fall below the valley current corresponding to D. Now V_2 is able again to supply energy to the inductor and the terminal current increases until the original steady state bias point A is reached. The operating point remains here until the next trigger pulse.

An alternate triggering action can be obtained by applying a negative pulse through a diode to the output terminal, as shown. This causes the peak current of the NRE to be momentarily exceeded and hence a switching action will occur. The current immediately after switching, however, will still be equal to I_A if the pulse width of the trigger is small.

ANALYSIS—Figure 1C gives the equivalent circuit for the monostable circuit as B is reached. Solv-

ing for t_1, the time required to go from B to C, yields

$$t_1 = \frac{L}{R_L + R_{bc}} \ln \left[\frac{\frac{V_1 - V_2}{R_L + R_{bc}} + I_A}{\frac{V_1 - V_2}{R_L + R_{bc}} + I_C} \right] \quad (1)$$

As the operating point moves from C to D, the dynamic resistance R_{cd} of the NRE is much higher and hence, t_2, the time required, is short.

$$t_2 = \frac{L}{R_L + R_{cd}} \ln \left[\frac{\frac{V_2}{R_L + R_{cd}} - I_C}{\frac{V_2}{R_L + R_{cd}} - I_D} \right] \quad (2)$$

In most instances t_2 may be neglected.

As the current through the inductor decreases below I_D, corresponding to point D, a switching takes place from D to E. Output voltage changes rapidly from a negative V_D, equal to the valley voltage, to a slightly positive voltage V_E.

The operating conditions are now such that V_2 supplies energy necessary to increase the current through L and move the operating point from E back to steady state A. The time required, t_3, is the recovery time.

$$t_3 = \frac{L}{R_L + R_{ea}} \ln \left[\frac{\frac{V_2 - V_E}{R_L + R_{ea}} - I_D}{\frac{V_2 - V_E}{R_L + R_{ea}} - I_A} \right] \quad (3)$$

If a trigger pulse is applied before the end of the recovery period, the monostable either will not start or t_1 will be shortened due to a lower initial current in the inductor.

Width of the trigger pulse should

PUTTING A NEW DEVICE TO WORK

Negative resistance elements are proving themselves to be versatile circuit elements. In the May 31 issue, the author presented characteristics of the NRE and mentioned the monostable multivibrator circuit briefly. Here he develops the design equations and shows how to get bias voltages from one supply

---

be shorter than t_1 or the circuit may fire a second time or more.

WAVEFORM

The output waveform is shown in Fig. 1D. Points labeled correspond to points on the characteristic curve of Fig. 1B.

The resulting waveform is nearly flat on both top and bottom because of the self limiting action of the characteristic curve. In the high-voltage state, as the operating point moves from B to C, the ouptut voltage changes only a few tenths of a volt. In like manner, the output voltage is nearly constant as the operating point goes from E to A.

Except for the transition represented by the line C-D, the rise and fall times are short and depend only upon the various shunt capacitances and the frequency response of the transistors used in the NRE. To eliminate this slower transition, the circuit biases are changed such that V_1 is equal to V_v, which is equal to $I_p \times R_n$.

The peak amplitude of the monostable output voltage is almost entirely dependent upon supply V_1. If the trigger pulse width is less than t_1, the output pulse width will be independent of the trigger.

LOADING

The preceding discussion assumed negligible loading at the output of the monostable. If a load resistor R_3 is connected, R_3 and the NRE form a composite characteristic as shown in Fig. 1E. The composite curve is formed by adding the respective currents of the load resistor and the NRE.

If the currents corresponding to C' and D' are used for those of C and D, Eq. 1, 2 and 3 still apply.

The three power supply circuit can be simplified. For the monostable bias condition where the steady state bias point is in the low voltage region, V_2 must always be less than V_1. From Eq. (1) the period t_1 is a function of (V_1-V_2), not just V_1 or V_2. This leads to Fig. 2.

Since at least a small current always flows through the inductor, R_L, and the breakdown diode, a relatively constant voltage exists across B_1. This supplies an equivalent V_2, which is equal to the difference between V_1 and the breakdown voltage V_{B1}; ($V_1 - V_2$) is thus V_{B1}, a constant.

The bias technique of Fig. 2, therefore, not only simplifies the supplies but yields relative immunity of the time period t_1 to changes in voltage supply V_1. The time t_2, to go from C to D, is still a function of supply voltage, as is recovery time t_3.

The output waveform is the same as for the three-supply circuit.

By using an additional breakdown diode as shown in Fig. 3, only one supply is needed. Bias current I_1 is developed by voltage regulator diode B_2 and resistor R_1. Voltage regulator diode B_1 provides V_2 supply as in Fig. 2.

With a few modifications, Eq. 1, 2, and 3 may still be used for the time periods. Note that the supply for V_1, connected between terminals 3 and 7 in Fig. 1 and 2, will now be equal to ($V_1' - V_{B2}$) in Eq. (1), V_2 will be ($V_1' - V_{B1} - V_{B2}$)

The output waveform will be different in that the voltage level is shifted by an amount equal to V_{B2}, as shown in Fig. 3.

DESIGN EXAMPLES

Assume a monostable circuit is to operate from -24 and $+24$ supplies and have a 1-ms output pulse.

An SC5140 NRE is used with a 10-volt regulator diode. Peak current of the NRE characteristics is determined by I_1. Assume I_p is to be -10 ma. For a 24-v source, R_2 should be 2,200 ohms.

The steady state bias point must intersect the NRE curve in the low-voltage positive resistance region. Since the required trigger current will be the difference of I_p and operating current I_A, I_A should be roughly 0.9 I_p to have a low trigger current with adequate margin.

The effective value of V_2 is the difference in V_1 and V_{B1}, or -14 volts. This gives a net value of ($V_1 - V_2$) of -10 volts. With V_2 and I_A fixed, the d-c load resistance is computed as (-14v)/(-9ma) or 1,560 ohms. This includes the dc resistance of the inductor.

Typically, R_{bc} is around 50 ohms for the SC5140. The value of H, the ratio of peak to valley currents, is roughly 50, giving a valley current equal to -0.18 ma. By choosing the value of R_n, determined by the value of resistance R_1 applied between terminals 1 and 2, C and D of Fig. 1B can be the same point. To do this, make R_1 equal to V_1/I_1; for this case, 2.4 ohms.

Solving Eq. (1) for L

$$L = \frac{(t_1)(R_L + R_{bc})}{\ln\left[\dfrac{\dfrac{V_1 - V_2}{R_L + R_{bc}} + I_A}{\dfrac{V_1 - V_2}{R_L + R_{bc}} + I_C}\right]}$$

$$= \frac{(10^{-3})(1560 + 50)}{\ln\left[\dfrac{\dfrac{-10}{1610} + (-9 \times 10^{-3})}{\dfrac{-10}{1610} + (-0.18 \times 10^{-3})}\right]} \quad (4)$$

$$= 1.9 \text{ h}$$

Waveforms of the circuit are given in Fig. 4. Output amplitude is approximately 25 volts peak; a 10 μs trigger pulse was used at 100 pps.

With the repetition rate reduced to 10 pps, the trigger pulse width was increased to 1 ms to obtain pulse bursts. While the trigger is negative, the circuit actually is operating in an astable mode. The amplitude of the trigger must remain constant. Overall circuit performance is indicated in Fig. 5.

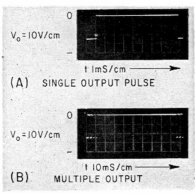

TYPICAL waveforms of NRE monostable circuit—Fig. 4

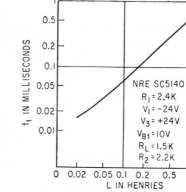

TEST RESULTS of two-supply circuit as a function of inductance—Fig 5

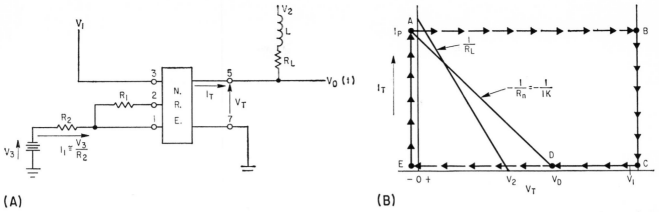

(A)　　　　　　　　　　　　　　　**(B)**

A STABLE MULTI *using the NRE (A), its operating char teristics (B), instantaneous equivalent circuit when voltage*

The NRE Free-Running Multivibrator

Design based on negative

resistance element

requires few components

By CARL DAVID TODD, Modular Circuits Department
Hughes Electronic Products Division
Hughes Aircraft Co., Newport Beach, California

NEGATIVE RESISTANCE elements are voltage stable or S-type negative resistance devices and require an inductor for energy storage in the relaxation or astable mode of operation. A typical circuit, Fig. 1A, includes all of the biasing arrangements needed.

Operating characteristics for the NRE under the conditions of the circuit given are illustrated in Fig. 1B. For astable operation it is necessary that d-c load line, determined by the resistance of R_L, intersect the negative resistance portion of the characteristic curve without intersecting either of the positive resistance regions.

Several conditions must be met in order that the load line pass through only the negative resistance portion of the characteristic curve. First, the value of the load resistor, R_L, must be less than R_n, the magnitude of the negative resistance of the NRE used. In addition, the supply voltage, V_2, must be made between $I_P R_L$ and a voltage, V_D, corresponding to point D in Fig. 1B. V_D may be computed from the value of the bias current, I_1, and the value of R_n by $V_D \cong -I_1 R_n$.

OPERATION—The intersection of the load line and the negative resistance portion of the NRE is not a stable point of operation and hence the operating point must slide either down the curve to point D or up the characteristic curve to point A.

Suppose the operating point is momentarily at point A. Conditions are such that the terminal current through the NRE under a stable state must exceed I_P when the terminal voltage is equal to V_A corresponding to point A. As the current attempts to exceed I_P, a switching action takes place. The current through the NRE is momentarily held equal to I_P by inductor, L, whose current may not change instantaneously, and the terminal voltage across the NRE increases to V_B corresponding to point B on the characteristic curve.

With the terminal voltage equal to V_B, however,

STABLE LINEAR *output is a feature of the NRE multivibrator*

MORE ON THE NRE

This is the third article we have published by the same author on the NRE and its uses. On p 21, May 31, 1963, he discussed basic operation and general characteristics, and on p 32, July 12, designing d-c switches

---

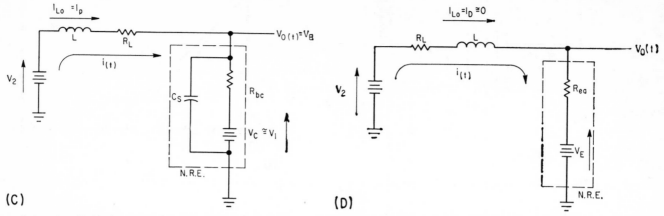

(C)   **(D)**

reaches point B of the operating characteristic (C), and equivalent circuit with operating point at E (D)—Fig. 1

conditions are not such that the supply voltage, V_2, may provide the energy necessary to sustain a current through the NRE equal to I_P. The instantaneous equivalent circuit at the instant that point B is reached is shown in Fig. 1C.

The NRE has been represented by a voltage source which is very nearly equal to V_c, corresponding to point C; a series resistance, R_{bc}, which is equal to the inverse of the slope from point B to point C on the characteristic curve; and an equivalent shunt capacitance, C_s.

For a medium or low speed circuit, the effect of the shunt capacitance, C_s, may be neglected. Making this assumption, the transient equation for the circuit of Fig. 1C may be written from which an expression for the time, t_1, to traverse the characteristic curve from B to C may be derived.

$$t_1 = \frac{L}{R_L + R_{bc}} \ln \left[\frac{\frac{V_1 - V_2}{R_L + R_{bc}} + I_P}{\frac{V_1 - V_2}{R_L + R_{bc}} + I_C} \right] \quad (1)$$

Since I_c is usually small

$$t_1 \cong \frac{L}{R_L + R_{bc}} \ln \left(1 + \frac{I_P (R_L + R_{bc})}{V_1 - V_2} \right) \quad (2)$$

Time, t_3, required for the operating point to move from point C to point D will be much shorter than t_1 and may be assumed negligible because the device resistance, represented by the inverse slope of the line from C to D, is large, typically from 50 to 300,000 ohms for the unloaded multivibrator depending on the source resistance of the supply providing I_1. Where t_3 may not be ignored

$$t_3 = \frac{L}{R_L + R_{cd}} \ln \left[\frac{\frac{V_2}{R_L + R_{cd}} - I_C}{\frac{V_2}{R_L + R_{cd}} - I_D} \right] \quad (3)$$

where R_{cd} represents the dynamic resistance represented by the slope from point C to point D.

As point D is reached and the current attempts to fall to a lower value than I_D, a switching action must occur and the operating point jumps to point E. Figure 1D illustrates the instantaneous equivalent circuit at the instant point E is reached.

Using the equivalent circuit of Fig. 1D, the tran-

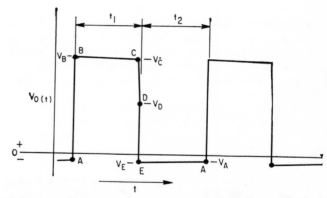

OUTPUT WAVEFORM *for astable multivibrator of Fig 1A—Fig. 2*

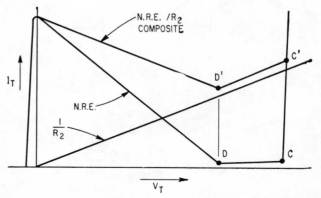

ADDING *the external load resistor modifies the terminal characteristic—Fig. 3*

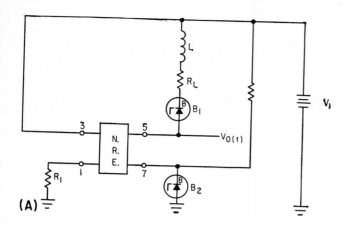

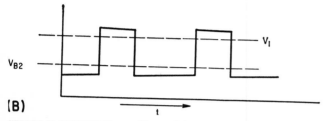

(A)

(B)

SINGLE SUPPLY *astable multivibrator (A) and its operating characteristics (B)—Fig. 4*

sient equation governing the current in the loop is

$$i_{(t)} = \frac{V_2 - V_E}{R_L + R_{ea}}\left(1 - \exp{-\frac{(R_L + R_{ea})t}{L}}\right) + I_L \exp{-\frac{(R_L + R_{ea})t}{L}} \quad (4)$$

A period time, t_2, will be required for the operating point to move from point E to the original point A where the switching action will again occur. The value of t_2 may be found by setting the value of $i_{(t)}$ in Eq. 4 to the value of the current at point A which is equal to I_P. The initial current in L will be equal to I_D

$$t_2 = \frac{L}{R_L + R_{ea}} \ln\left[\frac{\frac{V_2 - V_E}{R_L + R_{ea}} - I_D}{\frac{V_2 - V_E}{R_L + R_{ea}} - I_P}\right] \quad (5)$$

If I_D may be assumed zero, as for the normal unloaded multivibrator, Eq. 5 simplifies to

$$t_2 \cong \frac{L}{R_L + R_{ea}} \ln\left(\frac{1}{1 - \frac{I_P(R_L + R_{ea})}{V_2 - V_E}}\right) \quad (6)$$

If R_L is made large with respect to the dynamic resistances R_{be} and R_{ea}, which are typically less than 50 ohms each, then Eq. 2 and 6 may be simplified

$$t_1 \cong \frac{L}{R_L} \ln\left(1 + \frac{I_P R_L}{V_1 - V_2}\right) \quad (7)$$

$$t_2 \cong \frac{L}{R_L} \ln\left(\frac{1}{1 - \frac{I_P R_L}{V_2 - VE}}\right) \quad (8)$$

WAVEFORM—The output waveform (Fig. 2) is nearly flat on both top and bottom because of the self limiting action of the characteristic curve. In the high voltage state, as the operating point moves from B to C the output voltage changes only a few

tenths of a volt. In like manner, the output voltage remains nearly constant as the operating point moves from E to A.

Except for the area represented by the line $C\text{-}D$, the rise and fall times are short and depend only upon the various shunt capacitances and the frequency response of the transistors used in the NRE. If it is desirable to eliminate this slower transition, then the circuit biases are changed such that V_1 is made equal to the valley voltage, V_v, which is equal to the product of I_P and R_n. The peak voltage amplitude in the high voltage state is almost entirely dependent upon the value of the voltage supply, V_1.

LOADING—It has been assumed that the multivibrator has no external load connected to its output.

The easiest method of analyzing the effect of load R_2 is to consider the manner in which it modifies the equivalent NRE terminal characteristic. Since the NRE and R_2 are in parallel, the currents may be added graphically, Fig. 3.

For the example shown, output current is about one half the peak current. Points C and D are modified to C' and D', otherwise Eq. 1, 3 and 5 may be used as before.

PRACTICAL CIRCUITS—The circuit of Fig. 1A requires two positive supply voltages and one negative supply voltage from which I_1 may be derived. For the opposite polarity NRE family, V_1 and V_2 must be negative and V_3 should be positive. There are some variations in the circuit that require fewer supplies for biasing the NRE.

In a two-supply circuit, V_2 is always less than V_1 and it is possible to derive V_2 from V_1 by a normal resistive voltage divider if adequate power available. This may be done and the output resistance of the voltage divider may be used for R_L. Should this be impractical, V_2 may be developed by using a voltage regulator diode in series with V_1. Current flows at all times, so no bleeder resistor is necessary.

The bias current I_1 is obtained from a voltage supply opposite in polarity to V_1 by means of a series limiting resistor R_1.

The voltage output will switch between a minimum voltage which will be a few tenths of a volt negative for the positive voltage NRE as shown in Fig. 1A, or positive for the negative voltage types of NRE, and a maximum voltage nearly equal to V_1.

By using the arrangement shown in Fig. 4A, it is possible to use only one voltage supply for the NRE astable multivibrator. Bias current, I_1, is developed by voltage regulator diode B_2 and resistor R_1. Voltage regulator diode B_1 provides the proper voltage for V_2. Note that this approach for obtaining V_2 always gives a constant value for $V_1 - V_2$ even if V_1 should change from time to time. This is helpful in giving immunity to supply voltage variation on the time t_1, as seen by Eq. 1.

Switching levels for the output voltage will be changed from that given by the other circuits. The minimum voltage level will be fixed by the value of the breakdown voltage of B_1. The upper voltage level will still be limited by the value of V_1'. The value of V_1 in Eq. 1 will be equal to $V_1' - V_{B2}$.

How Diodes Keep Current to Constant Value

*Family of current
regulators can simplify
a variety of circuits*

By NEIL WELSH

Chief Engineer
CircuitDyne Corporation
Laguna Beach, California

CONSTANT-CURRENT diodes, called Currectors, are two-terminal solid-state devices that limit current. Current-limiting action of these units is comparable to the voltage-limiting action of zener diodes.

Departure from theoretical behavior of presently available types of Currectors is negligible for most applications. And designers now find their use can effect improvements for power supplies, linear amplifiers, multivibrators, and wave-shaping circuits.

CHARACTERISTICS — Typical first-quadrant characteristic of a polar constant-current diode of this type is shown in **Fig. 1A**. The operating region, that portion of the curve over which current is essentially independent of voltage, is bounded on its lower side

by an abrupt change in slope. A more gradual slope change marks the upper boundary of the operating region.

Nonpolar types Fig. 1B, have nearly identical forward and reverse characteristics. Deviations from exact symmetry are slight, and are confined to the extremes of the operating voltage range.

The linear equivalent circuit, Fig. 2, is appropriate to the operating regions of both polar and nonpolar types.

Shunt capacitance, C_c, has a voltage dependence similar to that of reverse-biased pn junctions. Magnitude of this shunt capacitance presently limits usefulness of these devices to frequencies below a few hundred kilocycles.

Shunt conductance is also a function of voltage. The peak absolute magnitude of the shunt conductance is held, in most cases, to one micromho per milliampere. However, conductance is negative over much of the operating range, reducing the average value to about one-tenth of the peak. This fact is significant for applications which involve operation over wide voltage spans.

Such an application is the circuit

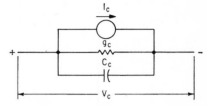

EQUIVALENT *circuit is applicable to both types of constant-current diodes—Fig. 2*

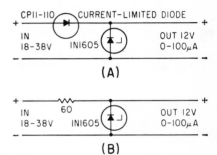

CURRENT-LIMITED *shunt-voltage regulator circuits utilizing Currector-zener diode (A) and resistor-zener (B)—Fig. 3*

shown in Fig. 3A. This circuit supplies 0-100 ma of load current at a nominal output voltage of 12-v d-c, from a 28 ±10-v d-c source. Currector selected has a current rating 10 percent higher than the maximum normal load current, and functions over extremes of input voltage for both normal and shorted loads. The isolation of output voltage from changes of input voltage varies less than ±4 mv for 16 to 40-v d-c inputs. Short-circuit current is similarly independent of input voltage, being 10 ±2 ma over the full input-voltage span.

MERITS—Unusual features of this design approach are illustrated by comparison with conventional resistor-zener voltage regulator shown in Fig. 3B.

Largest series resistance that can be used in this circuit is 60 ohms. Output voltage variation, for the rated input-voltage change, is ±425 mv—more than 100 times that of the Currector-zener cir-

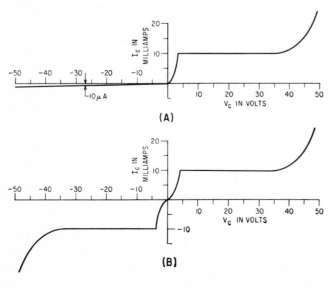

(A)

(B)

TYPICAL *diode characteristics are given for two types of diodes used to regulate current. Curves are shown for polar (A) and nonpolar (B) types —Fig. 1*

cuit. For normal load conditions, input current varies from 265 ma, at 28-v input, to 435 ma at 38-v input. Maximum zener-diode power dissipation is, therefore, almost four times as high as in the circuit of Fig. 3A. The output impedance of the resistor-zener circuit is about 20 percent lower than that of the Currector-zener circuit, because of the shunting effect of the 60-ohm resistor, and the lowering of the zener-diode impedance due to the higher zener current. Most impedance reduction is due to the latter cause, and so is expensive in terms of efficiency, power dissipation, short circuit-current and input-output isolation. The performance of the Currector-zener circuit compares favorably with more complex regulator circuits.

TEMPERATURE — Configuration of Fig. 3A, though generally valuable as a zener-drive circuit, has merit for use with temperature-compensated reference diodes, since their high impedance requires that they be driven with a constant current. This circuit is useful also in decoupling applications, for it provides excellent isolation even with a low voltage drop. Also, circuit does not introduce instability caused by the inherent phase shift of r-c decoupling networks.

The Currector in Fig. 4 isolates the output of the single-stage amplifier from changes in supply voltage, and acts as a collector-load impedance. Bias resistor establishes collector voltage at a quiescent value of −10v. With no signal input, collector voltage remains substantially constant for supply voltages between −12 and −35-v d-c. Decoupling, as measured by superimposing 1vrms on a supply of −25-v d-c is 30 db or greater for frequencies below 50 Kc, indicating that a stage of this configuration is unusually immune to power supply ripple and power supply-coupled feedback.

The voltage gain of this circuit is unusually high. Voltage gain in a common emitter amplifier stage approaches r_c/r_b (expressed in T-equivalent parameters) as load admittance approaches zero.

In Fig. 4, the effective load con-

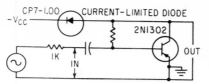

CONSTANT - CURRENT *diode used as a collector load—Fig. 4*

sists of the parallel combination of the Currector shunt admittance and the bias resistance, and is nearly equivalent to the bias resistor alone. Several transistors with betas ranging from 20 to 100, were tried in the circuit. In each case, appropriate bias resistors establish quiescent collector voltage at −10-v d-c. Bias resistor values ranged from 200 kilohms to 1 megohm. Mid-frequency voltage gains for the single stage varied from 57 to 66 db, and upper 3 db cutoff frequencies from 50 to 100 Kc. Low frequency response was limited by the input r-c circuit alone.

As a consequence of the high gain attained by using a Currector as a collector-load impedance, quiescent collector-voltage level must, for linear operation, be defined by feedback. This was the reason for selecting the biasing method used in Fig. 4. Without stabilization of the collector voltage by either internal or external feedback, linear amplification would be impossible. This presents no problem, of course, if operation in the switching mode is desired.

LINEARITY — A simple linear ramp generator utilizes a Currector for linearization. This circuit achieves performance ordinarily obtained only through the use of bootstrap techniques.

When the incoming gate signal turns off the transistor of the generator, Currector current is diverted into charging the capacitor. Rate of change of the capacitor voltage, remains constant until e_r reaches a level such that the voltage drop across the Currector is less than its minimum operating voltage. Thus the lower limit on the supply voltage is defined. Voltage must exceed the desired ramp magnitude by at least the knee voltage of the diode. Also, since the supply voltage is impressed directly across the current limiter when the transistor is gated on, supply volt-

age must not exceed the maximum rated voltage of the Currector. Within these limits, supply voltage has no influence on the ramp output, which is both linear and stable.

A number of familiar circuits can be improved substantially by substituting a constant-current diode for a resistor. However, application of the diode is not restricted to the modification of conventional circuits.

In a triangular-wave-shaping circuit, a non-polar constant-current diode limits the magnitude of a capacitor-charging current whenever the instantaneous generator voltage is such that the voltage drop across the diode exceeds its knee voltage. This simple circuit produces an output that is largely independent of input waveform characteristics.

Small truncations visible on the output waveform of the wave-shaping circuit are the result of the combination of low rate-of-change of the driving waveform near its points of polarity reversal, and the diode knee voltage. Truncation error can be reduced by increasing the magnitude of the drive voltage, or using a drive waveform which reverses polarity rapidly, such as a square wave. Similar circuits are easily adapted to the demodulation of pulse frequency, pulse wave and pulse repetition.

Chapter 12
OPTOELECTRONIC CIRCUITS

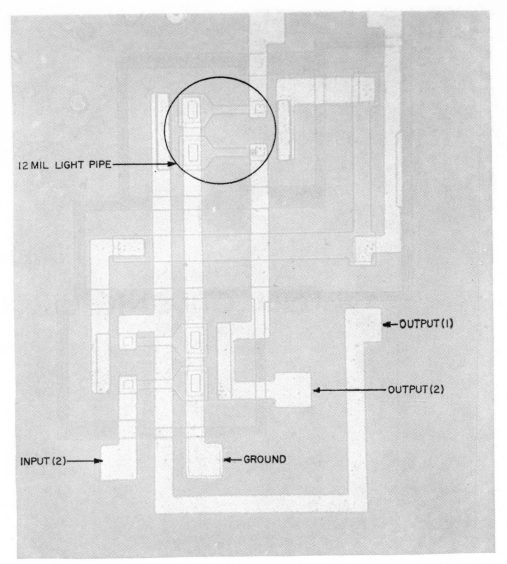

PHOTOMICROGRAPH at 135 times magnification shows microcircuit flip-flop driven through 12-mil light pipe (circled)

OPTICAL COUPLING:

NEW APPROACH TO MICROCIRCUIT INTERCONNECTIONS

Experimental techniques lead to success
with arsenic trisulfide light pipes

By **M. A. GILLEO** and **J. T. LAST**
Amelco Semiconductor, Mountain View, California

INDIVIDUAL MICROCIRCUITS in large number can be wholly formed on a silicon wafer an inch in diameter and a few mils thick. A group of such microcircuits can be mounted on a substrate for interconnection into a much larger array, or connected using thin, photoengraved metal film on the wafer sur-

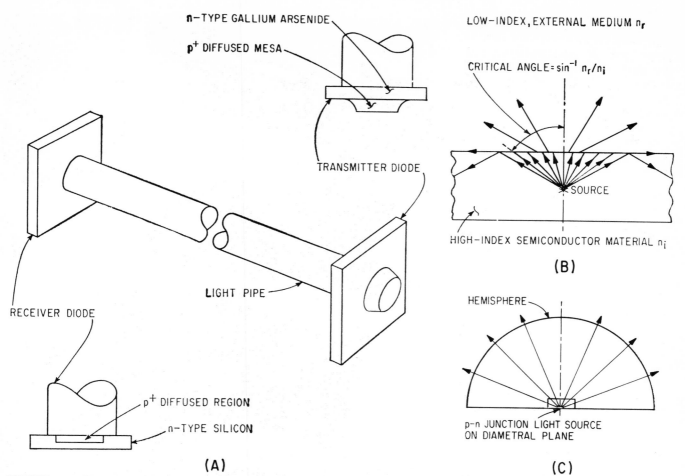

n–TYPE GALLIUM ARSENIDE

p⁺ DIFFUSED MESA

LOW-INDEX, EXTERNAL MEDIUM n_r

CRITICAL ANGLE = $\sin^{-1} n_r/n_i$

TRANSMITTER DIODE

SOURCE

HIGH-INDEX SEMICONDUCTOR MATERIAL n_i

(B)

HEMISPHERE

LIGHT PIPE

RECEIVER DIODE

p⁺ DIFFUSED REGION

n–TYPE SILICON

p-n JUNCTION LIGHT SOURCE
ON DIAMETRAL PLANE

(A)

(C)

OPTICAL coupling of microcircuit pair with light pipe (A) escape of light through plane surface from light source within semiconductor having high refractive index (B) and light source in Weierstrass sphere (C)—Fig. 1

face. To interconnect a stacked array of these plates, the wiring must cross the surface of one layer, make connection with external wiring, translate to another layer and cross its surface to the desired point. Direct connection between the layers would greatly decrease the problem of combining stacked plates of microcircuits. Optical means of interconnection between layers can add a new dimension both to the directions available for wiring and to system performance.

More Reliability—A signal carried by light can be transferred between layers without electrical contact or regard to any differences of electric potential. Consequently, in high-speed circuits, coaxial cables or strip lines of small dimensions are not needed and the labor involved is eliminated. In addition, reducing the number of external connections,

which have a lower reliability than the photoengraved wiring, improves overall system reliability.

Optical coupling between integrated circuits is possible because p-n junctions can efficiently convert current to radiation by charge-carrier recombination and reconvert radiation to current by the photovoltaic effect. In elementary form, an optically coupled circuit com-

prises two p-n junctions, one transmitting radiation and the other receiving radiation by means of a light pipe as shown in Fig. 1A. Although much refinement of detail remains, this method of circuit interconnection can now be used to change the state of a standard, microcircuit flip-flop optically.

Conversion of radiation to light in silicon has been brought to a high

GIANT STEP?

Reliability, simplicity and economy can all be expected from better methods of interconnecting microcircuit groups. The method described in this article has been only a topic of conversation until recently. Now that optical interconnection has been accomplished it has nowhere to go but in the direction of further improvement and refinement. Understanding the problem and utilizing recent discoveries has produced a successful experiment. It looks more like a quantum jump than an incremental advance

state of development through extensive work on solar cells. A yield of more than 0.5 charge-carrier pair per incident photon can be obtained from a solar cell at wavelengths between 0.45 and 0.9 microns to which its response is the greatest.[1] The photovoltaic effect in the collector-base junction of a transistor results in a phototransistor that may have a gain of 100 or more.

Radiation Production—When a forward current flows through a silicon *p-n* junction, radiation is produced with an efficiency as high as 5×10^{-4} photons per electron at a wavelength of about 1.1 microns.[2,3] The speed of response corresponds to the minority-carrier lifetime, which may be as long as one microsecond to give the efficiency stated.[3,4] In reverse-current operation the speed corresponds to the majority-carrier lifetime, which is three or four orders of magnitude shorter than the minority-carrier lifetime.[2] The efficiency for the production of radiation at wavelength less than about 1.1 microns is one to two orders of magnitude smaller for reverse than for forward-current operation.[2,3] The reverse-current radiation spectrum extends from 0.35 to perhaps 3 microns.[3,5] The photoresponse of a silicon diode is down almost an order of magnitude at 1.1 microns from its peak value and vanishes at wavelengths much beyond 1.2 microns.[1] Therefore, although silicon junctions can provide a current-transfer pair, it is not efficient.

Fortunately, the efficiency of radiative recombination in gallium arsenide, and in other III-V compound *p-n* junctions, was recently discovered to be as high as 0.1 photon per electron at room temperature.[6] Moreover, the radiation wavelength of about 0.9 micron for gallium arsenide at room temperature occurs in the region of high response for silicon diodes. A current transfer as high as 10^{-2} is therefore possible between a gallium-arsenide light source and silicon diode. The transfer could exceed unity if the receiver were a phototransistor. At or below the temperature of liquid nitrogen (77 K) unit current transfer could be approached with a diode receiver because the source efficiency approaches unity.[6,7] In addition, the charge-carrier lifetime in gallium arsenide is less than 10^{-8}

WELDING gold leads from a pair of diodes coupled by a light pipe

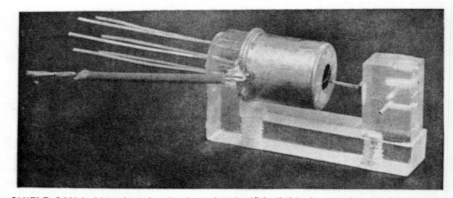

SHIELD CAN holds microcircuit. Arsenic trisulfide light pipe carries driving impulse from gallium arsenide light source (right)

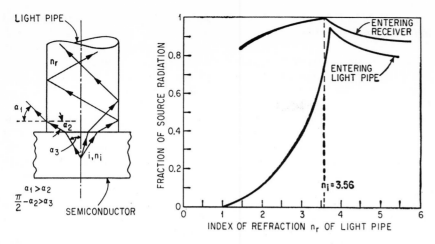

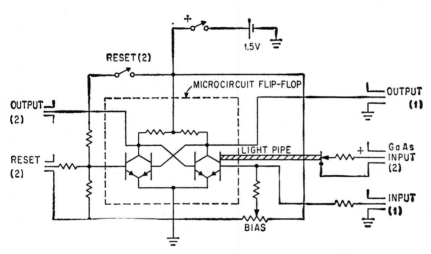

LIGHT PATHS from semiconductor source into light pipe (left) and curves showing fraction of light entering pipe from source and that reentering a receiving medium of same refractive index, as function of light-pipe refractive index—Fig. 2

MICROCIRCUIT flip-flop optically actuated by light pipe to GaAs diode in another circuit—Fig. 3

sec and may be shorter than 10^{-9} sec—even with relatively efficient light production—so response is fast.[6]

Optical Coupling—Difficulties in efficient optical coupling of integrated circuits are imposed by optical properties of semiconductor materials. Methods of achieving a high transfer coefficient are found by a detailed study of optical reflection and refraction problems.

Close optical coupling of the light source and the receiver is not readily achieved between separate units because the indices of refraction of gallium arsenide[8] and silicon[9] are large—about 3.6 at the emitted wavelengths. As a consequence of the high refractive index of the semi-conductor material in which the radiation is produced, much of the radiation is trapped by internal reflection. Less than three percent of the radiation incident on a plane surface from an internal source escapes into air. Only the radiation within a cone of about a 16-deg half-angle with an axis normal to the surface is available as shown in Fig. 1B. Because of refraction at the surface, the exit radiation that originates within the 16-deg cone is spread over a hemisphere in air.

Reflection loss for normal incidence at an interface between media with $n_i = 3.6$ and $n_r = 1$, given by $[(n_i - n_r)/(n_i + n_r)]^2 = 0.32$, is relatively small compared to internal reflection loss. Aigrain[10] has **shown that with a Weierstrass**

sphere (Fig. 1C) in which all radiation is incident normal to the surface the escape efficiency becomes high. Despite its efficiency, fabrication and assembly of such spherical sources is incompatible with the microcircuit approach to optoelectronics.

Appreciable light coupling can be achieved by immersing both source and receiver in a medium with a high index of refraction, ideally about the same as that of source and receiver. The receiver must subtend as large a solid angle as possible at the source; however, a large subtended angle means appreciable capacitive coupling, which is to be avoided.

Light Pipes — Radiation can be transferred from one point to another using the highly efficient, multiple internal reflection in a light pipe. Internal reflection coefficient is essentially 100 percent whereas each metallic reflection involves a few percent loss except at large angles of incidence. For good light transfer, a light pipe should have a high index of refraction to minimize interface-reflection losses at the source. In addition, a high refractive index also increases the angle of the acceptance cone for radiation because the critical angle for internal reflection is given by $\theta = \sin^{-1} n_m/n_r$, where n_r is the index of the light pipe and n_m is the index of the surrounding medium.

To compare the merits of various materials for light pipes, the light entry into a pipe has been calculated[3, 11] as a function of its refractive index (Fig. 2). In addition, the re-entry of light from the pipe into the receiving medium must also be considered in determining overall transfer. In these calculations, the Fresnel coefficients for transmission through a surface for both polarizations of light must be considered. It has been assumed here that the light source is unpolarized. For good performance, the index of refraction of the light pipe must closely approach that of the semiconductor material.

Glass Fibers—Materials suitable for practical application are inorganic glasses such as germanate glass with $n = 1.84$ at a 1 micron wavelength and arsenic trisulfide with $n = 2.47$ at 1 micron. A glassy material can be drawn into small-diameter rods or fibers with the highly polished surface essential to good internal reflection at angles approaching the critical. At present, arsenic trisulfide appears to be the best material available. It has the higher index of refraction and yields light pipes of good quality. Even better inorganic glasses can probably be developed.

When integrated circuit arrays of sources and receivers are to be optically coupled, many light pipes are required. It is impractical to use individual light pipes but two alternatives are possible. The light pipes can be assembled in a matrix with a lower refractive index. Or, many small-diameter fibers coated with a lower-index material can be formed into a fiber-optic plate. The individual light pipe with a unit packing fraction gives somewhat better transfer than a fiber-optic plate. However, the source and receiver arrays must be carefully registered with the light pipes. The fiber-optic plate has a poorer transfer efficiency with a probable packing fraction of about one-half to three-quarters, but no registration is required in assembly.

Assemblies are now being made with gallium-arsenide light sources, silicon receivers and arsenic-trisulfide light pipes. The principal problem is to obtain an optically satisfactory, mechanical bond between the light pipe and the semiconductor devices. An inorganic glass consisting of arsenic, sulfur and iodine in about equal weight proportions [12] adheres well to gallium arsenide but not so well to silicon or to arsenic trisulfide. A high index of refraction, high-viscosity liquid containing arsenic tribromide, arsenic disulfide, antimony bromide, and selenium obtained better wetting. By heating, the volatile components may be diffused into (or reacted with) an arsenic-trisulfide light pipe and partially vaporized to stiffen the joint.

Optical Actuation—To demonstrate directly the applicability of optical actuation to a device, an Amelco MC-303 microcircuit flip-flop was used. This unit employes four transistors of a new design (OMIC) that decreases the parasitic capacitance and the collector-emitter saturation voltage [V_{CE} (SAT)] in integrated microcircuits. Performance compares favorably to that achieved with epitaxial techniques.

Optical actuation of the flip-flop shown in Fig. 3 works despite inefficient light transfer arising from poor matching of refractive indices and present lack of a microcircuit designed expressly for optical coupling. A 12-mil diameter light pipe of arsenic trisulfide was cemented over the two transistors on one side of the microcircuit illustrated. On the other end of the half-inch light pipe a gallium-arsenide diode was attached with epoxy cement to serve as the light source. A can with a hole for the light pipe shown in the photograph was placed on the TO-5 header that bears the microcircuit. Grounding the can gave sufficient shielding to avoid electrostatic coupling. The poor light transfer resulting from use of epoxy cement was much below that achievable using improved techniques.

The speed of operation of optically coupled elements is very high as far as light-source and receiver diodes are concerned. The minority-carrier lifetime in gallium-arsenide diodes is usually in the subnano- or nanosecond region, though the most efficient units may have radiative-recombination lifetimes of tens of nanoseconds. Receiver diodes of the p-i-n type may have response times in the subnanosecond region. [13]

Achieving sufficient amplification to attain unit current transfer with presently available phototransistors could increase overall response time of the system to between 10 and 100 nanoseconds.

Light Sources — In some applications a light source operating in a laser mode could provide more efficient radiation. With radiation more nearly collimated, interface reflection losses could be reduced and transmission losses would be low owing to slight internal reflection required in the light pipe. The line-source form of most diffused solid-state lasers make a laminar light pipe suitable, and even advantageous in some cases.

For large-scale optically coupled microcircuits the use of individual sources separate from the receivers is cumbersome. Use of integral sources is not only advantageous but a necessity. This objective can probably be achieved with an epitaxial layer of an efficient electroluminescent material on silicon. Gallium phosphide is closely similar to silicon in lattice dimensions, but is not an efficient light-producing material. However, a mixture of gallium phosphide with 50 percent or more of gallium arsenide is an efficient electroluminescent composition. [14, 15] An epitaxial growth on silicon of gallium phosphide grading to the desired composition is a means of reaching the goal. The resulting material is one on which the microcircuit technology, including photo-receivers, could be carried out and on which light sources will be integral.

Work related to this article was supported in part by the Aeronautical Systems Division, Air Force Systems Command under contract AF 33(657)–8678.

REFERENCES

(1) M. Wolf, Limitations and Possibilities for Improvement of Photovoltaic Solar Energy Converters, Part I: Considerations for Earth's Surface Operation, *Proc IRE*, **48**, p 1,246, 1960.

(2) A. G. Chynoweth and K. G. McKay, Photon Emission from Avalanche Breakdown in Silicon, *Phys Rev*, **102**, p 369, 1956.

(3) M. A. Gilleo, Photronics: The Generation of Light in Silicon P-N Junctions and the Optical Coupling of Semiconductor Devices, Technical Documentary Report No. ASD-TDR-63-606, Contract AF 33(657)-8678, U. S. Air Force.

(4) W. P. Dumke, Spontaneous Radiative Recombination in Semiconductors, *Phys Rev*, **105**, p 139, 1957.

(5) A. G. Chynoweth, Bell Telephone Labs., Inc., private communication.

(6) R. J. Keyes and T. M. Quist, Recombination Radiation Emitted from Gallium Arsenide, *Proc IRE*, **50**, p 1,822, 1962.

(7) G. Cheroff, F. Stern, and S. Triebwasser, Quantum Efficiency of GaAs Injection Lasers, *Appl Phys Letters*, **2**, p 173, 1963.

(8) R. E. Morrison, Reflectivity and Optical Constants of Indium Arsenide, Indium Antimonide, and Gallium Arsenide, *Phys Rev*, **124**, p 1,314, 1961.

(9) H. B. Briggs, Optical Effects in Bulk Silicon and Germanium, *Phys Rev*, **77**, p 287, 1950.

(10) P. Aigrain, Light Emission from Injecting Contacts on Germanium in the 2_u to 6_u Band, *Physica*, **20**, p 1,010, 1954.

(11) M. A. Gilleo, to be published.

(12) S. S. Flaschen, A. D. Pearson, and W. R. Northover, Low Melting Sulfide-Halogen Inorganic Glasses, *J Appl Phys*, **31**, p 219, 1960.

(13) R. P. Riesz, High Speed Semiconductor Photodiodes, *Rev Sci Instr*, **33**, p 994, 1962.

(14) J. W. Allen and M. E. Moncaster, Injection Electroluminescence in Gallium Arsenide-Phosphide Alloys, *Phys Letters*, **4**, p 27, 1963.

(15) N. Holonyak, Jr., and S. F. Bevacqua, Coherent (Visible) Light Emission from $Ga(As_{1-x}P_x)$ Junctions, *Appl Phys Letters*, **1**, p 82, 1962.

Evaluating light demodulators

A method is proposed for comparing various designs of
a key element in laser communications or radar systems

By D.E. Caddes and B.J. McMurtry

Electronic Defense Laboratories, Sylvania Electronic Systems, Mountain View, California

The light detector is a key element in an optical communications or radar system. It determines the entire system's bandwidth, sensitivity and flexibility.

Yet there are no generally accepted criteria for evaluating the detector.

Since detectors are appearing in a widening array of designs, the time may come for users to consider a meaningful system for comparing them.

Three major criteria

It is possible to formulate objective criteria for evaluating these devices. The power and noise performance of a photodetector can be described in terms of three major factors:

1. Quantum efficiency of the photo process, expressed in current-carriers per photon input.

2. Current multiplication factor—the amount by which the amplitudes of the a-c and d-c components of photocurrent are increased.

3. Equivalent load resistance—a fictitious quantity comprising all the effects that participate in converting the a-c component of current into useful output power.

Other important considerations are modulation

bandwidth and frequency response, both of which affect the information-carrying capacity of the beam.

Illumination-handling capacity is also of interest, because devices that cannot survive moderate light levels are restricted to the detection of very weak signals. Such devices cannot, for example, be used in heterodyne receivers.

A-m and f-m systems

As in radio, an optical communications system transmits information by modulating the amplitude, phase or frequency of a carrier and transmitting the modulated carrier to a receiver, where the signal represented by the modulation is recovered by a detection process.

Most photoconductors respond to amplitude modulation (a-m). An a-m photodetector can be used in a frequency-modulation (f-m) receiver if the detector is preceded by elements that convert f-m to a-m. Such conversion can be accomplished by discriminators and ratio detectors. Since such converters have been demonstrated at optical-carrier frequencies[1-3], a discussion of a-m detectors will be applicable to f-m receivers.

A second f-m demodulation scheme, currently under investigation, involves converting f-m into "spatial modulation" by passig the beam through a prism or similar dispersing element, that physically deflects the beam in accordance with the modulating signal. This spatial modulation is then detected with a device that responds to the movement of the light beam.[4-5]

General a-m photodetector

The operation of any a-m photodetector can be divided into two processes, see bottom of page 55.

1. Conversion of light into photocurrent whose a-c component represents the detected modulation, and any subsequent current multiplication.

2. Conversion of the a-c component of photocurrent into output power.

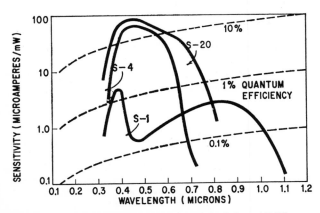

Typical spectral response curves for S-1, S-4 and S-20 photoelectric cathodes

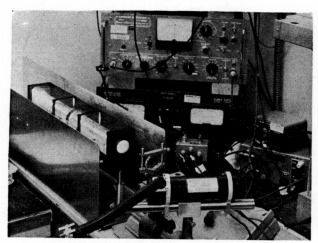

Test setup of an 11-to-20-gigacycle traveling-wave phototube and helium-neon gas laser.

In the first process, the input light produces a photocurrent of average amplitude

$$I_o = P_{light} \, \eta \, e/h \, \nu \qquad (1)$$

where P_{light} is the average input light power, η is the quantum efficiency of the photo-process (current-carriers out per photon in), e is the electron charge, h is Planck's constant, and μ is the optical carrier frequency. It is convenient to relate the peak a-c component of current, i, to the d-c current, I_o, by the definition $i = mI_o$; m will be referred to as the "modulation index," and is twice the conventional a-m modulation index. Current multiplication simply increases the amplitudes of both the a-c and d-c components by the multiplication factor m.

This current-generating process is a perfect "square-law" process in which the output current is directly proportional to the input power and hence to the square of the input amplitude. Therefore, two optical signals of different frequencies can be heterodyned by the square law photoelectric process. The peak a-c current at the difference, or "beat" frequency, is then $2(I_1 I_2)^{\frac{1}{2}}$, where I_1 and I_2 are the average currents due to the individual light signals.

This property of the photoelectric effect is exploited in optical heterodyne receivers, where a light source performs a role similar to that of the local oscillator in a radio-frequency heterodyne. Heterodyne reception is ideal for optical radar systems where the return signal, possibly doppler-shifted by reflection from a moving target, is mixed with a portion of the transmitter signal. The photo-mixing effect has also been used to study simultaneously oscillating laser modes.[7-9]

The second step shown in the figure is the conversion of the a-c component of current, which carries the a-m signal being transmitted, into useful output power. All the factors that participate in this process may be lumped into a fictitious "equivalent load resistance," R_{eq}, defined by

$$P_{out} = \frac{1}{2}(MmI_o)^2 \, R_{eq} \qquad (2)$$

Then, depending on the particular detector being

considered, R_{eq} may include the influence of such factors as carrier lifetimes, the frequency of modulation, and the voltage applied.

Sensitivity

The weak-signal detection capability of an optical communications receiver depends largely on the performance of its photodetector. It is of interest, therefore, how the signal-to-noise ratios of photodetectors depend on parameters η, M, and R_{eq}.

The noise sources usually include:

1. Thermal noise, kT per unit bandwidth, from the internal resistance of the device, where h is Boltzmann's constant and T the temperature in degrees Kelvin.

2. Shot noise, $2emI_T R_{eq}$ per unit bandwidth. Shot noise arises from the fact that the current is comprised of moving discrete charge carriers and is not a flowing continuum of charge. Average current I_T includes current from all sources, including background light and thermally generated current. In bulk photoconductors, where the carrier lifetimes are shorter than the transit time required for carriers to cross between electrodes, generation-recombination noise rather than shot noise must be considered.

3. Velocity fluctuation noise, due to the statistical distribution of carrier velocities about the average. This is usually negligible compared with shot noise, because the fluctuations are usually very small.

4. Low-frequency noise—"flicker" effect or "1/f" noise. Since this article is primarily concerned with broadband, and hence high-frequency applications, this will be ignored, although it would be important with audio-frequency modulation rates.

Thus, the signal-to-noise ratio for direct a-m detection is

$$S/N = \frac{1}{2}(MmI_o)^2 \cdot R_{eq} \, (kTB + 2emI_T \, R_{eq}B)^{-1} \qquad (3),$$

keeping in mind that the shot-noise term should be replaced by a generation-recombination noise term for bulk photoconductors for photoconductive insulators. In the high-frequency limit, the generation-recombination term is $8e\beta I_o BR_{eq}$, where β represents the average number of times an electron is trapped, which may be of the order of 10^3.[32]

Thermal noise

In general, thermal noise dominates shot noise at very weak light levels, and determines the minimum detectable signal. However, at high light levels, shot noise (or generation-recombination

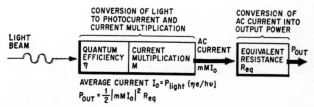

CONVERSION OF LIGHT
TO PHOTOCURRENT AND
CURRENT MULTIPLICATION

CONVERSION OF
AC CURRENT INTO
OUTPUT POWER

LIGHT BEAM → | QUANTUM EFFICIENCY η | CURRENT MULTIPLICATION M | → AC CURRENT mMI_o → | EQUIVALENT RESISTANCE R_{eq} | → P_{OUT}

AVERAGE CURRENT $I_o = P_{light} \, (\eta e/h\nu)$
$P_{OUT} = \frac{1}{2}|mMI_o|^2 \, R_{eq}$

Photodetector for a-m optical signals.

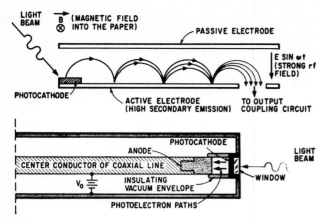

Dynamic crossed-field electron multiplier detector, top; simple planar photoelectric diode, bottom.

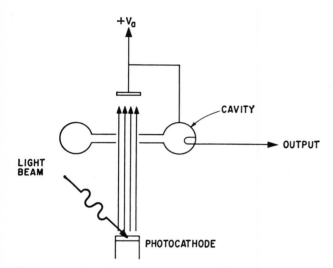

Cavity-type photoelectric diode, or photoklystron.

noise) fixes the signal-to-noise ratio. "High light levels" are high enough to make $2eMI_TR_{eq} >> kT$ (or $8\beta eI_oR_{eq} >> kT$ for the photoconductor.

For thermal-noise-limited operation, the appropriate sensitivity figure of merit is $\eta^2M^2R_{eq}$. That is, for any two thermal-noise-limited photo-detectors, the one with the larger $\eta^2M^2R_{eq}$ will have the better signal-to-noise ratio. The high-level, shot-noise-limited, S/N-dependent figure of merit is just ηM, if the current consists only of the carrier induced I_o. For high-frequency generation-recombination noise, the high-level figure of merit is η/β.

While the first figure, $\eta^2M^2R_{eq}$, is the important quantity for detection of weak a-m signals, a different situation prevails in the case of detecting weak signals by optical heterodyning. Here the signal-to-noise ratio is

$$S/N = 2M^2I_1I_2R_{eq}\ (kTB + 2eMI_TR_{eq}B)^{-1} \qquad (4)$$

If one of these currents, say I_1, is due to a strong enough local oscillator, this ratio can be shot-noise limited even though the light carrying the signal is weak. The appropriate sensitivity figure of merit for this case, where $I_T \cong I_1$, is just ηM. However, it will be recalled that dependence on R_{eq} is implicit,

since the requirement for shot-noise-limited operation is $2eMI_TR_{eq} >> kT$. At room temperature, this demands $MI_TR_{eq} >> 10^{-2}$, a condition that can be difficult to meet if MR_{eq} is not large.

Let's see how this proposed comparison system is applied to some of the major types of detectors.

Electrostatic photomultiplier tubes

Electrostatic photomultiplier tubes are unchallenged for direct detection of weak a-m signals with modulation frequencies below a few hundred megacycles with carriers in the visible region of the spectrum. Like other photoemissive devices, these tubes can be made with fairly high quantum efficiencies at visible and near-infrared wavelengths, as shown at bottom left of page 243. More important, the electron multiplication process can give current amplification of 10^5 to 10^7. Assuming R_{eq} of about 10^3 ohms at low frequencies, $M \cong 10^6$, and $\eta \cong 10^{-1}$, this gives a sensitivity figure of merit $\eta^2M^2R_{eq} \cong 10^{13}$. This is very high compared with other detectors, showing the great utility of photomultiplication in weak-signal, low-frequency detection.

Unfortunately, the R_{eq} of conventional electrostatic photomultipliers is so poor at higher frequencies, because of transit-time effects, that the current-multiplication advantage is negated. For multigigacycle bandwidths, other kinds of detectors must be chosen.

A familiar problem resulting from current multiplication is that high levels result in tube currents large enough to destroy the final multiplier-dynode stages. This limits the operation to weak optical signals or to attenuated strong signals. In optical heterodyning, this restriction, may limit the optimum noise performance, because it was required that the local oscillator-induced shot noise be the dominant noise source,

$$2eMI_1BR_{eq} >> kTB + 2eM(I_B + I_D)BR_{eq}$$

where I_1, I_B, and I_D are the average photocurrents due to the local oscillator, background light and thermionic (D for "dark") emission, respectively.

Since the thermal noise term is generally the smallest of the noise terms, the problem boils down to making $I_1 >> I_B + I_D$. However, this condition may mean a dangerously high total current. With laser systems, the background light may often be reduced with narrow-band optical filters; reducing the thermionic, or "dark," current requires refrigeration, which is not always feasible.

Crossed-field photomultipliers

A photomultiplier tube that has been proven capable of demodulation in the gigacycle range is the dynamic crossed-field electron multiplier.[10, 11] In this novel device, shown schematically at the upper left, current multiplication of about 10^5 by secondary emission is accomplished by the combined effects of a strong r-f electric field and a perpendicular d-c magnetic field to cause the trajectory shown in the figure.

Only those electrons are accelerated that are

emitted in the proper phase of the accelerating electric field, and these follow the trajectory. The current is initially "sampled," with further phase-focusing at each multiplication step. This process minimizes transit time spread, making possible the detection of microwave modulation if the r-f driving field is a microwave signal. This multiplier has, in fact, been used at three gigacycles (Gc).

The combination of the quantum efficiencies with current multiplication and an R_{eq} in the hundreds of ohms makes this device potentially valuable for sensitive detection. In experimental models, however, problems have been caused by amplification of noise from the magnetron source of the strong r-f field required. Elimination of this "external" noise should result in noise performance comparable with that of electrostatic multipliers.[8]

The predicted bandwidth is half the driving signal frequency, so gigacycle bandwidths should be possible. The requirement of a driving signal is one of the less attractive features of this multiplier, since it adds to cost and complexity. To the authors' knowledge, this multiplier is not commercially available, although it is being developed.

Vacuum photodiodes

The simplest photoelectric tube is the planar photodiode, which consists of just a photocathode and an anode. This device, mounted as part of the center conductor of a coaxial line, or in a waveguide, has detected signals at as high as X-band.[12, 13]

These experiments consisted of observing the difference-frequency signal generated by the photomixing of simultaneously oscillating modes of a high-power pulsed-ruby laser. However, these diodes are not "sensitive" detectors. Their quantum efficiencies are as shown on page 243; they have no current multiplication, and at high frequencies their equivalent resistance is small because of transit-time reduction.

Even when the transit time of electrons is reduced by operating at three times the rated diode voltage, R_{eq} is only about six ohms at X-band and 0.5 ohm at X-band. Hence, $M^2\eta^2R_{eq}$ is only 6×10^{-2} and 5×10^{-3}, respectively, even when operating at wavelengths for which η can be 10%.

Although these diodes can handle visible continuous-wave (c-w) light powers in the tens-of-milliwatts range, they are not as useful for heterodyning as might be desired. To reach shot-noise-limited operation at room temperature requires $I_1 \cong 10$ ma if R_{eq} is one ohm. This would mean a light power input of about 200 milliwatts in the visible part of the spectrum, which is both higher than is available from c-w lasers and dangerous to the small photocathode. At practical levels of a c-w optical local oscillator, the diode's operation would be limited by its thermal noise level, where its low R_{eq} is a serious liability.

Photoklystron

Another relatively simple high-frequency detector is the photoklystron, or cavity-type photodiode, shown at center left of page 245.[6, 14] The a-c current modulation induces a signal in the coupling cavity, tuned to the modulation frequency.

As in the other photoelectric devices, the figure on page 243 gives the quantum efficiency possibilities for the photoklystron. The R_{eq} of high-Q (and hence narrow-band) cavities can be over 100 ohms, even at high microwave frequencies; the transit-time limitation that plagues the planar photodiode is overcome because the beam is preaccelerated and passed through a narrow coupling gap. This device could, in principle, be built at any frequency at which klystrons are built—to over 100 Gc—although the tube would have to be quite small for these frequencies. The photoklystron has $M^2\eta^2R_{eq}$ of up to unity at high microwave frequencies, and is therefore markedly superior to the simple planar photodiode as a sensitive photodetector.

The major disadvantage of this device is its narrow bandwidth. The band can be broadened only at the expense of reducing R_{eq}, in which case it is no better a detector than the simple photodiode. Even over a narrow bandwidth, as shown below, the photoklystron is inferior to the traveling-wave phototube and solid-state photodiode.

Distributed-emission photodiode

The distributed-emission photodiode[15, 18] is a family of schemes proposed for broadband detection at millimeter modulation wavelengths. In this detector, a "running wave" of photocurrent is generated, which has the same wave velocity as the transmission line, so the current wave can couple power into the transmission line.

These devices are among the most promising for millimeter waves, since they permit using practical component dimensions even at 100 Gc. The coaxial line version has already been used over the frequency range 1.65 to 34.65 Gc to detect photomixing "beats" between modes of a ruby laser.[19] Quantum efficiencies are like those of other photoelectric tubes, and R_{eq} of 10 ohms or so is predicted at 100 Gc. Other detectors are better at lower microwave frequencies, but distributed-emission phototubes show promise at millimeter wavelengths.

Traveling-wave phototubes

The traveling-wave phototube[8, 20, 21] offers broad demodulation bandwidths and high R_{eq}, and is the best broadband photodetector for visible light. Octave instantaneous bandwidths are easily feasible at microwave frequencies, with R_{eq} typically in the range of 10^5 to 10^6 ohms.

In this phototube, shown schematically at the center of the top figure on page 248, the a-m light causes the emission of a current-modulated photoelectron beam passed near a broadband microwave circuit, such as a helix. Power at the modulation frequency is efficiently coupled to the circuit if the electron beam velocity is roughly equal to that of the electromagnetic wave on the circuit. As with traveling-wave tube amplifiers, these conditions may be instantaneously realized over an octave bandwidth also with travelling-wave phototubes.

The efficient beam-to-circuit power transfer results in R_{eq} of 10^4 to 10^7 ohms. This is not the output impedance, but a fictitious load resistor; the output is typically delivered to a 50-ohm line, or to a waveguide,. with low voltage standing-wave ratio. The quantum efficiency of the photocathode is given in the same figure as the other efficiencies. Assuming $\eta = 0.1$ and $R_{eq} = 10^6$ ohms, $M^2\eta^2R_{eq} = 10^4$, the sensitivity is far better than that of the other high-frequency photoemissive detectors, the photodiode and the photoklystron. However, photocathodes with useful infrared sensitivities are not yet available, so the traveling-wave phototube is limited to use with optical carriers below a micron.

A traveling-wave phototube was developed by Sylvania Electric Products, Inc., for the Air Force Cambridge Research Laboratories.[22] This tube has an S-1 cathode and an instantaneous detection bandwidth of 9 Gc, from 11 to 20 Gc, with R_{eq} in the 10^5 range.

Traveling-wave phototubes were used in the first continuous microwave modulation and demodulation experiments[23] and in the first heterodyne demodulation of microwave f-m and a-m light.[24]

Multiplier TWPs

As noted earlier, current multiplication is an important way of increasing the sensitivity of photodetectors. A proposed method of combining current multiplication with the high R_{eq} and broad bandwidth of TWPs is shown at the bottom of the top figure on page 248. Transmission secondary emission multiplication (CTSEM)[25] films are the current-gain multiplier elements. With about five kilovolts of applied voltage per stage, gains of about four per stage are possible.[26] Thus, even a single stage could improve $\eta^2M^2R_{eq}$, and hence the sensitivity, by a factor of 16.

Unfortunately, the present TSEM films cannot handle much more than one μamp of incident current per square centimeter,[26] which severely limits the safe light-input power. For example, if a cathode has $\eta = 0.1$ at 6,000A in an S-band TWP, the total light input cannot safely exceed about 0.5 microwatt, and in higher-frequency tubes with smaller cathodes even less light can be handled.

Thus, even if traveling-wave phototubes of the TSEM type were commercially available, their use would be restricted to the direct detection of very weak amplitude-modulated carriers.

It should be pointed out here that a current density restriction necessarily implies a signal-to-noise ratio limitation, as seen from equation 3. If shot noise is the dominant noise, and if $I_o \cong I_T, S/N$ is proportional to MI_o, then at lower I_o, where thermal noise is dominant, S/N is proportional to $(MI_o)^2$. The quantity MI_o is the product of the current density and the cross-sectional area of the electron beam, after the multiplication process.

To illustrate the limitation imposed on S/N by the beam current-density, equation 3 has been plotted for dimensions representing traveling-wave phototubes in-production for the L, S, C and X-band. In this figure, page 248, the M is included in I_o. R_{eq} was arbitrarily set at 10^6, 100% amplitude modulation was assumed. The one-gigacycle bandwidth was chosen for convenience as representing an instantaneous microwave bandwidth of which all four tubes are capable; for other bandwidths, it is enough to multiply the S/N of this graph by the ratio of one gigacycle to the new bandwidth.

The important points are the dependence of S/N on current density, and the fact that this limitation becomes more serious with tubes for higher frequency. For example, even if the maximum safe current density is as high as 4 μa/cm², the S/N at X-band is only 4; for an S/N of 30 db, the bandwidth would have to be reduced to 4 Mc.

In heterodyning, the situation is at best the same as the case described. That is, "100% modulation" is achieved when $I_1 = I_2$ in equation 4, and the graph applies. Other combinations of I_1 and I_2 give smaller signal-to-noise ratios. The change of slope of the curves represents the transition from thermal to shot-noise-limited operation and shows that shot-noise-limited operation often requires average currents of dangerously high amplitude.

Bulk photoconductors

Bulk photoconductors constitute a class of relatively simple, broadband photodetectors. Their advantages are high quantum efficiency and high capability for handling light power. Disadvantages

The authors

Burton J. McMurtry, a 29-year-old native of Houston, is head of the optics department at the Electronic Defense Laboratories of Sylvania Electronic Systems, a division of Sylvania Electric Products, Inc. He is a 1957 graduate of Rice University with master's and doctor's degrees in electrical engineering from Standford. At Sylvania he has worked on the design and development of klystrons, traveling-wave tubes and microwave optical devices. In 1961, working with Prof. A.E. Siegman of Stanford, McMurtry obtained the first conclusive results from optical-heterodyne experiments involving microwave-difference frequencies.

Donald E. Caddes has been employed since 1959 at the Microwave Device division of Sylvania Electric Products, Inc., at Mountain View, Calif. He has worked on the development of travelling-wave microwave phototube theory, and recently designed and developed a traveling-wave phototube capable of detecting microwave modulation of light over a nine-gigacycle bandwidth. Caddes was graduate from Rice University in 1959 with a B.S. in electrical engineering. He received his master's from Stanford in 1962 and is working on his doctorate there.

are high generation-recombination noise and a low R_{eq}, which varies approximately as the inverse square of the modulation frequency at microwave frequencies.[27-32]

The figure shows the device and its equivalent circuit. If the frequency of input light is higher than that corresponding to the energy gap between the valence and conduction bands of the photo-conductive semiconductor material, the light is absorbed, creating electron-hole pairs. Since practically every incident photon creates a pair of charge carriers, η is nearly unity for wavelengths between the "band-gap" wavelength, which can be well into the infrared, and that at which the material begins to be highly reflective—typically in the visible range. Some useful spectral ranges, estimated at room-temperature are: indium antimonide, 0.4 to 5.7 microns; indium arsenide, 0.4 to 3.4 microns; germanium, 0.6 to 1.5 microns; silicon, 0.5 to 1.0 microns; lead selenide, 0.4 to 3.5 microns; and cadmium selenide, 0.4 to 0.7 microns. Only cadmium selenide and indium antimonide have received much attention as high-frequency detectors.

The equivalent resistance is, unfortunately, low at microwave frequencies, due chiefly to the effects of carrier lifetimes, trapping effects and transit time. The amplitudes of the a-c and d-c currents are significantly reduced by trapping lifetime effects.[32] At microwave frequencies, R_{eq} is given approximately by $(4G_p\omega^2T_t^2)^{-1}$, where T_t is the transit time, ω is the radian frequency and G_p is the conductance. G_p does not depend largely on the illumination level, at least for cadmium selenide.[32]

For a recent cadmium selenide detector[32] that has $T_t \cong 10^{-7}$ sec, $G_p \cong 5 \times 10^{-5}$ $^{-1}$, and $\eta = \frac{2}{3}$, R_{eq} is about 10^{-3} ohm at 3Gc, so $M^2\eta^2R_{eq}$ is less than 10^{-3}. Hence, this type of bulk photoconductor is not a sensitive detector. However, better results may be possible with indium antimonide,[30] also useful far into the infrared region (about six microns).

If operation limited only by generation-recombination noise can be approached in heterodyning, sensitivity depends on η/β. But since β is of the order of 10^3, the bulk photoconductor is not particularly sensitive.

The outstanding property of the bulk photoconductor is its power-handling capability. Tens of kilowatts from pulsed-ruby lasers have caused no damage to CdSe samples. For very high power levels such as these, the bulk photoconductors seem to have the greatest potential.

Semiconductor phtodiodes

Another important type of solid-state photodetector is the semiconductor diode.[31-36] The figure above represents the PIN configuration. When a large back-bias is applied, photo-generated carriers will be swept out of the I-region, with the resulting current containing a-c components corresponding to the a-m of the incident light beam.

The active region is where the high-bias field exists, between or nearly between N and P areas.

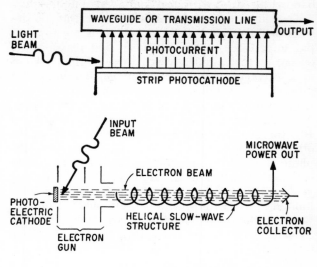

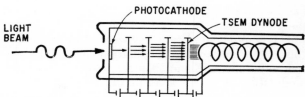

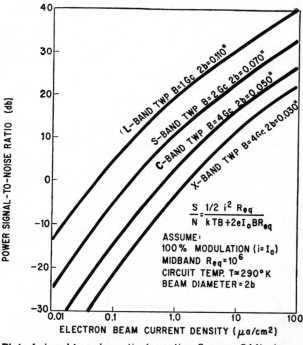

Distributed-emission photodiode, top; traveling-wave phototube, center; a traveling-wave phototube using transmission-type electron multiplication, bottom.

Plot of signal-to-noise ratio (equation 3, page 244) shows dependence of traveling-wave phototube signal-to-noise ratio on electron-beam current density.

Since the I-region is only of the order of a micron in thickness, it is not practical to focus light onto it in cross-section. Instead, the region next to the P-I junction is illuminated in the figure as shown. If a single spot of P-material is used, the sensitive area

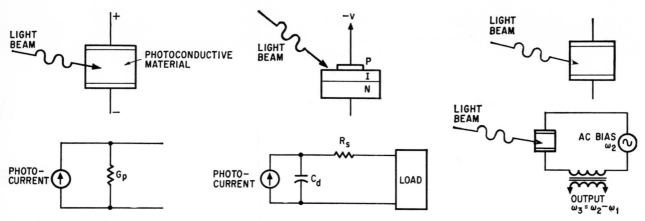

Bulk photoconductor and its microwave equivalent circuit, left; a fast PIN photodiode, and its microwave equivalent circuit, center; and a bulk photoconductor used as a combined photodetector-mixer, right.

is an annoyingly small target, demanding extremely precise positioning.

A more convenient arrangement, which also improves high-frequency response, is to use a grid of P-material. Thus, although η is essentially unity for light that reaches the I-region, the shadowing effect reduces the effective maximum η to about 0.4, somewhat poorer than that of the bulk photoconductor.

However, R_{eq} is much higher than it is for the bulk photoconductor, being given by $(4R_s\omega^2C_d^2)^{-1}$. Large back-bias across the narrow I-region results in only a little signal degradation due to transit-time effects. In fact, R_{eq} can be as high as 100 ohms at 3 Gc if the bias is high enough so the transit time is negligible.

However, the narrow I-region also has the disadvantage of producing the shunt capacitance shown. (For good diodes, it is about 2 pf, and the series resistance about two ohms). This capacitance

causes the $1/f^2$ frequency dependence of R_{eq}, so the diode with $R_{eq} \cong$ ohms at 3 Gc would have $R_{eq} \cong 10$ ohms at 10 Gc, neglecting the transit-time effects that also begin to be important in the 10-Gc range. In addition, the 100-ohm R_{eq} is realistic only if the diode is conjugate-matched, resulting in a relatively narrow bandwidth. Broader bandwidths are possible only at the expense of reducing R_{eq}.

For narrow-band detection, the photodiode then has $\eta^2R_{eq} \cong 10$ at 3 Gc, and about one at 10 Gc, both much higher than the bulk photoconductor. The traveling-wave phototube has much higher η^2R_{eq} at wavelengths below 0.7 micron but, as shown, this phototube is not useful beyond one micron.

As noted, some semiconductors can respond well into the infrared. At one micron, with an S-1 cathode, the traveling-wave phototube with $R_{eq} = 10^6$ ohms has $\eta^2R_{eq} \cong 1$, so the "cross-over wavelength"

References

1 S.E. Harris, "Conversion of FM Light to AM Light Using Birefringent Crystals," Applied Physics Letters, Vol. 2, p 47, Feb. 1962.
2 S.E. Harris and C.F. Buhrer, "An Optical Ratio-Detector," Paper presented at 1963 Conference on Electron Device Research, June 26, 1963.
3 E.O. Ammann et al, "Research on Techniques for Light Modulation Detection," Interim Engineering Report No. 6 on Contract AF 33(657)-8995, Sylvania Electric Products, Mountain View, California, Dec. 1963.
4 S.E. Harris and A.E. Siegman, "A Proposed FM Phototube for Demodulating Microwave-Frequency-Modulated Light Signals," IRE Trans on Electron Devices, ED-9, p 322, July 1962.
5 E.O. Ammann et al, "Research on Techniques for Light Modulation Detection," Interim Engineering Report No. 5 on Contract AF 33(675)-8995, Sylvania Electric Products, Mountain View, California, Sept. 1963.
6 A.T. Forrester, R.A. Gudmundsen, and P.O. Johnson, "Photoelectric Mixing of Incoherent Light," Phys Rev, 99, p 1,691, Sept. 15, 1955.
7 A. Javan, W.R. Bennett, Jr., and D.R. Herriott, "Population Inversion and Continuous Optical Maser Oscillation in a Gas Discharge," Phys Rev Let, 6, p 106, Feb. 1, 1961.
8 B.J. McMurtry and A.E. Siegman, "Photomixing Experiments with Ruby Optical Maser and a Traveling-Wave Microwave Phototube," Appl Opt, 1, p 51, Jan. 1962.

9 B.J. McMurtry, "Investigation of Ruby Optical Maser Characteristics Using Microwave Phototubes," Appl Opt, 2, p 767, Aug. 1963.
10 O.L. Gaddy and D.F. Holshouser, "High-Gain Dynamic Microwave Photomultiplier," Proc IRE, 50, p 207, Feb. 1962.
11 O.L. Gaddy and D.F. Holshouser, "A Microwave Frequency Dynamic Crossed-Field Photomultiplier," Proc. IEEE, 51, p 153, Jan. 1963.
12 P.A. Lindsay, S.F. Paik, K.D. Gilbert, and S.A. Rooney, "Optical Mixing in Phototubes," Proc IRE, 50, p 2,380, Nov. 1962.
13 K.D. Gilbert, H.C. McClees, P.A. Lindsay, and S.F. Paik, 'Photomixing Experiments at X-Band," Proc IEEE, 51, p 1,148, Aug. 1963.
14 M.D. Petroff, H.A. Spetzker and E.K. Bjornerud, "X-Band Microwave Phototube for Demodulation of Laser Beams," Proc IEEE, 51, p 614, April, 1963.
15 A.L. Cullen and P.N. Robson, "A New Principle in the Design of a Millimetric Photoelectric Laser Mixer," Third International Symposium on Quantum Electronics, Feb. 1963.
16 A.L. Cullen and J.A. Jones, "Proposals for Millimetric Photomixing Using Surface Waves," Proc Sym Optical Masers, April 1963, p 585, Polytechnic Press, N.Y., 1963.
17 A.E. Siegman, B.J. McMurtry, and S.E. Harris, "Microwave Demodulation of Light," Third International Symposium on Quantum Electronics, Feb. 1963.
18 B.J. McMurtry et al, "Investigation of New concepts in Optical Mixing," Final Report on Contract AF 19(628)-2472, Sylvania Electric Products Inc., Mountain View, California; 10 Oct. 1963.
19 N.C. Wittwer, "Detection of Higher Order Ruby Optical Maser Modes," Appl Phys Let,

between the two types of devices as narrow-band detectors is about one micron at 10 Gc and probably about 0.8 micron at 3 Gc. Of course, the traveling-wave phototube has many times the instantaneous bandwidth capability of the photodiode.

In narrow-band optical heterodyning, where only the quantum efficiency is important, the photodiode is superior to the traveling-wave phototube. With an R_{eq} of 100 ohms, shot-noise-limited operation at room temperature demands a total current in the 100-microamp range, which is not unreasonably high.

Photo-parametric detectors

In addition to the direct a-m detection and heterodyne schemes, the detection stage may be combined with parametric amplification to raise the apparent R_{eq}.[37-39] The last two figures show ways of accomplishing this with a diode used simultaneously as a photo- and a varactor-diode, and with a bulk photoconductor. Detailed experimental and analytical information on these schemes is still scarce. In addition, development directed toward producing a diode that is at once a good photodiode and a good varactor should improve the performance of that arrangement.

Conclusions

For direct detection of amplitude-modulated light, the photodetector sensitivity may be characterized by $M^2\eta^2R_{eq}$. The high current gain of photomultiplier tubes therefore makes them the most sensitive detectors of low-frequency modulation, for optical carriers in the visible range where good photoemission quantum efficiencies are possible.

Unfortunately, available photomultipliers cannot detect microwave-frequency a-m. The most sensi-

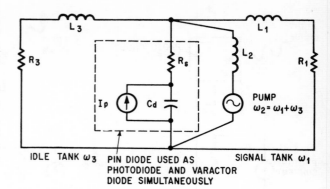

Photodiode parametric amplifier. A photodiode can be used simultaneously as the detector and as the varactor diode in a parametric amplifier which amplifies the detected signals.

tive broadband detector for the visible spectrum is the traveling-wave phototube, which has R_{eq} in the megohm range over octave bandwidths at microwave frequencies. For detection in the infrared regions, the semi-conductor photodiode is the most sensitive a-m detector, but junction capacitance makes a trade-off necessary between bandwidth and R_{eq}. Bulk photoconductors have better inherent bandwidth capability, but very low R_{eq}.

In optical heterodyne detection, sensitivity is determined solely by current multiplication and quantum efficiency, $M\eta$ (η/β for photoconductors), so long as $M(I_1 + I_2)R_{eq}$ is large enough so that shot noise dominates thermal noise. This is a difficult condition to meet with present c-w laser local oscillators, unless R_{eq} exceeds 100 ohms. Thus, for c-w microwave-frequency systems, the same two photodetectors, the traveling-wave phototube and the semiconductor photodiode, are of great practical importance.

2, p 194, May 1963.

20 B.J. McMurtry, "Microwave Phototube Design Considerations," IEEE Trans Electron Devices, ED-10, p 219, July 1963.

21 a) D.E. Caddes, B.J. McMurtrty, and A.E. Jacquez, "The Traveling-Wave Phototube: Theoretical Analysis," and
b) R. Targ, D.E. Caddes, and B.J. McMurtry, "The Traveling-Wave Phototube: Experimental Analysis," (both to be published in IEEE transactions on Electron Devices, April 1964).

22 D.E. Caddes, "Design and Development of a Photomixing Device," Final Report on Contract AF 19(628)-1671, Sylvania Electric Products Inc., Mountain View, Calif.; 9 Aug. 1963.

23 S.E. Harris, B.J. McMurtry, and A.E. Siegman, "Modulation and Direct Demodulation of Coherent and Incoherent Light at a Microwave Frequency," Appl Phys Let, 1, p 37, Oct. 1962.

24 R. Targ, "Optical Heterodyne Detection of Microwave-Modulated Light," Proc IEEE (to be published).

25 E.J. Sternglass, Rev Sci Inst, 26, p 1,202, 1955.

26 D.J. Blattner, J. Ruedy, and F. Sterzer, Third Quarterly Progress Report, Contract No. DA36-039-SC-90846 for USAERDL, Ft. Monmouth, N.J., March 1963.

27 M. DiDomenico, Jr., R.H. Pantell, O. Svelto, and J.N. Weaver, "Optical Frequency Mixing in Bulk Semiconductors," Appl Phys Let, 1, p 77, Dec. 1962.

28 A.W. Smith "Photoconductive Mixing in Bulk Semiconductors," Bull Am Phys Soc, 8, p 381, April 1963.

29 G. Lucovsky, R.F. Schwarz, and R.B.

Emmons, "Photoelectric Mixing of Coherent Light in Bulk Photoconductors," Proc IEEE, 51, p 613, April 1963.

30 E.N. Fuls, "Optical Frequency Mixing in Photoconductive InSb," Appl Phys Let, 4, p 7, Jan. 1964.

31 M. DiDomenico, Jr., and O. Svelto, "Coherent Photodetections: A Comparison Between Photodiodes and Photoconductors," to be published.

32 M. DiDomenico, Jr., and L.K. Anderson, "Signal-to-Noise Performance of CdSe Bulk Photoconductive Detectors," to be published.

33 R.P. Riesz, "High-Speed Semiconductor Photodiodes," Rev Sci Instr, 33, p 994, Sept. 1962.

34 H. Inaba and A.E. Siegman, "Microwave Photomixing of Optical Maser Outputs with a PIN-Junction Photodiode," Proc IRE (Correspondence), 50, p 1,823, Aug. 1962.

35 G. Lucovsky, M.E. Lasser, and R.B. Emmons, "Coherent Light Detection Utilizing Solid-State Photodiodes," Electrochem Soc, Electronics Div Abstracts, II, p 284, May 1962.

36 C.K.N. Patel and W.M. Sharpless, "Optical Heterodyning Using Point Contact Germanium Diodes," Proc IEEE, 52, p 107, Jan. 1964.

37 S. Saito, K. Kurokawa, Y. Fujii, T. Kimura, and Y. Uno, "Detection and Amplification of the Microwave Signal in Laser Light by a Parametric Diode," Proc IRE, 50, p 2,369, Nov. 1962.

38 P.D. Coleman, R. Eden, and J. Weaver, "Mixing and Detection of Laser Light in a Bulk Photoconductor," to be published.

39 M. DiDomenico, Jr., "Direct Demodulation and Frequency Conversion of Microwave Modulated Light in a CdSe Bulk Photoconductor," Jour Appl Phys, (in press).

Light-activated switch expands uses of silicon-controlled rectifiers

It eliminates coupling and feedback problems and opens
up a variety of applications in opto-electronic circuits

By E. Keith Howell

General Electric Co., Rectifier Components Department, Auburn, N.Y.

Designers of industrial control systems are employing a new light-activated switch to simplify photo-electric controls and to improve upon the use of silicon-controlled rectifiers in other control circuits. One problem was that most photocells required complicated circuits involving relays, power supplies and extra stages of amplification. Another problem was that ordinary silicon-controlled rectifiers required electrical coupling of the control signal, which sometimes produced feedback and limited the functions that could be formed without excessive complexity of the control circuit.

The light-activated silicon-controlled rectifier operates the load directly, without intermediate stages of amplification. It achieves complete isolation between the control (triggering) signal and the power circuit, thereby permitting applications in previously inaccessible control circuits.

Light-operated power switch

The light-activated silicon-controlled rectifier is a pnpn switching device in which incident light replaces, or adds to, the normal electrical gate current.

As the only available power switch that is light-operated, it extends the range of power, voltage and current-handling capabilities of light-sensitive resistors, diodes and transistors (see table). Its latching (holding) properties in direct-current circuits give the rectifier a built-in memory that can be valuable in opto-electronic logic circuits.

Being a high-speed power switch, the rectifier can directly activate solenoids, contactors, motors, lamps and similar 120-volt a-c loads more efficiently and at higher power levels than previous light-activated components. It can, therefore, be useful in card- and tape-reading, character recognition, static logic, general-purpose switching, phase control and monitoring. It is already being used in the preproduction stage of industrial-control and data-processing systems.

Characteristics and operation

The General Electric versions, types L8 to L9, are small rectifiers, similar to the C5 type, with glass windows to permit triggering by light as well as by the normal gate signals.[1,2] Rated for 440 ma d-c at 25°C ambient, these units are available in grades from 25 to 2000 volts.

The L8 differs from the L9 only in the amount of incident radiant energy (light) required to initiate switching. Types L811 and L911 are the same as L8 and L9 except that the added base increases the current rating to 770 ma d-c at 25°C ambient. When the rectifier is mounted on a heatsink, the rating can be increased to 1.6 amperes of direct current for case temperature below 75°C.

Operation and circuit handling are similar to other silicon-controlled rectifiers except that the external resistance between gate and cathode—

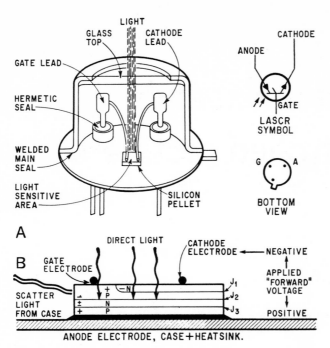

Construction (A) of the silicon-controlled rectifier includes a glass window to permit triggering by light. Current flows from anode to cathode when light enters the silicon (B) and creates electron pairs in the vicinity of the reverse biased junction J_2.

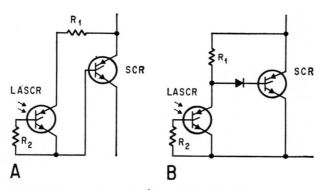

High power can be handled by circuit (A) using a light-activated rectifier as a gate amplifier to trigger a larger rectifier. Equivalent of normal closed contact circuit (B) is another useful configuration.

The author

E. Keith Howell joined GE's rectifier components department in 1962. He has specialized in application engineering and the preparation of technical literature in connection with the light-activated silicon-controlled rectifier and a three-electrode, symmetrical a-c switch.

He was graduated from North Carolina State College with a Bachelor of Science degree in electrical engineering, holds five patents and has 20 patent applications pending. He served in development engineering in the Radio and Television Department and the Outdoor Lighting Department since joining GE in 1948.

in addition to bias voltage and current—determines light sensitivity, because the gate current caused by light originates within the silicon pellet.

Thus electrical signals can be used to trigger the device as well as to modify the light sensitivity to give a shuttering effect. The gate connection also stabilizes the light sensitivity because the external resistance between the gate and cathode diverts some of the current generated internally by incident light around the junction. This serves to eliminate the effects of small leakage currents which, being variable, could affect stability.

How it's made

Construction of the rectifier pellet is illustrated at upper left. With the normally applied forward voltage, junctions J_1 and J_3 are forward-biased and they can conduct if free charge carriers are present.

Junction J_2 is reverse-biased, however, and blocks current flow. Light, entering the silicon, creates free hole- and electron pairs in the vicinity of J_2 which are swept across J_2, J_1 and J_3 to produce a small current from anode to cathode. As light is increased, this current increases, and the current gain of the npn and pnp transistor equivalents in the structure also increase. At some point the net current gain exceeds unity, and current will increase to a value that is limited only by the external circuit. The effect of an external resistance, connected between gate and cathode, is to bypass some current around J_1, thus reducing the gain of the npn transistor region and requiring more light and higher current to reach the unity-gain switching point.

To design circuits with these rectifiers it is necessary to make sure that the triggering threshold of light at which the device begins to conduct, is met. The considerations to be taken into account for this are described in the panel accompanying this article. Following are some circuits in which these rectifiers are particularly useful.

Relay replacement

This rectifier is basically a semiconductor version of the electromechanical relay. When so used, the device has the solid-state virtues of compactness, completely static operation, freedom from contact "bounce" microsecond response, ruggedness and long life, plus the unique feature of complete electrical isolation between input and output. Some basic relay configurations are illustrated and described on p 253.

Latching: without a triggering input, the rectifier is equivalent to an open single-pole, single-throw contact, rated at 200 volts peak and 440 ma d-c (25° C). With input, it will switch, latch and deliver power to the load. The input may then be de-energized and the circuit reset externally, taking care not to introduce too great a voltage transient.

Half-wave SPST: The latching circuit with an a-c supply to the rectifier is used here. The equivalent circuit is a single-pole, single-throw contact in series with a silicon rectifier. The circuit is non-

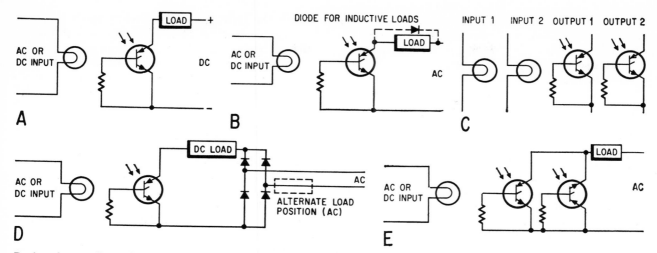

Basic relay configurations use the rectifier as: (A) d-c latching relay; (B) half-wave SPST switch; (C) full wave single-pole single-throw switch; (D) full-wave switch using two rectifiers, and (E) multipole input/multiple pole output combination.

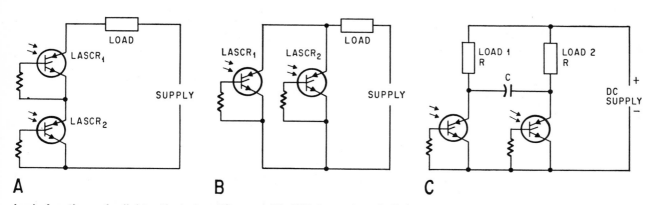

Logic functions of a light-activated rectifier are: (A) AND type where both inputs are required to energize the load and (B) OR type where either input will energize the load. Flip-flop or triggered multivibrator (C) uses inputs to rectifiers to activate the loads. For proper reset, RC must be greater than or equal to 100 microseconds.

latching on a-c, since the rectifier is reset for each cycle by the reversing supply voltage. The use of a diode across inductive loads allows stored coil energy to circulate current through the load while the rectifier blocks negative half-cycles of the supply. Relay or solenoid chatter is thus eliminated.

Full-wave SPST: A diode bridge converts the a-c supply to full-wave rectifier direct current. The load may be placed either in the a-c or d-c legs of the bridge. Care should be taken when using this circuit with inductive loads, since difficulty in rectifier commutation may be encountered.

Because of load power factor, rectifier current and supply voltage are not coincidentally zero. As load current goes to zero and the rectifier tries to commutate, a finite step of forward voltage will suddenly be impressed across it. This voltage step may possess sufficient rate of change of voltage to turn the rectifier on again.

The effect can be eliminated with d-c loads by placing a diode around the load. On a-c loads, a resistor connected between one side of the bridge and one side of the line eliminates this condition.

An alternate form of the full-wave SPST uses two rectifiers for full-wave control. Caution must be observed with this circuit, because a slight dissimilarity in the two rectifiers' sensitivity to light can, under critical or slowly changing irradiation, cause half-wave conduction. With loads such as transformers, motors solenoids and relays, saturation of the load and an abnormally large current can result. Where such loads are used with slowly changing or limited range light levels, the bridge circuit is preferable.

The power-handling ability of any of these relay arrangements may be increased as desired by using the rectifier as a gate amplifier to trigger a larger silicon-controlled rectifier. Repositioning the light-activated rectifier with respect to the driven silicon-controlled component converts the circuit into the equivalent of a normally closed contact, a useful configuration in many monitoring and alarm circuits requiring load-current flow in the absence of light.

Opto-electronic logic

The unique binary nature of the light-activated rectifier makes it an ideal element for opto-electronic logic circuits. A selection of the more common types of logic functions, as performed by the rectifier, are shown on p 253.

The use of light in logic circuits permits complete electrical isolation between functions and eliminates any possible feedback between the functions. The relatively high current and voltage capabilities of the L8 and L9 enable logic and load-control functions to be performed at the same level, eliminating stages of amplification.

Circuit (C) is of particular importance in working with d-c control circuits. Variations of basic flip-flop circuits are numerous because the loads do not have to be equal and a silicon-controlled rectifier can be used in one leg for handling large loads.

In a d-c circuit, the light-activated rectifier will conduct current indefinitely, until turned off by externally removing the current. The coupling capacitor C momentarily reverse-biases the conducting rectifier when the nonconducting rectifier is triggered. With the proper choice of the coupling capacitor the first load can be quite different from the second. For example, one may be a one-ampere load and the other may be one milliampere. If load currents higher than one ampere are required, a higher-current silicon-controlled rectifier may be used instead of one of the light-activated units.

Counting or delay circuit

When used with direct current, the rectifier will turn on with a short pulse of light and remain in that condition. Some control circuits require manual resetting, others require operation for a fixed time after being activated by the pulse of light with automatic resetting.

Simple and economical commutation (turning-off) for the rectifier in low-voltage d-c circuits can often be accomplished with a single boot-strapped unijunction transistor. The circuit may be used either as a pulser by differentiating the square-wave output with a capacitor, or as a light-activated time delay, by "stretching" the output square wave up to several seconds with suitable unijunction transistor constants.

When light hits the rectifier, the device delivers power to the load. The load voltage then energizes the timing-turnoff circuit. While the emitter capacitor C_1 is charging through R_1 to the peak-point voltage, C_2 charges rapidly to the load-voltage potential through R_3. When the transistor eventually fires—determined by (R_1 x C_1) and the transistor constants—the output pulse from R_4 is coupled through C_2 and CR_1 to the rectifier cathode, raising cathode potential above supply voltage long enough for the rectifier to commutate.

Variable on-time switch

In a-c control work, a short flash of light may be required to actuate a solenoid, counter or contactor for a definite period. For example, a solenoid-operated shear, controlled by a notch or hole in moving strip material, must have current applied for several cycles to complete its travel, even though the light pulse received through the hole lasts only a fraction of a cycle. The circuit shown on p.255 provides this delayed turn-off operation.

A random impulse of light fires the rectifier, applying current to the load. Capacitors C_1 and C_2 discharge through R_2 and R_3, and through R_1 and the rectifier. As long as this capacitor-discharge current is higher than holding current I_H, the rectifier cannot commutate, thus applying full-wave alternating current to the load. When the discharge current drops below I_H, the rectifier turns off at the next succeeding current zero, assisted by R_4 for inductive loads. Decreasing R_3 reduces the time the switch remains on.

The variable on-time switch, which is impulse-actuated, can turn on at any phase angle, but will turn off only at zero current. During conduction, the full sine wave is applied to the load, with virtually no harmonic distortion. Radio noise is therefore negligible.

This circuit is useful for operation of solenoids, contactors, small motors and lamps, particularly in conjunction with an optical programmer.

An optical programmer consists of a motor-driven paper tape with holes. Light passing through the holes, operates various rectifiers. This can be used to set up a predetermined program of operation of various devices such as machine-tool controls.

Smallest phase control

To provide a proportional control of low power with a small space, the light-activated rectifier may be triggered by a small lamp, with phase control provided by response time of the lamp filament.

The phase control circuit (p 255) uses a miniature lamp (No. 2128) that has a small, low-mass filament with a short delay time compared with most lamps. With a low applied voltage, the rectifier firing level for the lamp is reached in about three cycles. As applied voltage is increased, this time is reduced, reaching about one millisecond when it is directly across the rectifier terminals, thus providing phase control of the rectifier. Lamp voltage is removed when the rectifier fires, protecting the lamp and resetting it for the next half-cycle. Lamp and rectifier should be in direct physical contact for best results.

The circuit is useful for small heating elements, such as a soldering iron; or for dimming a lamp except at the low end of the range, where flickering occurs as a result of changes in lamp resistance.

Production-line flow monitor

This circuit has been used to monitor the smooth flow of small components down a high-speed conveyor chute. It can overlook or pass up, small self-clearing pileups, but will shut the line down rapidly in the event of an impending traffic jam.

As shown on p 255, the silicon-controlled rectifier is in series with a relay load, and is supplied from a 120-Volt a-c line. SCR_1 is normally off, being energized only when a fault occurs. With light on, the light-activated rectifier conducts current and

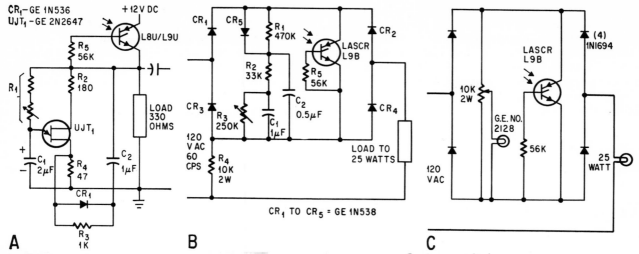

Applications of the rectifier switch include: variable pulse-width counting or delay circuit (A); impulse actuated **variable** on-line switch (B) and phase control (C).

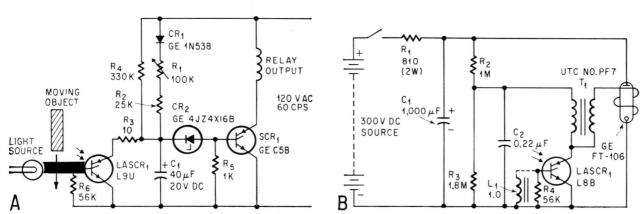

Circuit (A) will monitor the flow of a production line and shut it down in case of a jam. Modified with a rectifier, industrial flashgun circuit (B) triggers a slave unit used in multiple-light-source high-speed photography.

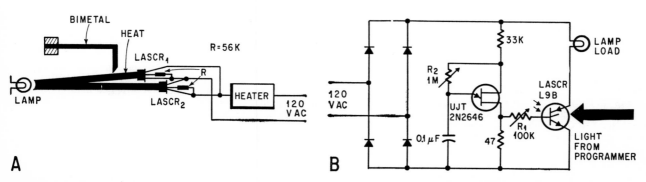

Rectifiers, lamp and a two-metal thermostat provide accurate temperature regulation (A). Unijunction transistor control circuit (B) provides preheating of the lamp by triggering the rectifier late in each half-cycle.

prevents voltage from building up across capacitor C_1. Each time a passing component momentarily interrupts the light beam, the $LASCR_1$ is briefly commutated by the 60-cps a-c line. During these off periods, capacitor C_1 does start to charge toward the peak a-c line voltage through R_1, R_2 and CR_1, but is shorted to zero again as light is restored to

$LASCR_1$. If the light path to $LASCR_1$ is blocked for more than a few milliseconds, however, capacitor C_1 continues to charge unimpeded by $LASCR_1$ and, at a time determined by the time constant C_1 x (R_1 + R_2), it exceeds the avalanche voltage of CR_2 and fires SCR_1. SCR_1 then activates the load.

Reset is automatic when light is restored to

Triggering the light-activated switch

The light-activated rectifier is triggered when the radiant energy falling on it exceeds a given level. The absolute value of this threshold is subject to change by junction temperature, by applied voltage, load impedance, supply frequency and gate condition. A production tolerance also must be taken into account. The equipment designer must see that the triggering threshold is adequately met under all conditions.

The triggering level for the L8 and L9 is given in terms of effective irradiance. This is related to total irradiance and illumination, and is given for the case of a tungsten lamp operating at 2,800° K color temperature.

For example, the L8 will trigger with incident irradiation of 0.010 watt per square-centimeter effective, which may be obtained from a 2,800° K tungsten lamp producing total irradiance of 0.04 watt per square centimeter, or 750 footcandles of illumination at the rectifier. This specification is based upon a junction temperature of 25°C, a supply voltage of six volts of direct current, a load resistance of 100 ohms and a gate-to-cathode resistance of 56,000 ohms.

Terminology

For the rectifier to be used most effectively, the terminology should be defined clearly. The term "light" in "light-activated silicon-controlled rectifier" refers to radiant energy. Technically speaking, however, light is electromagnetic radiation of such a frequency or wavelength as to be perceived by the human eye. Therein lies the fundamental difference between (physiological) photometric and (physical) radiometric systems.

In radiometry, the strength of the wave, or waves, is described in terms of power, or total flux, and of power-per-unit-area, for flux density. Frequency in cycles-per-second may be used, but wavelength is more common and is expressed in microns.

In photometry, the strength of the wave is expressed in terms of its effect upon the eye relative to a standard reference, and the units for flux and flux density are accordingly weighted in physiological effect. Frequency is expressed as color, with mixtures of waves of different frequencies often producing the same color as a single intermediate frequency.

Spectral considerations

The relative spectral response, typical of the human observer and of this rectifier, is a function of wavelength [see figure]. The luminosity curve for the human eye shows that twice as much power is required at 0.510 micron as is required to produce the same sensation of brightness at 0.555 micron. The rectifier responds to a much greater range of wavelengths than the eye,

extending slightly into the utlraviolet region but concentrated primarily in the near-infrared region. Since response is down to 50% at 1.09 and 0.76 microns, twice as much power is required for switching at these wavelengths as at one micron.

Relative response curves

Most light sources emit radiation whose wavelength is outside the visible region. Photometric measurements, concerned only with visual effects, do not indicate directly the effect upon silicon except when correlated with the total spectral output of the source. Therefore, if a particular LASCR triggers at 500 footcandles (visible) from a tungsten lamp operating at 2,800° K color temperature, the same LASCR will turn on at a different light intensity obtained from any other type of lamp, or even from the same lamp operating at a different color temperature.

Effective irradiance

To accurately specify and use the rectifier, radiometric units are required and must be weighed according to the response curve of the device. This is the "effective irradiance," H_E, which is expressed in terms of watts per square centimeter falling on the receiving surface.

Consider a rectifier that requires an "effective-irradiance-to-trigger", H_{ET}, of 7.5 mw/cm². If very narrow band radiation at one micron (such as from a laser) is directed on the pellet, a flux density of 7.5 mw/cm² will cause the device to trigger. If the wavelength is shifted to 1.09 microns (response down to 50%), the triggering flux density will be 7.5/0.5 or 15 mw/cm².

Now suppose we supply 5 mw/cm² at one micron. Then 2.5 mw/cm² additional energy will be required for triggering. This can be obtained by supplying 5 mw/cm² at 1.09 microns, because effective energy is additive.

For broad-band radiation, with a spectral distribution of energy H_λ, the total effective energy may be found by breaking up the wide band into many narrow bands, then multiplying the energy in each narrow band by the relative response, Y_λ, in the band, and then adding the resulting incremental effective energies together, thus H_E = total effective irradiance = $\int H_\lambda H_\lambda d_\lambda$.

The same method is used to evaluate the effective energy of light in which the relative response Y_λ is the "luminosity curve."

The equation above shows energy outside the response band does not contribute to the effective energy. Therefore the relationship between effective energy for the eye (light) and effective energy for silicon depends entirely upon the distribution of energy produced by a particular source. Similarly, the relationship between effective energy and total energy is source dependent.

LASCR$_1$. Circuit delay time can be adjusted from a few milliseconds up to several seconds with R$_1$.

Where solid state switching of the load is required, the relay shown can be replaced with the actual direct load, or by moving the SCR inside a diode bridge (C) full wave a-c output can be realized.

Electronic flash

There is a need in photography for a fast photo-sensitive switch capable of triggering the slave flashgun units used in high-speed photography. An industry-standard flashgun circuit can be modified with a light-activated silicon-controlled rectifier to

Measurement of H$_E$

Although there are several ways to calculate effective irradiance based upon lamp characteristics and physical dimensions, the accuracy of such calculations depends heavily upon data that is not generally available (see Ref. 2 for irradiance calculation details). Certainly the easiest way to determine effective irradiance is to measure it. The rectifier can be calibrated for current vs H$_E$ simply by connecting it as a pnp device in series with a battery and microammeter. The ZJ227UX4 is a factory calibrated LASCR available for evaluation of lamps and optical designs. In essence, this provides a light meter calibrated in terms of mw/cm^2 effective upon the rectifier, thus eliminating the need for conversion from other units of measurement, such as footcandles.

The ZJ227UX4 is a valuable laboratory instrument that can be installed in prototype rectifier systems to measure the maximum and minimum light produced by whatever source and optical system is employed. By measuring the photo-current in the ZJ227UX4 and referring to its calibration curve, the available effective irradiance, H$_E$, is found. This can then be compared with the specified triggering requirements H$_{ET}$ for the L8 or L9 to establish feasibility of the design.

Variations of H$_{ET}$

Since the total light-generated current in the light-activated rectifier is very low, the triggering level of these devices is much lower than in normal silicon-controlled rectifiers. As a result, the light-activated units exhibit greater sensitivity to operating conditions. The effective irradiance to the trigger (H$_{ET}$) is reduced by increasing anode voltage, increasing junction temperature, increasing the rate-of-change of anode voltage, and by increasing either gate-to-cathode resistance or externally supplied gate current. Therefore these devices should not be used as threshold detectors for light if accuracy is important. Stability is improved by holding temperatures, load currents and voltage constant and well below maximum.

Light sources

Tungsten lamps are well suited for operating the rectifiers. With proper choice of lamp and proper derating, excellent life and reliability can be achieved. For example, operating a tungsten lamp at half of its normal voltage extends its life about 10,000 times. This drop in voltage reduces the effective radiation about 20% of normal. Hence one must start with a lamp of higher power, but this is advantageous because it means a more rugged filament.

Xenon flash lamps are suitable sources for pulsed

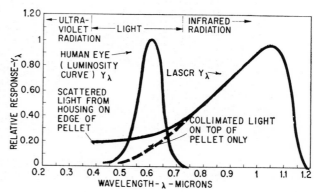

Relative spectral response characteristics of the human eye and the light activated rectifier as a function of wavelength.

triggering, and hence are useful for a-c phase-control or long-distance work. These lamps have very high peak output intensities and are a reasonably good spectral match to silicon.

Injection luminescent diodes of gallium arsenide, operating in either the laser or the noncoherent mode, are excellent sources for pulse triggering and will probably soon be useful for continuous work. The spectral match is practically perfect, and hence results in high radiant efficiency. These diodes operate at low voltage and can easily produce one-microsecond pulses of radiation. Since no visible radiation is produced, they are well suited for systems requiring visual security.

Optics

Innumerable lenses and reflectors are available that can increase irradiance on the rectifier, but always at the expense of restricting the "angle of view." The maximum irradiance that can be obtained with optical systems is limited to the emittance of the source.

Fiber optics provide the best coupling between a source and a rectifier. They can be used to couple several sources and several rectifier units in a complex matrix for logic operations.

Fiber optics can be optained in flexible, noncoherent bundles that provide reasonably efficient transmission of light over circuit paths. For example, a fan-out array of bundles can be used to conduct light information from a closely spaced punched-hole data recording to a larger array of rectifiers. Glass-clad optical fibers can be potted in plastic to hold and protect arrays.

Breadboard of a light activated silicon controlled rectifier "relay" circuit controls the 60 watt lamp.

Editor's note

In addition to the General Electric Co., other companies supply light activated SCRs: Hoffman Electronics Corp., Solid State Products, Inc. and Texas Instruments, Inc.   Some typical devices with manufacturers' ratings:

Mfgr:	Type Series	Package	Fwd blocking voltage	Max. fwd current	Light trigger intensity[1]
General Electric	L8	TO-5	25–200 V	1.6 a	0.68–10 mw/cm^2
	L9	TO-5	25–200 V	1.6 a	0.68–4.2 mw/cm^2
Hoffman	HLS	TO-5	25–200 V	200 ma	50–300 ft-candles
Solid State Products	3P	TO-18 (modified)	15–200 V	300 ma	30–150 ft-candles
Texas Instruments	LSX515	1/16" diam. (ceramic)	60 V	100 ma	5–17.5 mw/cm^2

(1) Conversion from ft-candles to mw/cm^2 is inadvisable since the light source must be defined when using ft-candles.

Operating characteristics of light-sensitive devices

Parameter	Photo-Transistor (PNP or NPN)	PNPN L8, L9, L811, L911	Photoconductive (Cds, Cd Se, etc)	Photovoltaic Si, Ge, Se	Photoemissive (Phototubes etc)
Max. Temp. Capability	85 C	100 C	65 C	150 C	65 C
Max Voltage	< 50 V D-C	200 V	500 V	V (generated)	1500 V
Type	Assymetrical	Assymetrical	Symmetrical	Assymetrical	Assymetrical
Current Capability	1 mA	1.4 A	10 mA to 1 A	150 mA	Up to 10 mA
Dissipation	50 mW	2 W	50 mW to 25 W	75 mW	10 mW → 1 W
Rise Time	2 μsec	2 μsec	0.2 ms → 100 ms	2 μs	1/10 μs
Fall Time	2 μs	2 μs (not t_o)	Somewhat longer than rise time	10 μs	1/10 μs
Frequency Capability	50 kc	1 kc	1 kc (best Pbs)	50 kc	10 mc
Useful Operating Light Levels	1 — 50 ft cn	50 → 10^4 ft cn	10^{-3} → 10^3 ft cn	10^{-1} → 10^6 ft cn	10^{-6} → 10^4 ft cn
Spectral Response	Visible → near IR	Visible → near IR	Visible → IR	Visible → near IR	UV → IR
Long Term Stability	Good	Good	Poor to Good	Best	Good
Adaptation Effects	None	None	Large (similar to eye)	None	Slight

Note — size: Photodiode smallest; photomultiplier tube largest

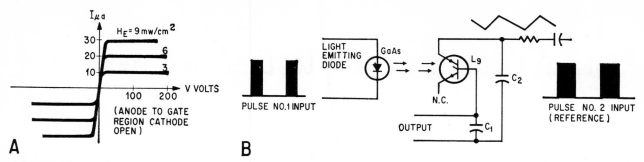

Typical voltage-current characteristics (A) of a rectifier as a symmetrical photo-transistor. A useful type of photo-transistor action is the phase-detection circuit (B).

serve as a fast-acting slave unit.

With switch S_1 closed, capacitor C_1 charges to 300 volts through R_1, and capacitor C_2, charges to approximately 200 volts through R_2 and R_3. When the master flashgun fires, triggered by the flash contacts on the camera, its light output triggers $LASCR_1$, which then discharges capacitor C_2 into the primary winding of transformer T_1. The transformer's secondary puts out a high-voltage pulse to trigger the flash tube. The flash tube discharges capacitor C_1, while the resonant action between C_2 and T_1 reverse-biases $LASCR_1$ for positive turnoff. With the intense instantaneous light energy available from modern electronic flash units, the speed of the rectifier's response is only a few microseconds, leading to perfect synchronization between master and slave.

High levels of ambient light may also trigger the rectifier, and hence the slave, when a resistor is used between the gate and cathode. Although this resistance can be made adjustable to compensate for ambient light, the best solution is to use an inductance of at least one henry, which will be a low impedance for ambient light and a high impedance for a flash.

Precision two-step thermostat

The elementary bi-metal thermostat has problems of mechanical loading, slow make and break of contacts, and self-heating with current flow. Two light-activated rectifiers, a lamp and a thermostat can provide accurate temperature regulation with two-step power control.

As temperature increases, the thermostat blocks light from the rectifier, reducing the heater to half its power. A further increase in temperature causes the thermostat to block light from a second rectifier turning the heater off completely. Since there is no mechanical loading, the differential of this thermostat is very small and is determined primarily by optics and the change in light-sensitivity of the rectifier with temperature and voltage.

Lamp-switching circuit

For programmed operation of lamps in which switching is repetitive for a large number of on-off cycles, thermal stresses on lamps and on control are severe. A unijunction transistor control circuit can provide preheating of the lamp by triggering the rectifier late in each half-cycle. The setting of R_2 will determine the minimum lamp current, as is required to maintain filament temperature just below the visible level. Gate resistor R_1 may be adjusted to control the rectifier's sensitivity to light. One unijunction circuit may be used in conjunction with several rectifier-and-lamp circuits by using a separate gate resistor (R_1) for each rectifier.

Temperature compensation

Since the rectifier's sensitivity to light is a function of junction temperature, some problems may be encountered where large variations in ambient temperature occur. If the changes in junction temperature caused by anode current are of negligible effect, some compensation for ambient temperature changes may be obtained by the use of a thermistor with series and parallel resistors in the gate circuit. Current is low in the gate circuit, permitting the use of a small thermistor that can follow rapid changes of temperature.

Photo-transistor action

The region between the rectifier's anode and gate of the rectifier behaves like a reasonably symmetrical photo-transistor. Typical voltage-current characteristics at several levels of irradiance are shown. This connection is used with the ZJ227UX4, which is a factory-calibrated unit used for measuring effective irradiance H_E (see panel accompanying this article).

The rectifier's photo-transistor action is useful in many ways, one of which is the phase-detector circuit.

The infrared emitting diode of gallium arsenide produces a pulse of radiation coincident with the input pulse. The L9 charges capacitor C_1 to a voltage determined by the phase relationship between pulse 1 and the integrated wave derived from pulse 2. Optical coupling provides balanced operating and isolation.

References

1. GE, SCR Manual 3rd Edition, March, 1964
2. E. Keith Howell, The Light Activated SCR, GE Application Note 200-34

Optical Coupling: Key to Design Freedom

*Photons hold answer
as signal carrier in
three important areas*

DETAILS of IBM's experimental gallium arsenide transistor, which uses optical coupling between diffused *p-n* junctions, was recently reported by company's R. F. Rutz (ELECTRONICS, Mar. 8, p 7).

Schematic drawing of the device is given in diagram, along with common base current voltage characteristics. Rutz says wider base region can be used in this type of configuration, which means lower base resistance.

Primary disadvantage right now is low current gain. But Rutz says improvements are possible by removing the highly light absorbing, heavily doped surfaces of the *P*- regions and adding reflecting coatings.[1]

Several three-layer *pnp* structures were fabricated by diffusing zinc at 850 C to a depth of approximately 2 mils into a 6-mil thick wafer of *n*-type gallium arsenide, tellurium doped, with a room temperature net impurity concentration of approximately 3×10^{17} atms/cms.[3]

From the wafer, small square chips of 10 mils to a side were cut and ohmic contacts were alloyed to the three regions. Width of the base region is about 2 mils.

The optically-coupling transistor may be useful as a fast inverter in the common connection, and as an impedance transformer. Devices were fabricated by R. McGibbon, and unit has been operated as a one megacycle oscillator by C. Lanza.

Greater band gap and potentially greater mobility of gallium arsenide over silicon and germanium has been generally known for some time. During the past few years, gallium arsenide compounds have been examined for potential use in

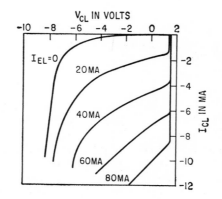

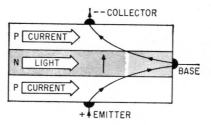

EXPERIMENTAL *optical-coupling transistor structure is examined by IBM's R. F. Rutz (standing) and R. C. McGibbon. Configuration uses light energy to create electron-hole combinations as photons are absorbed near junction between base and collector. Graph shows current-voltage characteristics of three-layer device*

high-frequency and high-temperature devices.[2]

PHOTONS—Key to new freedom in transistor design is fact that gallium arsenide differs from semiconductors like germanium and silicon in that light (photon) energy is produced in former, charged current carriers are produced in latter two.

Not only do gallium arsenide compounds offer possibility of supplying a light source[3], photon injection mechanism can be used as the transport between input and

output junctions of solid-state devices, and gallium arsenide compounds have potential in the laser area.

Light, used to carry signals, can open up new horizons for diodes and transistors[4, 5, 6], integrated solid-state networks[7], optoelectronic circuits, and laser action at higher pulsed current[8, 9].

Mechanism of photon emission from gallium arsenide structures is still not clearly understood. But phenomenon is being explored at many laboratories.

REFERENCES

(1) R. F. Rutz, Transistor-Like Device-Using Optical Coupling Between Diffused p-n Junctions in GaAs, *Proc of IEEE*, Mar., 1963.
(2) M. F. Tomaino, What Lies Ahead for Gallium Arsenide?, ELECTRONICS, Feb. 17, 1961, p 144.
(3) Will Gallium Arsenide Provide New Eleetronic Light Source?, ELECTRONICS, Dec. 28, 1962, p 52.
(4) L. K. Anderson, The PIN Junction Photodiode as a Detector of Light Modulated at Microwave Frequencies, Bell Telephone Labs, Murray Hill, N. J. (1963 Solid-State Circuits Conf, IEEE).
(5) R. V. Bez, Switching Light With Light: Absorption Edge Modulation, Sylvania Electric, Needham Heights, Mass (1963 Solid-State Circuits Conf, IEEE).
(6) J. R. Biard et al, GaAs Infrared Source for Optoelectronic Applications, Texas Instruments, Dallas, Texas (1963 Solid-State Circuits Cof, IEEE).
(7) M. F. Wolff, Advances in Microminiaturization, Special Report, ELECTRONICS, Feb 15, 1963, p 57, 59.
(8) F. H. Dill, Jr., Gallium Arsenide Injection Laser, Thomas J. Watson Research Center, IBM Corp, Yorktown Heights, N. Y.
(9) N. Holonyak Jr., Active Region in Visible-Light Diode Laser, GE Semiconductor Products, Syracuse, N. Y., ELECTRONICS, Mar 1, 1963, p 35.

Light Isolates Amplifier Stages

Optically-coupled device promises more accurate measuring instruments

By **LAURENCE D. SHERGALIS**
Regional Editor
San Francisco

PALO ALTO, CALIF.—Electrical isolation of input from output has been achieved with a relatively simple solid-state device that uses optical coupling. Developed at Hewlett-Packard Associates, the device is a four-terminal network that electrically isolates input from output while retaining the characteristics of conventional transistors, Fig. 1A. H-P Associates did the background work on the device under an Air Force contract for advanced functional block development in which the light emitting characteristics of the gallium-arsenide mesa diode were investigated. Now, the diode has been combined with a phototransistor. Results of this work will be reported in a paper, "An Optically Coupled Amplifying Device" by Dave Earle and Richard Soshea at the Electron Devices Meeting this week.

Basically, the device consists of a gallium-arsenide mesa diode mounted on a silicon phototransistor. Two methods are used to couple the two units. In one scheme, Fig. 1B, the *p*-layer of the diode is very thin. Thus, the distance from the light-emitting junction to the phototransistor is very small. The problem is in controlling this thickness, which can be of the order of only a few microns. Also the contacting surface is made in a screen

form. Using this type of construction, a light energy peak at 1.41 electron volts can be observed and utilized. This peak is absorbed in gallium-arsenide if the material is thicker than a few microns.

Although the effect is strong, the excitation mechanism isn't really understood. Light can be readily seen at liquid-nitrogen temperatures. But H-P is striving to produce a device that will be useful at room temperature. Thus, unless the thickness of the *p*-layer is made small, another method must be used.

The 1.41-ev light peak can be ignored and a 1.37 electron-volt peak, obtained from zinc-doped material, may be used. This peak, while not as strong as the 1.41 peak, may be observed at room temperature and is not absorbed in the gallium-arsenide material. Therefore, the diode is turned over and the *n*-layer

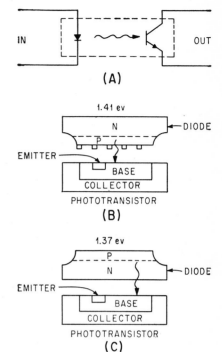

BASIC light amplifier circuit (A). Two methods are used to mount gallium arsenide diode to silicon phototransistor. (B) gives higher gain but requires more precise manufacturing tolerances. (C) uses light energy peak that is not absorbed in the diode and is visible at room temperature, Fig. 1

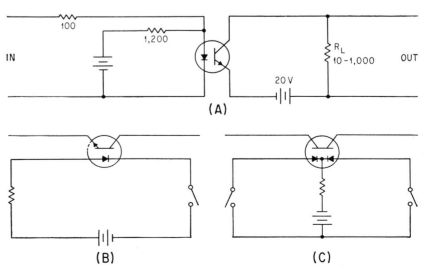

TYPICAL amplifier circuit (A). Load resistance R_L is kept to a minimum to increase operating speed. Applications include simple relay (B) and OR relay (C), Fig. 2

placed in contact with the phototransistor, Fig. 1C.

One disadvantage of this type of construction is that light is lost and overall gain of the device is less. But because of the ability of the devices to work at room temperature and the relative ease of fabrication, most of the experimental work has been carried on with units constructed in this way.

Efficiency—Light output varies with current to the diode. The authors say they are still conducting experiments to determine ways to achieve a linear relationship between current in and photons out. Conversion efficiency, they find, is dependent upon both current level and temperature. Another factor in determining efficiency is the difference in index of refraction of the gallium-arsenide material and the material through which the light passes upon leaving the diode. Index of refraction of the gallium arsenide is 3.5, and the high reflection at the surface makes it difficult to get light out. A very narrow critical angle—only 16 degrees—has been found. Light hitting the surface head on—at 90 degrees—suffers a loss of about one-third due to reflections.

The trick, say the authors, is to fill the space between the diode surface and the phototransistor with a material having an index of refraction approaching that of gallium-arsenide. Various potting materials and glasses are being tried.

Phototransistor—This is a conventional silicon unit with very high beta. Betas of the order of 500 to 1,000 are being used. This requirement puts tight tolerances upon the manufacturing processes. Presently, the phototransistor is the limiting factor in the speed of the amplifier.

Speed of operation—Two factors influence speed of operation. There appear to be a high lateral resistance in the base and a parallel capacitance between the base and emitter. A solution to this problem is being approached by designing various emitter configurations. A stripe and a vee shape are being tried.

Collector-base capacitance influences speed of operation also. While it is only a few picofarads, it is multiplied by the beta of the phototransistor in this type of operation and becomes a major factor. This capacitance plus the load resistor form an RC network with a finite time constant. Load resistance values are held to a minimum.

Characteristics — Combining the pair, some preliminary tests show a current gain of about 0.5 to 2.0, with a 100-ohm load resistance. Voltage gain is about 2.5 to 11 and power gain is about 1.5 to 22. Cutoff frequency is about 250 kc at 3 db down. Work is continuing to extend cutoff frequency by a factor of 3 or 4. Current-carrying capacity is limited by the thermal characteristics of the transistor. Total harmonic distortion from zero to 500 kc is about 3 percent, and needs to be improved by a factor of 10 to 100.

Applications—Work on the optically-coupled amplifier, Fig. 2A is now product oriented, on applications where no interaction between input and output is desired. Hewlett-Packard is interested in the device for measuring instruments.

Some interest has also been shown for telephone applications to replace certain types of relays. A few test circuits have been tried, including a simple relay, 2(B) OR relay, 2(C) and various configurations of choppers. Because of the high speed of this device, it may replace neon photoconductor devices and relays. The amplifier is still in the laboratory stage.

Chapter 13

MICROPOWER CIRCUIT TECHNIQUES

ELECTRON-BEAM *gun—extending below vacuum chamber—is part of equipment used in micropower technology. Equipment at left has pattern monitoring screen*

MICROPOWER CIRCUITS

NEW FRONTIER IN SOLID STATE

Micropower circuits combining thin-film and diffusion technology are now limited to operating below 1-Mc, but higher speeds appear feasible with further size reduction. Circuit design for micropower— both analog and digital—promises to be on a par with conventional design

By W. W. GAERTNER and M. SCHULLER, CBS Laboratories, Stamford, Conn.

BY BRINGING power consumption of individual circuit components down to microwatts, packaging densities of one million components per cubic inch become feasible since the heat generated is small and the circuits operate nearly at ambient temperature. Space electronics with a density of ½ million components per cubic foot have already been delivered to NASA and much greater size reduction is possible.

The technique developed to produce microwatt circuits integrates planar diffusion technology and deposited thin-film technology on the same silicon wafer. Microwatt power does not represent a lower limit for the process and even nanowatt power appears feasible. Nanowatt operation would bring micro- electronic circuits into the range of power of biological systems.

TECHNOLOGY — Integration of planar diffused technology and deposited thin-film technology on the same silicon wafer is indicated in Fig. 1. All the conventional processes of epitaxial growth, diffusion and alloying are performed first and then the grown silicon oxide on

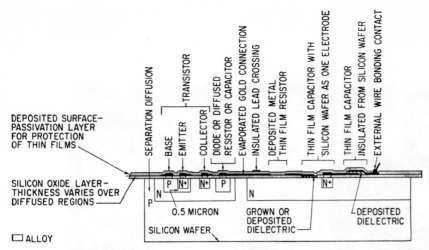

Labels in figure (top to bottom / left to right):

DEPOSITED SURFACE-PASSIVATION LAYER FOR PROTECTION OF THIN FILMS

SEPARATION DIFFUSION
BASE
EMITTER — TRANSISTOR
COLLECTOR
DIODE OR DIFFUSED RESISTOR OR CAPACITOR
EVAPORATED GOLD CONNECTION
INSULATED LEAD CROSSING
DEPOSITED METAL THIN FILM RESISTOR
THIN FILM CAPACITOR WITH SILICON WAFER AS ONE ELECTRODE
THIN FILM CAPACITOR INSULATED FROM SILICON WAFER
EXTERNAL WIRE BONDING CONTACT

SILICON OXIDE LAYER - THICKNESS VARIES OVER DIFFUSED REGIONS

□ ALLOY

0.5 MICRON
SILICON WAFER
GROWN OR DEPOSITED DIELECTRIC
DEPOSITED DIELECTRIC

PLANAR DIFFUSED *technology is combined with thin-film techniques to give microwatt circuits. The deposited surface-passivation layer allows a large reduction in volume—Fig. 1*

the wafer surface is used as a substrate for depositing thin-film components. Finally, an inert passivation layer is deposited over the thin-film components to protect them from mechanical and chemical damage. The result is a fully passivated function block, as in conventional microelectronics, but with thin-film components included.

The photograph on the cover of this issue shows such a surface-passivated thin-film semiconductor circuit wafer being subjected to a hot dichromic acid test. The circuit is unaffected. Thus the surface-passivation technique is an important step towards eliminating the present bulky package around the small semiconductor wafer. This increase in allowable packing density is not accompanied by a destructive temperature rise.

The new technology brings several additional degrees of freedom to the microelectronics field and offers some distinct advantages.

• *High Resistor Values*—Micropower operation requires resistances of the order of megohms. With a sheet resistance of only 400 ohms per square and a line width of 1 mil, a 1-megohm resistor covers an area of approximately 70×70 mils. A diffused 1-megohm resistor would take up twice this area.

• *Low RC Time Constants*—All microelectronics is plagued by stray capacitance between the closely spaced circuit elements and the bulk of the wafer, resulting in undesirable coupling, spurious oscillations and R-C time delays that slow down the circuit significantly at all power and impedance levels. It is particularly noticeable, however, in low power, high resistance circuits. The capacitance of silicon *p-n* junctions, which separate diffused resistors from the bulk and from other circuit elements, is typically about 0.2 pf per sq mil. But the capacitance across a 1-micron thick layer of grown silicon oxide that separates a deposited metal-film resistor from the substrate is only 0.024 pf per sq mil. Thus the time constant associated with a thin-film resistor of the same value and size as a diffused resistor

is almost 10 times lower.

In addition, the size of the deposited resistor itself will usually be at least 50 percent smaller. Furthermore, the silicon-oxide layer can still be made substantially thicker whereas there is a natural limitation to the thickness of a *p-n* junction depletion layer. Therefore the combination thin-film semiconductor technology can produce faster microcircuits at all power levels and not only in the microwatt range. Thin film resistors deposited on silicon oxide over silicon compare even favorably in response time with those deposited on ceramic substrates because the latter often have high dielectric constants which lead to high coupling capacitance between the closely spaced resistor lines.

• *Component Independence*—Since the fabrication of transistors and resistors—and sometimes of capacitors — occurs at different times, their characteristics are largely independent and each can be changed and optimized without affecting the others.

• *Versatility*—A direct result of the complete independence of transistor and resistor characteristics is design versatility. A number of universally useful transistors can be diffused into a silicon wafer and then various resistor and interconnection patterns can be added to produce a variety of different circuits for different speed and power ranges. When the transistors are fabricated it is not necessary to know whether a digital or analog circuit is to be built, or which package leads will be used for which purpose. Figure 2 shows six different resistor and interconnection patterns added to a basic transistor pair to form a variety of medium-power analog and digital circuits.

Another example is given in Fig.

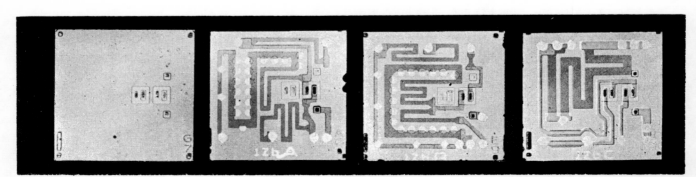

3, where several different NOR gates and a pair of emitter-followers have been evaporated onto the same transistor pattern. This not only aids efficient production but also allows quick reaction during circuit development. If a fast mask-making facility is available, a new circuit design can be ready for testing in microelectronic form in one day. New resistor and interconnection patterns are evaporated onto an existing universal transistor wafer, then tested after being scribed, mounted and bonded.

• *Tight Tolerances*—In some applications tight tolerances on components must be achieved. Resistor tolerances are a function of line width and sheet resistance. Tight tolerances are achieved by monitoring the sheet resistance of a thin-film resistor during deposition and stopping the evaporation as close as possible to the desired value, as well as by being able to predict the small resistance changes which occur during high-temperature stabilization. Readily achievable tolerances range at the present time from ±5 percent with a line width of 1.5 mils and a sheet resistance of 400 ohms per square to fractions of 1 percent with a line width of 5 mils and a sheet resistance of 100 ohms per square. These tolerances are continuously being improved. Since there is a direct relationship between component tolerances and speed and power consumption of a system, performance superior to systems produced with diffused components alone is expected. The accuracy of resistors evaporated on the same substrate is within a few tenths of one percent. Figure 4 shows a high precision resistor ladder network for microelectronic analog-to-digital converters.

• *Temperature Stability*—In applications such as f-m telemetry,

temperature stability of components is an absolute necessity. In other applications it is desirable because it increases the speed and decreases the power consumption of the entire system. Figure 5 shows the temperature variation of a passivated thin-film resistor deposited on silicon oxide over silicon. Its temperature coefficient is 10 to 100 times better than diffused semiconductor resistors.

• *Resistor Materials*—Any resistor material that can be evaporated or sputtered can be used in the thin-film semiconductor technology: the choice depends on sheet resistance, temperature coefficient or other property desired. Nichrome, chrome and tantalum are useful for many applications.

• *Scaling*—Many circuits depend on the ratios of resistances rather than on their absolute values. The speed, power consumption and fanout capabilities of a thin-film semiconductor microcircuit can be changed over wide ranges by depositing different amounts of resistor materials onto the same pattern.

• *No High-Temperature Leakage*—Unlike diffused semiconductor resistors, thin-film resistors on silicon oxide over silicon show no leakage currents between the resistor and the bulk of the wafer even at high temperatures and with large resistor areas.

• *Heat Conduction of Substrate*—The high heat conductivity of the silicon substrate as compared to ceramic substrates equalizes hot spots in the microcircuit much better, so permissible power dissipation for a resistor covering a given area is much higher. Figure 6 shows the long term stability of these resistors under loading at elevated temperatures.

• *Extremely Pure Substrate*—

CONTROL DESK *with optical bench in which pattern slide is sensed by a flying-spot scanner*

The extreme chemical purity of the grown silicon oxide substrate is considered a favorable factor for the long-range high-temperature stability of the thin film resistors.

• *Low Operating Temperature*—In microwatt operation and at packing densities dictated by present packaging and interconnection schemes, the microelectronic function block remains at ambient temperature rather than experiencing the significant temperature rise typical in systems consisting of uncooled tightly packed conventional microelectronic packages. This low operating temperature is expected to contribute greatly to reliability.

• *Packing Density*—Since one million transistor stages operating at one microwatt each will dissipate only 1 watt, micropower circuits alone will allow the size reductions previously predicted on the basis of size alone. Already delivered to NASA is microelectronic space hardware with a packing density of ½ million components per cubic foot, and an increase of many orders of magnitude is still feasible.

• *Secondary Advantages*—Indirect benefits derive from micro-

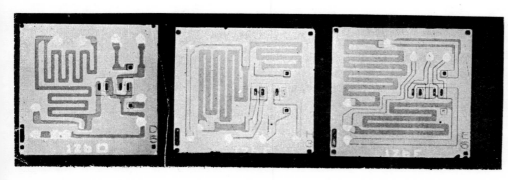

WAFER *with two transistors (far left) can be made into a variety of circuits by depositing different thin-film patterns. Circuit development can be rapid if mask-making equipment is available—Fig. 2*

BASIC *transistor wafer applied to various circuit designs. A few basic transistor chips can be applied to many circuits.*

APPLYING MICROPOWER

Microwatt and nanowatt circuits should go a long way toward freeing the circuit designer from the problems of heat dissipation and circuit volume, at least so far as the signal processing and computing part of the circuit is concerned. One result is that highly sophisticated techniques can be developed for military and space applications—and eventually for more prosaic uses

power operation of systems. The cost, size and weight of the power supply — storage batteries, solar panels—can be reduced sometimes by as much as 100. In air and spaceborne systems this results in a saving in transportation costs or in greatly improved capability for a given transportation cost.

PROBLEMS—Whereas the desirability of very low power operation and of complete integration of thin-film and semiconductor techniques is almost self-evident, the technological problems in the practical realization of these concepts have not been trivial.

• *Transistor Quality*—To achieve microwatt operation the microelectronic function block must contain transistors with high current gain at an emitter current of 1 microampere and a collector voltage of less than 1 volt. Such transistors, with high capacitances, are now

commercially available but are not necessary for and are not used in conventional milliwatt microelectronics.

Since high-quality performance is required of adjacent transistors on the same function block, the overall yield of the microwatt transistor production process must be high. Furthermore, in the interest of speed the high gain at low current must be combined with low junction capacitance. Since decreasing size increases the surface-to-volume ratio of the junctions, resulting usually in lower current gain at low currents because of surface recombination at the junction, high precision in mask line-up and photoresist processing is required. The transistors shown in Fig. 2 and 3 have betas as high as 80 at one microampere collector current and junction capacitance of 5 pf at zero volts.

• *Substrate and Resistor Quality*—In ordinary planar and microelectronic technology occasional pinholes and oxide flaws are not immediately harmful except near the junctions and may only later result in poor reliability. In the thin-film semiconductor technology, however, the oxide layer covering the silicon wafer is the substrate for the thin-film components and must be perfect and uniform over large areas, especially for resistors with long narrow lines closely spaced and for large capacitors. For resistors an irregularity may cause an im-

mediate break in a line, or a weak spot which opens up under high load and temperature. Or, the resistor may have leakage or a short to the substrate. In capacitors, imperfections cause leakage and low breakdown voltage.

Equally important to the quality of the silicon substrate are the controls on thin-film deposition. Since the substrate wafer contains transistors and diodes worth thousands of dollars, the yield of the deposition process must be near 100 percent. Subsequent trimming of resistors by abrasion, customary with some conventional thin-film resistors, is impossible and all components must be deposited within tolerances, and subsequent accelerated aging must not bring them outside tolerance.

• *Compatibility of Technologies*—Thin-film deposition requires cleaning the substrate with highly reactive chemicals and heating it to high temperature for a prolonged time. Cleaning, however, must have no ill effects on the transistors and diodes in the substrate. For micropower operation the transistors must maintain their high current gain throughout the treatment. Thin-film components must withstand thermocompression bonding temperature. Both these steps present difficulties.

• *Effect on Cost*—Several factors contribute to the present high cost of micropower microelectronics: the quality of the components required; the extra fabrication steps required by the addition of the thin films; the size of the megohm-range resistors which allows only a relatively small number of circuits on one wafer. With improved understanding and automation of all processes, however, and control of higher and higher sheet resistances, the cost of micropower microelectronics will come down close to that of conventional milliwatt

HIGH PRECISION *ladder network has 19 thin-film resistors accurate to 0.3 percent—Fig. 4*

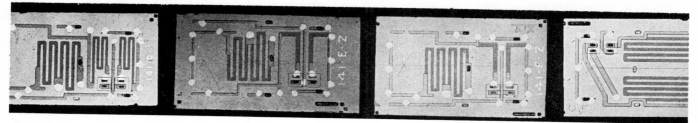

because of component independence—Fig. 3

electronic circuits.

• *Reliability*—This is one of the main reasons for using microelectronic building blocks. Thin-film semiconductor microelectronic technology is at this point too new for extensive reliability data and the technology itself still changes rapidly to take advantage of possible improvements. An unusually high degree of reliability is expected, however. It is well established that an increase in operating temperature causes a decrease in reliability, and since micropower microelectronic blocks operate virtually at ambient, they should eventually have the highest reliability possible at a given ambient—higher than any type of circuit that raises its operating temperature significantly due to heat dissipation.

The main source of reliability is in the fabrication processes. Although these are proprietary a few general rules can be mentioned. All work must be performed in white rooms with humidity, dust and temperature control; all fabrication should be carried out at the highest possible temperature to eliminate subsequent changes of component values in the operating range; the entire circuit is covered by a tough passivation layer such as silicon oxide, which allows the circuit to be submerged in hot dichromic acid ($H_2SO_4+H_2O+Na_2Cr_2O_7$) for almost an hour without damage to the thin-film components (see cover); each circuit chip can be monitored through all fabrication steps into final packaging. The letters and numbers on the circuit chips in Fig. 2 and 3 identify the location of the chip on a wafer, which may contain 40 to 1,000 circuits. These tight controls lead to high yield, which is another prerequisite for high reliability.

NANOWATTS—Microwatt operation is not a limit dictated by semiconductor physics and a reduction of supply power by several orders of magnitude into the nanowatt range appears feasible. This would bring microelectronics down into the biological-supply power range. Several research projects are presently underway to penetrate the nanowatt range, with emphasis on the following.

• Improved control on diffusion processes to achieve a high yield of transistors with sufficient current gain at emitter currents of 1 na

• The exploration of stable thin-film resistors with a sheet resistance of many thousands of ohms per square

• The replacement of visible light by electron and ion beams as the major technological tools to produce the minute geometries necessary for high speed at very low power. Transistors with a maximum area of 3 × 3 microns are forecast whose details could not even be observed under an optical microscope. Experimental electron and ion beam systems for such purposes are shown in the photographs.

SYSTEMS — Micropower microelectronics has been applied to several subsystems of moderate complexity, some already delivered for operational systems use; one application involves over 300 transistors and 600 resistors and capacitors, all on micropower function blocks. The applications have led to some general design rules and procedures.

• Micropower microelectronics lends itself to all types of analog and digital circuits. Transformers and inductances must be designed out of the circuits. Field-effect transistors and active R-C filters may sometimes be used.

• The large resistance values required, together with the *p-n* junction and stray capacitances in the circuit, limit the operating frequency to below 1 Mc. This limitation will be lifted as the size of the microcircuits decreases. Higher power circuits close to the frequency response of the transistors can be built.

• Interfaces between micropower microelectronics and conventional-

MONO-ENERGETIC *ion beam emerges from slit in top plate. Oven for generating neutral atomic beams is at lower right; evaporation well is under screw cap on top of oven*

component or microelectronic circuits operating at milliwatt level present no problem. Micropower function blocks can readily be driven by milliwatt circuitry and interface amplifiers (emitter-followers, see Fig. 3) can be provided wherever a micropower circuit must drive a milliwatt circuit. These amplifiers typically consume more power than all the microwatt circuits preceding; thus it is desirable to use microwatt circuits in as much of the system as possible.

• Power consumption in each circuit of a system should be minimized to provide only the speed and fan-out required and not more. Thus in a typical system the resistance values and power consumption of circuit blocks of the same type may vary by more than a factor of ten. In a binary counter chain, for example, the power consumption of each successive stage can be reduced by 2 because less speed is required. In many systems most circuits require only a fan-out of about 4 and these circuits can be designed for much lower power consumption than the few high fan-out circuits. By changing the amount of metal deposited on the resistor pattern, and thus changing the sheet resistance and the resistance value, or by adding a different resistor pattern to the basic transistor pattern, speed, fan-out and power consumption can be varied continuously over 4 orders of magnitude. The exact minimum power circuit desired can thus be realized.

• Micropower circuits can be used today where the reduced power and increased reliability justify present high prices.

At the present time, with micropower components not yet gener-

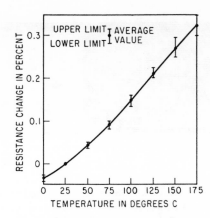

THIN-FILM *resistor (nichrome on silicon dioxide) with average value of 240,000 ohms is highly stable with temperature*—Fig. 5

ally available, circuit design should be done in collaboration with a fabricator of micropower circuits. The first step is to build a systems breadboard with conventional components but using the identical transistors that will later be used in the microelectronic function block, thus avoiding discrepancies in temperature, voltage and bias-current dependence of parameters. Next, the conventional resistors and capacitors are replaced by individual diffused and thin-film resistors and capacitors on a silicon substrate. This is the first step towards taking stray capacitance into account.

Adjustments are made in the breadboard using conventional components for trimming. Then partial integration is accomplished by putting five to ten active and passive elements on the same silicon chip. Taps are provided on the resistors and capacitors and test points are brought outside the package in addition to the input, output, power supply and ground

connections. Again conventional components or individual microelectronic components on silicon chips can be used for trimming. When the circuit design is frozen the circuit is fully integrated on a single silicon chip.

Engineering samples of various micropower logic and analog stages will soon be available for systems design and will provide short cuts in circuit development.

Experience in designing micropower systems accumulates rapidly; within a year circuit design will probably be no more difficult than with conventional components.

C. Heizman, J. Kostelec, C. Levy, E. Littau, W. Meyer and M. Urban have been instrumental in the design and fabrication of the microwatt function blocks.

The electron-beam system and the ion gun have been designed and constructed by A. Andrews and F. Cook respectively, under sponsorship of the U. S. Naval Avionics Facility in Indianapolis and the U. S. Army Research and Development Laboratory, Fort Monmouth, New Jersey.

Most of the other work has been sponsored by the National Aeronautics and Space Administration and the U. S. Air Force.

BIBLIOGRAPHY

(1) W. W. Gaertner, M. Schuller, C. Heizman, C. Levy, Microwatt-Microelectronics, paper presented at the 1961 Northeast Electronics Research and Engineering meeting, Boston, Mass., Nov. 1961.
(2) W. W. Gaertner, M. Schuller, C. Heizman, C. Levy, Microwatt-Microelectronics, lecture to Washington Chapter of *PGED*, Washington, D. C., Nov. 27, 1961.
(3) W. W. Gaertner, M. Schuller, C. Heizman, C. Levy, Microwatt-Microelectronics, lecture to Merrimack Valley Subsection of the *IRE*, North Andover, Mass., Jan. 15, 1962.
(4) W. W. Gaertner, M. Schuller, C. Heizman, C. Levy, Microwatt-Microelectronics, *Electro-Technology*, Feb. 1962.
(5) W. W. Gaertner, C. Heizman, M. Schuller, C. Levy, Microelectronics, Micro-Power Analog and Digital Circuit-Function Blocks for Space Applications, paper presented at 1962 National Symposium on Space Electronics and Telemetry, Miami Beach, Fla., Oct. 1962.
(6) W. W. Gaertner, C. Heizman, C. Levy, M. Schuller, Microelectronic, Micropower Digital and Low Level Amplifiers for Space Applications, *Spaceborne Computer Engineering Conference Proc.*, p 151, Anaheim, Calif., Oct. 1962.
(7) W. W. Gaertner, Nanowatt Devices, paper presented at the 1962 Electron Devices Meeting of the IRE Professional Group on Electron Devices, Wash., D. C., Oct. 1962.
(8) Descriptions of the CBS technology have also been given in the following Journals: Giants Jump Into Race for Tinier Electronics, *Business Week*, Aug. 25, 1962; Microwatt Computer Block, *Electronic News*, Oct. 1, 1962; Micromin, Communication Strive to Meet Space Needs, *Electronic Design*, Oct. 25, 1962; Nanowatt Range Devices Developed by CBS Labs, *Electronic News*, Oct. 29, 1962; Recipe for Stringbean Transistors, *Electronic Design*, Nov. 22, 1962; And Now—A Nanowatt Circuit Design, *Electronic Design*, Nov. 22, 1962; Nanowatt Power: How Low is Low?, *Electronic Design*, Feb. 15, 1963; Advances in Microminiaturization, Electronics, Feb. 15, 1963.

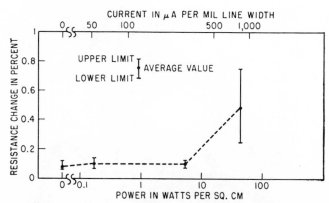

PERMANENT CHANGES *in thin-film resistors after 1,000 hours at 125 C—Fig. 6*

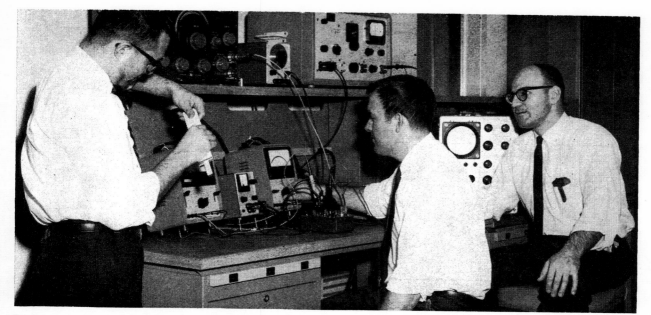

Engineers test common-emitter amplifier at the Army Electronics Research and Development Laboratory.

How to design micropower transistor amplifiers: part I

Technique provides specified output power capability over a wide temperature range, minimizes amplifier power drain and maximizes power gain

By J. D. Meindl, R. Gilson, O. Pitzalis and W. Kiss

U.S. Army Electronics Research and Development Laboratories, Fort Monmouth, N.J.

One of the chief problems in space electronics and portable military communications equipment, where size, weight and power drain are crucial, is designing circuits that consume little power. For this reason, increasing emphasis is being placed on micropower electronics—the design of circuits that consume microwatts rather than milliwatts.

Recent advances in semiconductor device technology have produced silicon planar transistors which exhibit junction reverse currents less than one nanoampere and common-emitter current gains greater than 50 for collector currents of 1 to 10 microamperes. Because of their ultralow-level operational capabilities, such micropower transistors offer attractive possibilities for alleviating the problem of excessive power drain in space electronics and portable military communications equipment.

This article is the first of two which give a design technique for micropower amplifiers, including the characteristics of commercially available micropower transistors, an optimum design theory for linear broadband micropower transistor amplifiers

Multichip common-emitter amplifier

and a cascode micropower amplifier configuration. A salient feature of this design technique is that for the first time it provides a single approach to both the d-c and large-signal a-c design of micropower amplifiers. Subject to the initial constraints on the design, the technique provides a specified amplifier output power capability over a wide temperature range, minimizes amplifier power drain and maximizes amplifier power gain. This performance is assured for the worst possible combination of transistor, resistor and supply voltage tolerance margins. Specifically, the technique permits designing micropower amplifiers that can provide an 0.18-volt peak a-c load voltage over the temperature range —50° to +100° C for a power drain of only 25 microwatts and a power gain of 25 db.

If the peak load voltage capability is reduced to 0.15 v, this amplifier can accept 10% worst-case tolerance margins on all circuit resistors. Depending on transistor barrier capacitances and stray circuit capacitances, amplifier bandwidth may vary from about 10 kc to 25 kc with five times and larger increases possible with the cascode circuit to be described in the second article.

Fabrication

The amplifiers described here were fabricated by using an approach to microelectronics known as the multi-chip technique. This involves using separate silicon chips for the active and passive components to cut parasitic capacitances to less than would be found in a comparable monolithic (single-chip) integrated circuit at present.

The silicon chips are bonded to metal islands on a ceramic substrate as shown in the photo. The active-component chips are simply planar transistors in a silicon substrate. The separate passive-component chips use diffused resistors or thin-film resistors deposited on top of a silicon substrate passivated with silicon dioxide.

This feature allows using resistors that have values of 300,000 ohms or more and provides another reason for the multi-chip approach because such

values are presently not feasible in monolithic integrated circuits.

Design theory

The initial consideration in designing micropower amplifiers is the characterization of the micropower transistor. Briefly, micropower transistors differ from ordinary silicon transistors in that they have:

1). Junction reverse currents less than one nanoampere at room temperature.
2). Forward current transfer ratios (h_{fe} and h_{FE}) greater than 50 for collector currents of 1 to 10 microamperes.
3). Greater sensitivity of the d-c forward current transfer ratio h_{FE} and four terminal parameters h_{11e} and h_{21e} to changes in quiescent collector current and temperature.
4). A relatively limited gain-bandwidth product f_T.

Micropower transistor characteristics

Six typical micropower transistors are characterized in the table below. The devices include three npn planar transistors (devices A, B and C), an npn planar epitaxial transistor (device D), an npn mesa transistor (device E), and a pnp planar transistor (device F). Each transistor is supplied by a different manufacturer. The tabulated d-c characteristics indicate that the temperature variation of transistor current gain h_{FE} at a 10 microampere collector current may often be greater than the corresponding variation at milliampere collector current levels. For example, device D exhibits a 5.5 times increase in h_{FE} from 23 to 128 for —50≦T≦100°C. In addition, it is evident that at temperatures above 100°C, collector junction reverse current I_{CBO} can become significantly large compared with base current, if not collector current, for collector currents in the 1 to 10 microampere range. Again considering device D, the I_{CBO} of 0.33 microampere at 100°C, which increases to about 2.5 microampere at 125°C, illustrates this point.

The variations with collector current of the small

D-C characteristics

	$I_C = 10\ \mu a$ $I_B = 1.0\ \mu a$		$I_C = 10\ \mu a$ $V_{CE} = 3.0$ v			$V_{CB} = 3.0$ v
T (°C) =	25		—50	25	100	100
Device	V_{CES} (v)	V_{BES} (v)	h_{FE}	h_{FE}	h_{FE}	I_{CBO} (na)
A (2N929)	0.10	0.55	23	66	106	1.0
B (unregistered)	0.09	0.52	14	54	125	3.8
C (2N2510)	0.13	0.53	62	91	156	9.0
D (2N2784A)	0.16	0.60	23	71	128	33.0
E (2N2251)	0.05	0.49	20	50	96	14.0
F (2N2604)	0.13	0.52	58	115	192	30.0

These properties are described in more detail in the panel (p 272) which also presents characterization data for six typical diffused silicon micropower transistors.

In designing a micropower amplifier, several problems arise that are far less severe or even non-existent at normal milliwatt power levels in silicon transistor linear circuits. In d-c operation, transistor bias point stabilization becomes more difficult due to three factors: 1) at 1 to 10 microampere collector currents, collector junction reverse current I_{CBO} can become significant at temperatures above 100° C; 2) the temperature variation of common emitter current gain h_{FE} is somewhat larger than that at collector currents of 1 to 10 milliamperes; a five-to-one variation for $-50°$ C $\leq$ T $\leq$ 100° C is not unusual: 3) temperature variation of base-emitter diode conductance g_{BE} makes the d-c operating point unstable. This effect becomes more difficult to counteract at the low battery voltages which usually accompany microwatt power levels, because V_{BE} is a greater percentage of the battery voltage.

In a-c operation, a major problem stems from the fact that quiescent collector currents in the micro-ampere range severely restrict the dynamic range of an amplifier and effectively contribute to a large signal mode of operation. Careful attention must be paid to the effects of temperature as well as transistor saturation and cut-off on the dynamic range of a design. The influence of both transistor and passive component tolerances assumes a greater importance in micropower amplifiers. Finally, poor high-frequency response of currently available silicon transistors at microwatt power levels seriously limits the bandwidth of micropower amplifiers. The design technique described has been found useful in pro-

signal, low frequency, common emitter parameters, $h_{11e}=h_{ie}$ and $h_{21e}=h_{fe}$, indicate the changes that occur in the values of transistor a-c input impedance and current gain as quiescent collector current is reduced. For example, h_{ie} increases markedly from 4,000 to 217,000 ohms while h_{fe} decreases moderately from 140 to 78 as I_c varies from a 1 ma to 10 microampere collector quiescent current as indicated. Typical low frequency values for the reverse voltage transfer ratio $h_{12e}=h_{re}$ and the output admittance $h_{22e}=h_{oe}$ for micropower transistors are indicated at the bottom of the table; h_{12e} and h_{22e} can generally be neglected in micropower circuits.

The three-decibel cutoff frequencies f_{3db} and current gain-bandwidth products f_T shown in the table illustrate the strong dependence of transistor frequency response on quiescent collector current. In the case of device D the current gain-bandwidth product decreases from 600 to 7 Mc as I_c is reduced from 1 ma to 10 microampere. By means of the conventional hybrid pi small signal equivalent circuit for a transistor, it can be shown[1] that the gain-bandwidth product of a micropower transistor is approximately directly proportional to collector current

I_c. The governing relationship is

$$f_T = h_{fe} f_{3db} = \frac{1}{2\pi} \frac{h_{fe}}{h_{ie}(C_{b'e} + C_C + C_s)}$$

$$= \frac{1}{2\pi} \frac{q}{kT} \frac{I_c}{(C_{Te} + C_C + C_s)}$$

where the total base-to-emitter capacitance $C_{b'e}=C_D+C_{Te}$ is essentially equal to the emitter junction capacitance C_{Te}, C_C is the collector junction capacitance, C_s is stray base-to-ground package capacitance, q is the electronic charge, k is Boltzmann's constant, and T is absolute temperature. Normal base diffusion capacitance C_D is virtually negligible at the low operating current levels of interest for micropower transistors. High frequency response must be achieved by reducing junction areas in order to minimize the barrier capacitances C_{Te} and C_C. The table indicates device D exhibits both the minimum barrier capacitances and the maximum gain-bandwidth product. For micropower applications, it is generally the best performing device of those listed.

A-C characteristics

$I_C = 10\ \mu a$ $V_{CE}=3.0$ v 25		$I_C = 100\ \mu a$ $V_{CE}=3.0$ v 25		$I_C = 1.0$ ma $V_{CE}=3.0$ v 25		$I_C = 10\ \mu a$ $V_{CE}=3.0$ v -50		$I_C = 10\ \mu a$ $V_{CE}=3.0$ v 100		$I_C = 10\ \mu a$ $V_{CE}=3.0$ v 25		$I_C = 100\ \mu a$ $V_{CE}=3.0$ v 25		$I_C = 1.0$ ma $V_{CE}=3.0$ v 25		$C_{Te}, V_{BE} = +0.3$ v $C_C, V_{CB} = -3.0$ v $C_D, I_C = 1.0$ ma 25		
h_{11e} (KΩ)	h_{21e}	h_{11e} (KΩ)	h_{21e}	h_{11e} (KΩ)	h_{21e}	h_{11e} (KΩ)	h_{21e}	h_{11e} (KΩ)	h_{21e}	f_{3db} (KC)	f_T (MC)	f_{3db} (KC)	f_T (MC)	f_{3db} (KC)	f_T (MC)	C_{TE} pf	C_C pf	C_D pf
184	71	26	95	3.2	120	73	37	350	107	24	1.7	150	14	935	112	16.7	6.2	27
200	76	38	141	6.4	230	46	22	460	146	42	3.2	184	26	532	123	9.0	2.4	35
335	125	65	248	10.6	390	172	91	600	188	30	3.7	118	29	286	112	5.0	3.0	43
217	78	30	110	4.0	140	66	33	435	134	90	7.0	595	65	4290	600	2.1	1.3	5
187	68	37	130	5.8	210	61	30	400	121	44	3.0	200	26	675	142	8.8	2.8	29
330	124	43	159	4.6	172	138	71	545	173	16	2.0	90	14	470	81	16.4	4.6	51

Typical characteristics	T (°C) =	$I_C = 10\ \mu a$, $V_{CE} = 3.0$ v			$I_C = 1.0$ ma, $V_{CE} = 3.0$ v
		-50	25	100	25
	h_{12e} =	2.3×10^{-4}	5×10^{-4}	1×10^{-3}	3.2×10^{-4}
	h_{22e} (ohms)$^{-1}$ =	0.013×10^{-6}	0.02×10^{-6}	0.032×10^{-6}	16×10^{-6}

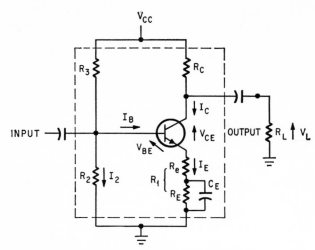

Common-emitter micropower amplifier schematic indicating circuit d-c currents and voltages, and peak a-c load voltage V_L.

the subscripts x and y refer to maximum and minimum temperatures, respectively.]

(a) From the schematic, write the d-c load line (DCLL) equation for the amplifier at the nominal operating temperature T_n. This equation is

$$V_{CC} = I_{Cn} R_C + V_{CEn} + V_{R1n} \qquad (1)$$

where

$$V_{R1n} = I_{En} R_1 \simeq I_{Cn} R_1$$

is the emitter d-c feedback voltage.

(b) Also, from the schematic write the a-c load line (ACLL) equation for the amplifier at T_n in terms of the quiescent collector current and voltage. This equation is

$$I_{Cn} = -(1/R_C + 1/R_L) V_{CEn} - V_{Ren} \qquad (2)$$

where

$$V_{Ren} = (I_{En} - I_o) R_e \simeq (I_{Cn} - I_o) R_e$$

is the emitter a-c feedback voltage. (I_o is the amount of offset from the transistor cut-off region.)

(c) In order to provide the specified peak a-c output voltage V_L at T_n for minimum d-c power consumption, the d-c operating point Q_n must bisect the ACLL in order for the output signal voltage swing to be a maximum. From the load line diagram the locus of ACLL midpoints can be shown to be

$$I_{Cn} - I_o = (1/R_C + 1/R_L) (V_{CEn} - V_o) - V_{Ren} \qquad (3)$$

with V_o the transistor saturation region offset and I_o the cut-off region offset.

(d) Since the quiescent collector voltage required to accommodate a peak output voltage V_L is

$$V_{CEn} = V_L + V_{Ren} + V_o \qquad (4)$$

simultaneous solution of equations (1), (3) and (4) yields the nominal collector current and the maximum allowable value of the collector resistance:

$$I_{Cn} = \frac{V_{CC} - V_L - V_{R1n} - V_{Ren} - V_o}{V_{CC} - 2V_L - V_{R1n} - V_{Ren} - V_o} \left(\frac{V_L}{R_L} + I_o \right) \qquad (5)$$

$$R_C = \frac{V_{CC} - 2V_L - V_{R1n} - V_{Ren} - V_o}{\dfrac{V_L}{R_L} + I_o} \qquad (6)$$

Given V_{R1n}, equations (5) and (6) define the smallest I_{Cn} and the largest R_C, respectively, that satisfy the initial design constraints on V_{CC}, R_L and V_L. This is advantageous since a small value of I_C decreases

viding amplifier designs to minimize these difficulties.

The initial constraints assumed in the design of the common-emitter broadband micropower amplifier shown schematically above are: (a) the amplifier supply voltage V_{CC} and operating temperature range $T_y \leqq T \leqq T_x$ are fixed; (b) the amplifier load impedance R_L, the peak a-c output voltage V_L, and the bandwidth f_{3db} are specified; (c) the d-c power consumption of the amplifier should be as small as possible.

Design procedure

Subject to the assumed initial constraints, the objectives of the design technique summarized below are to determine optimum values for the minimum and maximum temperature transistor quiescent collector current and voltage (I_{cy}, V_{cey}) and (I_{cx}, V_{cex}), as well as for the circuit resistances R_C, R_1, R_2 and R_3. [Note that throughout this article

The authors

James D. Meindl received a Ph.D. degree in electrical engineering from the Carnegie Institute of Technology in 1958. Prior to this he held positions at C.I.T. as a research assistant and at Westinghouse Research Laboratories and North American Aviation as a development engineer. He joined the Central Research Laboratories of the Westinghouse Electric Corp. in 1958 where he was engaged in advanced solid state circuit development. In 1959 he was called to active duty as a first lieutenant with the U.S. Army Electronics Research and Development Laboratories, Fort Monmouth, N.J., where he became engaged in microcircuit research. Following the completion of his military duty in 1961, Dr. Meindl remained with the Army laboratory where he is presently chief of the semiconductor and microelectronics branch. He is responsible for the development and application of a wide range of semiconductor devices and integrated circuits.

Russell A. Gilson joined the Electronics Research and Development Laboratories of the U.S. Army at Fort Monmouth in 1960. He has been engaged in microcircuit design techniques and is presently pursuing a master's degree at New York University. He obtained his bachelor's degree in engineering from the University of Wisconsin.

power dissipation P_D and a large value of R_C increases amplifier gain. The proper selection of V_{R1n} in equations (5) and (6) obviously constitutes a key point in the design.

A practical procedure for obtaining the d-c emitter feedback voltage V_{R1n} is to complete designs for several arbitrarily selected values of V_{R1n} and compare their over-all performance. The a-c emitter feedback voltage V_{Ren} and the saturation region offset V_o and cut-off region offset I_o should be judiciously selected (as zero in some cases) to satisfy the design constraints of particular applications. For instance, a major consideration in choosing I_o and V_o might be the acceptable limit of distortion for a particular design.

(e) From the load line diagram, it is evident that because the quiescent point bisects the ACLL at T_n, operating point drift will limit the output voltage swing to values less than the specified V_L when T does not equal T_n. A key feature of the present design theory lies in regulating the d-c operating point drift such that the amplifier can handle the desired a-c output voltage swings at the operating temperature limits ($K_y V_L$ at the minimum temperature T_y and $K_x V_L$ at the maximum temperature T_x with $0 < (K_y, K_x) < 1$). Furthermore, it is particularly important to insure that the already minimal dynamic range of a micropower amplifier is preserved in the face of worst case tolerances for both the transistor, the resistors and the supply voltage. From the diagram, it is apparent that the critical function of a worst case design technique for linear broadband micropower amplifiers is to insure that I_{Cy} will not be less than

$$I_{Cy\,(min)} = K_y V_L (1/R_{C\,(max)} + 1/R_L) + I_o \quad (7)$$

in order to provide an output voltage swing $K_y V_L$ at T_y and that V_{CEx} will not be less than

$$V_{CEx\,(min)} = K_x (V_L + V_{Ren}) + V_o \quad (8)$$

in order to provide an output voltage swing $K_x V_L$ at T_x.

(f) Employing worst case tolerances, the d-c output loop equation at T_y

$$V_{CEy} = V_{CC\,(min)} - I_{Cy\,(min)} (R_{1\,(max)} + R_{C\,(max)}) \quad (9)$$

together with $I_{Cy\,(min)}$ gives the operating point at T_y. The output loop d-c equation at T_x

$$I_{Cx} = (V_{CC\,(min)} - V_{CEx\,(min)}) / (R_{1\,(min)} + R_{C\,(max)}) \quad (10)$$

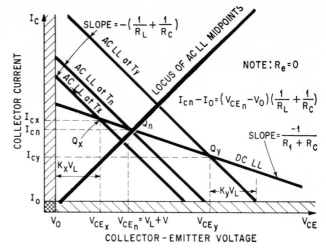

Load line diagram for common-emitter micropower amplifier.

gives the value of I_{Cx} which accompanies $V_{CEx\,(min)}$ at T_x. It is evident here that the selection of the factors K_y and K_x or the dynamic range constants of the amplifier effectively determines its d-c operating point stability or the temperature stability of the dynamic range. For the typical design constraints on the amplifiers described here $0.50 \leqq K_y$, $K_x \leqq 0.80$ is a useful range of values for K.

(g) The establishment of the transistor collector quiescent points at T_y and T_x in equations (8), (9) and (10) effectively defines the corresponding transistor base drive conditions. From the schematic (p 76) a solution of the four simultaneous worst case equations[1]

$$V_{CC\,(min)} = (I_{By\,(max)} + I_{2y}) R_{3\,(max)} + I_{2y} R_{2\,(min)} \quad (11)$$

and

$$0 = V_{BEy\,(max)} + I_{Ey} R_{1\,(max)} - I_{2y} R_{2\,(min)} \quad (12)$$

at T_y and

$$V_{CC\,(min)} = (I_{Bx\,(min)} + I_{2x}) R_{3\,(min)} + I_{2x} R_{2\,(max)} \quad (13)$$

and

$$0 = V_{BEx\,(min)} + I_{Ex} R_{1\,(min)} - I_{2x} R_{2\,(max)} \quad (14)$$

at T_x yields the maximum allowable values for R_2 and R_3, considering both worst case temperature and manufacturing tolerances for all circuit ele-

Octavius Pitzalis, Jr. specializes in microcircuit design techniques. He received his bachelor's degree from the University of Missouri in 1959 and is presently engaged in graduate study for a master's degree at New York University.

William F. Kiss is presently engaged in ultrahigh-frequency and very high frequency high-power transistor characterization for the semiconductor and microelectronics branch which he joined in 1959. Initial assignments were in characterization of switching transistors and uhf small-signal transistor evaluation. He received his electrical engineering degree from Drexel Institute of Technology and is presently doing graduate work at New York University.

ments, which will insure the specified output voltage swing at a minimum power consumption.

By its nature, this design technique yields a common emitter amplifier design which must comply with all initial constraints except the specified bandwidth. For the proper choice of V_{RIn}, the technique yields the maximum allowable values of R_C, R_2 and R_3 and thus minimizes the power dissipation in and the signal drain through these resistors. The design therefore exhibits the maximum power gain per unit of power consumption consistent with the specified supply voltage, operating temperature range, load impedance, dynamic range and element tolerances. Additional bandwidth can be achieved as required in the common emitter configuration by increasing the collector quiescent current.

In many cases a preferable alternative, which is far less costly in terms of power consumption although it requires more components, is to employ a cascode-circuit configuration. The salient features of the cascode stage and a comparison of its performance with that of the common emitter stage will be given in the second article of this series.

Reference

1. "Static and Dynamic Performance of Micropower Transistor Linear Amplifiers," R.A. Gilson, O. Pitzalis, W. Kiss, and J.D. Meindl; U.S. Army Electronics Research and Development Laboratories Tech Rep 2386 Fort Monmouth, N.J. Sept. 1963. (This material was presented in the Micropower Electronics lecture series of the AGARD of NATO in Paris, France; Malvern, England; Stuttgart, Germany; and Rome Italy, in June, 1963. It will be available soon in a book published by Pergamon Press and edited by E. Keonjian.)

Conventional-component version of common-emitter micropower transistor amplifier at top of chassis and multi-chip version at bottom.

Amplifier performance data

		1. Basic common-emitter amplifier		2. Feedback design		3. Worst case design		4. Cascode design	
Circuit constraints									
V_{CC}	(v)	3.0		3.0		3.0		4.0	
R_L, R_g	(K)	50, 50		50, 50		50, 50		50, 50	
V_L	(v)	0.3		0.3		0.3		0.3	
T_y, T_z	(°C)	−50, +100		−50, +100		−50, +100		−50, +100	
Circuit design									
V_{Rin}	(v)	1.0	—	1.0	—	1.6	—	0.6	—
V_{Ren}	(v)	0.00	—	0.03	—	0.00	—	0.00	—
V_o	(v)	0.3	—	0.3	—	0.3	—	0.00	—
I_o	(µa)	0.3	—	0.3	—	0.3	—	0.3	—
I_{Cn}	(µa)	8.02	—	8.02	—	10.1	—	7.75	—
R_C	(K)	175	—	175	—	79.4	—	206	—
$K = K_y = K_z$		0.6	—	0.6	—	0.5	—	0.5	—
Δ_R, Δ_V		0, 0	—	0, 0	—	0.10, 0	—	0, 0	—
R_1	(K)	125	—	125	—	159	—	77.4	—
R_4	(K)	0.0	—	3.89	—	0.0	—	0.0	—
R_2, R_4	(MEG)	2.77,	—	2.56,	—	5.66,	—	0.343,	1.63
R_3, R_3	(MEG)	2.54,	—	2.45,	—	2.60,	—	0.930,	1.44
Circuit performance		C	M	C	M	C	M	C	M
I_{Cy}	(µa)	4.93	4.90	4.93	4.90	5.02	5.04	4.03	4.1
V_{CBy}	(v)	1.52	1.50	1.54	1.60	1.69	1.67	1.85	1.9
I_{Cz}	(µa)	8.42	8.40	8.46	8.48	11.1	11.0	8.63	8.6
V_{CBz}	(v)	0.48	0.50	0.45	0.44	0.45	0.47	0.55	0.6
P_{Dz}	(µw)	27.1	27.0	27.3	27.9	34.7	34.5	52.9	52.8
A_{iy}	—	21.3	21.5	19.6	18.9	17.3	16.0	14.4	12.3
A_{iz}	—	63.2	60.0	50.0	49.2	56.8	54.0	33.2	30.7
A_{ry}	—	9.98	10.0	5.0	4.96	8.02	8.0	8.68	7.15
A_{vz}	—	10.2	10.3	5.06	5.00	10.6	10.0	10.9	10.3
G_y	(db)	23.3	23.0	19.9	19.7	21.4	21.0	21.0	19.4
G_z	(db)	28.1	27.9	25.0	24.0	27.8	27.3	25.6	25.0
R_{iy}	(K)	107	100	196	182	100	109	83.0	86.0
R_{iz}	(K)	311	290	493	482	269	249	152	149
R_{oy}	(K)	175	—	175	—	86	—	206	—
R_{oz}	(K)	175	—	175	—	86	—	206	—
$f_{1db_y}*$	(KC)	48.3	39.0	52.4	42.6	65	52.4	218	562
$f_{1db_z}*$	(KC)	10.1	9.9	12.5	12.2	17.4	17.0	110	82

* = Measured values corrected for stray circuit capacitance   C—calculated,   M—measured

How to design micropower transistor amplifiers: part 2

Commercially available transistors can be used to design
common-emitter and cascode micropower amplifiers

By J.D. Meindl, R. Gilson, O. Pitzalis and W. Kiss

U.S. Army Electronics Research and Development Laboratories, Fort Monmouth, N.J.

The salient characteristics of micropower transistors and an optimum design technique for their use in broadband common emitter micropower amplifiers were presented in the first article of this two-part series [Electronics, May 18, 1964, p. 73]. Now the problem of obtaining large amplifier bandwidths at microwatt power levels is discussed and the over all performance of both common-emitter

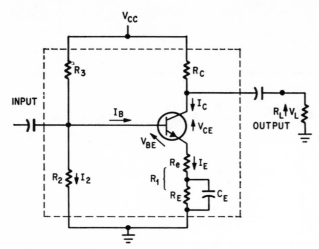

Common-emitter micropower amplifier operates from a three-volt supply with a load impedance of 50,000 ohms.

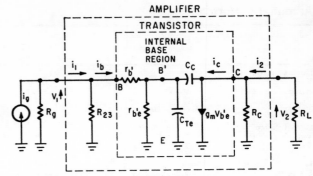

r_b' = BASE SPREADING RESISTANCE (CAN BE NEGLECTED IN MICROPOWER CIRCUITS)

$r_{b'e}$ = COMMON-EMITTER DIFFUSION RESISTANCE

C_{Te} = EMITTER JUNCTION CAPACITANCE

Small-signal a-c equivalent circuit of common-emitter micro amplifier incorporates the hybrid pi transistor equivalent circuit.

and cascode amplifiers, designed according to the procedure of the first article is examined.

The bandwidth of a common-emitter micropower amplifier can be exceeded significantly without loss of gain or increase in power consumption by means of a cascode circuit configuration (see below). A common-emitter broadband micropower amplifier operating from a three-volt supply with a load impedance of 50,000 ohms can provide a 0.18 v peak a-c load voltage over the temperature range $-50 \leq T \leq 100°C$ for a power drain of 25 microwatts and a power gain of 25 db. If the peak load voltage capability is reduced to 0.15 v, this amplifier can accept 10% worst-case tolerance margins on all circuit resistors. Depending on transistor barrier capacitances and stray circuit capacitances, amplifier bandwidth may vary from about 10 kc to 25 kc. Five times and larger increases are possible with the cascode circuit. Further extensions of bandwidth are readily possible for larger operating powers.

Amplifier a-c characteristics

The a-c equivalent circuit of the common-emitter broadband amplifier described in the first article is illustrated above at right. The transistor is represented by the familiar hybrid pi equivalent circuit. Under the noncritical assumption that R_g and $R_{23} >> r_{b'e}$ and $R_C >> R_L$, the current gain of the amplifier is

$$\frac{i_2}{i_1} \simeq \frac{h_{fe}}{1 + j\omega r_{b'e}\left[C_{Te} + \left(1 + h_{fe}\dfrac{R_L}{r_{fe}}\right)C_C\right]} \quad (1)$$

and the bandwidth is

$$f_{3db} \simeq \frac{1}{2\pi} \frac{1}{r_{b'e}\left[C_{Te} + \left(1 + h_{fe}\dfrac{R_L}{r_{b'e}}\right)C_C\right]} \quad (2)$$

Power dissipation, P_D, is given by the expression

$$\begin{aligned}P_D &= V_{CC}(I_E + I_2) \\ &= V_{CC}\left[I_E + \frac{V_{BE} + I_E R_1}{R_2}\right]\end{aligned} \quad (3)$$

Dividing this into the gain bandwidth product

$$G\omega_{3db} \simeq \frac{q}{kT} \frac{I_c}{C_c + C_{cs}} \frac{1}{1 + R_L/R_c} \quad (4)$$

gives a number that can be considered a figure of merit for micropower amplifiers. In virtually all instances, a major objective in designing a broadband micropower amplifier is to achieve maximum

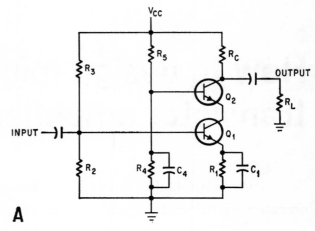

A

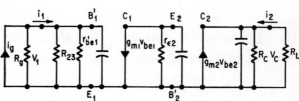

$r_{\epsilon 2}$ = COMMON-BASE DIFFUSION RESISTANCE OF Q_2

B

Cascode arrangement for micropower amplifier (A) and its a-c equivalent circuit (B) reduces the Miller effect limitation on bandwidth.

gain and a specified bandwidth for minimum power dissipation. Thus, the expression F. M. = $G\omega_{3db}/P_D$ defines a parameter whose relative magnitude is a useful indication of the quality of a given micropower amplifier design.

Equation 4 shows that the gain-bandwidth product of a common-emitter micropower amplifier can be improved by increasing the transistor collector current I_C (which increases power dissipation) and decreasing the transistor collector-to-base barrier capacitance C_C as well as the collector-to-base stray circuit capacitance C_{Cs}. Since C_C is usually of the order of 5 picofarads or less, the importance of minimizing the stray circuit capacitance C_{Cs} to maximize gain-bandwidth product is clear. It is evident from equation 1 that the usual Miller-effect capacitance

$(1 + h_{fe} R_L/r_{b'e}) C_C$

is an important limitation on micropower amplifier bandwidth. Frequently, the emitter junction capacitance C_{Te} is approximately equal to C_C for micropower transistors and the Miller-effect multiplier $1 + h_{fe} (R_L/r_{b'e})$, may be greater than 10 for a cascade of common-emitter stages.

A circuit found particularly effective in reducing the Miller-effect limitation on bandwidth is the cascode arrangement (bottom p 278). Again invoking the noncritical assumptions that R_g and $R_{23} \gg r_{b'e}$ and $R_C \gg R_L$, the current gain and bandwidth equations 1 and 2 for the common-emitter stage also apply to the cascode amplifier except that the Miller-effect multiplier

$$\left(1 + h_{fe} \frac{r_{b'e}/h_{fe}}{r_{b'e}} \right) \approx 2$$

in the case of the cascode circuit. This reduction

of the Miller-effect multiplier by a factor of five or more permits significantly larger bandwidths for essentially the same current and power gain and only a slight increase in power consumption compared with the common emitter amplifier. (In practical micropower circuits stray capacitances can severely degrade amplifier bandwidth if proper interconnection techniques are not employed.)

The optimum design of a cascode amplifier can be accomplished by following the general pattern outlined for the common-emitter stage in the first article of this series. The principal modification is the selection of the quiescent collector voltage for Q_1. This voltage may be small due to the low value of the load impedance for Q_1. The cascode configuration provides a building block which is as universally useful and flexible in its applications as the common-emitter stage. Both circuits require only a single power supply. The cascode configuration has inherently less undesired feedback than the common-emitter stage because there is no feedback capacitor for Q_2. In addition, the current and voltage gains for both circuits are virtually identical. There is no requirement for matched transistors in the cascode arrangement. Finally, of primary importance for micropower electronics is the capability of the cascode circuit to provide significantly larger bandwidths than the common-emitter stage for relatively small increases in power consumption. It should be kept in mind, however, that the cascode circuit requires more components than the basic common-emitter amplifier.

Amplifier performance

Detailed characteristics of four broadband micropower amplifiers designed according to the procedure in the first article are tabulated on p 277. The

---

Design example

To illustrate the application of the design procedure, the steps in the basic design given in column 1 (Table page 277) for the circuit on p. 278 are enumerated below: For convenience, the equations used in this example, which appeared in Part I of this series, are repeated first.

$$I_{Cn} = \frac{V_{CC} - V_L - V_{R1n} - V_{Ren} - V_o}{V_{CC} - 2V_L - V_{R1n} - V_{Ren} - V_o}$$

$$\left(\frac{V_L}{R_L} + I_o \right) \quad \text{(a)}$$

$$R_C = \frac{V_{CC} - 2V_L - V_{R1n} - V_{Ren} - V_o}{\dfrac{V_L}{R_L} + I_o} \quad \text{(b)}$$

$$I_{Cy(min)} = K_y V_L (1/R_{C(max)} + 1/R_L) + I_o \quad \text{(c)}$$
$$V_{CEy} = V_{CC(min)} - I_{Cy(min)}(R_{1(max)} + R_{C(max)}) \quad \text{(d)}$$
$$I_{Cz} = (V_{CC(min)} - V_{CEx(min)})/(R_{1(min)} + R_{C(max)}) \quad \text{(e)}$$
$$V_{CEx(min)} = K_x(V_L + V_{Ren}) + V_o \quad \text{(f)}$$
$$V_{CC(min)} = (I_{By(max)} + I_{2y})R_{3(max)} + I_{2y}R_{2(min)} \quad \text{(g)}$$
$$0 = V_{BEy(max)} + I_{Ey}R_{1(max)} - I_{2y}R_{2(min)} \quad \text{(h)}$$
$$V_{CC(min)} = (I_{Bx(min)} + I_{2x})R_{3(min)} + I_{2x}R_{2(max)} \quad \text{(i)}$$
$$0 = V_{BEx(min)} + I_{Ex}R_{1(min)} - I_{2x}R_{2(max)} \quad \text{(j)}$$

1. The assumed constraints are $V_{CC} = 3.0\ V$, $R_L = 50\ K$, $V_L = 0.3\ V$ and $-50°C\ T \le 100°C$.

2. Assume $K = K_x = K_y \le 0.6$ and $V_{R1n} = 1.0\ V$.

3. On the basis of the static collector characteristic curves for the transistor, select $V_o = 0.3\ V$ and $I_o = 0.3\ \mu A$.

4. From equations (a) and (b) compute $R_C = 175\ K$ and $I_{Cn} = 8.02$ microamperes.

5. From the relation $R_1 = V_{R1n}/I_{Cn}$ compute $R_1 = 125\ K$.

6. The lower ($I_{Cy} = 4.93$ microamperes, $V_{CEy} = 1.52\ V$) and upper ($I_{Cx} = 8.42$ microamperes, $V_{CEx} = 0.48\ V$) temperature quiescent points are computed from equations (c), (d), (e) and (f) respectively.

7. Corresponding to the operating points computed in step 6 obtain the transistor base current and base-emitter voltage at the extremes of the temperature range (I_{By}, V_{BEy}) and (I_{Bx}, V_{BEx}) from the transistor spec sheet.

8. Substituting these data in equations (g) through (j) and solving simultaneously yields

$$R_3 = \frac{V_{CC}[(I_{Ex} - I_{Ey})R_1 - (V_{BEy} - V_{BEx})]}{(V_{BEx} + I_{Ex}R_1)I_{By} - (V_{BEy} + I_{Ey}R_1)I_{Bx}}$$

and

$$R_2 = \frac{R_3(V_{BEx} + I_{Ex}R_1)}{(V_{CC} - I_{Bx}R_3 - V_{BEx} - I_{Ex}R_1)}$$

which may be used directly to compute $R_2 = 2.77$ megohms and $R_3 = 2.54$ megohms.

9. From standard formulas such as 1, 2 and 3, the gain, bandwidth and power consumption of the amplifier should be computed. Their values are listed in column 1.

10. At this point, it is advisable to repeat steps 4 through 9 for several different values of V_{R1n} near the original 1.0 V value. Thus the design yielding the maximum gain-bandwidth product per unit of power consumption is determined.

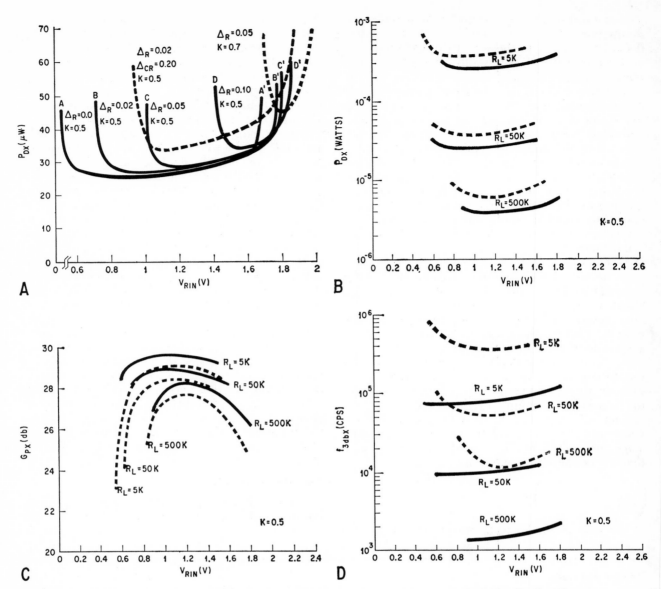

Power drain of circuit designed with a given resistor-tolerance margin can be minimized by adjusting the d-c emitter feedback voltage. V_{Rin} (A). Power drain of cascode amplifier (dashed curves) is less than twice the drain of the common-emitter amplifier (B), while there is less than 1 db difference in power gain between the two circuits (C). Key advantage of cascode stage over common-emitter amplifier is the increased bandwidth (D).

transistor used in these circuits is similar to the 2N2784A planar epitaxial transistor. The common emitter amplifier designs of columns 1, 2 and 3 assume a supply voltage $V_{CC} = 3v$, a load imped-ance $R_L = 50,000$ ohms, a required peak load volt-age swing $V_L = 0.3v$ and an operating temperature range $-50 = T_y \leq T \leq T_x = 100°C$. The initial constraints of the cascode amplifier of column 4 differ only in that the supply voltage $V_{CC} = 4v$.

The optimum emitter d-c feedback voltage V_{Rin}, determined by comparing the power consumption and gain of several trial designs per column, ranges between 0.6v and 1.6 v as indicated. Only the de-sign of column 2 employs a-c emitter feedback V_{Ren} which is selected as 10 percent of the peak load voltage swing, or 0.03v. The offset voltage which prevents saturation is $V_o = 0.3v$ for all designs except the cascode where, due to the common-base

output transistor, $V_o = 0$ is permissible. The offset current which prevents cutoff is $I_o = 0.3$ micro-ampere for all designs. The minimum load voltage swing permitted at the operating temperature lim-its of $T_y = -50°C$ and $T_x = 100°C$ is $KV_L = 0.18v$ for the designs of columns 1 and 2 and $KV_L = 0.15v$ for the designs of columns 3 and 4. K is considered the dynamic range constant of the am-plifier. Resistor and supply voltage tolerance mar-gins are taken as 0% for all cases except for the design of column 3 where worst case resistor toler-ances of 10% are assumed ($\Delta R = 0.1$).

The optimum values for the resistors R_C, R_1, R_2, R_3, R_4 and R_5 are listed at the bottom of the cir-cuit design portion of the table for each of the four amplifiers. The relatively small $R_C = 79,400$ ohms for the worst case design results from the larger V_{Rin} required to combat the 10% resistor tolerance margins. The larger $R_C = 206,000$ ohms for the cascode design results from the lack of necessity for an offset voltage (that is, $V_o = 0$) and the smaller optimum $V_{Rln} = 0.6v$ resulting from a supply voltage $V_{CC} = 4v$. The relatively large R_2 and R_3 values for the worst case design are a consequence of greater d-c feedback ($V_{Rln} = 1.6v$) and smaller limiting dynamic range ($KV_L = 0.15v$). The reduced d-c feedback of the cascode design ($V_{Rln} = 0.6v$) requires that R_2 and R_3 be relatively small for that circuit. A design example is provided in the panel on bottom of p 279.

Comparing designs

A comparison of the calculated and measured circuit performance indicated in the table on page 277, reveals reasonable agreement. The quiescent point (I_C, V_{CE}), the current, voltage and power gains, A_i, A_v and G respectively, the input and output impedances, R_i and R_o respectively, and the bandwidth f_{3db} of the amplifiers were measured and calculated at both of the operating temperature limits T_y and T_x. Considering the calculated performance of the basic amplifier of column 1, it is evident that over the operating temperature range: 1) collector current drifts from $I_{Cy} = 4.93$ microamperes to $I_{Cx} = 8.42$ microamperes; 2) collector voltage drifts from $V_{CEy} = 1.52v$ to $V_{CEx} = 0.48v$; 3) power drain at T_x is $P_{Dx} = 27.1$ microwatts; 4) current gain varies from $A_{iy} = 21.3$ to $A_{ix} = 63.2$; 5) voltage gain varies from $A_{vy} = 9.98$ to $A_{vx} = 10.2$; 6) power gain varies from $G_y = 23.3$ db to $G_x = 28.1$ db; 7) input impedance varies from $R_{iy} = 107,000$ ohms to $R_{ix} = 311K$; 8) output impedance is fixed at $R_o \cong R_C = 175,000$ ohms; and 9) bandwidth varies from $f_{3dby} = 48.3$ kc to $f_{3dbx} = 10.1$ kc.

Compared with this performance, 1) the feedback design exhibits expected small improvements in the temperature stability of gain, input impedance and bandwidth; 2) the worst case design displays a slight increase in power consumption, slight decreases in gain and input impedance and a slight increase in bandwidth; and 3) the cascode design shows a moderate increase in power consumption, a moderate gain reduction and a substantial increase in bandwidth.

The tabulated data shows that a linear broadband micropower amplifier can be designed to accept 10% worst-case tolerance margins on all circuit resistors. In the past considerable attention has been given to worst-case d-c design techniques for digital circuits. While the effects of component tolerances generally have been considered more severe in linear circuits, apparently, practical analytical techniques for worst case design of linear circuits are not in wide use.

In terms of the most senitive indicator of component tolerance margins, circuit power consumption, graph (A) displays the effects of resistor tolerances in linear micropower amplifiers designed according to the procedure outlined in part I.

The graph shows power consumption P_{Dx} of a common-emitter amplifier, similar to that of column 1 in the table (p 277) at a temperature of 100°C versus the nominal emitter d-c feedback voltage V_{Rln} for various worst-case resistor tolerance margins Δ_R constant-ratio resistor tolerance margins Δ_{CR} and dynamic range constants K. Curves AA', BB', CC', and DD' indicate that for worst-case resistor tolerance margins of 0%, 2%, 5% and 10% respectively, and a dynamic range constant $K = 0.5$ (the dynamic range at T_x and T_y is $KV_L = 0.5 V_L$) circuit power consumption can be held to acceptable amounts by increasing the minimum value of V_{Rln} and holding it below a nearly fixed maximum. The sharp minimum in curve DD' indicates an extremely narrow design range for 10 percent worst case resistor tolerances.

The colored curve with $K = 0.7$ illustrates the adverse effect of attempting to design for a dynamic temperature stability which is too demanding. This curve is comparable to the curve CC' ($K = 0.5$) except for the dynamic range constant.

The dashed curve illustrates the combined effects of a 2 percent worst case resistor tolerance combined with a 20% constant ratio tolerance in which all resistors are assumed to be off the design center by 20% in the same direction. This case occurs in the batch processing used to fabricate resistors in silicon integrated circuits and thin film circuits. Graph (A) indicates that given constant ratios, rather large (20 percent) absolute tolerance margins can be accepted by a linear circuit.

Graphs (B), (C) and (D) compare the critical performance features of power consumption P_{Dx}, power gain G_x and bandwidth f_{3dbx} at the maximum operating temperature T_x for a large number of common emitter and cascode circuit designs with load impedances extending from $R_L = 5 K$ to $R_L = 500,000$ ohms. The remaining circuit constraints are similar to those in the table on p 277. Graph (B) indicates that the power consumption (colored curves) of a cascode amplifier runs about twice that of a common emitter stage (black curves). Graph (C) indicates that there is less than 1db difference in power gain between the two circuits. Finally, (D) indicates that there is a five-to-ten-times increase in bandwidth for the cascode stage. In general, the results of (B), (C) and (D) show that a cascode stage is capable of delivering a significantly larger gain-bandwidth product per unit of power consumption than a common-emitter stage. This capability combined with the over all flexibility of the cascode configuration mark it as a strong candidate for a general purpose micropower amplifier stage.

It is evident that the principal obstacle to be overcome in the broader application of micropower transistors in portable military communications equipment is the limited gain-bandwidth product of micropower devices and circuits. In order to improve device and circuit frequency response, transistor junction capacitances, header capacitances and stray circuit capacitances must be reduced about an order of magnitude.

Saving Microcircuit Power With

replacing a resistance type between stages of a digital

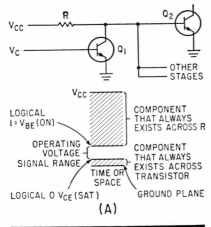

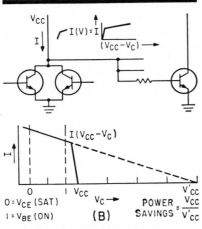

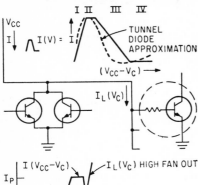

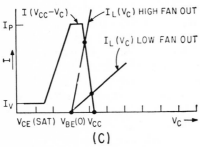

TYPICAL *resistance shunt coupling and potential distribution (A), shunt coupling with breakup characteristic and comparison with resistance-shunt coupling with identical performance (B), shunt coupling with a —R characteristic (C)—Fig.1*

TWO-TERMINAL coupling elements in conventional transistor logic stages are normally resistive, being elements with linear V-I characteristics. But typical coupling functions are often better served by nonlinear two-terminal V-I characteristics. Substantial reduction in static power dissipation is a principal advantage if coupling is achieved by the type of V-I characteristic produced by tunnel junctions.

LINEAR COUPLING—A familiar shunt configuration shown in Fig. 1A, uses a resistance coupling element, along with the potential distribution in the system. When Q_1 is nonconducting (logical 1 state), the coupling device and d-c supply are driving the load. The coupling device should have low resistance to accommodate large fan-out loading resulting from effects of other stages. When Q_1 is conducting (logical 0 state), the load current is zero (owing to the threshold nature of the load V-I characteristic). All the current supplied by the coupling device is shunted to ground, serving no useful functional purpose. The coupling device should have high resistance in this state. These requirements cannot be met by a linear coupling characteristic, and resistance shunt coupling is wasteful of power as indicated in Fig. 1A by the large unvarying and, useless component of voltage

found across the coupling resistor.

NONLINEAR COUPLING—Shunt coupling with a break-up (the dual of break-down) type of two-terminal characteristic is illustrated in Fig. 1B. As long as V_{cc} is higher than the voltage that exists at the collector node in the logical 1 state, the operation of this circuit will be identical to that of a resistance coupled stage having the same coupling device V-I locus in the signal voltage range. Power savings result because V_{cc} is much lower.

To reduce current drain in the logical 0 state below that of the logical 1 state, the shunt coupling characteristic must have a region exhibiting dynamic negative resistance. Such a characteristic, and its use in shunt coupling, is illustrated in Fig. 1C. This type of characteristic may be approximated by a tunnel-diode static V-I curve, resulting in a new digital logic scheme named tunnel diode transistor logic (tdtl). For the logical 1 state when $I_c = 0$ the load current and supply voltage should be such that the coupling device is in region I. For logical 0, the coupling device must be in region IV. The load characteristic is assumed to have an ideal threshold nature. The slope of $I_L(V_c)$ above the threshold voltage, $V_{BE}(0)$, depends on the number of fan-out load units. Note that load current decreases when fan-out is reduced.

NOVEL AND USEFUL

The workhorse role for the tunnel diode as nonlinear coupling between transistor logic stages employs some but not all of the td's attributes. Power dissipation, a major problem in microsystems, is reduced. Device characteristics may be relaxed compared with resistive coupling methods. System power supply voltage problems are found to be unique. Bistable operation, based upon td negative-resistance characteristic is not, however, utilized. Although switching action is regenerative (an advantage in itself) logic state control is through transistor action

---

Tunnel-Diode Coupling *Employed as a nonlinear coupling,*

circuit, the tunnel diode's characteristics can save considerable power

By H. C. JOSEPHS and J. T. MAUPIN, Honeywell Research Center, Hopkins, Minnesota

This is a favorable relationship since the drive to each stage is almost independent of fan-out. Therefore, the power dissipation per stage and the amount of transistor overdrive with accompanying saturation storage time are kept at their design optimum, regardless of changes in fan-out.

Static power dissipation is reduced compared to resistance coupling capable of the same maximum load current because V_{cc} is lower, load current tends to vary with number of load units and current in the logical 0 state is much lower.

A comparison can be made of static dissipation for linear and nonlinear shunt coupling based on typical characteristics available from discrete component devices. Since all the system operating power enters through paths provided by the shunt coupling elements, it is convenient to examine system power dissipation per shunt coupling element. This is the product of V_{cc} and the static current flowing in the coupling element. This is the same as the worst case power dissipation per stage if the fan-in and fan-out are equal.

STATIC PARAMETERS —

These are applicable to the logical 0 and 1 states, respectively, of a tdtl inverter stage, are shown in Fig. 2. Comparison is made with a resistance coupled stage capable of the same fan-out loading. A 3-volt supply is used with resistance coupling, as this seems to be a typical value for systems such as direct-current transistor logic, dctl. Current in the coupling element may be determined from the intersection of static characteristics. This leads to the comparison of static dissipation in the table. To simplify the comparison, it is assumed in Fig. 2B that all load units have the same threshold characteristics.

The transistor collector current in the on state in Fig. 2A is much lower with td coupling. Thus, the effect of an ohmic component in V_{CE} (SAT) is less, yielding a larger voltage switching transition and improved noise margins. However, propagation delay is also increased if parasitic capacitance loading at the collector node is a major factor in determining delay.

A GaAs tunnel diode type, with reasonable C/I_P values of approximately 10 pf per ma was chosen. Speed cannot be ignored in considering power requirements. A figure of merit for low duty cycle systems may be derived by taking the product of the average static power dissipation per stage times propagation delay per stage. This parameter will be called the delay-power product. Propagation delay per stage is the time interval between 50 percent points on the $V_c(t)$ waveforms in a chain of re-alistically operated inverter stages.

A chain of tdtl stages has been operated experimentally, using type XA653 GaAs tunnel diodes and type 2N744 transistors. Data on propagation delay and delay-power product are compared with resistance coupling in Fig. 3.

WAVEFORMS —

Experimentally observed waveforms at collector nodes are shown in Fig. 3C. Switching action is regenerative during the transition through the $-R$ portion of the td characteristic. The regenerative effect is best seen in the exponentially rising turn-off transient. Once the stage is driven into the $-R$ region, from either direction, it switches of its own volition, and the waveform is independent of the number of stages through which a logical decision

AUTHORS *J. T. Maupin (left) and H. C. Josephs (right) work up schematic circuit diagram for a tunnel-diode-coupled logic circuit*

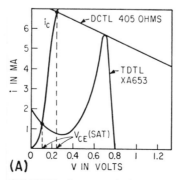

(A)

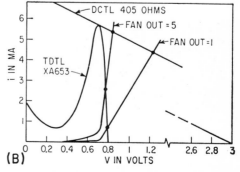

(B)

STATIC *characteristics of dctl and tdtl in logical 0 state (A) and the logical 1 state (B)—Fig. 2*

has been propagated. The long, slow portion of the turn-off transient corresponds to the valley current region of the td characteristic. The rate of transition through this region is controlled by the C_{TD}/I_v ratio, and this is the major factor contributing to propagation delay. Ideally, a coupling characteristic would be preferred in which the $-R$ portion of the total voltage transition is larger than in the example discussed. Total switching action in this type of stage is extremely complex.

A possible scheme for constructing the tunnel diode and transistor in integrated form is shown in Fig. 4A. This inverter can be the basic building block for a complete tdtl system. Gating would normally be accomplished by paralleling transistor collectors as in the dctl NOR gate. For example, a tdtl half-adder is shown schematically in Fig. 4B.

CURRENT HOGGING—A logic system constructed using tdtl gates

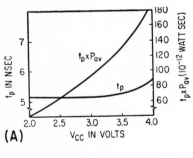

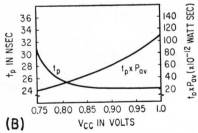

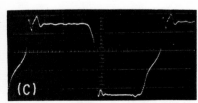

PROPAGATION *delay and delay-power product for dctl (A) and tdtl (B). Regenerative switching action in tdtl 3-stage ring oscillator collector voltage waveform (C) when horizontal is 20 nsec per division and vertical 0.2 v per division* —Fig. 3

will be less susceptible to the familiar current hogging problem of dctl. The problem is illustrated in Fig. 5 for worst-case conditions with a fan-out equal to N in both dctl and tdtl. For tdtl, the resistor $R_c \approx V_P/I_P$ is the tunnel diode resistance in region I. The transistor input characteristics are approximated by a threshold voltage V_{BE} (0) having linear series resistance R_B. An overscored symbol means that the parameter symbolized has its maximum permissible value under worst-case conditions, while an underscore means it has its minimum value. From the requirement that I_B must be large enough to provide a certain minimum overdrive ratio, $D = h_{FE} \ \underline{I_B}/\overline{I_c}$, an expression is obtained for the maximum permissible spread in transistor input threshold voltages.

$$\Delta \overline{V_{BE}} (0) = \overline{V_{BE}} \ (0) - \underline{V_{BE}} (0) \leqq$$

$$\frac{\Delta V_C - [\rho R_B + R_c + (N-1) \ \overline{\rho R_c}] \ I_B}{1 + (N-1) \ \overline{R_c}/R_B} \quad (1)$$

where $\Delta V_C = V_{CC} - \overline{V_{BE}} \ (0)$ and
$\rho = \overline{R_C}/\underline{R_C} = R_B/\underline{R_B}$.

This must be large enough to accommodate voltage differences owing to production variabilities, differences in temperature within the system, and noise.

As an experimental verification of Eq. 1, the circuit of Fig. 5B was constructed. For the parameters used in the experiment, the equation predicts failure at ΔV_{BE} (0) = 34 mv. In the experiment, Q_3 failed to operate when the oven temperature was raised 16 C. Since dV_{BE} (0)$/dT \approx 2$ mv per deg C, the agreement is excellent. The collector resistors were then replaced by tunnel diodes and the experiment was repeated. This time Q_3 failed to operate when the oven temperature was raised 57 C. Equation 1 predicts failure when ΔV_{BE} (0) = 112 mv, so the agreement is good.

On the debit side, tdtl is sensitive to systematic changes in the difference $V_{CC} - V_{BE}$ (0). This difference must lie in the range given by Eq. 2 if all load characteristics are assumed equal.

$$\frac{I_P}{h_{FE}} \ (NR_I + R_B) < V_{CC} - V_{BE} \ (0) <$$

$$\frac{I_P}{N} \ (NR_I + R_B) \quad (2)$$

where $1/R_I$ = slope of coupling characteristic in region I
$1/R_B$ = slope of input characteristic above $\overline{V}_{BE}$ (0)
N = fan-out
I_P = peak current of coupling characteristic

This is not a severe limitation if the supply voltage is also made sensitive to the system temperature, so that $V_{CC}-V_{BE}$ (0) remains constant.

NONLINEAR COUPLING—Sensitivity to $V_{CC}-V_{BE}$ (0) may also be improved if the transistor input is modified to include a series connected break-up characteristic, as illustrated in Fig. 6A. It is possible to approach this type of characteristic with a tunnel diode or backward diode having I_P/I_v approaching unity. The combination of negative resistance shunt coupling and break-up characteristic series coupling is illustrated in Fig. 6B. If the intersection of $I(V_{CC}-V_C)$ and $I_L(V_C)$ always occurs in the constant current region of the latter, the logical 1 state is insensitive to $V_{CC}-V_{BE}$ (0). Also, current hogging cannot occur.

There are two general ways to combat current hogging. One method is to reduce the effective coupling resistance R_c so the group of driven transistors is fed from a more nearly perfect voltage source. When the currents are not limited, there can be no problem with unequal sharing. This cannot be accomplished in dctl without excessive power waste. The tdtl, however, accomplishes this with a reduction in power, through the nonlinear tunnel diode characteristic. The coupling resistance in the operating range of importance is lower by a factor of 50 to 100 than that commonly used in dctl.

The other method is to increase the base resistance so each individual transistor is driven from a more nearly perfect current source. Again there can be no problem with unequal current sharing if the current to each load is fixed. This has adverse effects on switching speed in both dctl and tdtl. Furthermore, it cannot be accomplished in tdtl without an increase in supply voltage and a corresponding increase in power dissipation. It cannot be carried far in either system in integrated form without isolating the base resistor.

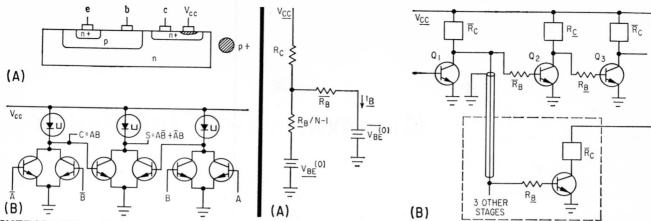

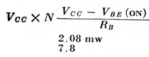

(A)

INTEGRATED *tdtl inverter (A)
and tdtl half adder (B)—Fig. 4*

(A)   **(B)**

WORST-CASE *current hogging equivalent circuit for dctl and tdtl (A)
and experiment for susceptibility to current hogging and permissible
spread in $V_{BE}(0)$ (B)—Fig. 5*

STATIC POWER DISSIPATION COMPARISON—TABLE

	Logical 0 State $V_C = V_{CE}(\text{SAT})$ $I_L = 0$	Logical 1 State $V_C = V_{BE}(\text{ON})$ $I_C = 0$
Resistance Coupling		
Approx. Formula	$V_{CC} \times \dfrac{V_{CC} - V_{CE}(\text{SAT})}{R_L}$	$V_{CC} \times \dfrac{V_{CC} - V_{BE}(\text{ON})}{R_L}$
From Fig. 2	20.4 mw	16.1 mw for $N = 5$
TD Coupling		
Approx. Formula	$V_{CC} \times I_V$	$V_{CC} \times N \dfrac{V_{CC} - V_{BE}(\text{ON})}{R_B}$
From Fig. 2	0.96 mw	2.08 mw
Reduction Factor	21.2	7.8

TDCL—The ideal situation of using a low resistance to couple the circuit to the power supply and a high resistance to couple stages together can be approached through the use of two tunnel diodes per stage as shown in Fig. 6C. This form is termed tunnel diode coupled logic (tdcl). A possible integrated form of a tdcl inverter is shown in Fig. 6D. Gating would normally be performed in the same manner as dctl and tdtl.

In Fig. 6C, D_1 is the ordinary tdtl tunnel diode with its n-region integral with the collector. Unit D_2 is a low current tunnel diode and could presumably be constructed in the base region in the manner shown in Fig. 6D. Both tunnel diodes should have low peak-to-valley current ratios.

The static requirements for this combination can easily be derived. The composite input characteristic of the transistor D_2 combination is shown in Fig. 6E, superimposed on the D_1 characteristics. The voltage V_f is the voltage at which the D_2 current in the diffusion region is equal to the D_2 peak tunneling current. From Fig. 6E are obtained

$$M < I_{V1}/\overline{I_{P2}}$$
$$I_{V2} \geqq \overline{I_{P1}}/h_{FE}$$
$$2\overline{V_\rho} + \overline{V_{BE}(0)} < V_{CC} < \underline{V_{BE}(0)} + \underline{V_f}$$

When the oven experiment was repeated using a tdcl circuit, Q_3 continued to operate with the supply voltage anywhere between 0.75 and 1.6 volts even when the oven temperature was raised to 200 C. At this temperature the transmission line carrying the signals into the oven failed, so the experiment was terminated.

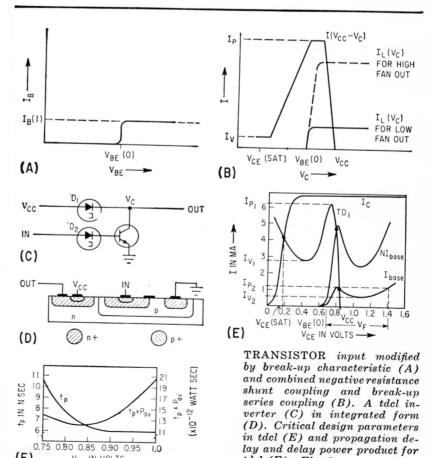

TRANSISTOR *input modified by break-up characteristic (A) and combined negative resistance shunt coupling and break-up series coupling (B). A tdcl inverter (C) in integrated form (D). Critical design parameters in tdcl (E) and propagation delay and delay power product for tdcl (F)—Fig. 6*

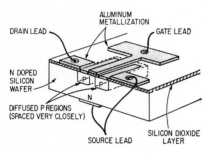

STILL *in design stage at CBS, 19-nanowatt free-running vibrator, is yet to be built—Fig. 1*

AROUND THE CORNER *device—the insulated gate field effect semiconductor—can be produced with n-type as well as p-type structures—Fig. 2*

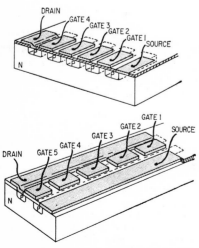

ARRAYS *of insulated-gate field effect semiconductors point to nanowatt memories with 2,500 elements packed in one-inch square wafers—Fig. 3*

Micropower Goes International

NATO talks hardware, suggests candidates for future equipment

PARIS—NATO's Micropower road Show (ELECTRONICS, p 38, June 28) has continued on to engineering audiences in Malvern England, Stuttgart and Rome. Talks analyzed basic requirements for micropower devices and also stressed practical hardware—existing and imminent.

A. W. Lo of Princeton and IBM looked beyond the polar transistor, and listed the following candidates for succeeding generations of micropower equipment:

• Thin-film cryrotrons. They consume no power except when switching, and switching power can be held very low for a cryrotron on a superconducting substrate; however, refrigeration presents a problem.

• Square loop magnetics. Although they require circuit artifices to obtain directivity of signal flow, they have distinct advantage of storage.

• Parametric phase-locked oscillators. They operate in majority logic and therefore reasonable variations in circuit parameters are not disturbing as long as the variations are uniform among individual components. Also, the system is immune to noise.

Thin-film magnetics or low-loss variable-capicitance diodes point to practical micropower in the very near future.

TECHNIQUES—European engineers also learned about CBS techniques for depositing thin-film passive elements right on wafer, company's nanowatt linear vibrators and a free-running multivibrator (Fig. 1) recently designed by CBS.

Fairchild's G. E. Moore told European designers that technology of the insulated gate field effect semiconductor (Fig. 2) has been advanced enough to produce n-type as well as p-type structures. Moore presented diagrams of arrays that have as many as 2,500 elements packed on a wafer 1-inch on a side (Fig. 3).

A. W. Lo of Princeton University and IBM showed a universal transistor logic circuit, Fig. 4, that uses base resistors to even out distribution of base current to the driven transistors.

At first glance, this circuit seems an unlikely candidate for optimum low-power operation. But Lo explained the base resistances were so low, compared to the collector resistance, that the circuit acts more like direct-coupled transistor logic than transistor-resistor logic.

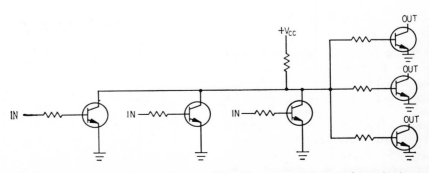

UNIVERSAL *transistor logic acts like direct-coupled transistor logic—Fig. 4*

Chapter 14

CRYOGENIC CIRCUITS

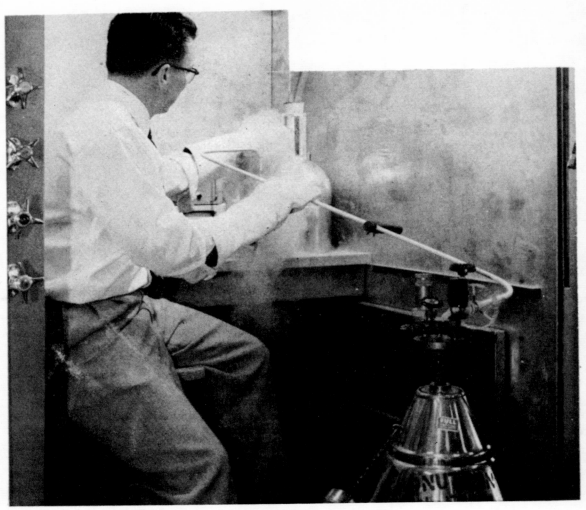

AUTHOR *Lambert filling a nitrogen jacketed cryostat with nitrogen*

The Cryosar: Promising Element For Tomorrow's Computers

A recent cryogenic development, the cryosar operates by the impact ionization of germanium at liquid helium temperatures. Its outstanding features are low element cost, low power dissipation and simplicity of construction

By L. M. LAMBERT and J. E. McATEER,
Research Laboratories,
Aeronutronic Division of Ford Motor Company,
Newport Beach, California

DATA PROCESSING is becoming more important as experimental knowledge of the physical world increases, as industrial and military facilities increase productivity and efficiency, and as the ever-expanding volume of the written word accumulates almost geometrically. To cope with these problems, increased effort has been expended toward systems that are faster, that are smaller in physical size, that have larger capacities and that have better input-output facilities. The cryosar has been investigated

PARAMETER DEFINITIONS

V_p — Peak or breakdown voltage of the compensated cryosar

V_s — Sustaining voltage or voltage after breakdown of the compensated cryosar

I_p — Current at the peak or breakdown point of the compensated cryosar

I_s — Sustaining current just after breakdown of the compensated cryosar

V_b — Breakdown voltage of the uncompensated cryosar

I_b — Current just after breakdown of the uncompensated cryosar

V_a — Voltage between storage cryosar and selection cryosar of Fig. 2A

V_c — Cryosar supply voltage in Fig. 2A

V_{int} — Interrogation voltage. Applied in order to read out information stored in cryosar

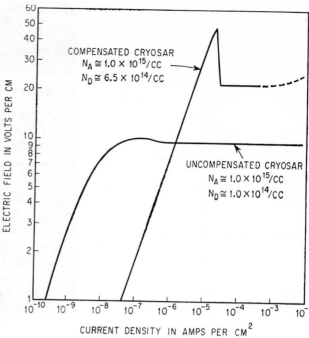

GRAPHS *of electric field versus current density in a typical uncompensated cryosar and compensated cryosar. N_A and N_D refer to number of acceptor or donor atoms, respectively*—Fig. 1

to evaluate its potential as a new device for faster, smaller, and larger-capacity digital systems.

Cryogenic systems of any type must compete with standard systems operating at essentially room temperature. To be practical, the cryogenic system must have something to offer that the standard systems does not. Present systems fail to provide:

(1) Adequate device characteristics to permit low-power (for example, one-microwatt) and high-speed (such as 100 Mc) operation, so that high-density packaging techniques can be fully utilized.

(2) Simple automatic or semi-automatic means of assembling high-component-count circuits. Even in principle, the solution to this problem is difficult to visualize because of the critical constructions involved in the various devices used.

(3) High enough reliability in the active devices; however, significant gains in this area are now being made through surface passivation techniques.

(4) Low enough cost in all phases so that it is economical to throw away faulty circuits or even subsystems.

(5) Means of engineering large systems, since high-component-count systems utilizing even moderately high-density packaging techniques and operating in the low megacycle region are difficult to assemble because of circuit noise cou-

pling and ground potential gradients.

It would be instructive to see whether the cryosar is able to make contributions to the solution of some of the present problems in these five areas. The categories may be examined in order for ease of comparison:

(1) The nature of the device phenomena often places bounds on the power capabilities of a device. By proper design, the breakdown current of the cryosar can be smaller than one microampere, with the corresponding sustaining voltage as low as a few tenths of a volt. One microwatt operating power is not a lower bound, but appears to be a reasonable value of power dissipation. The speed of switching at these low powers will probably be less than 100 Mc, but nevertheless should be in the megacycle region.

(2) Because of the simplicity of construction of the cryosar (essentially two contacts on a germanium wafer) important innovations in circuit assembly would be possible. The wafer itself could form the substrate for circuit construction. Multilayer interconnections may be possible using present evaporation technology.

(3) Since the impact ionization phenomenon used in the cryosar is a bulk phenomenon, the device is extremely reliable. Surface passivation and other precautions are not required, because surface proper-

ties are not that important.

(4) The cost of the unassembled cryosar device is essentially the cost of single-crystal germanium. It is difficult to visualize cheaper devices, since no individual yield problems are involved. In addition, if modern evaporation and masking techniques are employed, the cryosar circuitry would still be extremely cheap, and replacement would appear more feasible than repair of subsystems. The film deposition is noncritical; it is just a convenient way to put on ohmic contacts. If the films are thicker than about 3,000 A, they are suitable for ohmic contacts. Unlike the cryotron, the films serve no function other than for contacts and therefore impurities, structure and other parameters have no meaning, whereas they are important to cryotron fabrication.

(5) It seems reasonable that if ground planes of lead (which is superconducting at liquid helium temperatures) are used in cryosar systems, perfect shielding and ideal ground planes can at last be realized.

In addition, since the cryosar is a majority carrier device, radiation damage should be less than with other existing semiconductor devices. For space exploration or high-radiation environment systems, this may well be an important factor.

Other cryogenic devices, such as the cryotron, also offer some

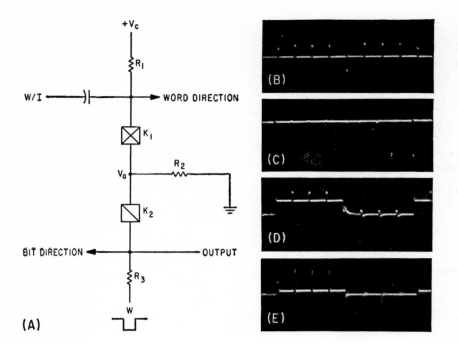

DOUBLE CRYOSAR *storage cell (A) and its waveshapes at various points: W/I (B); W (C); V(R_2) (D); output (E). Horizontal scale is 4 μsec per cm; vertical is 0.5 v per cm in (B) to (D), 0.1 v per cm in (E)—Fig. 2*

generation of a large number of free carriers by impact ionization of un-ionized impurity atoms. The finite conductance prior to breakdown is of interest, and for moderate concentrations of a single impurity type (for example, donor or acceptor atoms less than 10^{16} atoms per cubic centimeter) it appears to be due, at least in part, to the mobility of thermally generated electrons or holes. The pre-breakdown mobility is governed by the scattering of the free carriers by the neutral and thermally ionized impurity atoms. (Intrinsic generation of carriers is of course completely negligible.) A formula for the mobility due to scattering by ionized impurity atoms has been proposed by Conwell and Weisskopf[12-14] and appears to be approximated to a reasonable degree by considering only the Rutherford scattering due to the coulomb interaction of the carrier and the impurity center and also by considering the scattering potential caused by strains in the crystal lattice because of the presence of the charged impurity atom in a substitutional site. This latter scattering mechanism is essentially a discontinuity in the wave transmission properties of the periodic crystal structure.

Erginsoy[15] has approximated the effect of the neutral impurity atom by analogy with the scattering of slow electrons by hydrogen atoms.

The cryosar of most interest, from the standpoint of device possibilities is the two-impurity or the heavily compensated cryosar. The presence of compensating impurity atoms cause the voltage-versus-log current characteristics to appear as shown in Fig. 1. The considerations concerning neutral and ionized impurity scattering are still valid in this case. However, the ionized impurities are now the entire population of compensation atoms, plus those majority atoms which gave up their electrons (for example, in *n*-type material) to the acceptors, plus those donors which

advantages in these categories. However, the cryotron is critically dependent on temperature for its operation (typically ±0.1 K). Since localized heating is inevitable in a practical digital system, this presents a grave problem and possibly a limitation in the speed of the device since the thermal conductivity of liquid helium is about that of air at room temperature. Temperature is not a critical control parameter with cryosars: ±2 deg K is satisfactory for most applications, for which operational temperature is about 4.2 deg K.

IMPACT IONIZATION — Impact ionization of germanium at liquid helium temperatures has been investigated as a physical phenomenon by many workers.[1-5] The negative resistance process and device possibilities were first investigated by Rediker and McWhorter[6-8] who assigned to the device the name *cryosar*. *Cryo* pertains to the low-temperature environment involved in the device's operation. *Sar* is made up of the initial letters *s* for the switching, *a* for the avalanche, and *r* for the recombination processes. In short, the device switches ON by avalanche or ionization, and switches OFF by recombination of the free carriers. The avalanche process is an impact-ionization process whereby electrons, for example, in an *n*-type material, are accelerated to high enough energies

by the applied electric field so that when they collide with an un-ionized impurity atom, the impurity atom is then ionized, and its carrier is released to be accelerated and to ionize even more impurity atoms. The low-temperature environment of the cryosar is necessary to ensure that un-ionized impurity atoms exist in the semiconductor. The low temperature also permits the ionization to occur at lower electric fields because of the lower losses to the lattice. Electric fields of about a volt per centimeter are sufficient to ionize germanium at helium temperature. In a sense, the semiconductor crystal lattice at this temperature is a lossless waveguide for the propagating electron wave, except for the neutral and ionized impurity atoms and to a lesser extent, except for the dislocation and imperfections in the crystal lattice. This latter scattering mechanism has been estimated by Dexter and Seitz[9] and is generally regarded as negligible in high-quality single crystals of silicon and germanium.

The impact ionization of single-crystal germanium containing a single-impurity type has been investigated by several workers since Hung and Gliesman published their findings of low temperature anomalies in Hall coefficient and resistivities in 1950.[10, 11] A typical plot of field-versus-log current is as shown[2] in Fig. 1. The sudden change in conductivity is due to the

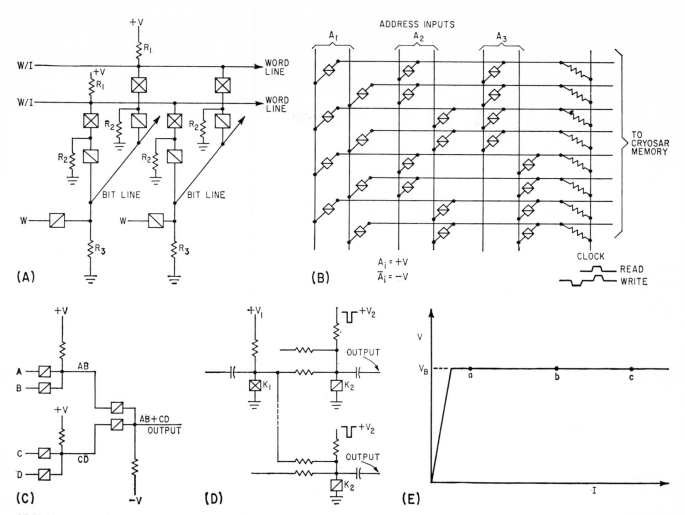

CRYOSAR CIRCUITS: *memory (A); decoder (B);* AND-OR *gate (C); pulse-type logic (D). Graph of uncompensated cryosar operation for pulse-type logic circuit (E)—Fig. 3*

provide thermally activated electrons for the conduction band. The remaining neutral-impurity atoms are those donor atoms which have not participated in either of the above donor-ionization processes. Because of the presence of the compensating atom, however, another pre-breakdown conduction process is in evidence. This conduction mechanism appears to be due to the finite probability of a carrier tunneling from an occupied or unionized impurity atom to an equivalent unoccupied or ionized impurity atom. This conduction process differs from the normal conduction process of thermally generated carriers in that it does not occur in the conduction or valence bands as is normal for n or p semiconductors, respectively. A compensating impurity is necessary to this phenomenon in order to empty the donor atom of its electron and thereby ionize it. The electron of the unionized donor then has a vacant site

to which it can tunnel. The probability of charge transfer within the impurity level increases rapidly with impurity concentration. At higher doping, concentrations greater than 10^{16} atoms per cubic centimeter in germanium, a different impurity conduction process occurs which does not require compensation. At very high impurity densities, the overlap of the wave functions of adjacent impurities is so strong that the carriers are no longer localized, and an impurity band is formed in which conduction can readily occur in a manner comparable to a metal. This second mechanism is not of present interest.

As the applied field is increased, the generation of carriers by impact ionization occurs; however, the breakdown field and the sustaining field no longer coincide in the heavily compensated case, the sustaining field being decidedly smaller. Such a situation can be recognized as

negative resistance. The origin of this negative resistance as suggested by McWhorter[16] and investigated by Callaway and Cummings[17] appears to be due to a loss mechanism analogous to scattering from an ionized hydrogen molecule, H_2^+. Suppose, for example, that a pair of donor atoms in an n-type material are located adjacent to each other as well as in the vicinity of an acceptor impurity atom. Since the acceptor will certainly be ionized by capturing one of the two electrons associated with the two donor atoms, this leaves two donor atoms with one electron in addition to the newly ionized acceptor atom. Now if the donor atoms are properly spaced in their substantial lattice sites, the energy situation will be similar to that of an ionized hydrogen molecule, H_2^+. This atomic configuration presents itself to conduction carriers as an additional inelastic scattering mechanism which absorbs energy, as do the phonons, by being excited from the symmetric to antisymmetric state. The calculations of this loss mechanism agree favorably with experiment. It is necessary therefore that a larger electric field be provided to accelerate the conduction carrier to high enough energies to overcome this additional loss mechanism and to ionize the un-ionized impurity atoms by collision. Once the breakdown occurs, and therefore essentially all impurity atoms are ionized, the H_2^+ ion disappears and becomes just two ionized donor atoms. The field necessary to sustain this breakdown should be essentially the same as that required in an uncompensated material, where the proper consideration is given to the fact that the total number of ionized impurity scatterers is now the sum of the two impurity types.

CRYOSAR CIRCUITS—The very low operating currents and voltages of the cryosar element offer very intriguing possibilities for low power, large capacity storage systems.

Because the cryosar is a two-terminal device and has such a low resistance in the ON condition, the problem of coupling to the element on a system basis becomes quite severe. Johnston's[18] approach to the solution of this problem was to fabricate a "compound" cryosar which essentially is a compensated and uncompensated cryosar in series. This gave rise to a two-terminal device having a double break and provided some isolation from element to element on a system basis.

Capacitive and electromagnetic coupling schemes were investigated and found unattractive for various reasons. The storage cell to be described, while somewhat similar to Johnston's, has several important differences.

The basic cell is shown in Fig. 2A. Component K_1 is a compensated cryosar while K_2 is an uncompensated cryosar. If the cell contains a one, K_1 is in the ON condition and K_2 is in the OFF, or high-impedance state. The ON current that flows through K_1 produces a voltage across R_2 which is slightly less than the breakdown voltage of K_2. To read the information, a positive pulse is applied to the W/I (Write/Interrogate) terminal. Since K_1 is

in the ON condition, the voltage will appear across R_2, causing K_2 to break down, and an output to appear across R_3. The amplitude of the voltage is a function of the dynamic resistance of K_1 and K_2 and the bias point of K_2 with K_1 in the ON state. The signal which appears on the output is a positive pulse; therefore, all other K_2 cryosars in the bit direction have the voltage across them reduced if the cell is in the one state. If the other cells are in the zero state, the output is not large enough to break down K_2; therefore, all K_2 elements in the bit direction will remain in their high-impedance (several megohms) state, and good isolation is achieved.

In the zero state, K_1 is OFF and the interrogate pulse is insufficient to break it down, therefore no output will appear across R_3.

Writing is accomplished by a two-pulse write cycle that consists of a negative pulse on the W/I line which clears all cells to zero. The ones are then written in by a positive pulse on the W/I line (equal to the interrogate pulse) and a negative pulse on the W line. The amplitude of the negative pulse is such that when it is in coincidence with the positive write pulse, both K_1 and K_2 are in their low-impedance state. When the pulses are removed, K_1 remains ON (low-impedance) while K_2 returns to its high-impedance (OFF) state.

Resistor R_1 is small enough so that the voltage drop across it is negligible though not small enough to unduly load the W/I driver.

Figures 2B through 2E show the waveshapes obtained with an experimental double-cryosar storage cell. The cryosars had the following characteristics: For K_1, $V_p = 1.35$ v, $V_s = 0.6$ v, $I_p = 1.2$ μa. For K_2, $V_b = 0.52$ v, $I_b = 0.8$ μa, and $R_{off} \approx$ 2 megohms.

The cryosars were those used for obtaining characteristics and had large contact areas, and hence fairly large capacities; they do not represent the optimum design. From the waveshape it can be seen that with an interrogate signal of 350 mv that the ONE output is approximately 150 mv and the signal-to-noise ratio is about 5. Most of the noise is attributed to capacitive feedthrough and pickup in the lines into the helium bath. It should be possible to improve this ratio with smaller

contact size and good packaging techniques.

The storage cell described is, as mentioned, not optimum. The following design is based upon planar cryosars which appear to be obtainable and have the following characteristics:

For K_1: $V_p = 0.3$ v, $V_s = 0.15$ v, $I_p < 0.5$ μa, $I_s < 1$ μa, and $R_{on} \approx 0$.

For K_2: $V_b = 0.1$ v, $I_b < 0.1$ μa, $R_{off} > 2$ megohms, and $R_{on} \approx 0$.

Should it prove unfeasible to use planar cryosars, then the bulk-type cryosar would be used. The only difference in the system would be that the voltages used would be higher. Therefore, more power would be consumed.

Using the above parameters and referring to Fig. 2A, assume $I_{on} = 2$ μa. Let $V_a = 0.09$ v when K_1 is on. Therefore, $R_2 = V_a/I_{on} = 0.09$ v/2 μa = 45,000 ohms.

If it is assumed that R_1 is small so that the voltage drop across it is negligible, then $V_c = V_a + V_s = 0.09 + 0.15 = 0.24$ v. Then the interrogate signal is given by $V_{int} \leq V_p - V_c = 0.06$ v. Let $V_{int} = 50$ mv.

If it is assumed that the output current through R_3 is to be limited to 2 μa then $R_3 = V_{out}/I_{out}$.

The output voltage will be given by $V_{out} = V_{int} - circuit losses$, which in the idealized case is given by $V_{out} = V_{int} - (V_b - V_a)$, so that $V_{out} = 0.04$ v, and therefore, $R_3 = 20,000$ ohms.

Because both cryosars are in their high-impedance region when the cell is in the zero state, the noise signal will be determined by the capacity of the cryosars. If a S/N ratio of ten is desired, the capacitance allowable per element is found to be 0.05 Δt pf, where Δt is the rise time of the interrogate pulse in nanoseconds. Even for fast rise times it is easy to achieve capacities well below the allowable.

Figure 3A shows the connection in more detail. The cryosar on the W line serves as an isolator. The amplitude of the W pulse necessary for writing a one can easily be calculated and is found to be 0.21 v if the isolator cryosar has the same characteristics as the previous uncompensated cryosar.

It can be seen from Fig. 3A that uninterrogated storage cells on the bit line present a high impedance to the output signal on the bit line, since the uncompensated cryosar is always in its high impedance state unless interrogated. However, any current which is caused to flow because of the capacitance of the element is in such a direction as to decrease the current through the compensated cryosar in the one (ON) state, and hence would tend to turn it OFF. This then is another restriction on the amount of capacitance an element may have. As mentioned previously, the ON current is taken as 2 μa while the sustaining current is assumed to be less than 1 μa; therefore $C < 0.025 \Delta t$ pf, and as mentioned previously, this is not difficult to achieve.

The value of R_1 should be fairly low for the reasons mentioned previously. A reasonable value would be 50 ohms, so that the voltage drop would be negligible for a reasonable number of elements. When all cells common to a word line are in the one state, the impedance seen by the W/I driver during interrogate is

$$Z_{W/I} = R_1 \; \Big\| \; \frac{R_2 \| R_3}{n}$$

where the vertical lines denote that the resistors are in parallel and n is the number of bits in the word. In the present case, if $n = 64$, $Z_{W/I} = 42$ ohms. Thus, the W/I driver does not see a widely varying impedance.

The power consumption of the cell in the ON state is 0.48 μw. If a fairly large system were built with a three-watt refrigerator, there would be considerable cooling power left for any circuits that might be put into the bath with the array.

It is worth noting that all the necessary pulse voltages are readily obtainable with tunnel diode circuitry. Tunnel diodes work quite well at liquid helium temperatures although no long-time storage data are available. It may be possible to construct a fairly large storage system where only a small number of connections to the outside environment are necessary.

CRYOSAR LOGIC—With the possibility of very small element capacities and extremely large OFF resistances, performing logic functions with fairly complex structures may be possible.

Johnston has described a decoder[19] which could be used with the storage cell described previously. Figure 3B shows this decoder which is made up of uncompensated cryosars. If, for the sake of illustration, it is assumed that the uncompensated cryosars have a breakdown voltage of one volt and that the true state is denoted by an input of one volt, the operation is as follows:

During read, the normal of the address is applied to the decoder input lines and a positive clock signal is applied at the clock terminal as indicated. A positive pulse will then appear on the output of the true line. No output will appear on the other lines because of the clamping action of the cryosars which return to the false (negative input) input lines.

For writing into the memory, the complement of the address is applied to the decoder input lines and a negative clock pulse (clear operation) is applied to the clock input. A negative pulse will appear on the output that clears the word to zero. No negative pulse appears on the other lines because of the clamping action of the cryosars which return to the positive inputs. The address is then returned to normal and followed by a positive clock pulse, and the decoder operates as for the read operation. This positive pulse on the word line in coincidence with the information signal (negative pulse) on the bit line selectively writes ones into the proper bit location.

The decoder described above is, of course, a logical AND gate. Used by itself, this gate has a level shift between input and output. It is possible to restore the original levels and perform an OR function by adding a second level of logic. This configuration is shown in Fig. 3C.

If it is assumed that the logic levels are +1 volt (true) and 0 volt (false) and the cryosars have a one-volt breakdown, then the output of the AND portion of the gate will be at +2 volts only if A and B are both at +1 volt. If either one or both of the inputs are at the lower voltage, then the output is at +1 volt. Thus, the first stage performs the logical function AB with the true output being represented by +2 volts. The output of the OR section will be +1 volt if either of the inputs are at +2 volts (true) so that a logical OR is performed. The configuration thus accomplishes the AND-OR function with the input and output levels corresponding.

Because of the low-loss nature of the elements in the ON state it may prove possible to perform many levels of logic before regeneration is necessary. Regeneration and inversion could possibly be accomplished with compensated cryosars or tuned diodes. The fan-in, fan-out capabilities should also be quite good because of the large resistances in the OFF state and small

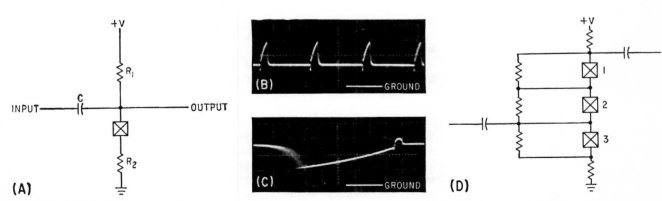

CRYOSAR PULSE GENERATOR (A); *pulse generator waveshapes (B and C); another possible cryosar pulse generator (D). In waveforms, horizontal scale is 10 μsec per cm in (B) and 1 μsec in (C), vertical scale is 0.5 v per cm in both—Fig. 4*

capacities of the elements.

Another possible logic configuration is shown in Fig. 3D. This is essentially a current summing type of logic. The uncompensated cryosar (K_2) is biased to point a of Fig. 3E and has a breakdown voltage equal to the sustaining voltage of the compensated cryosars (K_1) which provide the logical inputs. If all the K_1 cryosars inputs to one gate are in their low voltage state, then K_2 remains at point a. When the unit is clocked with a negative pulse, the current through K_2 is reduced and a negative pulse output produced. If any of the K_1 units are in their high voltage state, the K_2 unit has more current flowing through it and will be at point b for one input, point c for two inputs, etc. No output results when the negative clock is applied.

The output of this unit could turn off a K_1 cryosar of a succeeding stage, which had been turned on by a reset pulse, thus storing the information. This type of system would use a multiphase clock.

The fan-out capabilities of the K_1 unit are potentially excellent, being determined by the values of the voltage and resistors chosen for the circuit.

PULSE GENERATOR — Figure 4A shows a pulse generator circuit which has several different modes of operation, depending on the supply voltage. If the supply voltage is less than the cryosar peak voltage, a positive pulse triggers the device to the ON state and the output voltage remains at V_s providing

$$\frac{V - V_S}{R_1 + R_2} \geqq I_s$$

where I_s is the sustaining current. The device may be returned to the high voltage state by a negative pulse at the input or by momentarily decreasing the supply voltage so that the current falls below I_s.

If the supply voltage is larger than V_p and

$$\frac{V - V_p}{R_1 + R_2} > I_p$$

where I_p is the peak current then the cryosar is on in the quiescent state. The application of a negative pulse at the input will turn the cryosar off and the output voltage will begin rising to $+V$ with a time constant essentially determined by

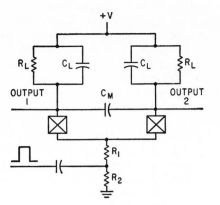

CRYOSAR T FLIP-FLOP *and output waveforms. Horizontal scale is 10 μsec per cm, vertical scale is 0.5 v per cm—Fig. 5*

R_1 and C. When the voltage reaches V_p, the device will break down and return to the ON condition. Waveshapes of a circuit operating in this mode are shown in Fig. 4B and 4C. The input was a negative pulse of about 150 mv amplitude and the circuit values were $R_1 = 1,600$ ohms, $R_2 = 100$ ohms, $C = 0.0047$ μf, and $V = +2$ volts. Resistor R_2 is included in the circuit to prevent the signal source from being short circuited by the cryosar in its ON state.

This general type of circuit could be useful as a sense amplifier for the memory described and for storing of logical information. Its speed is primarily limited by the RC time constant as the voltage goes toward V_p (for the circuit tested). However, it should prove possible to make the circuit much faster than that presented.

Pulse generators capable of giving larger outputs, without increasing the inputs, should be possible using cryosars placed in series as shown in Fig. 4D. In this circuit each cryosar would have a voltage across it less than its peak voltage. The third cryosar is turned on by a positive pulse and goes to its low-voltage state, thus applying more voltage across the first two cryosars which are then turned on.

Figure 5 shows a cryosar flip-flop circuit together with the waveshapes obtained at the two outputs.

The circuit works in the following manner.

The values of resistors are chosen so that in the quiescent state only one cryosar is in the ON condition. This is accomplished by assuring that if both cryosars attempt to be in the ON state, the sustaining current that must flow through each cryosar will result in a voltage drop across $R_1 + R_2$ and R_2, so that the voltage across the cryosar must be less than the sustaining voltage and thus one must be in the OFF state.

The flip-flop is triggered by a positive pulse input which turns the ON cryosar off. The two capacitors, C_L, serves as "memory" by virtue of the different voltages which are across them, assuring that the cryosar which was off turns on and C_M aids in regeneration. The manner of triggering shown in Fig. 5 provides isolation between input and output.

The main disadvantage of this cryosar flip-flop circuit is that the design depends on an accurate knowledge of the value of sustaining current, I_s. At this time the sustaining current appears to be the least designable parameter of the cryosar and is sometimes even difficult to determine as it appears to vary over a given wafer.

This research has been sponsored in part by the Electronics Research Directorate of the Air Force Cambridge Research Laboratories, Air Force Office of Aerospace Research under Contract AF 19(604)-8458.

REFERENCES

(1) F. J. Darnell and S. A. Friedberg, *Phys Rev*, **98**, p 1,860, 1955.
(2) N. Sclar and E. Burstein, *J Phys Chem Solids*, **2**, p 1, 1957.
(3) S. H. Koening and G. R. Gunther-Mohr, *J Phys Chem Solids*, **2**, p 268, 1957.
(4) G. Finke and G. Lantz, *Fs. f. Naturforsch.*, **12(a)**, p 223, 1957.
(5) S. H. Koenig, *Phy Rev*, **110**, p 986, 1958.
(6) A. L. McWhorter, Semiconductor Dev. Conf; Boulder, Colo., July 1957.
(7) R. H. Rediker and A. L. McWhorter, Int. Conf. on Solid State Physics in Electr., and Telecomm, Brussels, Belgium, June 1958.
(8) A. L. McWhorter and R. H. Rediker, *Proc IRE*, **47**, p 1,207, 1959.
(9) D. H. Dexter and F. Seitz, *Phys Rev*, **86**, p 964, 1952.
(10) C. S. Hung and J. R. Gliessman, *Phys Rev*, **79**, p 726, 1950.
(11) C. S. Hung and J. R. Gliessman, *Phys Rev*, **96**, p 1,226, 1954.
(12) E. Conwell and V. F. Weisskopf, *Phys Rev*, **77**, p 388, 1950.
(13) H. Brooks, *Phys Rev*, **83**, p 879, 1951.
(14) C. Herring (not published).
(15) C. Erginsoy, *Phys Rev*, **79**, p 1,013, 1950.
(16) A. L. McWhorter, MIT Lincoln Lab Rpt. 85G-0006.
(17) J. Callaway and F. W. Cummings, *Phys Rev*, **126**, No. 1, 1962.
(18) R. C. Johnston, MIT Lincoln Lab Rpt. 53G-0044.
(19) R. C. Johnston, *NEREM Record*, Nov. 1960.

HOMOGENEOUS SEMICONDUCTORS

A NEW GENERATION OF DEVICES

*Bulk properties, rather than impurity variations, are
the key to a new family of solid-state active components*

By JULIEN BOK, Laboratoire de Physique, Ecole Normale Superieure, Paris, France

DEVICES OPERATING on semiconductor bulk properties have been available for some time. Thermistors, for example, take advantage of the variation of carrier concentration with temperature. Photocells depend on production of excess free carriers by incident radiation. And a variety of devices use the Hall effect: multipliers, gyrators and the like.

But semiconductors have still other bulk properties that point to an entirely new family of devices. These properties arise from the existence in semiconductors of a solid-state plasma, analogous to a gaseous plasma. The plasma breaks down by impact ionization; electromagnetic waves can propagate through it; and under certain conditions, it becomes unstable and oscillates. All these phenomena

have been used to develop new homogeneous semiconductor devices.

Compared to a gaseous plasma, a solid-state plasma shows several important differences. For one thing, a certain free carrier density exists at thermal equilibrium because of the low ionization energy for the impurity atoms in the semiconductor; so no appreciable outside energy is necessary to ionize the plasma. Also, the free carrier density can be varied easily over wide limits by doping or temperature changes. And the density can run very high, as much as $10^{22}/cm^3$ for metals.

Further, the low-mass free carriers can be either electrons or holes, whereas in a gaseous plasma electrons are the only light particles. Finally, the ions are tightly linked to the crystal lattice, so

much so that they can be considered completely immobile, that is, of infinite mass.

IMPACT IONIZATION — The cryosar—Electrons bound to impurity atoms in a semiconductor lattice have low ionization energies (for example, 0.01 electron volt for arsenic in germanium). At room temperature these electrons are free, but at low enough temperature they are bound to the impurities. When a high electric field is applied, electrons are accelerated to energies high enough to ionize impurity atoms by impact. The released electrons in turn ionize other impurity atoms, causing the large decrease in resistivity called breakdown.

This phenomenon has been observed in germanium at liquid helium temperature by many workers[1-3]. A typical I-V characteristic for breakdown in uncompensated germanium is shown in Fig. 1. McWhorter and Rediker found that for compensated germanium the I-V curve has a negative resistance characteristic (Fig. 1). They proposed to use this as a bistable memory element and baptized their device the "cryosar"[4, 5]. Cryosar circuits have already been developed (ELECTRONICS, Aug. 17, 1962, p 39).

Obviously, the liquid-helium temperature requirement of operation is a major drawback for the compensated germanium cryosar. But with other semiconductor materials, impact ionization at higher temperatures becomes possible. At the Ecole Normale Superieure, im-

BYPASSING THE JUNCTION

Most present-day semiconductors amplify or oscillate because of their nonhomogeneous regions. This usually involves one or more **p-n** junctions, and leads to surface-effect difficulties, calling for delicate production techniques such as passivation.

These difficulties are sidestepped by devices that use the bulk properties of semiconductors for their operation.

Author Bok experiments with one of his brainchildren

pact ionization was obtained at 20 K (liquid hydrogen temperature) using silicon doped with phosphorus (ionization energy level of 0.04 ev)[6]. Here also, compensated samples had negative resistance.

Even better results were obtained with deep-level impurities in germanium. Using zinc-doped germanium compensated with antimony, Zylbersztejn[7] obtained at liquid nitrogen temperature a negative-resistance characteristic (Fig. 1), and room-temperature operation may be possible for silicon doped with indium. However, room-temperature devices consume considerably more power than the liquid-helium cryosar.

HELICON WAVES—Presence of free carriers in a medium modifies electromagnetic wave propagation because of the current produced by motion of the free carriers in the wave's electric field. Appleton[8] investigated this in detail for wave propagation in the ionosphere, and in fact the "helicon" propagation mode in solid plasmas described by Aigrain[9] was earlier noted in the ionosphere by Storey[10], who dubbed the mode "whistler".

The mode occurs under the following conditions: first, the wave is TEM with a steady magnetic field B_0 imposed on it in the direction of propagation. The medium is then anisotropic and the dielectric constant a tensor; however, the constant reduces to a scalar for a circularly polarized wave. Second, the frequencies considered are

$\omega << \omega_c$, where ω_c is the cyclotron resonance frequency of the carriers. In MKSA units, $\omega_c = e\,B_0/m$, where m is the effective mass of the free carriers under consideration. Third, the magnetic field must be strong enough so that $\omega_c \tau >> 1$ (τ is the carrier relaxation time, that is, the average time between two collisions). $\omega_c \tau = \tan \theta_H = \mu\,B_0$, where θ_H is the Hall angle and μ the carrier mobility. Physically, this means the Hall angle is in the neighborhood of 90 deg; the current and the electric field lie almost at right angles.

When these three conditions are satisfied, Libchaber and Veilex[11] have shown, the real component of the dielectric constant is

$$\epsilon = \epsilon_e \pm \frac{Ne}{\epsilon_0 \omega B_0}$$

where ϵ_e is the dielectric constant of the lattice, N the number of free carriers, e the electron charge and ϵ_0 the permittivity of free space in MKSA units ($\epsilon_0 = 1/4\pi 10^9$). The $\pm$ signs correspond to the two directions of rotation of the circularly polarized wave.

For most solids, the value of ϵ_e lies between 10 and 20 and is negligible compared to the second term of Eq. 1. Thus in helicon propagation a left-hand wave ($\epsilon > 0$) propagates but a right-hand wave ($\epsilon < 0$) does not. Thus the medium is gyromagnetic, as ferrites are, which suggests similar applications—isolators, directive couplers and the like, at frequencies where ferrites aren't satisfactory.

The dielectric constant ϵ for helicon waves can be very high, especially when the number of carriers is high and the frequency low. Metals, for example, show values in the order of 5×10^{17} ($N = 10^{22}/cm^3$, $\omega = 2\pi \times 50$ cps, and $B_0 = 10{,}000$ gauss). Under these conditions, the wavelength in the medium is about 1 cm and 50-cycle resonant cavities have reasonable dimensions, about 1 cm (Fig. 2). Helicon action in metals has been achieved by Bowers et al[12].

For an indium antimonide (InSb) homogeneous semiconductor, again with B_0 of 10,000 gauss but frequency ω of $2\pi \times 10$ Gc, the dielectric constant ϵ is 30 at 77 K ($N = 10^{14}/cm^3$) and 5,000 at 300 K ambient temperature ($N = 1.6 \times 10^{16}/cm^3$). Here the helicon wave in the semiconductor has a wavelength of about 1 mm. Libchaber and Veilex[11] have observed helicon waves in semiconductors.

The equation (1) for dielectric constant holds only if losses are negligible. The angle of loss δ in a solid plasma is given by

$$\tan \delta = \frac{1}{2\,\omega_c \tau} = \frac{1}{2\,\mu B_0}$$

Since for practical purposes B_0 can't go higher than 10,000 gauss, μ must be high—at least 10,000 $cm^2/v\ s$—to observe helicon resonance. For metals, then, liquid helium temperature becomes a condition for resonance; at that temperature $\mu \cong 10^5$ cm/²v s. However for indium antimonide semiconductor material, $\mu = 5 \times 10^5$ at 77 K and 7×10^4 at 300 K ambient temperature. In fact InSb is the only material found so far in which helicon waves propagate at room temperature.

Already, practical applications for the InSb helicon are in sight. Figure 3 shows a possible configuration for an isolator that would operate with a magnetic field of 10,000 gauss. The loss $\tan \delta$ runs about 1 percent at 77 K and 15 percent at 300 K.

Certainly, a magnetic field of 10,000 gauss represents an inconvenience; but there are important advantages that offset the drawback. For one thing, there's no lower limit on frequency—in metals helicon resonance occurs at frequencies as low as several cps. True, coupling to ordinary circuits

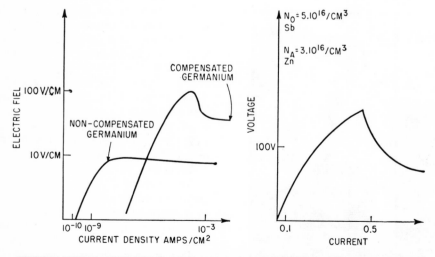

GERMANIUM CRYOSAR *characteristics, left, shown for compensated and uncompensated unit. Right, I-V characteristic for germanium cryosar doped with zinc and compensated with antimony (Zylbersztejn)—Fig. 1*

becomes difficult at such low frequencies because of the very high dielectric constant ($\cong 10^{18}$). But although waveguides can't be used, it seems likely that coaxial structures could provide the necessary circular polarization. An InSb isolator covering the 100—1,000 Mc band is under development at CSF —Compagnie Generale de Telegraphie sans Fil by a research team headed by Gremillet (Fig. 4).

A second important advantage of the helicon isolator is an upper frequency limit in the millimetric and even the sub-millimetric range. The condition $\omega << \omega_c$ sets the upper limit. However, the cyclotron resonance frequency ω_c can be very high. For InSb at 10,000 gauss, for example, the value is in the order of 10^{13} cps ($\omega = eB_0/m$).

INSTABILITY DEVICES—Plasma

instabilities in solids may lead to a new class of homogeneous semiconductor devices: oscillators and even amplifiers.

So far, two main kinds of instabilities have been described. Pines and Schrieffer[13] demonstrated theoretically that in some solids "two-stream" instability can produce longitudinal oscillations. This supposes the existence in the solid of two different carriers with opposite charge. But up to now no one has been able to devise an experiment that establishes the conditions required.

However, several researchers have been able to make semiconductors oscillate by applying a longitudinal magnetic field[14–16]. An InSb oscillator, developed at the Ecole Normale Superieure, operates at liquid nitrogen temperature with a longitudinal magnetic field of 1,000 gauss. It has peak power output of several tens of watts at a maximum frequency of 600 Mc. Steele and Larrabee[16] have described similar oscillators using germanium, silicon and InSb and suggested calling them "oscillistors".

Two different theoretical mecha-

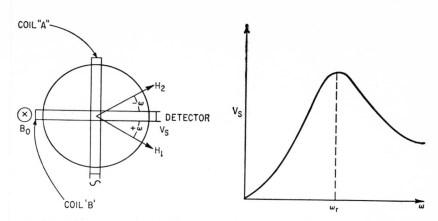

HELICON RESONANCE *in metals. Coil A is fed with a-c at frequency* ω, *creating a magnetic field that can be resolved into two rotating fields* $+ \omega$ *and* $- \omega$. *One is evanescent, the other propagates and induces an emf in coil B. Output voltage (plotted) in B is a function of frequency* ω. *Resonant frequency maximum* V_s *is determined by thickness* $\lambda/2$ *of metal sample—Fig. 2*

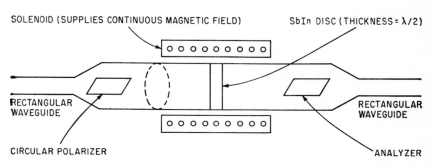

ISOLATOR *uses indium antimonide disk in waveguide—Fig. 3*

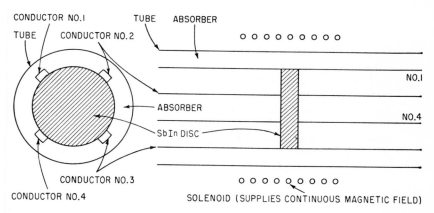

LOW FREQUENCY *isolator (100 Mc). The four conductors are fed in quadrature to obtain circular polarization at the center—Fig. 4*

nisms have been proposed to explain the instabilities that develop when a longitudinal magnetic field is applied to a solid-state plasma. One, called "screw instabilities", supposes a helical fluctuation of density of electrons and holes. The second attributes oscillation to an action analogous to that of a traveling-wave tube.

REFERENCES

(1) F. J. Darnell and S. A. Friedberg *Phys Rev* **98**, p 1,860 (1955)
(2) N. Sclar and E. Burstein *J Phys Chem Solids* **2**, p 2 (1957)
(3) S. H. Koenig and G. R. Gunther-Mohr *J Phys and Chem Solids* **2**, p 268 (1957)
(4) R. H. Rediker and A. L. McWhorter Int. Conf. on Solid State Physics Brussels, Belgium, June 1958
(5) A. L. McWhorter and R. H. Rediker *Proc IRE* **47**, p 1,207 (1959)
(6) J. Bok, J. C. Sohm, A. Zylbersztejn Int Conf on Semiconductor Physics Prague (1960)
(7) A. Zylberstein *J Phys Chem Solids* **23**, p 297 (1962)
(8) E. V. Appleton *J Inst Elec Engrs Japan* **71**, p 642 (1932)
(9) P. Aigrain Int. Conf. on Semiconductor-Physics, Prague (1960)
(10) L. R. O. Storey—*Phil Trans Roy Soc* (London) A **246**, 113 (1953)
(11) Libchaber et Veilex *Phys Rev* **127**, p 774 (1962)
(12) R. Bowers, C. Legendy and F. Rose *Phys Rev Letters* **7**, p 339 (1961)
(13) D. Pines and J. R. S. Schrieffer *Phys Rev* **124**, p 1,387 (1961)
(14) Ivanov and Ryvkin *Sov. Phys J.E.T.P.* **3**, p 722 (1958)
(15) J. Bok *Annales de la Radioelectricite*—**XV** No. 60 (1960)
(16) M. C. Steele and R. D. Larrabee *J Appl Phys* **31**, p 1,959 (1960)

Cryogenic flux pump switches high currents

The cryotron was developed for computer circuits;
now a modified version has even a brighter future in high
power circuits for superconducting magnets

By Theodor A. Buchhold

Advanced Technology Laboratories, General Electric Co., Schenectady, N.Y.

In a work room at General Electric's Advanced Technology Laboratories, a superconductive coil and a flux pump (cover) sit in a liquid helium bath conducting very large d-c currents—up to 500 amps. When a signal from a phase shifter, one of the components, makes a coil superconducting, the magnetic flux generated by another superconducting coil (another of the components) connected to it rises. If the coil flux decreases, energy flows back into the power supply circuit.

This is a new kind of d-c power supply or flux pump. It depends on the properties of superconducting materials operating at 4.2 deg. K. Small a-c current carried by small wires powers the flux pump. It depends on the properties of superconnetic field strength, the field is maintained by induced, loss-free, superconducting currents even though the power supply is disconnected.

The small feeder wires carrying the a-c current are a big asset. In superconducting studies, the trend is to generate bigger magnetic fields in larger and larger solenoids, built of heavy conductors. But these heavy conductors also carry large amounts of heat into the low-temperature container (or cryostat), reducing the efficiency of the cryogenic setup. The new flux pump could handle thousands of amperes of current without heavy conductors.

Improving on the cryotron

What makes this flux pump work is a new component called the reactor cryotron. A saturable reactor is added to a specially-made cryotron unit. The reactor can sense when the cryotron is to be switched on or off to make it superconducting.

The main difference between the conventional small-current computer cryotron and this new com-

The author

As technical consultant to GE's Advanced Technology Laboratories cryogenic projects, Dr. Buchhold holds five patents for cryogenic devices and has more pending. One of the V-2 missile guidance scientists, he also served as chief of the control and guidance branch of the Guided Missile Development Division at Redstone Arsenal, and there pioneered in gyros and accelerometers with air bearings, special servos, magnetic amplifiers and transistors for missile control. He developed the basic concept for the Redstone Missile Guidance System. Before joining General Electric in 1956, Dr. Buchhold was consultant to the vice-president of engineering of the Ford Instrument Co.

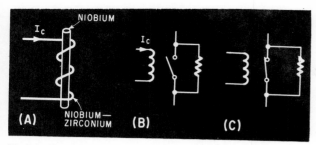

Model of cryotron, (A); equivalent circuit of cryotron when energized, (B); when not energized, (C)

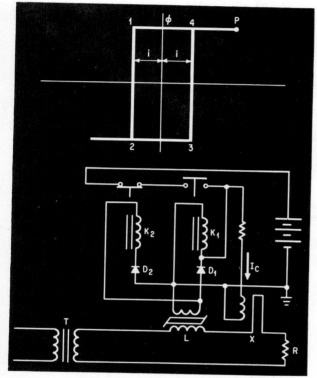

Reactor cryotron control of superconducting coil, bottom; hysteresis loop for saturable reactor used in circuit, top

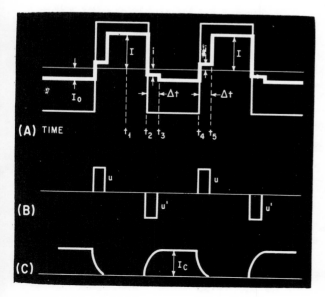

Waveforms occurring in reactor cryotron: voltage and current, (A); reactor signal, (B); control current, (C)

ponent is the different geometry and the much larger dimensions. The computer cryotron is made of a superconducting wire or metallic film—called a gate—placed near a coil or second metallic film—called the control—which applies a magnetic field to the gate. In a typical cryotron, the gate may be a thin niobium wire and the control coil is a niobium-zirconium alloy which has a higher critical field than plain niobium. With this construction the cryotron can handle milliampere currents.

For large currents, in the reactor cryotron, the gate is made of niobium tape of proper width and length, bifilarly wound. The tape can be folded so that it occupies only a small space and can be surrounded by a control coil of niobium-zirconium.

In either case, when the coil is energized, producing a strong enough magnetic field around the gate, the niobium wire is made resistive. A cryotron corresponds to a switch which is open when the control coil is energized, closed if the control current is interrupted. The resistance of the open cryotron, however, is finite, not infinite like the resistance of an ordinary switch. For most applications, the resistance of the cryotron is sufficient for it to operate as a switch.

The tiny computer cryotron is employed in computer logic and in computer memories. Its most desirable features: simplicity, fast response and potential small size with very low switching currents. The new power cryotron can be used in a variety of applications; for example, as a cryogenic rectifier for large currents.

Cryogenic rectifier

The operation of a reactor cryotron can best be explained in a half-wave rectifier circuit (left), which is also a basic element for the more important full-wave rectifier circuit. Transformer T is maintained at 4.2 deg. K and has its secondary winding connected through saturable reactor L and the power cryotron X to the resistive load, R. The reactor flux ϕ exhibits the hysteresis characteristic shown. It is assumed that transformer T delivers a rectangular voltage pulse V. At time t_1 a large current I flows in the power circuit and the saturable reactor is saturated, represented by point P on the hysteresis loop. At time t_2, voltage V reverses and the current tends to follow. However, when the small negative magnetizing current i is reached, the saturable reactor leaves its positive saturation state and flux ϕ moves along path 1-2 on the loop. The full voltage V now appears across the reactor, inducing in its secondary winding a negative voltage u′, which energizes relay K_1 via rectifier D_1. Its contact closes and control current I_C can flow from the battery through the closed contacts of relay K_2 and K_1 to the control coil of cryotron X. During the interval Δt, in which the reactor goes from positive to negative saturation, only the small magnetizing current i flows and control current I_c builds up.

At time t_3, negative saturation is reached. The power-circuit current becomes $I_o = V/r_o$, determined by resistance r_o of the now resistive cryotron. After t_3, the saturated reactor consumes no voltage and its secondary voltage u' becomes zero. Relay K_1 remains energized through its contact. At time t_4, voltage V becomes positive again and the current again tries to follow. However, the reactor now limits the current to the small positive magnetizing current $+i$ and the flux ϕ follows path 3-4 on the hysteresis loop. In the secondary winding of the reactor, an opposite voltage u is induced. Due to rectifier D_2, this energizes relay K_2, and opens K_1, thus interrupting the control current I_c in the control winding of X. In the absence of a control field, the cryotron becomes superconductive. After this time interval Δt, positive saturation is reached at t_5 and full current $I = V/R$ flows.

The time interval established by the reactor, during which the current is kept small, is quite important since it gives the cryotron time to change from the normal to the superconductive state. Without the current limitation during Δt, the decreasing cryotron resistance would cause an increasing current I and such losses that the cryotron might reach its transition temperature and not to go superconducting.

In the actual experimental circuit, the two relays shown in the diagram were replaced with solid-state switching devices.

In this circuit, the reactor cryotron was switched on and off by voltages derived from the reactor. For many applications only the "on" signal from the reactor is used to produce a high resistance to reverse currents. The "off" signal, which makes the cryotron superconductive, can be derived from any signal source; e.g., the output of a phase shifter. Then the controlled reactor cryotron resembles a controlled rectifier, which is made conductive by a gate signal, and offers very high resistance to reverse currents.

All circuits suitable for controlled rectifiers can be used for controlled reactor cryotrons; for instance, it is possible to build a full-wave rectifier circuit for large d-c currents which can be connected to a superconductive coil. Such a circuit can be made entirely of superconductive material. Since a cryotron has zero resistance in the forward direction, the circuit represents a d-c supply with no internal resistance, having an approximately constant d-c output voltage. Therefore, the current supplied to a superconductive coil increases linearly with time. If the primary current into the transformer is interrupted, the d-c current continues to flow as a persistent current since at least one of the two cryotrons acts as a superconducting short circuit across the coil.

If the reactor cryotron is controlled by a phase shifter, as mentioned above, the magnetic field in the coil can be controlled, and, in fact, a flux decrease can be achieved; energy is then fed back into the power supply. Such a circuit controls the flux in an inductive load with no moving mechanical parts and so might be called an electrical flux pump.

Experimental model

A feasibility model of a full-wave rectifier circuit with reactor cryotrons controlled by a phase shifter was built and connected to a superconducting coil of $L = 1.8 \times 10^{-3}$H. The maximum d-c current was somewhat above 500 A and produced a field of about 25,000 oersteds with a stored energy of 220 joules. When exceeding this value of current, the cryotrons became resistive. With phase shifting, it was possible to adjust the field to any desired value, and also to obtain persistent currents or fields by disconnecting the power supply. The supply could be reconnected at any time to permit changing the field setting. The rectifier circuit was fed with a rectangular voltage of 10 cps and the a-c currents were below 1 ampere. The low frequency allowed sufficient switching time for the cryotrons.

More development work was indicated by the experimental model, especially toward building cryotrons with higher maximum currents, but it is believed that in the future, reactor cryotrons for electrical flux pumps can be built to carry several thousand amperes.

The author thanks P.J. Molenda, R.K. Terbush, S.H. Minnich and R.E. Morgan for their assistance.

Bibliography

J. Volgers and P.S. Admiral, A. Dynamo for Generating a Persistent Current in A Superconductive Circuit, Phys Letters, 2, 5, 1962

H.L. Laquer, An Electric Flux Pump for Powering Superconducting Magnet Coils, Cryogenics, 3, 1, 1963

C.F. Hemstead, Y.B. Kim and A.R. Strand, Inductive Behavior of Superconductive Magnets, J Appl Phys, 34, 11, 1963

H. VanBeelen, A.J.P.T. Arnold, H.A. Syphens, R. DeBruyn Ouboter, J.J.M. Beenakker and T.W. Taconis, A 25,000 Gauss, 175 Amperes Nb-25% Zr Wire Magnet Fed by a Flux Pump, Phys Letters, 7, 3, 1963

S.L. Wipt, A Superconductive DC Generator Paper presented at Cryogenic Conference in Boulder, Colorado, 1963

The art of Q measurement has been extended to permit evaluation of superconductive resonant circuits. Three circuits have been devised to measure high values of Q obtained in the h-f/vhf range

Novel Test
Techniques
Measure Q in

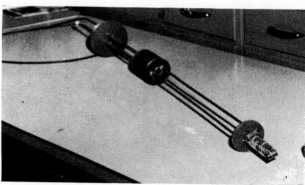

MOUNTING *and coupling probes for 58-Mc (above); solid dielectric configuration (below)*

Cryogenic Resonant Circuits

By WILLIAM H. HARTWIG, Department of Electrical Engineering, University of Texas, Austin, Texas

ACCURACY is improved and the time needed to measure high values of Q is reduced by three newly devised measurement circuits. They are being used in experiments with superconducting resonant circuits, which are being investigated in an effort to obtain high values of Q (greater than 100,000) in the h-f/vhf range. The work is being conducted in the Electronic Materials Research Laboratory, Department of Electrical Engineering, University of Texas.

The Q of a resonant circuit is a measure of its usefulness in an oscillator, filter or other frequency-sensitive circuit. The use of superconductors permits lumped circuit components to have values of Q comparable to quartz crystals and cavities in the h-f/vhf region. The problems of measuring Q of such devices require unconventional approaches.

SUPERCONDUCTING TANKS—The range of frequencies under investigation dictates the use of lumped L-C circuits. Although the attainable Q from

HOT SOLUTIONS FOR A COLD PROBLEM

The intriguing phenomenon of superconductivity may prove useful in still another area—high-Q resonant circuits. However, measurements associated with these circuits defy conventional methods. Some ingenious solutions have been devised that not only permit these high values of Q to be measured but are helping to pinpoint the loss mechanisms that affect Q in cryogenic tanks

a helical inductor and parallel-plate configuration is less than from a cavity, economy in the use of liquid helium and physical size make the use of distributed structures prohibitive.

Lead and alloys of lead and tin are the most convenient among the available metals. Transition temperature from normal to superconducting is 7.2 deg K, which permits operation in liquid helium baths.

Circuits can be fabricated in any of several ways to suit the purpose. A 17-Mc configuration made of a single piece of lead foil using glass as a supporting structure and as the dielectric material is shown in Fig. 1. The 58-Mc circuit in the top photograph was made of brass coated with an alloy of 75 percent lead and 25 percent tin, which can be applied like solder. Superconducting shield cans are used to prevent losses from radiation.

Circuits are being constructed in other forms using a variety of bulk and thin-film techniques. However, all of the techniques used provide a clean, smooth surface, which is essential to ensure minimum losses.

The circuits are mounted as shown in the photographs. The outer shell of the capacitor and the shield can that slips over the entire assembly are at ground potential. Energy is coupled in and out through two coaxial cables made of thin-walled stainless steel tubes. Since this material is a poor conductor of heat, it reduces boil-off of liquid helium.

The probes in the upper photograph couple r-f energy to the inner capacitor shell through a small hole in the outer shell. The probes can be rotated away from the hole, which permits a 40-db variation in coupling during the experiment.

COOLING SYSTEM—The circuit is placed in the double dewar system shown in Fig. 2, which is composed of an evacuated outer dewar containing liquid nitrogen and an evacuated inner dewar. The circuit is placed in the inner dewar, and the air is replaced by gaseous helium. This procedure prevents water frost and frozen air from interfering with the experiment when liquid helium is poured into the system.

The outer dewar is filled with liquid nitrogen to precool the system before the liquid helium is introduced. The liquid helium is transferred in through a special evacuated double stainless steel tube from a large storage vessel. The resonant circuit can be cooled to 4.2 deg K in this manner with the expenditure of about 4 liters of liquid helium, 1 liter of which will have blown off as a gas in the transfer process. The remaining 3 liters keep the circuit at constant temperature for over 12 hours without refilling.

RESONANT CIRCUIT Q—The Q of a resonant system is

$$Q = \frac{\omega_o \text{ peak energy stored}}{\text{average power loss}}$$

where ω_o is the resonant frequency in radians per second. Therefore

$$\frac{1}{Q} = \frac{1}{\omega_o} \frac{\text{loss } 1 + \text{loss } 2 + \dots \text{loss } n}{\text{peak energy stored}} = \frac{1}{Q_1} + \frac{1}{Q_2} + \dots \frac{1}{Q_n}$$

The second form of the equation accounts for n loss mechanisms. Thus, $1/Q_c$, $1/Q_R$, $1/Q_D$ and $1/Q_o$ can be considered measures of the losses resulting from coupling, radiation, dielectric dissipation and the intrinsic loss in the superconductor. Their sum is the reciprocal of the loaded Q, which is indicated by the symbol Q_L, so that

$$\frac{1}{Q_L} = \frac{1}{Q_c} + \frac{1}{Q_R} + \frac{1}{Q_D} + \frac{1}{Q_o}$$

MEASURING METHODS—Because the techniques usually used to measure Q at lower frequencies (substitution, bridges) become prohibitively tedious at values of Q much above 10^2, they were not seriously considered. Instead the circuit was driven with a pulse-modulated carrier at the resonant frequency, and decay time was measured. This method is superior in this application because it does not require an ultrastable signal source nor an unrealistic pulse rise time.

The only precision measurement needed is of time. The oscilloscope has sweep speeds accurate to ±3 percent, and time required for the decay is in milliseconds. Therefore, relatively short-term instability is permissible in both circuit and signal generator without introducing significant measurement error.

Decay time is proportional to Q and is difficult to measure at low values of Q. However, this presents no problem because Q can be measured by more conventional means if it is low.

The decrement method of Q measurement gives a value of Q in terms of resonant frequency and decay rate of the signal in which

$$Q_L = \frac{\omega \Delta t}{2 \ln (e_1/e_2)} \text{,}$$

as shown in Fig. 3A. Several values of Q_L can be gotten from a single record simply by measuring several sets of voltages and time intervals and averaging them.

Two systems have been in use that provide an adequate measurement using the decrement method. The circuit in Fig. 4A is the simpler means for observing the rise and decay of r-f energy in a high-Q tank with a resonant frequency within the passband of the cathode-ray oscilloscope (CRO). Its greatest limitation is the tight coupling needed to obtain a sufficient signal level for the cro.

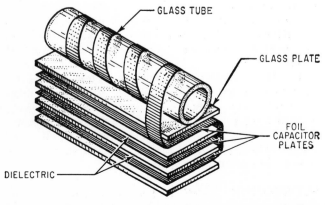

SUPERCONDUCTIVE *circuit using lead foil and glass dielectric is resonant at 17 Mc*—Fig. 1

In principle, the higher gain of the i-f amplifier used in the heterodyne circuit in Fig. 4B permits the coupling to be reduced below the level where it would limit Q. The heterodyne circuit also allows the frequency range to be extended. The ultimate limitations in this method are imposed by linearity, bandwidth and noise in the mixer and i-f amplifier. The adjustable coupling that has been incorporated in the resonant circuit design is adequate to ensure linear operation.

The minimum Q that can be measured is one having a time constant, $2Q/\omega$, about 10 times the rise time of the amplifier and associated circuits. When the time constant of the tank circuit drops below 10 μsec, conventional bandwidth measurements are used to determine Q_L.

TIME-DELAY METHOD—A variation of the heterodyne method is shown in Fig. 4C. The cro sweep is triggered by the delayed leading edge of the pulse that keys the oscillator. Vertical gain of the cro is increased until a presentation is obtained similar to curve a in Fig. 3B. Some point is chosen (1) as a fiduciary mark. Attenuation is increased by a known amount, A, which is less than 0 db, resulting in curve b. Time delay is then reduced, which causes curve b to move to the right an interval Δt where point 2 coincides with the fiduciary mark. The derivation follows directly from the equalities

$$A \epsilon \exp - \omega t_2/2Q = \epsilon \exp - \omega t_1/2Q = \epsilon \exp - \omega(t_2 + \Delta t)/2Q$$

From the equation, Q is calculated

$$Q = 4.34\ \omega \Delta t/A \text{ (in db)}$$

This method of measurement requires that the cro have good d-c balance since a vertical shift between the horizontal axes of curves a and b would introduce an error in the time delay. The time-delay method for measuring Q in resonant circuits is convenient for high signal-to-noise ratios.

ELAPSED-TIME METHOD—Measurement time is decreased and accuracy increased by the elapsed-time method, which provides automatic measurement suitable for a continuous recording or print-out system. Basically, time interval Δt is measured between two points on the decay curve using an elapsed-time counter.

The setup for this technique is shown in Fig. 5A. The pulse that triggers the r-f generator is inverted, differentiated and passed through a negative clipper. These processes provide a positive spike at the end of the r-f pulse.

Amplitude of the output pulse from the receiver is set at a predetermined level by adjusting it for a red-line reading on the peak-reading voltmeter. The Schmitt trigger circuit is adjusted to fire when the pulse reaches a predetermined lower level. Schmitt trigger output is differentiated and clipped to provide a positive spike at the time that the exponential decay reaches a convenient value, such as $1/\epsilon$. The

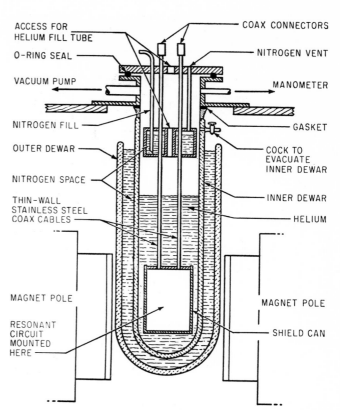

DOUBLE *dewar system maintains tank circuits at superconducting temperatures—Fig. 2*

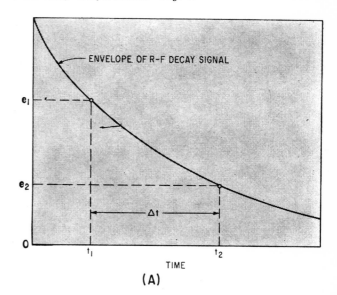

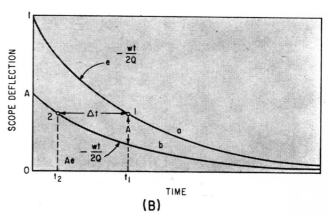

DECREMENT *method measures Q in terms of resonant frequency and decay rate (A), and time-delay circuit provides scope presentation like that at (B)—Fig. 3*

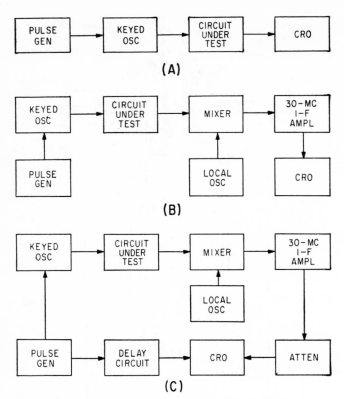

DECAY *can be displayed directly (A), the decay envelope can be displayed using the heterodyne circuit (B), or the time-delay circuit (C) can be used to measure Q—Fig. 4*

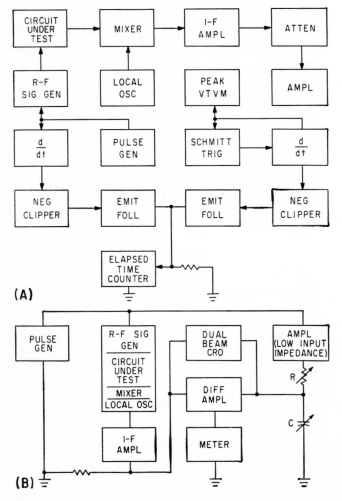

(A)

(B)

spikes from the pulse generator and the Schmitt trigger are fed into separate emitter followers that work into a common load. Thus, a pair of identical pulses are provided that are separated in time by an amount proportional to Q of the circuit under test. The leading spike starts the elapsed-time counter and the lagging spike stops it. The Q is simply this elapsed time multiplied by a constant. The constant is determined from the settings of the amplifier and Schmitt trigger and from the frequency. After the system has been set up, Q is calculated from the equation

$$Q = K\Delta t$$

The advantage of this method is that the error resulting from noise can be reduced significantly by averaging a large number of time measurements.

R-C BRIDGE METHOD—In the last of the three methods, a circuit reads Δt accurately, even in the presence of considerable noise. Two exponential decay signals are compared and one is adjusted to coincide with the other. The comparison can be made with a dual-beam cro or by obtaining a minimum output from a differential amplifier.

Output of the i-f amplifier in Fig. 5B is a partially integrated rectangular pulse. The time constant of the receiver output pulse is $2Q_L/\omega$, and the time constant of the integrator is RC. Therefore, when the equipment is adjusted for minimum meter deflection,

$$Q_L = \omega RC/2$$

These methods for measuring Q are designed to yield accurate results quickly. They are very satisfactory over a range of many decades of decay times and resonant frequencies. Accuracy is limited by noise in the mixer and i-f amplifier; however, as Q increases, required bandwidth decreases proportionately.

LOSS MECHANISMS—To achieve the highest possible Q consistent with mechanical stability, every loss mechanism must be minimized. The effect of reducing the temperature of even normal metals like copper and silver improves Q fivefold. When the metal becomes superconducting, additional improvement of several orders of magnitude can occur.

At room temperature, the dominant loss mechanism is I^2R in the conductor. Radiation losses depend on frequency. At lower frequencies, a shield may actually degrade Q, but this is almost never true in superconducting resonant circuits. A superconductive shield on a 58-Mc circuit at this laboratory raised Q from 5,000 to more than 200,000. The shield must be designed with care since it can be considered a single shorted turn loosely coupled to the resonant inductor. As a consequence, a closely wound coil of many turns may induce a current in the shield with a surface density equal to or greater than that in the coil itself. The high Q denotes high circulating current, which may exceed the critical current and cause the super-

ELAPSED-TIME method (A) increases accuracy, while R-C bridge method (B) can be used with considerable noise present—Fig. 5

conductor to switch back to the normal state during the peaks of the cycle. If this possibility is recognized, the statement about shields never degrading Q in superconducting resonant circuits need not be qualified by the word almost.

Losses in the shield are of the same nature as the intrinsic losses in the superconductor itself. Thus

$$\frac{1}{Q_R} + \frac{1}{Q_o} = \frac{\alpha}{Q_o},$$

where α exceeds unity.

DIELECTRIC LOSSES

At room temperature, losses in the capacitor dielectric rarely limit Q of a resonant circuit, but this is not the case for a superconducting tank. With only dielectric dissipation, Q_D of a circuit is simply

$$Q_D = 1/\tan \delta,$$

where $\tan \delta$ is the loss tangent of the material. Values of $\tan \delta$ for glass, polystyrene and other common insulators range typically from 10^{-3} to 10^{-4} at room temperature in the frequency range of interest. At low temperatures, the losses drop appreciably. Little is known about dielectric losses at helium temperature, but teflon and quartz appear to be the best selections. Using these materials, values of Q above 100,000 might be expected and possibly as high as 1 million.

To avoid the limitations imposed by dielectric losses, capacitors should be built with a minimum of dielectric support. With only a fraction of the electric field in a dissipative medium, Q_D can be raised until inadequate support introduces mechanical instability. The relationship is

$$Q_D = \frac{1}{\tan \delta}\left(1 + \frac{C_o}{C_D}\right),$$

where C_D is the capacitance of the dissipative material, C_o is capacitance in a nondissipative medium and the circuit capacitance is $C_D + C_o$. In the circuit in Fig. 1, Q was only 22,600 at 17 Mc, which was shown to be limited to dielectric dissipation in the glass dielectric.

COUPLING LOSSES

Coupling losses may prove to be the limiting mechanism for a practical superconducting resonant circuit. Using capacitive probes, the equivalent circuit for the r-f decay is shown in Fig. 6A. Tank inductance and capacitance are L and C, and R is the intrinsic surface impedance of the device plus the equivalent resistance of the dielectric dissipation process. Total coupling capacitance is C_1, and r_1 is the resistance seen looking toward the generator and detector circuits. Coupling capacitance is about 10^{-13} farad and can be reduced a hundredfold during the experiment. The value of r_1 is about 25 ohms, which is much less than the reactance of C_1.

The presence of the coupling circuits causes a decrease in resonant frequency in accordance with the relationship.

$$\omega = \frac{\omega_o}{(1 + x)_{1/2}} \approx \omega_o (1 - \tfrac{1}{2}x)$$

where $x = C_1/C$ and $\omega_o = 1/(LC)^{\frac{1}{2}}$. In practice, x

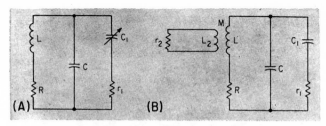

EQUIVALENT circuits of superconductive tank have capacitative (A) and mixed (B) coupling—Fig. 6

$< 10^{-3}$ and may reach 10^{-6} with suitably sensitive detectors. The effect on resonant frequency is less serious than the losses introduced. Calculating Q results in

$$\frac{1}{Q_L} = \frac{1}{Q_o} + \frac{r_1 x^2}{\omega_o L} = \frac{1}{Q_o} + \frac{1}{Q_C}$$

For Q_o to be measured as $10^6 \pm 10$ percent, Q_C must be 10^7 or greater.

If minimum detuning is desired, one coupling circuit can be inductive and the other capacitive. The dependence of Q on an inductively coupled circuit terminated in a resistance is

$$\frac{1}{Q_L} = \frac{1}{Q_o} + k^2 Q_2$$

where $k^2 = M^2/LL_2$, $Q_2 = \omega_o L/r_2$ and $\omega = \omega_o (1 + \tfrac{1}{2} k^2 Q_2{}^2)$. With the mixed coupling of the circuit in Fig. 6B, resonant frequency is essentially independent of coupling when

$$C_1/C = k^2 Q_2{}^2$$

An interesting design problem and a useful possibility is the conception of single vernier adjustment that can perform this function in the cryogenic environment.

SUPERCONDUCTIVE TANK Q

Loaded Q in excess of 10^6 has been measured at 36 Mc. When corrected for the effects of loading, unloaded Q was 1.3×10^7. This value is not regarded as an upper limit. More recent experiments using improved techniques indicate further increase in Q_L and Q_o can be expected. In fact, since surface resistance of a superconductor approaches zero as frequency or temperature approach zero, there is little reason to limit Q_o unless circulating current exceeds the critical value.

The improvement in Q_L when a circuit becomes superconducting is indicated by Q measurements of 200 at room temperature, 500 at 77 deg K in liquid N_2, 1,100 at 7.2+ deg K and 10^6 at 4.2 deg K.

As a matter of practical interest, the loaded Q of a superconductive resonant circuit will probably be limited by coupling losses below a few hundred megacycles. Above that frequency, the reduction in surface impedance in a superconducting resonant circuit is not as pronounced.

The author acknowledges the assistance of Thomas G. Milner, now of Minneapolis-Honeywell Development Laboratory. This project is sponsored by the U. S. Army Research and Development Laboratory, Fort Monmouth.

SUPERCOOLED COILS

PROMISE INDUCTIVE ENERGY STORAGE

May replace capacitor
banks and batteries in
high-energy applications

By **P. R. WIEDERHOLL**
D. L. AMEEN
Ion Physics Corp.,
Burlington, Mass.

ENERGY STORAGE, a frequent requirement in aerospace and terrestrial applications such as lasers, high-energy physics, nuclear and fusion experiments, conventionally has been accomplished by one of two means: capacitors and batteries. Recent advances in superconductivity will soon be adding a third method: inductive storage in superconducting coils.

Capacitor banks are particularly suited for supplying high power for short periods of time. Although the storage capacity of batteries is about three orders of magnitude greater than that of capacitor banks, they are not suited for high-rate discharges of the order of milliseconds or microseconds.

Energy densities obtainable in capacitor banks are low, of the order of 3×10^5 joules/m³. Storage of 1 kw-hr, or 3.6 megajoules, would require over 10 m³ of dielectric material, or a very large capacitor bank.

Another method of energy storage that allows release of the stored energy in the form of pulses, is in the magnetic field of an air-core inductor. The field energy of an inductor is

$$W = \frac{B^2}{8} \times 10^7 \text{ joules/m}^3$$

where B is flux density in webers/m². For a field of 10 webers/m² this yields a density of 4×10^7 joules/m³, considerably higher than for capacitor banks.

However, there are several problems associated with conventional inductive energy storage. Due to I^2R losses in windings, energy is lost at twice the rate of storage during an interval equal to the coil's time constant. Therefore only short charging periods are allowed and a large power supply is needed. Further problems lie in the removal of energy from an inductive store. Consequently, few inductive storage

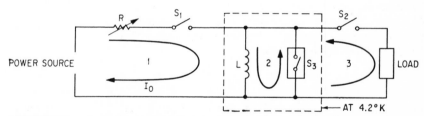

INDUCTIVE energy storage using a superconducting coil and discharge switch

FIRING LASER flash tube with superconducting inductive power supply. Cryogenic energy storage dewar is at right, in right center is a gaussmeter atop the thermal switch control instrument; the power supply and associated circuitry is at left

COMPACT 375-joule energy source developed by Ion Physics. A 50-liter coil, including dewar, can store 100 joules, while capacitor banks require 750-liter volume for the same job

applications existed until recent advances in superconductivity.

Superconductive storage—The elementary form of inductive energy storage in a superconductive coil is shown in the figure. The superconducting storage coil L is charged with S_1 closed and S_2 and S_3 open. Series resistance R controls the time constant and thus the charging time. After the desired current is achieved in L, S_2 is closed and S_1 opened, disconnecting the energy store from the supply. S_2 is a superconducting switch, causing the current in circuit 2 to be a persistent current. Energy discharge is obtained by closing S_3 and then opening S_2.

Such a system has several advantages:

(1) Once stored, the energy can be kept in storage for indefinite periods, as long as the 4.2 deg K temperature is maintained, because the persistent current in circuit 2 encounters no resistance.

(2) The coil can be charged over a long period of time with a small, low-voltage power supply.

(3) Unlike capacitor banks, energy is stored at low voltage; high voltages appear only during discharge.

Short discharges in the millisecond range are possible, provided that a suitable superconducting switch is available.

Several modifications of the circuit are possible; for instance, the stored energy may be discharged by a secondary winding and discharge initiated by causing the coil to go to normal conductivity.

Materials—The most widely used material at this time is Nb—25 percent Zr (niobium-Zirconium alloy) with a critical field of about 70 kilogauss, and a critical current density approaching 10^9 amps/m² at 50 kilogauss. Another material, Nb$_3$-Sn, has a critical field of about 200 kilogauss. This material is brittle and more difficult to use than the Nb—Zr alloys. The estimated critical field of V$_3$Ga (vanadium-gallium) is even higher, up to 500 kilogauss, but this material is not available in suitable forms.

Storage coils — Although energy storage coils are similar to superconducting coils used for magnet systems, their design differs considerably, and is aimed at optimizing the stored energy rather than the magnetic field properties. The coils must withstand field transients and high voltages occurring during discharge. It will generally be necessary to operate storage coils at high currents, which may involve the use of rectangular conductors or parallel windings. Although high energy densities can be obtained in properly designed superconducting solenoids, the large external fields may present problems; for fast discharges it becomes undesirable for the magnetic field to link any closed metal loop other than those necessary for the operation. A more desirable configuration in this respect is the toroidal coil, which completely contains its magnetic field.

Energy densities of more than 10^7 joules/m³ can be obtained with presently available Nb-Zr wires, and densities of at least 10^8 joule/m³ should be possible when the newer materials have reached a more advanced state of development allowing their use in larger coils.

Applications—Energy stores of this type, using superconductive coils and switches, have been used for experiments with flash tubes for optical pumping of lasers. One such experiment conducted at Ion Physics has delivered about 350 joules to the flash tubes with efficiencies of up to 90 percent. A 1.5-kilojoule energy store is now under test.

Chapter 15

FIELD-EFFECT DEVICES AND APPLICATIONS

Novel Field-Effect Device

Hole-conducting metal-oxide-semiconductor transistor characteristics
provide a three-stage gain of 1,350 from 5 cycles to 72 kc

By F. M. WANLASS, Fairchild Semiconductor Research and Development Laboratory, Palo Alto, California

---

THE p-MOST AS AN A-C AMPLIFIER

Field-effect hole-conducting metal-oxide semiconductor transistors (p-MOSTs) are easily applied to a-c coupled amplifier circuits because of two operating characteristics. The device does not conduct appreciable current unless its input gate is biased in the same polarity as its output. Its gate is voltage-operated, never drawing d-c. By contrast, the p-n junction input field-effect transistor, like the electron tube, requires input bias opposite to the polarity of its output for small-signal amplification. Ease of biasing the p-MOST to a correct operating point makes practical wideband a-c amplifiers without large coupling or bypass capacitors

---

BASIC STRUCTURE of a p-MOST, shown in Fig. 1A, comprises a silicon substrate of n-type conductivity into which are diffused two adjacent islands of p-type conductivity. A silicon-dioxide insulating layer overlays the area between the two diffused regions and a thin metal gate electrode is deposited on top of this SiO_2 layer. In addition to the gate electrode, one of the p islands is tied to the n-type substrate to act as the source electrode, and the other p island is the drain electrode.

The operation of this insulated gate p-MOST is based on the fact that when its gate is biased negatively, electrons will tend to be repelled out of the n-type silicon immediately beneath the gate and holes will be attracted to this region. If the gate is made negative enough, the n-type

silicon will actually convert to p-type in the region close to the Si-SiO_2 interface, so that there will be a p-type link connecting the diffused source and drain islands. The negative gate voltage at which conduction between source and drain can first occur is called the gate threshold voltage V_{GST}. As the gate is made more and more negative beyond V_{GST} the p-type link connecting source and drain will progressively widen resulting in lower and lower source-drain resistance. Since, when current does flow between source and drain, it is carried by holes, which are the majority carriers, the device shown in Fig. 1A is called a p-type MOST or p-MOST.

To have a low threshold voltage V_{GST} and high transconductance in a MOST, it is necessary to have a

thin oxide beneath the gate and close spacing between source and drain islands. It is presently possible to obtain reproducible spacings down to about 5 microns and thicknesses to about 1,000 A. These critical geometrical parameters are controlled using standard manufacturing techniques. Compared to active elements such as the p-n junction input field-effect transistor the MOST is simple and several can be integrated in the same slice of silicon without isolation problems or increase in the number of processing steps.

Characteristics—In operation (Fig. 1B) the bias voltage V_{DS} applied to the drain of a p-MOST with respect to its source must always be negative, so the drain p-n junction is reverse biased. If the gate voltage

Provides Broadband Gain

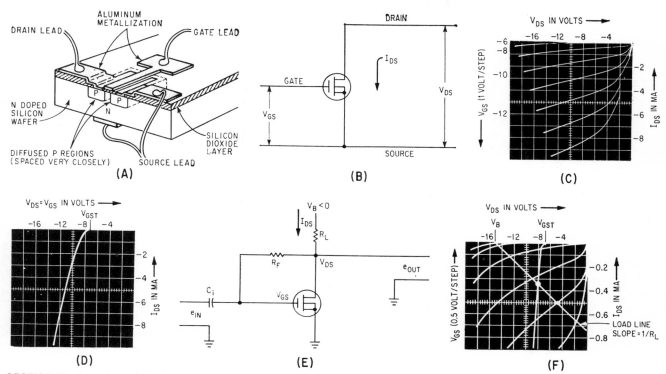

SECTIONAL view of p-MOST (A), suggested symbol and terminal notation (B), drain current vs drain voltage with gate voltage a parameter (C), drain current vs drain voltage with gate tied to drain with gate threshold voltage —8 v (D), automatically biased a-c amplifier stage (E), graphical operating point determination (F)—Fig. 1

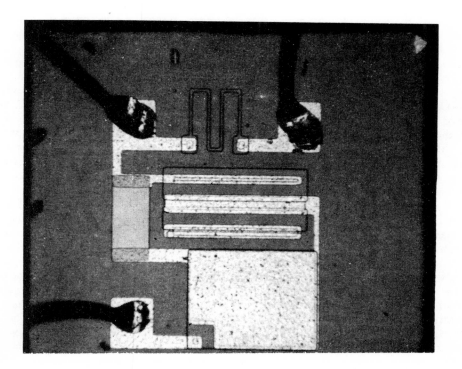

INTEGRATED a-c amplifier of Fig. 2E shown as a microphotograph

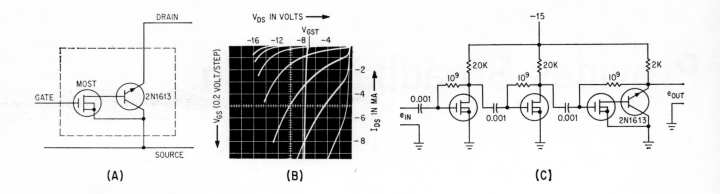

(A)   (B)   (C)

V_{GS} is more positive than V_{GST}, the drain current I_{DS} is small (it will be that flowing in a reverse biased silicon junction, or $< 10^{-9}$ amp). When V_{GS} is made more negative than V_{GST} drain current will increase and it will increase considerably if V_{GS} is made negative enough. Data on typical present devices are shown in Fig. 1C, where for $V_{DS} = V_{GS} = -11$ volts, I_{DS} is approximately -5 ma. For gate voltages more negative than V_{GST} the characteristic curves resemble those of a pentode, in that the dynamic output resistance is high.

A convenient way to determine the gate threshold voltage V_{GST} at which drain current I_{DS} first flows is to tie the gate to the drain and then plot I_{DS} vs V_{DS} on a transistor curve tracer as in Fig. 1D. Usually it is desirable to have devices for which $|V_{GST}|$ is as small as possible. But V_{GST} is a parameter that can be adjusted within wide limits during manufacturing, by adjusting the oxide thickness under the gate. If desirable, $|V_{GST}|$ can be made large for high-power, high-voltage amplifier applications.

Automatic Biasing—Consider the single-stage amplifier of Fig. 1E with a supply voltage V_B that is several volts more negative than the gate threshold voltage of the MOST. Without input signal ($e_{IN} = 0$) drain voltage V_{DS} is determined as follows. Gate $V_{GS} = V_{DS}$ independent of the value of R_f (since no gate current flows). Voltage V_{DS} cannot equal V_B, because then the MOST would conduct current causing a voltage drop in R_L. Also, V_{DS} must be at least as negative as V_{GST} to produce any drain current flow at all. It appears, therefore, that V_{DS} will be automatically biased to a value between V_{GST} and V_B. This

is a bias region in which the MOST has appreciable small signal gain. To find exactly the small signal operating point for the circuit of Fig. 1E I_{DS} vs $V_{DS} = V_{GS}$ is plotted for the particular MOST used. On the same graph is superimposed a load line of slope $1/R_L$, with an x intercept of V_B. The intersection of these two curves (Fig. 1F) gives the operating point current I_{DSO} and voltage $V_{DSO} = V_{GSO}$. If the characteristic curves are now also superimposed on the same graph, the variations ΔI_{DS} and ΔV_{DS} owing to small variations ΔV_{GS} about V_{GSO} can be obtained. This graphical operating point determination is performed in Fig. 1F for the same MOST that was used to obtain the data of Fig. 1C and D. It is evident from Fig. 1F that the stage will automatically bias itself to a point of useful gain for almost any value of its load resistor R_L. The value of R_L is not critical, since it is difficult to saturate V_{DS} at extreme voltage.

For determining static bias conditions the values of R_f and C_i are unimportant in the circuit of Fig. 1E. Consider the conditions necessary for amplification of a small input signal e_{IN}. For a small change e_{gs} in the gate voltage the drain voltage will change in the opposite direction. Thus, the first requirement to obtain a-c gain is that the input coupling capacitor C_i must be much larger than the gate-drain capacitance C_{GD}. This is satisfied because a typical MOST has only about 0.2 pf for C_{GD}. More importantly, the degenerative effect of signal coupling through R_f from drain to gate must be kept small in comparison to the signal coupled to the gate through C_i. This means that a-c amplification can only be obtained down to a frequency f_e equivalent to $1/R_fC_i$.

To make an amplifier stage that is flat down to 1 cycle means that the product of R_f and C_i should be several seconds at least. The advantage of a MOST becomes apparent since the gate requires no d-c input current, R_f can be made extremely large in value and C_i fairly small to obtain the large R_fC_i product. Feedback resistors R_f having values beyond 10^{12} ohms have been successfully used. With such large feedback resistors, input capacitor C_i must have an exceedingly low leakage current.

An accurate value for R_f is not important as long as the product R_fC_i is much greater than the period of the lowest frequency signal to be amplified.

Transistor Addition—In an a-c amplifier stage driving a heavy load, an *npn* transistor can be added as an emitter follower, so the drain of the MOST need only supply base current to the transistor. This arrangement is shown in Fig. 2A. This combination of MOST and transistor can be considered a new species of three-lead device. This composite has some characteristics, shown in Fig. 2B, that are similar to a single MOST. For example, the gate threshold voltage V_{GST} is a comparable negative value. However, the transconductance of the composite, when it has started to conduct, is much larger than for a single MOST. The composite g_m is the product of the g_m of the MOST and the β of the transistor. Another slight difference between the composite and the single MOST is that, regardless of gate voltage, the drain of the composite must be more negative than approximately -0.7 volt to have conduction. This is the voltage required between the base and the emitter of the transistor before

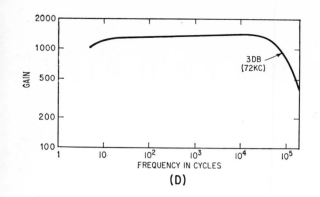

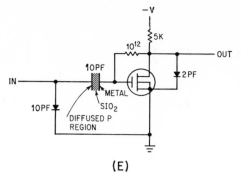

COMBINATION of MOST and npn transistor gives increased g_m (A), input-output characteristics for combination shown previously (B), high input impedance amplifier circuit (C), gain of amplifier vs frequency (D), circuit of integrated a-c amplifier stage showing parasitic reverse-biased diode capacitance (E)—Fig. 2

any base current will begin to flow.

The composite can be used in self-biased stages like that of Fig. 1E. If desirable, load resistor R_L can be made smaller to get more power gain. In fact, several transistors can be connected from a MOST in a Darlington configuration, so that practically any size load can be driven with automatic bias point stabilization.

A-C Amplifier—Figure 2C shows a practical high-input-impedance, low-output-impedance voltage amplifier comprising cascaded stages, each like that of Fig. 1E. The 10^9 ohm feedback resistors were made especially for this application by depositing a thin film of amorphous silicon onto an insulating substrate, etching into a pattern and bonding on leads. The resistors are physically small, in the order of 0.01 by 0.01 in. Together with 0.001-μf coupling capacitors they produce a low-frequency response of about 5 cycles at 3 db down.

At low frequencies such that the interelectrode capacitances of the MOST can be neglected, but at frequencies high enough that there is not too much degenerative feedback through R_f, the gain of one stage of the amplifier of Fig. 2C should be $G_8 = e_o/e_{IN} = g_m r_D R_L/(r_D + R_L)$, where r_D is the dynamic output resistance of the MOST. The total voltage gain should be the product of three such terms and when calculated is $G = 1,290$, using values of g_m and r_D from the characteristic curves in Fig. 1C and Fig. 2B. The measured gain of about 1,350 agrees favorably with this calculated value over a bandwidth from 5 cycles to 72 kc (3 db down points) as shown in Fig. 2D.

The constant gain bandwidth could be extended, at the sacrifice of low frequency gain, by connecting more degenerative capacitance from drain to gate of each MOST in the circuit of Fig. 2C.

Input Impedance—For a solid-state amplifier the circuit of Fig. 2C has an extremely high input impedance Z_{IN}. Above a few cps Z_{IN} results almost exclusively from gate-drain capacitance C_{GD} of the first MOST multiplied by the gain of the first stage, plus the gate-source capacitance C_{GS}. With typical values of $C_{GS} = 1.5$ pf, $C_{GD} = 0.2$ pf, and G about 8, we get C_{TOTAL} about 3 pf. At a signal frequency of 50 kc the input impedance is still greater than 1 megohm.

Transients—Since the gate of the MOST is insulated from its body it can never draw current for either positive or negative voltage excursions. Therefore, if the a-c amplifier shown in Fig. 2C has a momentary extra large input pulse, normal low level signal amplification can proceed immediately afterwards. No capacitor blocking phenomenon will occur like that in a-c coupled vacuum-tube amplifiers. An upper limit is set by the breakdown voltage of the oxide layer beneath the gate, but this voltage can be made 100 volts or higher depending on the thickness used.

Integration—An attractive feature of the a-c amplification scheme is the ease with which it might be integrated into a single silicon chip. An a-c coupled amplifier with gain down to very low frequencies is generally impossible to integrate because large values of coupling capacitance are needed. Here, if the feedback resistance R_f of a stage is made about 10^{12} ohms the input capacitor C_i can be as low as 10 pf,

and gain is obtained down to a few cycles per second.

Figure 2E is the equivalent circuit of the integrated stage shown in the microphotograph. The input capacitor to this stage consists of a metal electrode separated from a p island by a thin SiO_2 insulating layer. The metal electrode goes to the gate of the MOST and the p island is the input terminal to the stage. This MOS capacitor with SiO_2 as its dielectric has low leakage current to the metal electrode, so that it is possible to use a thin film silicon resistor of about 10^{12} ohms connected from drain to gate to set the bias level. However, there is an unavoidable parasitic capacitance of about 10 pf between the p island and the n-type substrate. This parasitic capacitance basically limits the stage to relatively low frequency amplification. Other types of thin-film input capacitors still to be developed could extend the high frequency response.

The integrated stage has a voltage gain of about 5. Several cascaded stages without other components produce any total desired gain. The stages are not critical with respect to supply voltage or to internal component tolerance.

BIBLIOGRAPHY

C. T. Sah, A New Semiconductor Tetrode—The Surface-Potential Controlled Transistor, *Proc. IRE*, **49**, p 1,623, Nov. 1961.

P. K. Weimer, The TFT—A New Thin-Film Transistor, *Proc. IRE*, **50**, p 1,462, June 1962.

D. Kahng and M. M. Atalla, Solid-State Device Res. Conf. at the Mellon Inst. & Carnegie Inst. of Technology, Pittsburgh, Pa., June 1960.

M. F. Wolff, Advances in Microminiaturization, ELECTRONICS **36**, p. 51, Feb. 15, 1963.

F. M. Wanlass, Field-Effect Metal-Oxide-Semiconductor-Transistors and Microelectronics, WESCON Preprint for 1963.

Using a New Device: Field-Effect

Variable frequency Wien-bridge has 20-cps to 40-Kc range, delivers 3.5

WIEN-BRIDGE THEORY

The oscillator (Fig. 1A)—a two-stage, RC-coupled, class-A amplifier—has two loops (Fig. 1B) linking input and output. One, the positive feedback loop, causes the oscillation; the other, the negative feedback loop, stabilizes the amplitude of the oscillations.

Oscillations occur when there is zero phase-shift between V_{AD} and V_{CD}, at a frequency f_o determined by R_1, R_2, C_1, and C_2 and given by: $f_o = 1/2_\pi (R_1 R_2 C_1 C_2)^{\frac{1}{2}}$; the attenuation is calculated from $V_{AD}/V_{CD} = 1/(1 + C_2/C_1 + R_2/R_1)$. If $R_1 = R_2$ and $C_1 = C_2$, then zero phase-shift occurs at $f_o = 1/(2_\pi RC)$ and the attenuation becomes 1/3.

The negative feedback loop—a resistive voltage divider—has zero-phase shift at all frequencies and an attenuation $V_{AB}/V_{CD} = R_S/(R_S + R_F)$; R_S is the a-c resistance of lamps I_1 and I_2.

The voltage transfer ratio, β, of the bridge network is the difference between the attenuation of the positive and negative feedback loops: $\beta = V_{AB}/V_{CD} = [1/(1 + C_2/C_1 + R_1/R_2)] - [R_S/(R_S + R_F)]$. If $R_1 = R_2$ and $C_1 = C_2$, then $\beta = (1/3) - (R_S/R_S + R_F)$.

A necessary condition for oscillation is that the product of gain and feedback attenuation be equal to one. Therefore the gain of the amplifier, expressed by the feedback ratio is $A = (1/\beta) = [(1/3) - R_S/(R_S + R_F)]$, or, the necessary feedback for a particular oscillator is a function of the open-loop amplifier gain, $R_S/(R_S + R_F) = (1/3) - (1/A)$. With large open-loop gain, the oscillator has more stability and less distortion .

Two lamps, in series with the negative feedback loop, keep $A\beta$ independent of component aging or temperature changes; their nonlinear resistance increases with signal amplitude—thus bringing amplitude back to normal

BECAUSE OF their high input-impedance, vacuum tubes, rather than transistors are normally used as active elements in Wien-bridge oscillators. In this circuit, the active element is a 2N2498 field-effect transistor that is smaller and more efficient than a tube and has an equivalent high input impedance. The two stage oscillator is followed by a buffer that delivers 3.5 volts to 2,000-ohm load.

The oscillator's frequency ranges from 20 cps to 40 Kc in four steps and is continuously variable between steps. Both frequency and amplitude stability are good, except at the lower frequencies. Several ways of improving the stability and frequency range are suggested.

EXPERIMENTAL CIRCUIT—The breadboard model Wien-bridge oscillator, Fig. 2, consists of a two-stage oscillator and an emitter follower or buffer. With the buffer, power stages can be added without degrading the oscillator.

The four frequency ranges, selected by a four-position switch S_1, are: 20 to 200 cps; 200 cps to 2 Kc; 2 Kc to 20 Kc; and 4 Kc to 40 Kc. The signal amplitude is adjustable from zero to 3.5 v rms into a 2,000-ohm load. An 8-ma, 24 v d-c supply is required.

The amplitude is controlled by potentiometer R_{14}; R_{11} attenuates the amplifier signal slightly to prevent unsymmetrical clipping by the emitter follower. The bias point of Q_2 is adjusted by rheostat R_8, to insure symmetrical clippings, and the

SIMPLIFIED WIEN-BRIDGE *oscillator, with two-stage amplifier, (A) and redrawn in bridge form; lamps I_1 and I_2 are part of the negative feedback loop (B)—Fig. 1*

Transistor Oscillators

By VERN GLOVER
Applications Engineer,
Texas Instruments Inc.,
Dallas, Texas

volts to a 2,000-ohm load. Other field-effect transistor circuits suggested

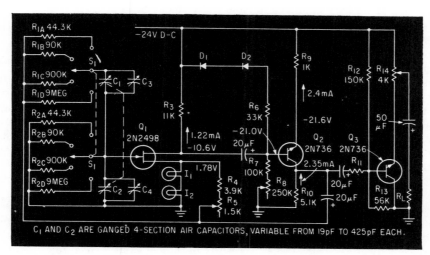

BREADBOARD MODEL *oscillator uses field-effect transistor 2N2498. Switch S_1 selects one of four frequency ranges; transistor Q_3 is the buffer stage—Fig. 2*

gain is adjusted by R_5 which must be set for minimum distortion. Both R_5 and R_8 need only initial calibration.

Diodes D_1 and D_2 help stabilize the bias point of Q_2 over the temperature range 15 C to 45 C. The lamps I_1 and I_2 are nonlinear resistors in the negative-feedback loop.

The positive-feedback loop consists of ganged variable capacitors, paralleled by mica trimmers, and two sets of resistors connected by a double-pole, four-position switch.

Trimmer capacitor C_3 compensates for inequalities in the variable capacitors and in the input capacitance of the field-effect transistor. The breadboard model operated satisfactorily with several 2N2498 units, even using limit samples having maximum and minimum data sheet values of $I_{D(on)}$, zero-gate-voltage drain current.

FREQUENCY STABILITY — A maximum random variation of 2.77 percent was observed in the low-frequency scale range. All other scale ranges exhibited less than 0.25-percent variation. The maximum variation of frequency on any scale with a 10-percent voltage variation was no more than the maximum random variation of 2.77 percent. The frequency variation observed over the temperature range of +45 C to +15 C was also no more than the maximum random variation of 2.77 percent observed at room temperature.

The maximum amplitude variation over the 20-cps to 40-Kc frequency range was +4.7 percent to −12.3 percent compared to the amplitude at 1 Kc. The amplitude variation with temperature at 15 C was negligible but increased to 6.25 percent from the amplitude at 25 C as the temperature reached 45 C. Below 10 C the waveform started to distort, and above 50 C the amplitude decreased sufficiently to stop oscillation.

DISTORTION — Maximum distor-

tion measured from 20 cps to 20 Kc was 0.81 percent; distortion measurements were not made above 20 Kc because of limitations in the measuring equipment. Visual examination of the waveform indicated no increase in distortion from 20 Kc to 40 Kc.·

FREQUENCY LIMITATIONS — The high- and low-frequency ends of the oscillator were determined by the resistors in the positive feedback loop. The maximum value of R_2 was limited by the finite input impedance of the field-effect transistor. At 200 cps—high end of the low-frequency scale—the transistor's input impedance began to reduce the effective value of R_2. Thus, R_2 was made slightly larger than R_1 on this scale range. But this was not sufficient compensation, and the low-frequency scale was the least stable. The worst-case amplitude variation and distortion occurred on this scale.

The voltage developed across R_2

by the source-to-gate leakage current further limits the maximum resistance. If the voltage developed by this temperature-dependent current increases sufficiently to cause the field-effect transistor to approach pinch-off, the oscillator will cease functioning.

Both limitations can be overcome by a larger variable air-capacitor, which would permit the use of a smaller resistor on the low-frequency scale. A larger capacitor would also permit the use of additional larger trimmer capacitors to ease frequency adjustment during calibration. The capacitor used in this circuit was employed only because it was available.

The high-frequency limitation is determined by the minimum permissible resistor values which do not load down the oscillator's second stage. The positive feedback resistors required for the high-frequency range are 44,300 instead of the theoretical 45,000 ohms (from Eq. 1). The output impedance of the second stage is significant enough to increase the effective value of R_1 and explains this apparent discrepancy. Corresponding vacuum-tube oscillators that operate at 20 cps usually also employ a larger variable capacitor than the one used in the breadboard model.

POSSIBLE IMPROVEMENTS —
A larger variable air capacitor would permit the use of smaller resistors in the bridge circuit when operating on the low-frequency scale. This would result in improved frequency and amplitude stability.

Another improvement is to increase the open-loop amplifier gain of the oscillator. The calculated voltage gain of the oscillator was

$$A \cong g_m R_3 \frac{R_{10}}{R_9}$$

$$= (1 \times 10^{-3})(11K)\left(\frac{5.1K}{2K}\right) = 28$$

where g_m = transconductance of the field-effect transistor. The measured gain was 27.3. According to Millman[1], frequency stability could be improved if this gain could be increased. This could be accomplished if constant-current biasing of the field-effect transistor were employed. It would permit the use of a larger source load resistance in the field-effect transistor stage in conjunction with a larger supply voltage. An additional transistor amplifying stage could also be added, to prevent loading of the field-effect transistor stage and for additional amplification.

Another circuit improvement is a continuously variable frequency control using two ganged variable rheostats; however, unequal rheostat tracking results in radical variations in output amplitude at the rheostats, and thus varying frequency. If rheostats are used, the large air-dielectric capacitor is eliminated and a smaller package can be achieved.

OTHER CIRCUITS — Several oscillator circuits employing field-effect transistors were investigated. Phase-shift oscillators were found to work satisfactorily except for the disadvantage inherent in such circuits, that is, no simple compensating negative feedback such as the variable lamp resistance in the Wien-bridge oscillator. A phase-shift oscillator which was breadboarded is shown in Fig. 3A. The attenuation of the 4-mesh feedback network is 18.36. The frequency of oscillation is determined by:

$$f_o \approx \sqrt{\frac{7/10}{2\pi RC}}$$

where R and C are the values of one mesh in the ladder feedback network.

A three-mesh network would have an attenuation of 29 and a frequency

$$f_o \approx \frac{1}{2\pi RC \sqrt{6}}$$

The frequency of oscillation of the circuit shown in Fig. 3A can be varied several cycles around 10 cps by varying R_{11}. The variable resistor R_3 permits the gain to be adjusted exactly to compensate for the attenuation of the feedback network.

Another circuit possibility is shown in Fig. 3B. R_1 adjusts the bias for symmetrical clipping and R_2 adjusts the gain. It has possibilities as a fixed, low-frequency oscillator. It appears that for a fixed frequency oscillator, a lamp in the negative feedback loop is not as important and a resistor can be used with reasonable success.

BIBLIOGRAPHY

Jacob Millman, Vacuum Tubes and Semiconductor Electronics, McGraw-Hill Book Co, New York, 1958, pp 479-493.

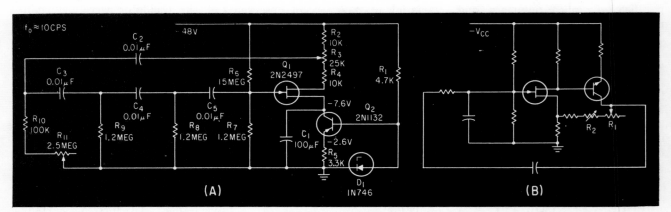

PHASE-SHIFT oscillator for 10 cps, also uses field-effect transistor (A); fixed low-frequency oscillator does not require lamps in feedback loop; its gain and bias are adjusted by R_1 and R_2 respectively (B)—Fig. 3

FILLING TRANSISTOR PERFORMANCE GAPS

Despite the profound influence of transistors on circuit design, practical use of these devices has not been without problems. For example, the difficulty of designing transistor amplifiers with high input impedance still makes the vacuum tube the logical choice in many applications. The commercial availability of the field-effect transistor is changing this situation. Here's how its characteristic high input impedance can be used to design a practical low-noise preamplifier suitable for many applications

LOW-NOISE PREAMPLIFIER
Uses Field-Effect Transistors

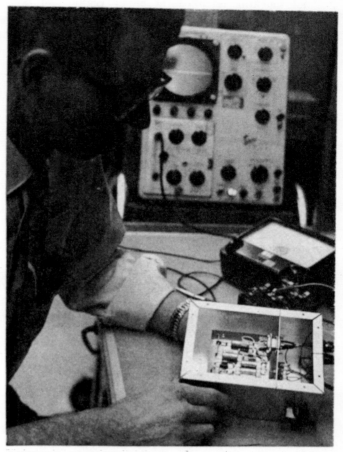

AUTHOR FLEENOR *checks performance of low-noise field-effect transistor preamplifier*

Few parts are needed in multiple-purpose preamplifier design using off-the-shelf field-effect transistors. High input impedance and low noise are combined with gain stability despite temperature change

By E. G. FLEENOR, Senior Electronics Research Engineer
Lockheed Missiles & Space Company, Sunnyvale, California

FIELD-EFFECT transistors have input impedances and optimum source impedances that are typically two orders of magnitude higher than those of ordinary bipolar transistors. These characteristics have been used to design a general-purpose preamplifier that is suitable for use with any low-level, high-impedance source. A commercially available field-effect transistor is used in the circuit, which has an input resistance greater than 100 megohms. Noise figure can be less than 1 db. The preamplifier operates from 12 volts and draws 1.4 ma.

CHARACTERISTICS—The electrical characteristics of the field-effect transistor are similar to those of a vacuum tube, and the same equivalent circuit can be used. The field-effect transistor terminal designations and the analogous tube electrodes are gate for grid, source for cathode and drain for plate. The equivalent circuit is shown in Fig. 1A. Typical values for the 2N2497 field-effect transistor at drain-source voltage V_{DS} of −7 volts and drain current I_D of 0.5 ma are transconductance g_m of 800 micromhos, drain resistance r_d of 100,000 ohms, gate-drain capacitance C_{gd} of 4 pf, drain-source capacitance C_{ds} of 4 pf and gate-source capacitance C_{gs} of 16 pf.

The TI 2N2497 is a silicon p-channel field-effect transistor, so polarity of the biasing voltages are opposite to those of an n-channel field-effect transistor or a tube. The characteristics, shown in Fig. 1B, are similar to those of a pentode tube.

In the field-effect transistor in Fig. 1C, the bar of p-type silicon has had n-type impurities introduced into opposite sides creating p-n junctions. Ohmic connections for the source and drain are made at opposite ends of the bar, and an ohmic connection for the gate is made to the two n regions. If the gate-source and gate-drain junctions are reverse biased, depletion layers are formed between the two n regions, which effectively reduces the size of the p channel through which majority carriers flow. Thus, source-drain conductance can be modulated by varying gate-source or gate-drain voltage.

The operating range in which the depletion layers

are not touching is called the ohmic region and is shown on the curves in Fig. 1B. If gate-drain voltage is increased sufficiently, the two depletion layers touch and pinch off the channel. The constant-current operating range that results is called the pinch-off region. The field-effect transistor is operated in the pinch-off region in linear amplifiers where high transconductance and drain resistance must be maintained.

PREAMPLIFIER—The low-noise field-effect transistor amplifier in Fig. 2A has a voltage gain of 10.5 and an input resistance of 100 megohms. It can be used as a preamplifier for piezoelectric transducers (microphones, hydrophones, accelerometers, pressure cells), capacitor microphones and radiation detectors (thermistor-bolometers, photodiodes, phototubes, and lead-sulfide, cadmium-sulfide and gallium-arsenide detectors).

The input field-effect transistor stage is d-c coupled to a common-emitter transistor stage, and 26 db of feedback is used. The circuit can provide a 3-volt peak-to-peak output into a 5,000-ohm load. Performance can be calculated from the equivalent circuit in Fig. 2B.

Gain can be calculated from the approximation $(R_1 + R_2)/R_1$, which yields a value of 11, compared to the measured gain of 10.5. Precision resistors with low temperature coefficients are used for R_1 and R_2 to stabilize gain. The circuit was tested over a temperature range of -40 to $+100$ deg C, and gain changed less than 1 percent. This highly stable gain can be partly attributed to the large amount of feedback. In addition, there is a partial cancellation of the negative temperature coefficient of transconductance of the field-effect transistor (-0.6 percent per deg C) by the positive temperature coefficient of beta of the output transistor ($+0.5$ percent per deg C).

INPUT IMPEDANCE—The equivalent input circuit of the preamplifier is a 100-megohm resistor, R_i, shunted by an 8.3-picofarad capacitor, C_i. The high input resistance is obtained by bootstrapping Q_1 so that the source voltage is fed back through C_2 to the bottom of R_3. Feedback voltage across R_1 also reduces the effect of gate-source capacitance C_{gs} and consequently of C_i.

The value of C_i is determined by gate-drain capacitance C_{gd}, which is increased by the Miller effect, and by gate-source capacitance C_{gs}, which is reduced by the feedback, as shown in Fig. 2B. Thus

$$C_i = C_{gd}\left(1 - \frac{E_d}{E_i}\right) + C_{gs}\left(1 - \frac{E_s}{E_i}\right)$$

The value of R_i is determined by R_3 and the amount of feedback. Gate-source and gate-drain leakage resistances are assumed to be negligible. Thus

$$R_i = R_3/(1 - E_s/E_i) = R_3(1 + R_1 g_m h_{fe}')$$

The value of R_3 was selected to be low enough so that gate leakage current (0.1 μamp at 100 deg C) would not disturb bias at high temperature.

The 3-db frequency response of the preamplifier extends from 0.5 cps to 700 Kc using a 600-ohm source. The lower 3-db frequency is determined by $R_4 C_4$ and the amount of feedback. Thus, the lower

3-db frequency is $f \cong 1/2\pi R_4 C_4 R_1 g_m$. If a resistive source such as a radiation detector is used, the upper 3-db frequency is limited by the R-C circuit formed by external source resistance R_s and C_i of the preamplifier (8.3 pf). For a 1-megohm source, the upper 3-db frequency is 20 Kc. If gain at high frequencies is not needed, it can be reduced to minimize pickup problems by shunting R_2 with capacitor C_6. Thus the upper 3-db frequency is $f \cong 1/2\pi f R_2 C_6$.

Measured output impedance is 250 ohms. The equation is

$$R_o = \left(\frac{1 + R_2/R_1}{h_{fe}' g_m}\right)\left(1 + \frac{R_1 R_2}{R_1 + R_2} g_m\right)$$

Output impedance can be reduced by a factor of 3 by replacing the 2N910 with the higher beta 2N930.

NOISE FIGURE—The noise figure of the preamplifier is detemined primarily by the noise performance of the field-effect transistor because it has a large power gain and furnishes approximately optimum source impedance to the second stage. Noise figure of a field-effect transistor is limited fundamentally by thermal noise of the conducting channel,[2] but shot noise of the gate current and $1/f$ noise of the gate and channel currents contribute to the noise.

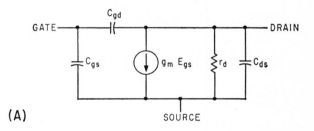

(A)

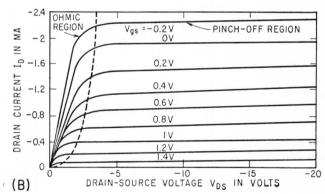

(B)

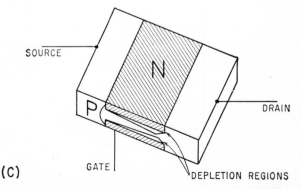

(C)

EQUIVALENT *circuit (A) and characteristics (B) are shown for field-effect transistor (C)—Fig. 1*

At frequencies below 1 Kc and with a high-impedance source, $1/f$ noise of the gate current tends to predominate. The noise figure varies with frequency and source impedance. A test setup for measuring noise figure is shown in Fig. 2B. The following equation can be derived from the definition of noise figure

$$NF = 10 \log \left(\frac{V_{no}^2}{A^2} \right) \left(\frac{1}{4kt\Delta f R_s} \right) \left[(2\pi f R_s C_i)^2 + \left(\frac{R_i + R_s}{R_i} \right)^2 \right]$$

where A is voltage gain of preamplifier-amplifier combination, f is center frequency, Δf is bandwidth of wave analyzer, k is Boltzman's constant, t is temperature in deg K and V_{no} is rms noise voltage out. Another method of determining noise figure involves measuring the equivalent short-circuit noise voltage and the open-circuit noise current.[3]

Noise figure is plotted as a function of source impedance and frequency in Fig. 3. In this preamplifier, optimum source impedance is about 0.5 megohm at 1,000 cps, but the preamplifier is useful over an impedance range of 20,000 ohms to 20 megohm. The noise figure is typically less than 3 db referred to 1 megohm at frequencies between 100 cps and 10 Kc.

For ultralow noise applications, the 2N2500 field-effect transistor, which has a guaranteed noise figure of 1 db at 1 Kc, can be used by determining the value of R_6 experimentally for the proper bias level.

BIASING—Transistor Q_1 is biased by returning gate resistor R_3 to a fixed bias level determined by the resistance divider formed by R_6 and R_7. Stability of the bias was analyzed, and the results indicate that the temperature coefficient of drain current is reduced from −0.6 percent per deg C to −0.15 percent per deg C by the d-c feedback.

Bias is stable enough so that any 2N2497 having the 3 to 1 range of drain current values can be used without changing the bias resistors (specified drain current of the 2N2497 is between 1 and 3 ma when gate-source voltage is zero and drain-source voltage is −10 volts). The ratio of drain currents for field-effect transistors at the limits is 77.5 percent.

REFERENCES
(1) W. Shockley, A Unipolar Field-Effect Transistor, *Proc IRE*, **40**, p 1365, November 1952.
(2) A. van der Ziel, Thermal Noise in Field-Effect Transistors, *Proc IRE*, **50**, p 1808, August 1962.
(3) A. E. Sanderson and R. G. Fulks, A Simplified Noise Theory and Its Application to the Design of Low-Noise Amplifiers, *IRE Trans on Audio*, p 106, July-August 1961.

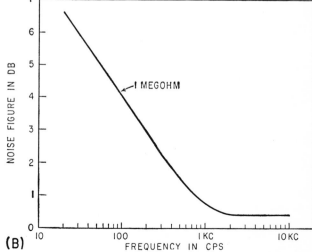

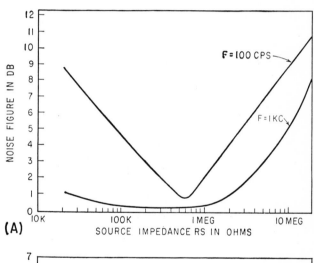

LOW-NOISE *preamplifier (A) is shown with equivalent circuit (B) and noise measurement setup (C)—Fig. 2*

NOISE FIGURE *is plotted as a function of frequency (A) and source impedance (B)—Fig. 3*

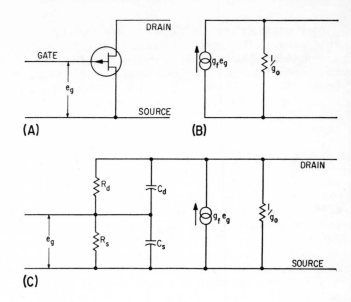

NARROWING THE GAP

The introduction of field-effect transistors has significantly narrowed the gap between tube and transistor circuit design. This discussion illustrates a typical case, in which the techniques used in vacuum-tube circuits have been successfully adapted to the field-effect transistor. As new semiconductor devices are developed, and a wider range of applications is recognized, a combination of the best attributes of both tubes and transistors will result

EQUIVALENT CIRCUITS: *actual circuit (A); simplified equivalent circuit (B); equivalent circuit (C)—Fig. 1*

HOW TO GET Maximum Input Impedance

THE FIELD-EFFECT transistor, being a voltage-controlled device, is more nearly the equivalent of a vacuum tube than of a current-controlled conventional transistor. The main advantages of the field-effect transistor over the tube are its low power consumption with the elimination of excess heat, and its small size. In d-c amplifiers it eliminates the drift due to filament voltage variations, although it does have a drift term associated with the leakage current of the reverse-biased gate diode. Its advantages over conventional transistors are its high input impedance (that of a reverse-biased diode), its reduced noise figure, and its high power gain, which approaches that of a good vacuum tube. The application ideally suited to the characteristics of a field-effect transistor is an amplifier requiring a low-level input, high input impedance and low power consumption.

For this type of amplifier, a number of parameters are of interest. A high d-c input resistance is needed; this can be deduced from the gate-diode leakage current on the specification sheet for the device. At frequencies above a few cycles per second, the input impedance is determined principally by input capacitance, which therefore should be kept to a minimum. An additional factor of importance is the noise figure, which in low-level applications will determine the minimum signal amplitude that can be passed by an amplifier. Finally, a high gain is desirable, since this will effectively reduce the noise contributed by succeeding stages. In the field-effect transistor, the gain is determined by the forward transfer conductance.

The characteristic curves of field-effect transistors are similar to those of a pentode, and show the drain (plate) current as a function of gate (grid) bias and drain-to-source (plate-to-cathode) voltage. As in a pentode, a simple equivalent circuit can be used to represent the field effect transistor; a current generator $g_f e_g$ in parallel with a resistance $1/g_o$, where g_f is the forward transfer conductance, and g_o is the output conductance. Figures 1A and 1B show the actual and simple equivalent circuits.

Typical values for present devices show g_f with a range from less than 1,000 micromhos to about 5,000 micromhos, and g_o from about 1 to 500 micromhos.

EQUIVALENT CIRCUIT—In the equivalent circuit shown in Fig. 1C, R_d and R_s represent the reverse-bias resistances of the gate diode, which are reflected into the drain and source circuits respectively. These resistances have typical values of hundreds or thousands of megohms. Shunting these high-resistance paths are small values of capacitance C_d and C_s, which have values of 15 pf or less. Above a few cycles per second, the input impedance of the device is determined mainly by these shunt capacitances.

In designing a high input impedance stage, the input capacitance must be kept at a minimum. A source (cathode) follower can be utilized to minimize the gate-to-source capacitance C_s, as shown in Fig. 2A and 2B.

The addition of a source resistance R_s produces negative feedback which, in addition to the stabilizing effect it has on the circuit, reduces the voltage appearing across the gate-to-source capacitance C_s. This voltage e is the difference between the input and output signals which are in phase

$$e = e_{in} - e_o \qquad (1)$$

The voltage gain of the amplifier can be computed

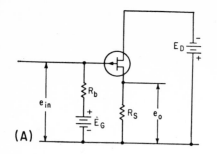

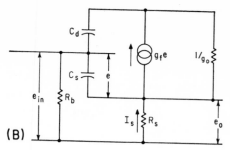

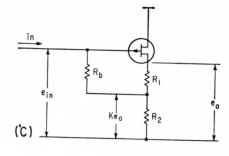

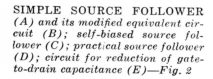

SIMPLE SOURCE FOLLOWER
*(A) and its modified equivalent cir-
cuit (B); self-biased source follower (C); practical source follower
(D); circuit for reduction of gate-
to-drain capacitance (E)—Fig. 2*

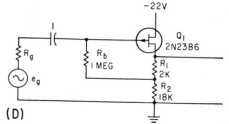

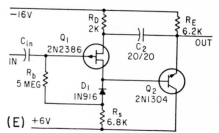

With Field-Effect Transistors

By T. ROSS BIGNELL
Project Engineer
Electro Instruments, Inc.,
San Diego, California

$$e_o = I_s R_s = g_f e R_s = g_f (e_{in} - e_o) R_s \qquad (2)$$

This simplifies to

$$G = \frac{e_o}{e_{in}} = \frac{g_f R_s}{1 + g_f R_s} \qquad (3)$$

The gate-to-source capacitance C_s is now equivalently reduced to

$$C_{eq} = C_s (1 - G) \qquad (4)$$

As the gain approaches unity, C_{eq} approaches zero. The virtual elimination of C_s almost doubles the a-c input impedance of a source follower over other conventional circuits. By the application of similar feedback techniques to the drain, the gate-to-drain capacitance C_d also can be substantially reduced. However, the controlling factor at low frequency still remains R_b and in the interests of stability this should be kept below a maximum value of about one megohm. As in most other applications, a compromise between stability and input impedance must be made.

SELF-BIASING—By a self-biasing technique common in vacuum-tube design, the equivalent gate bias resistance can be increased by bootstrapping, as shown in Fig. 2C.

The d-c input resistance of the stage will be considered as being due entirely to R_b. The input resistance is the ratio of input voltage to input current

$$R_{in} = \frac{e_{in}}{i_{in}} \qquad (5)$$

If the gate presents an open circuit to the input, then all the input current will flow through R_b. A portion of output voltage, Ke_o, is used to bootstrap the resistance R_b and the input current becomes

$$i_{in} = \frac{e_{in} - Ke_o}{R_b} \qquad (6)$$

where $K = \dfrac{R_2}{R_1 + R_2}$, and $e_o = Ge_{in}$ (7)

and finally $\quad R_{in} = \dfrac{e_{in} - \dfrac{R_2}{R_1 + R_2} Ge_{in}}{R_b} \qquad (8)$

which reduces to $\quad R_{in} \approx R_b \left(\dfrac{R_1 + R_2}{R_1} \right) \quad$ if $\quad G \approx 1 \qquad (9)$

The circuit shown in Fig. 2D uses the techniques of a self-biased source follower. It has a d-c input impedance of 10 megohms and at least 1 megohm input impedance at 10 Kc. The required range of input signal level is from 1 millivolt to 10 volts, with a bandwidth of from 10 cycles to 10 Kc.

The theoretical input impedance derived from Eq. 9 is 10 megohms. The actual input impedance at 10 cycles is slightly under 8 megohms. The frequency at which the input impedance drops to 1 megohm is about 25 Kc, corresponding to an input capacitance of about 6 pf.

Figure 3 (top) is a graphical comparison between actual and theoretical input impedance of the circuit in Fig. 2D, expressed as a function of frequency.

From Eq. 3, using $g_f = 1{,}500$ micromhos, the theoretical voltage gain is 0.97. Actual voltage gain was 0.96. The 3-db bandwidth of the stage extends from below 1 cycle to above 10 Mc. The voltage gain is linear over the specified range from 1 millivolt to 10 v., and, using a 1-megohm generator resistance, the output signal-to-noise ratio at 1 millivolt input is greater than 20 db.

STABILITY—Although temperature considerations were not part of this design study, the stability of the stage as a function of temperature shows an improvement over other configurations, due to the large negative feedback imposed by the source resistance. Temperature stability is less of a problem with field-effect transistors than with conventional ones. The base-emitter voltage variation due to temperature is eliminated, and only the leakage current of the gate diode needs to be considered. The change in forward transfer conductance, g_f, also is somewhat less than the change in h_{f_e} in conventional transistors.

From Eq. 3, since the gain is always less than unity, it follows that the output voltage drift will always be less than the input voltage drift. If the worst case condition is assumed ($\Delta e_o = \Delta e_{in}$), then Δe_o can be considered independent of variations in g_f. Assuming that all temperature variation in field effect transistors is due to leakage current, then

$$\Delta e_{in} = I_l R_b \qquad (10)$$

where I_l is the gate diode leakage current, and R_b is the gate bias resistor.

Again if worst case conditions are assumed; that

is, I_l is the maximum specified (10×10^{-9} amp at 25 deg C), and if it doubles every 8 deg C, then the maximum input voltage drift from 0 to 50 deg C generated across the 1-megohm bias resistor is

$$\Delta e_{in}(\text{max}) = 10 \times 10^{-9}\,\text{amp} \times 2^{3.1} \times 10^6\,\Omega = 0.086\ \text{volt}$$

The actual input drift over this temperature range is slightly less than 0.02 volt.

The gate-to-drain capacitance can be reduced by bootstrapping to produce an extremely low overall input capacitance for the stage. In the circuit shown in Fig. 2E, the design goals and actual values obtained were

	Design	Actual
$R_{in} =$	50 megohms	47.5 megohms
$C_{in} =$	< 0.5 pf	0.45 pf

The diode D_1 gives maximum a-c bootstrapping of the gate bias resistance, while providing the required d-c bias. A signal in phase with the input is coupled by the emitter follower Q_2 to the drain circuit of the field effect transistor. Capacitor C_2 provides a low-impedance a-c path between drain and emitter, while maintaining the d-c relationship between source and drain.

Figure 3 (bottom) is a graph of the theoretical and actual values of input impedance as a function of frequency for the circuit in Fig. 2E.

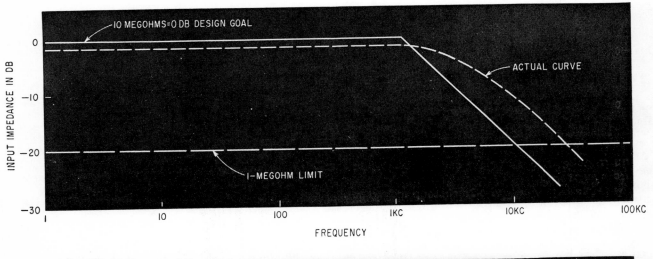

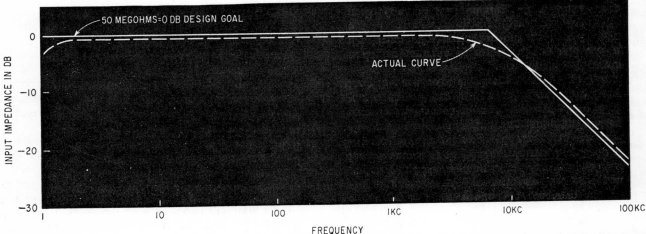

NORMALIZED *theoretical and actual input impedances versus frequency for circuit of Fig. 2D (top) and Fig. 2E (bottom)—Fig. 3*

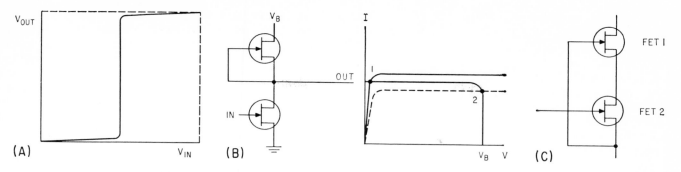

OUTPUT *voltage versus input voltage for an ideal logic element (A); basic circuit for near-ideal output-input relationship and interaction of* **FET** *and current-limiter characteristics (B); and screen-electrode principle with two field-effect transistors (C)—Fig. 1*

Put More Snap in Logic Circuits
With Field-Effect Transistors

Circuits using field-effect transistors with a current-limiter load achieve a snapaction rapid transition between switching states with a very small range of input voltage

By G. CSANKY and R. M. WARNER JR., Semiconductor Prod. Div., Motorola, Phoenix, Arizona

FULL EXCURSION of output voltage in an ideal logic element occurs within a very small range of input voltage. Moreover, the output excursion should occur near the middle of the input range as shown in Fig. 1A. An analogous relationship between input and output currents would serve as well. This type of logic element is efficient because switching occurs within minimum input drive. Furthermore, large margins are allowed for the initial and final values of the input drive and a switching speed-up effect is realized to the minimum τ_{switch} of the logic element.

The ideal characteristic can be closely approximated in several respects by using a field-effect transistor[1] in combination with a current-limiter[2] load as shown in Fig. 1B. Here the characteristic of the current limiter is plotted as a load

line and is nearly parallel to the field-effect transistor characteristic over a wide voltage range. As a negative voltage is applied at the input, the transistor characteristic is driven down, and the intersection of the two curves moves very rapidly from point 1 to point 2. As a result, a behavior similar to that

shown in Fig. 1 is realized.

The transition can be adjusted to the center portion of the input range by proper selection of relative pinch-off currents. The speed of transition from point 1 to point 2 is dependent upon the transconductance of the field-effect transistor as well as the slope of the

---

SNAPPY LOGIC

Field-effect transistors are naturals for logic elements because switching occurs within minimum input drive when the FET's are combined with a current-limiter load. Moreover, both NAND and NOR functions can be performed with this circuit by varying FET and current-limiter diode pinch-off currents.

In this article, the authors describe the operation and applications of their circuit and point out the advantages that should allow it to find wide use

---

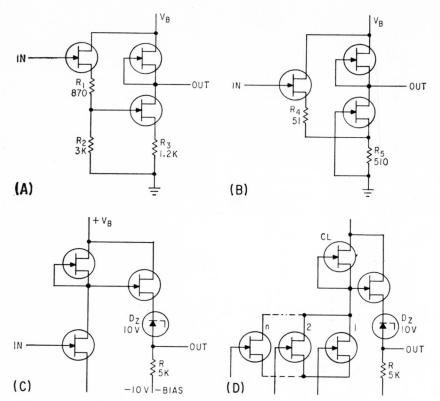

PHASE-INVERTING *logic element with source follower (A); nonphase-inverting element with source follower (B); element with high fan-in/ fan-out capability (C); and snap-action circuit for NAND and NOR functions (D)—Fig. 2*

characteristic curves. Switching becomes more abrupt if the two interacting characteristics are flattened.

An appreciable increase in output impedance of a field-effect device can be achieved with the screen electrode principle.[3] This principle may be applied to either or both of the devices shown in Fig. 1B. In the screen electrode principle two field-effect transistors are connected as shown in Fig. 1C. The basic requirement is that FET 1 has greater pinch-off current and voltage than FET 2. In this case, FET 1 will act like a voltage sponge; therefore, the drain of FET 2 will remain at a nearly constant voltage. This drain is the screen electrode which is analogous to the screen grid of a vacuum tube. This effect increases the output impedance of the field-effect transistor by two orders of magnitude; it has been shown experimentally that this reduces the switching time of the logic circuit comparably since the transconductance of the screen-electrode transistor is similar to that of FET 2 alone.

A steplike switching characteris-tic can also be obtained with a negative resistance device under conditions where its characteristic makes multiple intersections with the load line during some portion of the switching cycle; however, in a case like this, hysteresis will occur. If the configuration shown in Fig. 1B is used, there is no hysteresis because the two characteristics intersect at only a single point during the entire cycle.

The circuit shown in Fig. 1B is a low-frequency configuration because the drain-gate capacitance imposes a frequency limitation that is similar to the Miller effect. During the transition from point 1 to point 2, the overall gain of the circuit approaches the μ of the field-effect transistor, and the input capacitance rises to a point where it has an important frequency limiting effect.

This circuit also poses a voltage translation problem. That is, negative voltages are required at the input, while positive voltages are delivered at the output. Therefore, a complementary element must follow this circuit, or a fairly large off-set voltage must be provided.

MODIFICATION—Both problems can be solved with a slight modification of the basic element and two different solutions exist[4,5]. Both optimize the frequency response and eliminate the voltage translation problem by basically adding a source-follower stage to the circuitry. The two positions for the source follower lead to differing properties for the two circuits; however, both circuits make direct coupling possible (without voltage translation) and enhance frequency response. Moreover, they can be used to perform logic.

In case one, the source-follower stage is added to the input as shown in Fig. 2A. The source-follower voltage gain is close to unity so the effect of drain-gate capacitance is minimized. The output impedance of the source-follower stage is low, mitigating the high input capacitance of the field-effect transistor current-limiter combination.

The voltage translation problem is eliminated because the source of the field-effect transistor is kept above ground by R_3; therefore, the source-follower stage and voltage-divider $R_1 R_2$ can carry the gate of the field-effect transistor negative with respect to its source. Voltage divider $R_1 R_2$ is introduced only to compensate for voltage drop occurring in the field-effect transistor.

This circuit inverts the phase; if increasing voltage is applied at the input, decreasing voltage is delivered at the output. However, it is possible to modify the circuit so that it will be noninverting. A circuit that possesses all the advantages previously discussed and does not invert phase appears in Fig. 2B. Basically, it is a special type of difference amplifier with the snap-action feature added.

Logic functions can be performed with either phase-inverting or non-phase inverting circuits by the parallel connection of input source follower stages. However, in this way, NOR or OR circuits can be produced having a fan-in of only 3 to 5, because the range of currents permissible in the voltage divider is limited for satisfactory operation. The fan-out factor is also about 3 to 5 because of the high output impedance of the logic element that is sensitive to capacitive loads.

In case two, a greater flexibility of circuit design is achieved with the added feature of high fan-in and fan-out. Here, the source-follower state is added to the output of the snap-action switch, as shown in Fig. 2C. This provides a low output impedance with the required voltage translation. Zener diode D_z acts as a level-translator voltage buffer; thus, approximately the full voltage swing is realized at the output of the source follower.

The input of the logic element is the gate of the field-effect transistor in the FET-CL combination. A great variation of input capacitance during the switching cycle is realized through the Miller effect; however, its effect is mitigated by driving with the source follower of a similar preceding stage.

Both NAND and NOR logic functions can be performed with this circuit by varying the pinch-off currents of the field-effect transistors and current-limiter diode. A circuit which will perform the two functions is shown in Fig. 2D. It is a single circuit and only the choice of current determines the type of function performed. If the currents of field-effect transistors 1 to n are selected so that when all are on, their current sum exceeds the current of the current-limiter diode CL, but will be less if any one is off, then the function performed will be NAND as this circuit inverts phase. However, if the drain current of any field-effect transistor 1 to n, if on, exceeds the current of the current limiter diode CL, the function will be NOR. This relationship is shown in Fig. 3A & 3B.

A limitation of the circuit shown in Fig. 2A is its relatively low fan-in and fan-out capability. The fan-in of the circuit shown in Fig. 2C and 2D is extremely high. An ultimate limitation is the value of the cut-off currents of the field-effect transistors. Another limitation for the NAND circuit is technological; how close can the drain currents of the FET's be held? The value of drain current is geometry dependent and therefore the problem reduces to one of geometry control. It appears possible to obtain a fan-in of 50.

The fan-out of the logic element is high too. When the logic element is driven by a 10-Kc sinusoidal input having a peak value of 10 volts and operating into one and ten paralleled inputs, respectively, the waveform for ten inputs, though slightly distorted, is still quite satisfactory. A greater distortion of the output waveform results if the logic element is driven by fast pulses having a greater repetition rate.

An interesting feature of these elements is that if driven with a sinusoidal input, the switching time is a constant percentage of the complete cycle $1/f$ of the sine wave up to the maximum operational frequency. Also, the dimensionless factor of $f \, \tau_{switch}$ is constant within this frequency range.

It is possible to achieve snap action in a circuit analogous to that of Fig. 1B by substituting conventional transistors for the field-effect devices. The fact that an FET is voltage operated and can be self biased produces significant simplifications. Moreover, in all circuits, any kind of FET can be employed; that is, the principles are general and not applicable merely to an FET of certain special properties.

CONCLUSIONS — These elements cannot compete in speed at present with circuits employing conventional transistors, since the frequency range within which proper operation can be obtained is a few hundred kilocycles. However, in applications where speed is not a basic requirement, such as for periheral equipment in computers, their advantages can be fully exploited.

In addition to snap-action and direct d-c coupling, these circuits have the potential advantage of very low power dissipation. This relates again to the fact that an FET is voltage operated, and that very low operating currents can be chosen.

Field-effect transistors can be easily integrated in a monolithic configuration, because the current axis of a field-effect transistor integrated circuit lies in the plane of the wafer, rather than normal to it. Since certain electrical parameters are geometry dependent, simple concentric patterns can be used to integrate the circuit.

Finally, an advantage of the circuits is temperature compensation, because both the current limiter and field effect transistor have the same relative temperature coefficient. This means that the shift in operating point caused by temperature variation is small. In addition, the negative temperature coefficient of the devices will prohibit the thermal runaway of the circuits, making it a useful tool for higher temperature operation.

REFERENCES

(1) W. Shockley, A Unipolar "Field-Effect" Transistor, Proc. IRE, 40, p. 1365-1376; Nov 1952.
(2) R. M. Warner, Jr., et al., A semiconductor Current Limiter, Proc IRE, 47, p. 44-56; Jan 1959.
(3) G. Csanky, The Screen Electrode Principle with Field Effect Transistors, to be published.
(4) G. Csanky and R. M. Warner, Jr., Two New Compatible Logic Elements, Digest of the 1963 ISSCC, p. 30-31, Feb 1963.
(5) G. Csanky and R. M. Warner, Jr., High Input Impedance, Low Output Impedance, Snap-Action Logic, Digest of the 1963 Pacific Computer Conference. p 5-7 March 1963.

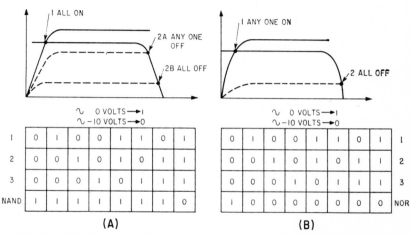

NAND *function and table for 3 inputs (A) and NOR function and table for 3 inputs (B)*—Fig. 3

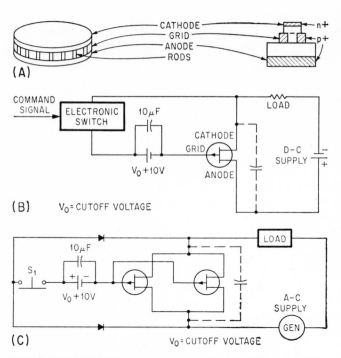

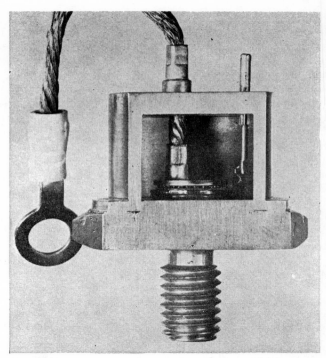

ROD ARRANGEMENT and cross-section through rod (A). Basic circuits for d-c switching (B) and a-c switching (C)

CUTAWAY view of new high-power Tecnetron. Note gear-like rod arrangement

New Tecnetrons Switch 15 Amp

French now planning field-effect devices to switch 50 amp

By ARTHUR ERIKSON
McGraw-Hill World News

PARIS—A French-developed field-effect semiconductor device that can switch high d-c currents made its official debut today at the International Exhibition of Industrial Electronics held at Basle, Switzerland.

Prototype versions of the device, called the high power Tecnetron, have nominal continuous ratings of 10 amp and break capability higher than 15 amp. They handle a-c or d-c to 150 v, with forward drop less than 2 v and residual current of 20 ma or less. Peak-inverse voltage rating is 300 to 400 v.

The device switches fast, too; on time is in the order of 1 μsec and off time is 10 times faster. And since it acts as a diode in the conducting state but as a cutoff pentode in the pinched condition, the high-power Tecnetron can be used for proportional control as well as on-off applications.

Slated to follow the 10-amp versions that will be in pilot production by early next year are 50-amp units both in germanium and silicon. The silicon units will have voltage ratings to 500 v and piv of 1,000 to 1,200 v (see table). But most important, the power-handling potential of this family of devices is practically unlimited—units can be connected in parallel directly with no special matching.

DESIGN—The high-power Tecnetron differs from the high-frequency communications version (ELECTRONICS, p 18 May 17) in structure and operation. Instead of a single n-type germanium rod, it has many rods sandwiched between a common base or anode plate and a cathode plate. The rods are n-type germanium of relatively high resistivity with a $p+$ layer at one end and an $n+$ layer at the other. A grid of $p+$

material surrounds the n-type rods over part of the height between the plates.

With a forward voltage applied between the anode and cathode plates, but no voltage applied to the grid, the device acts as a diode with carrier injection at both electrodes. But when a negative cutoff voltage is applied to the grid, it extracts minority carriers and a donor space charge develops to block carrier flow between anode and cathode.

For complete cutoff, grid bias ranges from —60 to —90 v. Up to cutoff, the I-V curve flattens out as bias increases so the family of curves resembles that of a pentode. With no grid bias, however, the curve has a diode-like look. Bias for complete cut-off will be reduced to —30 to —60 volts for the future 50-amp versions.

SWITCHING CIRCUITS — Basic circuit for using the high-power Tecnetron as a d-c switch is shown. The electronic switch in the grid circuit can be built around a fast low-power silicon controlled rectifier, or

CHARACTERISTICS OF BIPOLAR HIGH-POWER TECNETRON

	Available Now Germanium	Projected Germanium	Silicon
Continuous current rating (I_n)....	10 amp	> 50 amp	> 50 amp
Circuit break rating.............	$\geqq$ 15 amp	> 100 amp	> 100 amp
Forward voltage drop (at I_n).....	$\leqq$ 2 v	$\leqq$ 2 v	$\leqq$ 2 v
Residual current...............	0.002 I_n	0.001 I_n	< 0.0001 I_n
Grid bias (V_{go}) for complete pinch-off......................	60–90 v	30–60 v	30–60 v
Peak energy drawn by grid (transient)......................	$\simeq I_n V_{go} 10^{-6}$j	0.5 $I_n V_{go} 10^{-6}$j	0.5 $I_n V_{go} 10^{-6}$j
Average power drawn by grid....	2 $I_n V_{go} 10^{-3}$w	$I_n V_{go} 10^{-3}$w	< $I_n V_{go} 10^{-4}$w
Peak inverse voltage............	300–400 v	400 v	1,000–1,200 v
Duty voltage rating............	$\simeq$150 v	150–200 v	400–500 v
Intrinsic *OFF* switch time.......	$\simeq$0.1 μsec	$\simeq$0.1 μsec	$\simeq$0.1 μsec
Intrinsic *ON* switch time........	$\simeq$1 μsec	$\simeq$1 μsec	$\simeq$1 μsec

a power transistor, switched by a low-power bistable Tecnetron or a unijunction transistor.

To function properly in the grid switch, the scr must be able to pass in the conducting state during an interval of 2 to 3 μsec a peak current equal to one-third of the load current. In the blocking state, the scr must withstand the Tecnetron's cutoff grid voltage. An scr rated for 0.5 amp and 100 v, for example, could handle a Tecnetron with 30-amp breaking capacity.

Requirements are the same for a power transistor used to switch the cutoff voltage onto the Tecnetron grid. A Texas Instruments' 2N1046, for example, would suffice for Tec-netrons with breaking capacity up to at least 30 amp.

For highly inductive loads, an R-C network is added in the grid circuit to control the speed of applying cutoff voltage to the grid. Otherwise, the inherent 0.1-μsec off time of the Tecnetron is so fast overvoltages may develop across the load. At the same time, so that injection of minority carriers at the anode won't upset cutoff, the speed of voltage builtup across the anode and cathode must be matched to the slower breaking time by a capacitance shunt (indicated by dotted lines in the basic schematic).

A-C SWITCH—To switch a-c, the basic circuit is two Tecnetrons inverted in parallel with a common grid circuit. The grid source is connected through two diodes so that the voltage between the grid and the cathode-anode connection at each end is always at least equal to the cutoff voltage. The two diodes also isolate the grid and power circuits. No special circuit tricks are necessary for a-c switching, but the Tecnetrons must be mounted on separate heat sinks insulated from each other. An electronic switching circuit would in actual practice replace the mechanical switch shown for simplicity's sake in the grid circuit.

The high-power Tecnetron (*Te* for its inventor Dr. Stanislas Teszner, *cnet* for Centre National d'Etudes des Telecommunications where Teszner developed his original high-frequency communications field-effect devices, plus *ron*) was developed by a Franco-Belgian pair of electrical equipment manufacturers—Forges et Ateliers de Constructions Electriques de Jeumont and Ateliers de Constructions Electriques de Charleroi. In the United States, Atlantic Instruments and Electronics Inc. of Boston will produce and market the device under the tradename Fieldtron.

Chapter 16

UNCONVENTIONAL
SEMICONDUCTOR COMPONENTS

MORE RELIABILITY WITH

Controlled Avalanche

High reverse dissipation capabilities of these new silicon semiconductor devices

make them hundreds of times more immune to voltage transients. Application

in a variety of circuits significantly reduces required voltage safety factors

VOLTAGE safety factors can be significantly reduced and even eliminated in some applications using controlled avalanche silicon rectifiers. These semiconductor devices can dissipate typical circuit transients without being damaged. Their high surface stability at high voltages ensures the reliability of controlled avalanche rectifiers at normal operating voltages below avalanche. Since clipping takes place at well defined voltage levels, other circuit components are protected.

Long series strings of controlled avalanche rectifiers can be operated at high voltages without equalizing resistors, and shunting capacitors can also be eliminated in some applications. Because these diodes are unharmed by insulation high-potential and megger tests, they need not be disconnected or short circuited during such tests.

POWER DISSIPATION—The conventional silicon rectifier has made substantial contributions to electronics by its long life, small size, efficiency and low cost. However, the silicon rectifier is sensitive to overvoltage transients, in addition to some other shortcomings. One of the primary advantages of the silicon controlled avalanche rectifier is that it overcomes this fundamental limitation. Thus, controlled avalanche rectifiers permit a fuller realization of the potential of silicon in broader areas of application.

Three typical controlled avalanche rectifier diodes are shown in the photograph. Their current ratings range from $\frac{1}{2}$ to 250 amperes, and their working peak reverse voltage (prv) ratings from 150 to 1,200 volts.

A conventional silicon rectifier may be permanently damaged by only a few watts of reverse power dissipation, although the same device can momentarily dissipate thousands of watts in its forward direction. This disparity exists because the reverse dissipation in a conventional silicon rectifier may occur at a localized spot at the junction surface. Conversely, losses resulting from forward current flow are uniformly distributed over the entire junction area.

A silicon controlled avalanche rectifier can dissipate about as much heat in the reverse direction as in the forward direction whether it is steady state or transient. High reverse energy dissipation in this type semiconductor occurs in the avalanche breakdown region of the diode characterisic. This inherent non-destructive characteristic of the silicon rectifier diode is widely used at relatively low power and voltage levels in the zener diode.

No damage from true avalanche action results to a diode with a uniform junction if current is limited by the external circuit to the thermal capability of the diode. Hence, a rectifier diode, with uniform avalanche breakdown occurring at a voltage below that at which local dielectric surface breakdowns occur, can dissipate hundreds of times more reverse energy during transient overvoltage conditions.

By ensuring that true avalanche action occurs at voltages below the level of surface instability, there is no way that voltage across a controlled avalanche rectifier can reach levels where surface damage might occur. Such a semiconductor might be regarded as having a built-in transient voltage suppressor.

CHARACTERISTICS—In addition to conventional silicon rectifier characteristics, for a controlled avalanche rectifier to be generally useful, it should have rigidly specified maximum and minimum avalanche characterisitics. It should also be capable of steady-state operation in its avalanche region without damage and be able to dissipate momentary current surges in the avalanche region without damage (with ratings defining this capability).

An oscilloscope display of the reverse current-voltage characteristic of a typical A27 rectifier with 800 volts peak reverse voltage rating at room temperature is shown in Fig. 1A. The horizontal scale is 200 volts/cm and the vertical scale is 10 ma/cm. While it has the same sharp transition characteristic as a conventional zener diode, avalanche occurs at a much higher voltage (1,280 volts). The slope of the characteristic in the avalanche region, generally designated dynamic resistance, is typically 200 ohms for this 12-ampere diode. The avalanche breakdown voltage has a positive temperature coefficient, increasing about 0.1 percent per deg C of increasing junction temperature relative to the voltage at 25 deg C.

The outstanding feature of the controlled avalanche rectifier, its ability to dissipate high levels of transient energy, is defined in Fig. 2, which shows the reverse current surge curve of the A27. This graph

Rectifiers

By F. W. GUTZWILLER

Rectifier Components Department
General Electric Company
Auburn, N. Y.

CONTROLLED *avalanche rectifier diodes have current ratings of ½, 12 and 250 amperes*

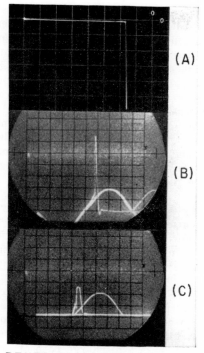

REVERSE *voltage-current trace (A) is for diode with 800-volt prv rating at room temperature. Peak 7,500-volt transient (B) produced when transformer primary is switched is reduced to 2,500 volts; (C) two controlled avalanche rectifiers—Fig. 1*

illustrates the peak reverse current capability for various pulse durations under nonrecurrent conditions.

In the forward direction, the controlled avalanche rectifier behaves similarly to any high-quality conventional silicon rectifier. Load current is distributed uniformly across the entire junction at both normal and surge levels, and load current ratings are similar to conventional silicon rectifiers of identical size.

SERIES OPERATION — Operation of controlled avalanche rectifiers in series strings can have favorable effects on efficiency, reliability, space utilization and cost. Because of their ability to operate reliably in the avalanche region, series strings of controlled avalanche rectifiers require no shunting resistors to equalize reverse voltage. If total applied voltage remains less than total avalanche voltage of all diodes in series, reverse current is limited to a value well within the continuous dissipation ratings of the controlled avalanche rectifiers. Since each diode operates well within its tested voltage and power dissipation capabilities, reliable operation is assured.

With series strings of conventional silicon rectifiers, shunting capacitors are used to equalize voltage between diodes during transient conditions, such as steep rises in applied voltage or during diode commutation. However, since series strings of controlled avalanche rectifiers can dissipate substantial reverse transient power, the need for shunting capacitors as well as resistors is eliminated in some cases, depending on the commutating cycle.

These characteristics of controlled avalanche rectifiers operated in series can also be used to force peak voltage sharing among series-connected conventional rectifiers and silicon controlled rectifiers. For example, small selected controlled avalanche rectifiers can be used in parallel with series-connected silicon controlled rectifiers to balance forward and reverse blocking voltage across each silicon controlled rectifier. This approach is more efficient than using voltage-equalizing resistors.

Small controlled avalanche rectifiers can also be used in the anode-gate circuits of silicon controlled rectifiers to protect them from excessive anode voltage. A back-to-back pair of silicon controlled recti-

AVALANCHE SIMPLIFIES RECTIFIER DESIGN

Silicon rectifier circuit design is complicated by the limited ability of these devices to dissipate power in the reverse direction without being permanently damaged. However, the familiar mechanism of the zener diode, avalanche breakdown, causes no permanent damage. This phenomenon occurs in the reverse direction in controlled avalanche diodes, which otherwise behave like conventional silicon diodes. These semiconductor devices can simplify rectifier circuit design

fiers for phase control of alternating current is protected by the pair of controlled avalanche diodes in Fig. 3A. The A7 diodes are selected so that avalanche occurs below the forward and reverse voltage ratings of the silicon controlled rectifiers. Hence, any voltage exceeding the avalanche level triggers the silicon controlled rectifiers into conduction, protecting them from the effects of high-voltage line surges.

PARALLEL OPERATION—Like conventional silicon diodes, controlled avalanche rectifiers can be operated in parallel if precautions are taken to assure that forward load current is equalized. Factory matching of the forward current characteristics of the diodes or forced current sharing techniques could be used to equalize current.

Since a controlled avalanche rectifier must conduct in the reverse direction to dissipate transient circuit energy, parallel sharing of reverse current during pulse operation is necessary if the diode array is to dissipate more than the reverse pulse rating of a single diode. In controlled avalanche diodes having the same prv ratings, the avalanche characteristics are automatically matched to a considerable degree by the minimum and maximum avalanche limits of the diodes. The dynamic resistances of individual diodes in the avalanche region provide an additional mechanism of transient reverse current sharing, as does the positive temperature coefficient of the avalanche voltage.

In a single-phase bridge, diametrically opposite diode elements operate in parallel in the reverse direction. Therefore, transient reverse dissipation is also greater than that of a single diode even though the diodes are not connected directly in parallel.

TRANSIENTS — Transient voltages that damage conventional silicon rectifiers generally arise when inductive circuits are switched. When current through an inductance is abruptly interrupted, the stored energy seeks a discharge path other than the switch. Voltage increases until a current discharge path is established by arcing or flashover or until destructive reverse current or dielectric breakdown is caused in the silicon rectifier.

Controlled avalanche rectifier diodes can conduct momentary discharge currents in the reverse direction at the avalanche level without damage if the currents are within the diode ratings. Voltages are thereby harmlessly limited to the avalanche voltage of the rectifier diode, protecting the diode, minimizing arcing and lowering the voltage on other components.

Clipping by controlled avalanche rectifiers connected to the secondary of a step-up transformer is shown in Fig. 1B and C. The vertical scale is 1,000 volts/cm and the horizontal scale is 2 millisec/cm in both traces. With no rectifier diodes across the 1,400-volt (rms) secondary, switching voltage transients of 7,500 volts peak were encountered regularly. With two A27N diodes in series in each leg of the secondary, the transient was clipped at 2,500 volts, which is the avalanche voltage of two diodes in series. The clipping action takes place just above the repetitive circuit voltage peak of 2,000 volts, indicating the success that has been achieved in this application

without requiring a substantial prv safety factor.

The maximum reverse dissipation limits of controlled avalanche rectifiers are hundreds of times higher than those of conventional silicon rectifiers. In applications where the diodes are relatively well matched to the stiffness of the system by their forward current ratings (diode Kva rating equals transformer Kva), these diodes can often be applied using a low prv safety factor. However, a rectifier operating from stiff a-c lines without the softening influence of its own transformer may require supplemental transient suppression.

Applications guidelines have been established defining the capabilities and performance of controlled avalanche rectifiers in basic circuit configurations. To simplify the analysis and presentation, several conservative assumptions are made. Circuit interruption is assumed to be instantaneous with no contact arcing and no energy dissipated in the switch. These assumptions are conservative in that practical switches in inductive circuits do arc and seldom chop currents above a few amperes. Thus, in practice, controlled avalanche rectifiers may handle many times the calculated value of stored energy.

It has also been assumed that circuit inductance is constant (no saturation effects exist) and that the avalanche voltage has zero dynamic impedance.

INDUCTANCE IN D-C LINES—A controlled avalanche rectifier is connected in the discharge path of an inductor in Fig. 3B. This circuit is equivalent to many relay, power supply and free-wheeling rectifier circuits. When the switch is closed, current I flows from the d-c source through inductor L. When the switch is abruptly opened at time $t = 0$, current i from inductor L discharges through the controlled avalanche rectifier. The relationship among the voltages around the discharge loop is described by the equation $0 = L \, di/dt - nV_A$, where V_A is avalanche voltage of each diode and n is the number of series-connected controlled avalanche diodes. Solving for i

$$i = I - (nV_A/L)t \qquad (1)$$

Time τ for current to reach zero (see Fig. 3C) can be determined by solving Eq. 1 for $i = 0$

$$\tau = LI/nV_A \qquad (2)$$

These equations are useful in determining drop-out time of solenoids and relays. For correlation with the reverse surge current curve of the controlled avalanche diode (see Fig. 2), the triangular current waveshape in Fig. 3D can be translated into the equivalent rectangular current waveshape in Fig. 3E. Peak current I is the same in this waveshape as in Fig. 3D and has the same current-time integral $I \, (\tau/2)$ so the time base of the rectangular current waveshape is $\tau/2$. The duration of the equivalent rectangular current waveshape can be determined from Eq. 2

$$\tau/2 = LI/2nV_A \qquad (3)$$

For nonrecurrent conditions, maximum allowable inductor current I can be obtained for design purposes directly from the reverse current surge curve (Fig. 2) for pulse duration $\tau/2$. As expected, higher discharge currents can be handled by controlled

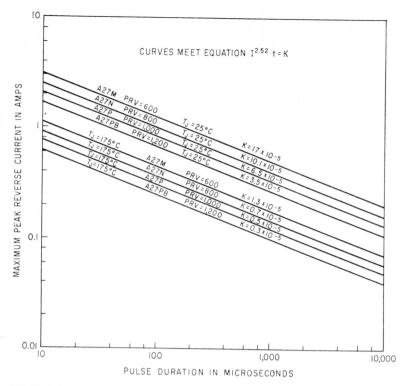

NONRECURRENT *reverse current surge curve indicates capabilities of 12-ampere rectifier at different pulse durations—Fig. 2*

INVERSE *parallel pair of silicon controlled rectifiers (A) is protected from voltage transients by controlled avalanche rectifiers. Controlled avalanche rectifier (B) in discharge path of inductor has voltage (C) across it and current (D) through it, which can be translated to rectangular waveshape (E)—Fig. 3*

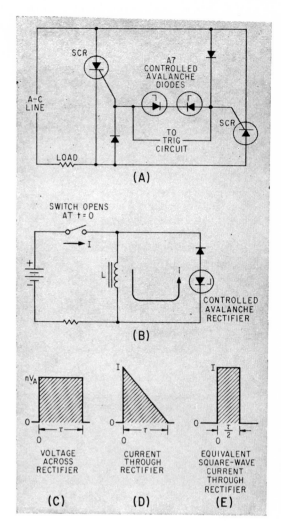

avalanche diodes with lower prv ratings.

Two general rules can be derived from these data. For maximum reverse current capability as well as maximum energy dissipation capability into the reverse diode characteristic, the lowest possible prv rating for each diode should be used that is consistent with recurrent circuit prv requirements. Moreover, for faster suppression of the inductive transient, higher prv ratings or a series string of diodes with higher total avalanche voltage should be used. Similar methods can be used to analyze other circuits.[1]

INDUCTANCE IN A-C LINES—When a controlled avalanche rectifier is subjected to the discharge of an inductance connected to an a-c line, peak allowable current I_L through the inductor is

$$I_L = (1.41 \omega K n V_A/V_S)^{1/a} \qquad (4)$$

where V_s is a-c line rms voltage, ω is frequency in radians per second, K is a constant for a diode with a specific prv rating at a specified temperature (see Fig. 2), and a is a constant for a given diode type (a is 2.52 for the A27).

A similar approach can be used for the transient that occurs when the primary of a single-phase transformer feeding a rectifier is switched. The maximum size transformer for which the magnetizing current can be instantaneously switched into the reverse char-

acteristic of a controlled avalanche rectifier is

$$VA_{max} = (V_S/1.41m)(1.41 \omega K n V_A/V_S)^{1/a} \qquad (5)$$

where VA_{max} is transformer volt-ampere rating, V_s is transformer rated secondary rms voltage, and m is magnetizing current on per unit basis.

It is unlikely that a switch would abruptly interrupt current in an inductive circuit without arcing. Also, in practical circuits, distributed capacitance and other storage and dissipative elements are present in addition to the controlled avalanche rectifier. Therefore, these analyses are conservative. In addition, when more than one controlled avalanche rectifier is in the circuit, they share the dissipation duty.

Where the reverse transient capability of controlled avalanche rectifier diodes is not sufficient to dissipate system energy, a capacitor can be used in parallel with the diodes to increase the overall power level of the circuit. For solving transformer switching problems, the capacitance in farads necessary to increase the transformer rating from VA_o (without capacitor) as determined in Eq. 5 to VA_c (with capacitor) is

$$C = [2mVA_C/\omega (nV_A)^2][1 - (VA_O/VA_C)^2] \qquad (6)$$

REFERENCE

(1) F. W. Gutzwiller, An Introduction to the Controlled Avalanche Silicon Rectifier, *Application Note* 200.27, General Electric Company, Auburn, N. Y.

The PIN Diode: Versatile Microwave

Absorption-type attenuators formed of pin diodes amplitude modulate all r-f sources without disturbing oscillator or amplifier elements. Jitter in the voltage-controlled modulator is unmeasurable and harmonic content is low

SINE-WAVE, square-wave and pulse modulation of microwave generators including klystron oscillators is achieved with *pin* diodes and a transmission line. Transistors can be used to drive the voltage-controlled modulator, which exhibits unmeasurable jitter on a 1,000-Mc sampling oscilloscope. The *pin* diodes can also be used to level output of an r-f generator throughout its frequency range.

Advanced techniques are making more evident the limitations of modulators now used for instrumentation. For example, it has been nearly impossible to modulate a klystron oscillator directly with anything but a square wave or pulse. Sine-wave modulation can result in significant frequency shifts with changes in amplitude.

Conventional klystron oscillators have relatively slow rise and decay times and poor frequency stability. Jitter in the r-f pulse is too high for precise pulse measurements. Klystron r-f pulse misfires are such a problem that one manufacturer makes a misfire counter to test its radar system. Also, modulators for lower frequency triode and pentode

generators have low on-off ratios, and speed of rise and decay of the modulated signal is limited by Q of the modulated stage.

A high-speed absorption-type attenuator that can be placed in series with the output of any signal generator can be made using *pin* diodes. As diode bias is changed in accordance with the modulating signal, greater or lesser amounts of power are absorbed from the signal source, effectively amplitude modulating the output. Frequency band and power limits must be observed.

THEORY — An intrinsic silicon wafer is used to make *pin* diodes. This slice of high-purity silicon has nearly equal *p* and *n* traces, but additional *p* type impurities are diffused from one side and additional *n* type impurities from the other. The middle intrinsic layer is left, which accounts for the name *pin*. The wafer is sliced into diode chips, which are placed into appropriate mounting configurations.

At frequencies below 100 Mc, the *pin* diode assembly rectifies as any other junction diode. Because the intrinsic layer acts as a dielectric

barrier separating the *p* and *n* regions, capacitance is low. However, rectification efficiency drops rapidly as frequency increases above 100 Mc because of carrier storage in the intrinsic layer.

When forward bias current is flowing through the *pin* diode, holes and electrons are stored in the *i* layer. The number of stored charge carriers increases with bias current. Before a back bias can be applied to the diode, all these charge carriers must be removed. Above several hundred megacycles, currents do not flow in the reverse direction long enough to remove these charge carriers. Thus microwave currents do not significantly change the instantaneous number of charge carriers stored, and there is negligible rectification.

However, there is a resistance to microwave current flow in the *pin* diode. It is inversely proportional to the number of charge carriers stored in the *i* layer, which in turn is proportional to forward bias current. By varying the bias from back bias (no stored charge) to about ½ ma forward bias, resistance to microwave currents varies from

PIN DIODES MODULATE MICROWAVES

The behavior of a semiconductor device has again provided the basis for overcoming some long-standing problems. This time it is the pin diode, and it is performing modulation functions formerly regarded as nearly m-possible. The mechanism that governs the flow of microwave currents through these devices is discussed with a variety of practical applications

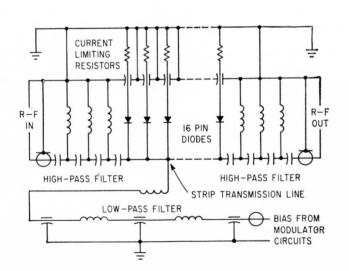

BIAS *controls absorptive properties, permitting reflectionless modulation or attenuation—Fig. 1*

Component

By ROBERT E. HELLER
Applications Engineer
Microwave Division
Hewlett-Packard Company,
Palo Alto, California

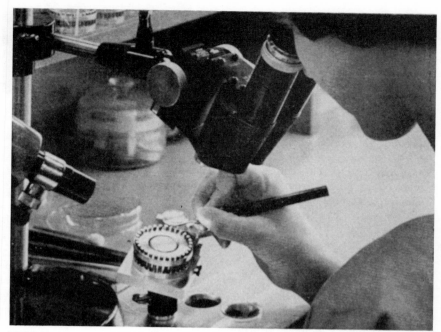

DIODE *posts are shown on rotary assembly jigs but pin chip is visible only under microscope*

about 5,000 ohms to 30 ohms.

This concept can be demonstrated by assuming that the *pin* diode has been mounted across a transmission line with a characteristic impedance of 50 ohms. When the diode is back biased to about 5,000 ohms, the microwave signal on the transmission line is not attenuated because 5,000 ohms compared to a 50-ohm line impedance has little effect. However, when the diode is forward biased to about 30 ohms, most of the microwave current flows through the 30-ohm diode instead of propagating down the 50-ohm line. Since this diode current represents microwave energy dissipated as heat, the diode actually absorbs microwave energy.

Negligible rectification means that resistance of the *pin* diode is about the same throughout a microwave cycle, and the diode behaves essentially as a linear microwave resistor. On the other hand, operation of the diode harmonic generator is based on the change in its resistance during the cycle. If resistance of the *pin* diode is constant throughout the microwave cycle, harmonic content of the modulated output must be low compared to other diode devices.

MODULATOR BOX—To use the microscopic *pin* diode, it must be mounted on a metal post. Reactance of the post is compensated by selecting dimensions that give proper values of capacitance and inductance, leaving only the resistive component. These posts are shown in the photograph of a typical setup for *pin* diode assembly. After assembling the diodes on the posts, they are placed at quarter-wavelength (at midband) intervals along a 50-ohm strip transmission line.

A series of diode-post elements is used to achieve the required maximum attenuation. Higher resist-

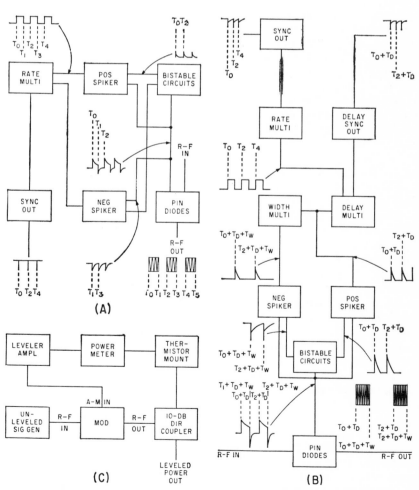

CIRCUITS *enable pin diodes to be programmed for square-wave (A) or pulse (B) modulation. Output of signal generator (C) is leveled by feeding back sample of output power to modulator—Fig. 2*

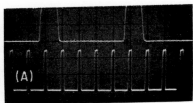

ance *pin* elements are used at each end of the stripline to improve attenuator match and reduce reflections. Loss characteristics of the modulator box are shaped like those of a resistance card in a waveguide flap attenuator.

The typical modulator box in Fig. 1 has 16 *pin* units, although any number may be used depending on required attenuation. The quarter-wavelength spacing is not critical since the attenuator works well over a 3:1 frequency range. However, quarter-wavelength spacing at midband produces the lowest average swr because reflections from each element tend to be absorbed and cancelled by adjacent diodes. This internal reduction of reflections is important in achieving low overall swr. Diode series resistors give equal current distribution. Modulation circuits external to the box are protected by the low-pass filter in Fig. 1, which prevents r-f leakage. If leakage were present, it could cause erratic action in the driving circuits and objectionable r-f interference. The high-pass filters permit r-f energy to enter and leave the stripline while keeping the low-frequency modulating signals from entering the r-f circuits preceding or following the *pin* modulator.

In constructing the *pin* diode box, care must be taken to assure good r-f matches for maximum power transfer. Not only does each *pin* diode represent a possible mismatch or reflection point, but the filters and connectors also contribute to mismatch. Mechanical tolerances of the box and the stripline are also important.

Modulator boxes have been successfully constructed having bandwidth ratios of 3:1 with low swr in both on and off conditions. For example, a typical 16-diode box for 800 to 2,400 Mc has a minimum insertion loss of 1 to 2 db and maximum attenuation of at least 80 db. Maximum swr may range from 1.5 to 2, and a response time of about 20 nsec is typical. Power handling capabilities are about 1 watt, and r-f harmonic content is low.

DRIVING CIRCUITS — The *pin* diode box can be modulated with any desired amplitude-time function. When modulating with sine waves, minimum distortion is obtained by setting d-c bias so that it is centered on the most linear portion of the *pin* diode characteristic curve. For normal modulation values (such as 50 percent), bias level is about 7 db down from no attenuation bias. Nonlinear distortion can be decreased even more by using diode shaping circuits to approximate the inverse of the *pin* characteristic curve. A feedback arrangement of the detected output would also be useful in reducing distortion in sine-wave systems. However, even without shaping circuits or feedback, harmonic distortion of less than 8 percent can be achieved with over 50 percent modulation.

For maximum speed in pulse and square-wave modulation, enough energy must be supplied to the intrinsic layer to sweep charge carriers rapidly into and out of each diode. Therefore, a spiked driving front is applied to the *pin* modulating pulse during changes of state. The energy levels required are readily obtained with transistors.

In the typical square-wave modulator in Fig. 2A, a square-wave rate multivibrator initiates the modulating circuits. Care must be taken to design a symmetrical square-wave device and to maintain this symmetry through the r-f output. In fact, the ratio of the integrated square wave to c-w power should be exactly 3 db. This 3-db figure can also be useful when measuring degradation in microwave systems.

The bistable circuits driving the *pin* diodes have a holding characteristic and provide a back bias of several volts for no attenuation. For maximum attenuation, the bistable circuits provide the required bias current. The diodes are held at minimum microwave resistance by bias current throughout the off period of the r-f pulse.

In the pulse modulator in Fig. 2B, modulation is again initiated by the rate multivibrator. Output of the rate multivibrator is symmetrical, and a width multivibrator provides the required pulse width. The delay multivibrator is useful for oscilloscope synchronization, target simulation or other instrumentation. The delay feature is particularly desirable when the modulator is operated with a sampling oscilloscope. All three functions—pulse rate, width and delay—are front panel controls. Time sequences are indicated in Fig. 2A and B. Commercial units have been constructed with internal square-wave and pulse repetition rates from 50 cps to 50 Kc. Pulse length and pulse delay are adjustable from 0.1 to 100 microseconds.

To permit external pulse modulation or synchronization, an externally actuated Schmitt trigger is substituted for the rate multivibrator. In commerical units, repetition rates have been extended up to 1 or 2 Mc with the Schmitt circuit. Pulse length and pulse delay are also adjustable from 0.1 to 100 microseconds for external synchronization. In external modulation, the modulating pulse determines length.

AMPLITUDE MODULATION—In conventional amplitude modulation, power output from the signal generator is usually varied by changing the d-c power supplied to one of the oscillating or amplifying elements. However, this method may introduce extraneous f-m and spectral impurities. Frequency characteristics are not always the same at all generator amplitudes. For example, klystron oscillator frequency depends heavily on klystron amplitude control, so that the klystron cannot be successfully amplitude modulated in the conventional manner. However, the *pin* diode

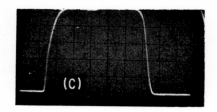 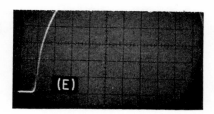

system does not disturb the oscillating or amplifying elements. It can amplitude modulate signals from all r-f sources and provides a practical way to amplitude modulate signals from klystron oscillators.

PULSE MODULATION — In conventional pulse modulation, klystron repeller potential is switched between two voltages or beam current is switched on and off. A reasonably stable frequency output can be achieved if the modulating pulse applied to the klystron is clamped when the generator is full on. However, frequency shift can be introduced if, for example, the clamp voltage shifts with modulation rate. In the full-off position, the klystron modulation pulse must be switched off completely. Even with these precautions, there are still frequency shifts and spectral problems because of the start-up and shut-down characteristics of the klystron oscillator.

Rise and fall times of the modulator pulse are also important. Poorly shaped wave fronts can introduce serious spectral problems that can cause errors in slotted-line and reflectometer measurements. With the *pin* modulator, however, the klystron oscillator operates continuously. The output r-f is switched on and off by the high-speed *pin* absorptive attenuator without disturbing klystron operating conditions.

Occasionally, high-speed switching diodes are used as r-f switches for klystrons and signal generators, but they can introduce reflections and mismatch errors during switching. They present different impedances to the generator for maximum and minimum conduction. Switching diodes are usually narrow-band devices, and this technique provides no filtering for control or transmission of r-f energy. The *pin* diode modulator has no disturbing effect on the r-f source as a result of loading and can introduce no erroneous pulse reflections. Klystron frequency pulling because of loading is not a problem because *pin* modulators present a constant impedance during modulation.

HIGH-SPEED SWITCHING—The *pin* diode modulator is useful for high pulse rates. Rise times of 20 nsec are easily obtainable. Since jitter times are unmeasurable with a 1,000-Mc sampling oscilloscope, jitter must be well below 1 nsec. Some typical high-speed *pin* modulator waveforms are shown in Fig. 3. All traces were made using a 1,000-Mc carrier frequency, a 0.1-μsec pulse width and a 2-Mc repetition rate. A 50-Mc oscilloscope was used for Fig. 3A and a 1,000-Mc oscilloscope for all others.

High-speed, pulse-code modulation of r-f signals by the *pin* diode modulator is well suited to telemetry and data transmission systems. For example, it is possible to frequency modulate a klystron and also pulse modulate or sine-wave modulate the r-f output. The amplitude channel might carry digital data while the f-m channel was used as a communications link. Other applications include synchronous pulsed f-m systems, such as pulsed-doppler and chirp radar. The modulator for high-speed switching provides increased accuracy and better r-f pulse resolution.

R-F LEVELING—Because the *pin* modulator is a current-controlled

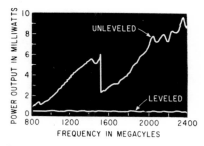

LEVELED *and unleveled outputs of signal generator are shown as a function of frequency with identical output attenuation setting—Fig. 4*

r-f attenuator, it can control level in r-f systems, as in Fig. 2C. A conventional signal generator is used. The variation in r-f output over the frequency range of a typical unleveled signal generator can be from $\frac{1}{2}$ to 5 mw or 10 db, but it is possible to level within $\frac{1}{2}$ db. The signal generator power that flows through the *pin* box is sampled from the directional coupler and fed to a temperature-compensated thermistor-type power meter. Power meter output is amplified and fed back to the modulator to control *pin* diode bias. System response time, which is limited by gain in the feedback loop and thermal lag of the thermistor, may be a fraction of a second. Accuracy is limited by the thermistor mount and characteristics of the directional coupler.

If faster response is needed, a crystal detector with negative output voltage could be used in place of the power meter. Response characteristics of the detector mount would have to be considered because they are not always as flat as thermistor mounts. Changes in crystal rectification efficiency with temperature might also be a problem.

SIGNAL GENERATORS—A commercial signal generator for 800 to 2,400 Mc has been built using a *pin* diode modulation system. The klystron operates continuously, and output is leveled within ± 1 db across the band. Output as plotted with a temperature-compensated thermistor power meter and recorded by an x-y recorder is shown in Fig. 4.

Weight and size of this compact signal generator have been reduced by using the *pin* diode modulator. Amplitude modulation is a standard feature. Performance has been improved by eliminating spurious f-m during square-wave modulation, increasing power output and providing uniform power output at all frequencies by *pin* diode leveling.

Improving Pulse Rise Time With

Tenfold improvement in pulse rise time is provided by cascading charge-storage diodes. Snap-off effect of the cascaded diodes is also used to generate ultrashort pulses that can be used for sampling oscilloscope

By K. C. HU, RCA Laboratories, Princeton, N. J.

CASCADED charge-storage diodes can improve rise time of a 30-volt pulse across 50 ohms from 5 to 0.5 nanosecond. Ultrashort pulses for oscilloscope sampling and other applications can also be provided by cascading these snap-off diodes. The recurrence rate of the snap-off action can be as high as several hundred megacycles.

Available pulse generators can supply pulses having a rise time of about 5 nanoseconds. These pulses of 500 milliamperes to 1 ampere can be supplied to a load of 50 to 100 ohms at recurrence rates of 1 Mc and higher. However, even with the best available components, such performance requires elaborate and careful circuit design, such as a negative power supply to enable d-c coupling. Several forward-biased charge-storage diodes in cascade across the output transmission line of the pulse generator can materially improve pulse rise time.

The extra loading on the generator output by the charge-storage diodes is more than compensated by the impressive improvement in rise

---

GETTING MORE OUT OF SNAP-OFF

If snap-off in one charge-storage diode can improve pulse rise time, two or three cascaded diodes should improve it even more. Here is how suitably biased charge-storage diodes provide a tenfold improvement in rise time and also enable generation of ultrashort pulses

---

time. Rise time is about 0.5 nanosecond for a typical 30-volt pulse across 50 ohms, which is a tenfold improvement.

SNAP-OFF—When a reverse voltage is applied to the charge-storage or snap-off diode after it has been conducting in the forward direction, it conducts in the reverse direction because of the charges stored near the junction.[1] The reverse current decreases during a period called the transition phase

until the charges have been removed. The transition period is short and is related to structure of the semiconductor device. When the diode is driven from a source with low internal impedance, the sudden stoppage of reverse current (snap-off) causes a sharp step change in voltage across the diode. The snap-off action has been used during the past few years, but its usefulness can be considerably extended by cascading several charge-storage diodes.

Three charge-storage diodes have been cascaded in Fig. 1. If the generator pulse were positive instead of negative, the diodes and their associated biases would be reversed. A coaxial cable of matched characteristic impedance is generally necessary to transmit the fast-rising pulses from the generator to the load. The coaxial transmission line is also convenient for mounting the diodes. The mechanical construction of the mounting is shown in Fig. 2. The r-f path is made as short as possible while preserving the continuity of the transmission line.

The instant that snap-off occurs

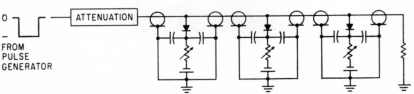

BIASES *for cascaded charge-storage diodes are adjusted separately to control instant that snap-off occurs—Fig. 1*

Snap-Off Diodes

for a given applied pulse depends on forward bias current. Therefore, forward bias current for each diode must be adjusted separately to increase steepness of the entire leading edge where this is desirable.

In some applications, only the step in a portion of the leading edge is of interest, such as when the diode is followed by a differentiator to generate short pulses. Although not yet fully investigated, the slope of the snap-off for a given diode depends on rise time of the applied reverse voltage. Thus, the resultant step is sharper if the snap-off step of a previous diode is used to drive the subsequent diode. The bias required is different from that needed for uniform steepness of the complete leading edge, and separate adjustment of the bias for each charge-storage diode is again necessary.

IMPROVING RISE TIME — A pulse is shown in Fig. 3A before and after the effects of three cascaded charge-storage diodes, and the leading edges of the pulse are shown in Fig. 3B. A Model 121 E-H Research Labs, Inc., pulse generator and three FD-100 charge-storage diodes were used in these experiments. A Tektronics type N sampling attachment and 543 oscilloscope were used to make these recordings. The sampling unit has a rise time limit of about 0.6 nanosecond.

The experimental results shown in Fig. 3C were obtained using a Lumatron 112A sampling oscilloscope adjusted for maximum bandwidth. The rise time limit of this oscilloscope is about 0.2 nsec. The biases used on the first, second and third charge-storage diodes were 100, 75 and 50 ma, respectively. In general, the first diode increases steepness of the last half of the

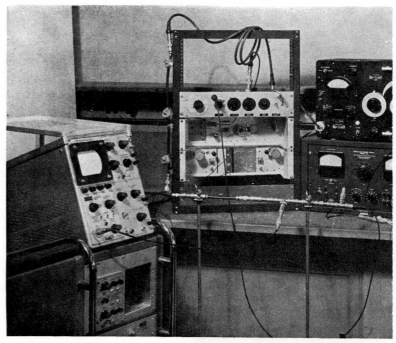

STROBOSCOPIC *sampling oscilloscope was used to observe the effect of the three charge-storage diodes mounted on the coaxial cable at the left of the rack*

leading edge; the third diode increases steepness of the initial portion of the leading edge; the second diode improves rise time of the remainder of the leading edge.

ULTRASHORT PULSES — Ultrashort pulses have been generated by differentiating the step voltage resulting from snap-off in charge-storage diodes. Differentiated pulses as short as 0.2 nsec have been measured at an amplitude of 0.5 volt across 50 ohms. Such pulses have been used in strobing sampling oscilloscopes by some instrument manufacturers.[2]

For a given voltage, the cascading of charge-storage diodes tends to generate pulses having shorter

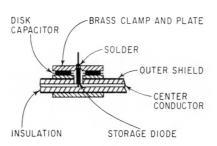

MOUNTING *of charge-storage diode is provided by generator coaxial cable—Fig. 2*

rise times than those that have been reported using a single diode. The reason is again that a faster rising driving pulse is supplied to each successive diode by the snap-off action of the previous diode. Differentiation of the fast-rising waveform was achieved by placing an inductor (a piece of metal) between the center conductor and the shield of the transmission line at a position between the last diode and the load.

The pulses that resulted using one, two and three charge-storage diodes are shown in Fig. 4. Again, the Lumatron Model 112A sampling oscilloscope was used. Since the rise time limit of the oscilloscope is about 0.2 nsec, the difference between using two or three charge-storage diodes is not obvious. However, the difference can be seen when the resulting pulses are used for strobing in a specially built sampling oscilloscope. The waveform in Fig. 5 with the different strobe pulses shows the difference in signal rise time.

The oscilloscope was designed to display fast-rising waveforms having repetition rates up to several gigacycles. The signal in Fig. 4 was obtained from a tunnel diode monostable switching circuit with a 500-Mc sinusoidal input in addition to a d-c bias. Strobing rate is phase modulated around a center frequency of about 5 Mc, which is synchronized with the signal.[3] A GaAs sampling diode was used as a mixing gate.

As with other sampling oscilloscopes, rise time of a displayed waveform indicates maximum width of the strobing pulse. Thus, in Fig. 5C, maximum width of the top portion of the strobing pulse that opens the gate is 0.1 nanosecond. It could be much narrower, since switching time of this circuit as determined from calculations and by other methods is nearly 0.1 nsec. If bandwidth of the sampling diode is not a limiting factor, the performance limit of this sampling system using strobing pulses obtained herewith has not yet been determined.

Biases were 85, 45 and 80 ma for the first, second and third diodes, respectively. The initial 5-Mc driving pulses had a rise time of about 8 nsec and a peak amplitude of 30 volts across a 50-ohm load.

The experimental results indicate that charge-storage diodes can be used more widely either in fast-rise pulse generation or in short pulse generation for sampling or similar purposes. Some of the advantages of using charge-storage diodes are the relatively low cost and circuit simplicity. Also, the recurrence rate of the snap-off action can be as high as several hundred megacycles, and so far no generator can provide pulses at these repetition rates and these amplitudes.

Some precautions should be taken in using this technique, such as loading from forward-biased diodes. Also, slowly rising pulses cannot be improved by this method. The slower the reverse driving pulses rise, the higher the forward bias must be. When pulses rise too slowly, either the diode is unable to carry the forward current or the generator is loaded too heavily. In general, the original pulse rise time should not be more than 10 nsec.

A minimum reverse driving voltage is also necessary to obtain proper snap-off action. For a 50-ohm load, about 10 volts is required.

When the diodes are conducting, the low impedance across the coaxial line causes reflections in the line between the diodes and the generator output. Attenuators must be properly placed between the generator output and the diodes to minimize the effects of the reflections.

This work was sponsored by the Bureau of Ships.

REFERENCES

(1) J. L. Moll, S. Krakauer and R. Shen, P-N Junction Charge-Storage Diodes, *Proc IRE*, **50**, p 43, January 1962.
(2) W. M. Goodall and A. F. Dietrich, Solid State Generator for 2 x 10[-10] Second Pulses, *Proc IRE*, **48**, April 1960.
(3) J. M. L. Jansen, An Experimental Stroboscopic Oscilloscope for Frequencies Up to About 50 Mc, *Philips Tech Rev*, **12**, p 52, August 1950.

EFFECT *of three charge-storage diodes on pulse leading edge is shown at 5 nsec (A), 1 nsec (B) and 0.5 nsec (C) per cm with vertical scale of 10 volts per cm—Fig. 3*

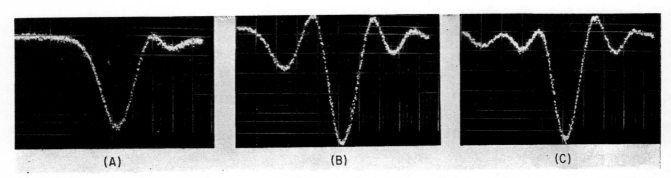

SAMPLING *pulses using one (A), two (B) and three (C) charge-storage diodes are shown at 0.2 nsec per division and 0.32 volt per vertical division—Fig. 4*

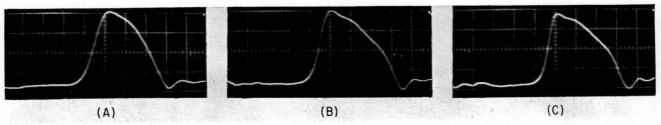

STROBE *pulses using one (A), two (B) and three (C) charge-storage diodes are shown at 0.2 nsec per division—Fig. 5*

CIRCUIT TRENDS IN

Nanosecond Switching

Tunnel diodes and storage diodes permit design of fast switching

circuits essential in gigacycle computers.   Now circuit size and

interconnections are the limiting factors, not device capabilities

By **PETER MEYERS**, Electronic Systems and Products Div., Martin Co., Baltimore, Maryland

HIGH SPEED switching techniques have been developed significantly during the past year. More suitable semiconductor devices plus circuits combining transistors, tunnel diodes and storage diodes have made possible the higher speeds. Particularly noticeable are tunnel diode hybrid circuits, which have renewed interest in the tunnel diode as a switching device. Tunnel-diode/storage-diode logic and tunnel-diode/transistor logic have moved into the forefront as practical general-purpose computer circuits. Circuits available today actually have such high switching speeds that the size and location of circuits and interconnections are becoming more of a problem than speed, particularly in general-purpose computer systems.

Of the various approaches[1] to high-speed switching for new generation computers, transistor circuits, tunnel-diode circuits, transistor/tunnel-diode circuits and storage-diode/tunnel-diode circuits are the main contenders.

Transistor Circuits—Transistors are close to ideal for many uses up to 100 Mc. They are the most widely used components for switching circuits because they provide gain, signal inversion and a wide range of design trade-offs. Transistor logic

CHECKING the speed, fan-out and tolerance limits of a modified tunnel-diode logic system

NEW DRIVE TOWARDS MICROMIN

Time was when radio and light waves traveling at 186,000 mps were thought to be fast moving. They still seem so to most people, the exceptions being some advanced computer designers, who ask to be included out.

The speed of light can also be expressed as 0.98 feet per nanosecond. If you need to build a computer that will be so complex and so fast that only one nanosecond delay can be allowed from one stage to some other randomly located stage, you are going to have to keep things cozy.

Thus the drive towards microminiaturization, first started by the armed services to save power and weight, pushed further by the rocket booster limitations of our space program, is now being pushed in an even more fundamental sense—there isn't any other way to solve the computer's speed-complexity problem

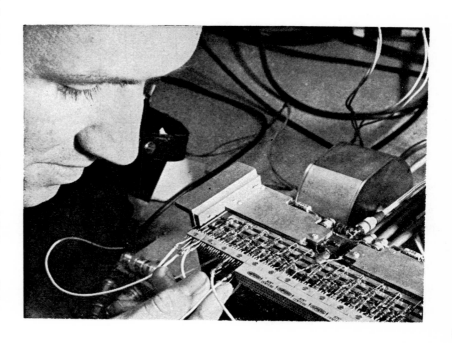

building blocks are presently limited to the 100-Mc region in practical circuits by a gain-bandwidth product of about 1 Gc. Although minor increases in this limit may be made, it is unlikely that semiconductor technology will have an order of

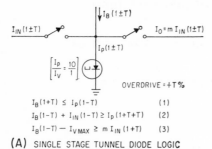

$$I_B(1+T) \leq I_p(1-T) \qquad (1)$$
$$I_B(1-T) + I_{IN}(1-T) \geq I_p(1+T+T) \qquad (2)$$
$$I_B(1-T) - I_{V\,MAX} \geq m\,I_{IN}(1+T) \qquad (3)$$

(A) SINGLE STAGE TUNNEL DIODE LOGIC

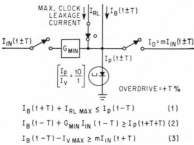

$$I_B(1+T) \leq I_p(1-T) \qquad (1)$$
$$I_B(1-T) + G_{MIN}\,I_{IN}(1-T) \geq I_p(1+T+T) \qquad (2)$$
$$I_B(1-T) - I_{V\,MAX} \geq m\,I_{IN}(1+T) \qquad (3)$$

(B) TRANSISTOR COUPLED LOGIC

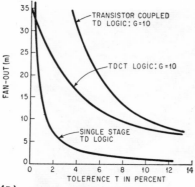

$$I_B(1+T) + I_{RL\,MAX} \leq I_p(1-T) \qquad (1)$$
$$I_B(1-T) + G_{MIN}\,I_{IN}(1-T) \geq I_p(1+T+T) \qquad (2)$$
$$I_B(1-T) - I_{V\,MAX} \geq m\,I_{IN}(1+T) \qquad (3)$$

(C) TDCT NOR LOGIC

(D) GAIN TOLERANCE CURVES

EQUIVALENT circuits with worst-case equations for three tunnel-diode logic schemes (A), (B), (C). Gain-tolerance comparisons (D) show that modified circuits are much less sensitive to changes in circuit current than straight tunnel-diode stages—Fig. 1

magnitude improvement in the next few years.

By virtue of the inherent input-output isolation and inversion properties of the transistor it is possible to design complete asynchronous systems.[2] Asynchronous systems need no high-power high-frequency clock supply, have logical flexibility, and have relatively simple interface circuit problems. Disadvantages include slower operating speed (based on worst-case propagation delay), low information rates, and program timing problems.

A device that cannot be left out of consideration in nanosecond switching, although it has as yet

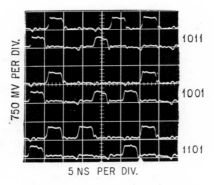

WAVEFORMS recirculating in a 10-bit memory loop at 250-Mc phase rate

found little or no use in logic systems, is the avalanche transistor. It can switch watts of power in fractions of a nanosecond but unfortunately requires too long a time to return the junction to its off state. Because avalanche mechanisms are not fully understood analytically, device manufacturers have had great difficulty in obtaining reasonable yields without allowing a wide spread in the breakdown voltage.

Tunnel Diode Circuits—Tunneling type diodes were received initially with great enthusiasm, but this was followed by a period of disillusion over tolerance limitations. Recently there is renewed interest based on improved components and circuit complementing techniques. Improved devices are now being used in computer-switching logic in the 100 to 200-Mc range. Even so, because of its gain-tolerance characteristics, the tunnel diode is severely limited in fan-in and fan-

out. One of its important uses is driving transmission lines at up to 5 Gc, an application made possible by its low-impedance and current-drive capability.

But tunnel-diode tolerances create severe problems in making reliable switching circuits. Some of the arrangements that have been investigated [3, 4, 5, 6, 7, 8, 9, 10] in an attempt to overcome tolerance problems include: resistor tunnel-diode threshold logic; resistor tunnel-diode majority logic; diode tunnel-diode threshold logic; monostable threshold logic; constant-current-operated threshold logic; locked-pair tunnel-diode logic; voltage-mode tunnel-diode logic.

Unfortunately, all the above schemes fall in the same category of having lower gain tolerances than have normally been used in computer systems.

Transistor-Tunnel Diode—One important attempt to overcome the gain-tolerance situation in tunnel-diode circuits is the transistor tunnel-diode hybrid. Although giving interstage current gain, the circuit is limited in gain speed by the gain bandwidth of the transistor. Superficially these circuits have no advantage over the transistor configuration; however, the transistor circuits are enhanced by using the tunnel diode as a low-impedance driver for transmission-line coupling, and tunnel-diode circuits are improved in gain tolerance by using the transistor as a coupling isolator. [11, 12, 13, 14, 15] The circuits are useful up to 500 Mc.

The design philosophy of this hybrid scheme is that the advantages of the transistor logic are combined with the advantages of the tunnel diode. Unfortunately, the hybrid cannot realize the tunnel diode's potential of operating in the Gc region.

TDCT—A unique approach to tunnel-diode circuits is to use a storage diode or charge transformer as an interstage current amplifier.[16, 17] This results in tunnel-diode charge-transformer logic (TDCT). Because the gain bandwidth of the storage diode or diode amplifier can be on the order of 10Gc for recently available retarded-field diodes, the combination of tunnel diode and storage diode has a 10 to 1 improvement over previously discussed nanosecond circuits. Other advantages are simple circuits, availability of several logical functions, wide tolerances and low cost.

The technique allows practical circuits with current gains of 14 at 250 Mc and 7 at 500 Mc, which shows that the tunnel-diode gain-bandwidth capability has been utilized without limiting the gain to less than two for tolerance requirements. The gain represents high fan-in and fan-out capability. Additional advantages of this approach are greater resistance to nuclear radiation, and ultimate low cost. Increasing use of tunnel-diode charge-transformer (TDCT) logic seems probable in the near future. Developmental systems utilizing 250-Mc phase rate synchronous logic are already appearing. By 1965 both military and commercial systems operating at these speeds should appear in quantity.

Circuit Comparisons—It is difficult to compare the various design approaches on an absolute basis since such factors as cost, size, flexibility, fan-out, reliability and professional egos are involved. However, it is possible to place a conservative upper bound on the gain tolerance characteristics by using a simplified worst-case analysis. From the equivalent circuits in Fig. 1 the fan-out tolerance relationships are derived. Fan-out is m and T is tolerance, with T expressed as a decimal: 1-percent tolerance is 0.01.

For single stage tunnel-diode threshold logic

$$m = \frac{0.8 - 3T + 3.2T^2}{5T + 6T^2}$$

For transistor tunnel-diode hybrids with interstage gain G

$$m = \left[\frac{0.8 - 3T + 3.2T^2}{5T + 6T^2}\right] \times G$$

Tunnel-diode charge-transformer logic with interstage gain G

$$m = G \times \left[\frac{0.7 - 1.9T + T^2}{0.2 + 4.8T + T^2}\right]$$

The relationships are plotted in Fig. 1D and show the superiority of both approaches that have an interstage current gain. The final consideration in assessing the merits and demerits of the various approaches must be based on gain tolerance and speed, as shown in Fig.

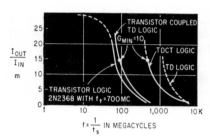

GAIN-BANDWIDTH comparisons, with practical operating regions indicated by solid lines—Fig. 2

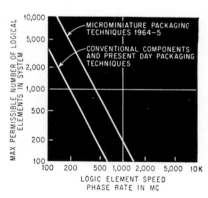

CIRCUIT DELAYS through interconnections place a limit on circuit speed, with speed decreasing as complexity increases. Smaller circuits offer some hope for the immediate future—Fig. 3

2. Tunnel-diode charge-transformer logic has a definite gain-bandwidth advantage.

Interconnections — Interconnecting high-speed switching circuits is a problem for both system and circuit designers. A simple example of a high-speed logic system will be used to illustrate the nature of present and future problems. Based on recent nanosecond circuit developments a tolerable delay for a 250-Mc phase rate system (synchronous logic) would require that the maximum allowable coaxial lead length be approximately 9 inches. Working from this point of reference, a plane of logical elements could tolerate a diagonal interconnection cube leaving one side open for access to interconnections. Any one side of the cube would then be limited to $9\sqrt{3}$ inches, to keep the longest interconnection (diagonal) ≤ 9 inches. This geometry is brute force and can be improved by a clever system layout of logical elements, but the improvement would be less than two in most cases. With present-day NAND, and NOR logic (250 Mc), the area required in the interconnection plane for one logical element with 5 input and 5 output connections is approximately 0.22 sq in. Since the area per element is fixed by packaging and interconnections, the number of elements will vary with the frequency of operation. A simple plot of phase frequency versus number of logic elements (Fig. 3) shows the limitations on high-speed computer design. Microminiaturization should provide a factor of 5 improvement in interconnection area per logic element during the next year or two, and this is included in Fig. 3.

Thus the size of the circuits rather than device speed or circuit design is becoming the predominant limitation on speed of operation.

REFERENCES

(1) Douglas L. Hogan, Ronald L. Wigington, Raymond W. Sears, Jr., Nanosecond Computing, *Science and Technology*, Oct. 1962.
(2) F. K. Buelow, Improvements to Current Switching, *International Solid States Circuits Conference*, p 30, Feb. 1960.
(3) H. K. Gummel and F. M. Smits, Margin Considerations for an Esaki Diode-Resistor OR Gate, *Bell Sys. Tech. J.*, **30**, p 213, Jan. 1961.
(4) R. H. Bergman, Tunnel Diode Logic Circuits, *IRE Trans Electronic Computers*, **EC-9**, p 430, Dec. 1960.
(5) G. W. Neff, S. A. Butler and D. L. Critchlow, Esaki Diode Logic Circuits, *IRE*

Trans Elec Comp, **EC-9**, p 423, Dec. 1960.
(6) H. S. Yourke, S. A. Butler and W. G. Strohm, Esaki Diode NOR-OR Logic Circuits, *IRE Trans Elec Comp*, **EC-10**, p 183, June 1961.
(7) B. E. Sear, Kilomegacycle Tunnel-Diode Logic Circuits, *Proc Int S S Cir Conf*, p 50, 1962.
(8) B. E. Sear, Constant Current Design of Tunnel Diode Logic Circuits, *IEEE Trans Circuit Theory*, **CT-10**, March 1963.
(9) J. J. Gibson, G. B. Herzog, H. S. Miller and R. H. Powlus, Tunnel Diode Balanced Pair Switching Characteristics, *Proc Int S S Cir Conf*, 1962.
(10) G. B. Chaplin, Voltage Mode Tunnel Diode Circuits, *Proc Int S S Cir Conf*, Feb. 1961.
(11) D. W. Murphy, High-Speed Non-saturating Switching Circuits Using a

Novel Coupling Technique, *Proc Int S S Cir Conf*, p 48, 1962.
(12) W. Peil and R. Marolf, Computer Circuitry for 500 Mc, *Proc Int S S Cir Conf*, p 52, 1962.
(13) R. W. Lade, Directly Coupled Tunnel Diode-Transistor Logic, *Solid State Design*, **3**, p 43, Jan. 1962.
(14) J. R. Turnbull, 100 Mc Nonsynchronous Esaki Diode Computer Circuitry, *Proc Int S S Cir Conf*, 1961.
(15) J. F. Kruy, High Speed Arithmetic Unit Using Tunnel Diode, *Int S S Cir Conf*, 1962.
(16) B. E. Sear, Charge Controlled Nanosecond Logic Circuitry, *Proc IEEE*, Aug. 1963.
(17) B. E. Sear, J. S. Cubert and W. F. Chow, The Enhanced Tunnel Diode Logic Circuit, *Proc Int S S Cir Conf*, 1963.

GATE TURN-OFF—UNIQUE

*Parameters and operating characteristics of a new
solid-state pnpn switch with some promising applications.*

CONTROLLING power, both a-c and d-c, is a unique capability of a new *pnpn* structure called the gate turn-off (GTO) switch. It differs from its counterpart, the silicon-controlled rectifier, in that conduction in the GTO can be stopped by applying a short-duration negative signal to the gate. With the SCR, conduction can be stopped only by interrupting the anode-cathode current.

Operation of a *pnpn* structure can be described by considering a configuration consisting of a *pnp* and and an *npn* transistor with a common collector junction, Fig. 1A. The *pnp* section of the bar has an αpnp defined as a fraction of hole current

injected at emitter 1 that reaches collector 1. The *npn* structure has an αnpn defined as a fraction of electron current injected at emitter 2 that reaches collector 2. By combining these two structures, the total current I flowing in a *pnpn* structure is the sum of the currents flowing in the individual transistor sections.

$$I = I_{Jc} = I\,\alpha pnp + I\,\alpha npn + I_{co}\ (\text{Leakage Current}) \quad (1)$$

$$I = \frac{I_{co}}{1 - (\alpha pnp + \alpha npn)} \quad (2)$$

Thus, if I_{co} is small and $(\alpha pnp + \alpha npn)$ is not close to unity, I will be small. Since I_{co} in a silicon p-n

junction can be made very small, I will also be small. This corresponds to the OFF condition of the device. If $\alpha pnp + \alpha npn$ is close to unity, I is limited only by the external circuit. This corresponds to the ON condition of the device. Physically in the ON condition, the two center regions are saturated with carriers, making all three junctions have forward biases. The entire potential drop across the device will be about 1 volt, that of one forward biased p-n rectifier.

FIRING—Two methods can be used to increase alphas of the component junction transistors and thus fire the GTO. One method is to

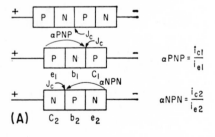

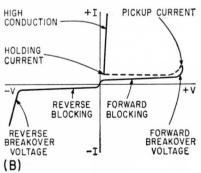

TWO TRANSISTOR *analogy of a pnpn structure (A), and its typical operating characteristics (B) —* Fig. 1

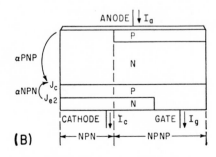

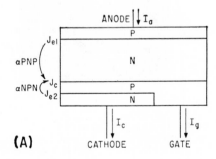

PNPN STRUCTURE *with wide n base and different p-base widths (A), and a more complex pnpn structure with a shorted anode emitter (B)—Fig. 2*

SOLID STATE SWITCH

By FRANK BRUNETTO, Material Laboratory, New York Naval Shipyard, Brooklyn, N. Y.

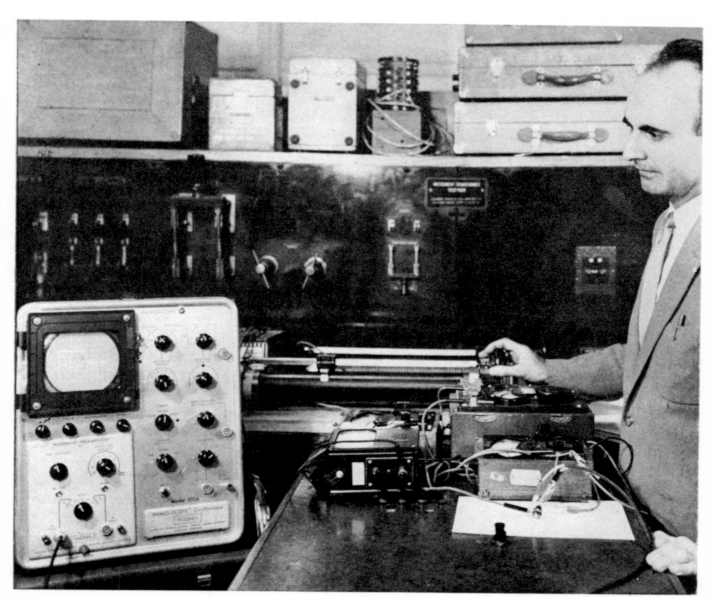

GATE TURN-OFF *switch under test has the same physical configuration as a silicon-controlled rectifier*

increase collector to emitter voltage to a magnitude where the energy of carriers arriving at the collector *p-n* boundary dislodges additional carriers producing an avalanche breakdown analogous to a Townsend discharge in gases. The other, and the recommended method, is to increase emitter current by introducing current at one of the bases. In most typical silicon transistors, α is low at low emitter currents, but increases rapidly as emitter current is increased. This is because of special impurity centers in the silicon. The latter method of firing is recommended because of reliability and simplicity of design. It is possible to use a GTO having a forward breakover voltage higher than any that will be normally encountered in the circuit and needs only a moderate amount of trigger power to start high conduction. As soon as the total current is sufficient to maintain the sum of the α's $\geqq 1$, the device will go into the conducting state provided the current (through the device) remains greater than the minimum value. This current is called the holding current. If the current (through the device) drops below the holding current, the GTO will revert to the forward blocking state, Fig. 1B.

REVERSE BLOCKING

—In the reverse direction the GTO is essentially two reverse biased *p-n* junctions in series. It exhibits characteristics similar to ordinary reverse biased silicon rectifiers. Care should be taken to see that reverse bias does not approach reverse breakover voltage because it may bring about destruction of the device.

TURN-OFF REQUIREMENTS —

Construction of a device that can be turned off with a low energy pulse while carrying a relatively large amount of current is more difficult than the construction of a high turn-on gain device. This is because a *pnpn* structure in the conducting state has an inherent regenerative feedback mechanism that resists attempts to turn it off. Thus it is necessary to change the operation from regeneration to degeneration if high turn-off gains are to be realized.

In Fig. 2A, a four-region, wide *n*-base, three junction *pnpn* structure is shown with contacts applied to the two external regions, and a

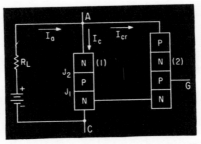

TURN-OFF GAIN *can be increased by combining the gate turn-off switch with a transistor—Fig. 3*

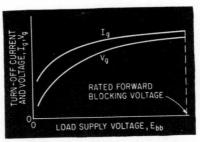

VARIATION *of turn-off current and voltage with load supply voltage—Fig. 4*

gate contact attached to one of the base layers. Assuming charge neutrality, negligible multiplication at J_c, and saturation currents small compared to the gate current, the load current I_a can be presented by any one of the equations

$$I_a = I_a\,\alpha pnp + I_c\,\alpha npn \qquad (3)$$
$$I_a = I_a\,\alpha pnp + I_a\,\alpha npn - I_g\,\alpha npn \qquad (4)$$
$$I_a = I_g\frac{\alpha npn}{\alpha npn + \alpha pnp - 1} \qquad (5)$$

These equations hold true only when ($\alpha npn + \alpha pnp - 1$) in Equ. 5 approaches zero. Once the unit is conducting, I_a is no longer determined by these equations but by the supply voltage and load resistance. To determine turn-off requirements, these equations can be considered to hold true if it is assumed that the alphas, αpnp and αnpn, adjust themselves so that the collector junction current I_{Jc} is equal to the anode current I_a.

$$I_{Jc} = I_a = I_a\,\alpha pnp + I_c\,\alpha npn \qquad (6)$$

When gate current I_g is increased, $I_c\,\alpha npn$ decreases unless it can readjust itself to a higher value. Since each alpha has a maximum readjustment limit for a given load, $I_c\,\alpha npn$ will eventually start decreasing as gate current flow is increased. At this point, junction current I_{Jc}, will become smaller than load current I_a. This means that the the unit is limiting the current and is in the OFF state.

Turn-off gain can be denoted by

$$\frac{I_a}{I_g} = \frac{\alpha npn}{\alpha npn + \alpha pnp - 1} \qquad (7)$$

Turn-off gain is defined as the ratio of load current turned off by gate current. It also tells what combination of alphas will result in a high turn-off gain, or ($\alpha npn + \alpha pnp - 1$) as small as possible with αnpn as large as possible.

TURN-OFF OPERATION

— With simple *pnpn* structures, Fig. 2A, it is difficult to obtain relatively high gains and still maintain a reasonable holding current. More complex structures, Fig. 2B, are necessary.

Turn-off of this structure is achieved in the same manner as that already shown in Fig. 2A, i.e., by removing current through the gate load. In this structure, the middle *n*-region is attached to the same ohmic anode contact as is the *p*-region. During normal operation the *p-n* junction on the anode side is partially shorted causing sufficient electrons to flow parallel to this junction thus biasing the GTO into forward conduction.

The thermal field built up on the left side of the structure by the electron majority carrier will cause the injected holes to be crowded towards the other side of the device. Since the base current for the *npn* consists of collected holes from the *pnp*, and since more holes are collected to the right side, more cathode *n*-region electrons are injected and collected near the right ridge of the cathode emitter.

When a negative gate current is introduced, the distribution of electron current density shifts to the left because the cathode junction nearer to the gate has less effective base hole current. This also reduces the lateral distance of biasing electron current in the *n*-type base, thus reducing its density in the region bordering the anode junction. Since the forward bias across this junction will lower, injection will drop and result in lower alpha sum. As the alpha sum drops below unity, the device will turn off.

INCREASING GAIN

—To get turn-off gains greater than the capability of a GTO, it is possible to combine the GTO with a transistor, Fig. 3. Structure 2 is the GTO and is in series with the forward biased junction, J_1, of transistor 1. With sufficient positive bias to gate, G, the GTO will conduct. Junction J_2 of the transistor will be a high parallel impedance across the GTO because it is a reversed biased junction. Current I_{cr}, flowing through the GTO, will be acting as base current for transistor 1 and the forward drop across GTO 2 will be the collector bias for J_2. If the transistor has appreciable current gain, β, most of the load, I_a, will flow through transistor 1.

Collector current I_c for transistor 1 equals βI_{cr}. Assuming β equal to 50, then $I_a = I_c + I_{cr} = 50\,I_{cr} + I_{cr} = 51\,I_{cr}$.

If the GTO 2 has a turn-off gain of 25, it can turn off a current, I_{cr}, with a negative current of 0.04 I_{cr}. Since transistor 1 will not conduct any appreciable current without the base current, I_{cr}, a load current of 51 I_{cr} is turned off with a current of 0.04 I_{cr} and thus have a turn-off gain of 51/0.04 or 1275.

TEMPERATURE SENSITIVITY—
Like any other semiconductor device, the GTO is sensitive to temperature variations. A rise in temperature will increase alpha and, conversely, a drop will bring about a corresponding reduction in alpha efficiency. Thus, a rise in temperature will increase the turn-on gain but reduce the turn-off gain. A relatively high junction temperature can reduce gain to a point where turn-off becomes unattainable and could destroy the device. It is important that the GTO or any other semiconductor device be operated within the temperature limits prescribed by the manufacturer which, for silicon, are usually never higher than 150C and never lower than −65C junction temperature.

RISE TIME—Other factors that affect the turn-off parameters of a GTO is the rise time of the triggering gate signal. Generaly, a smaller turn-off current gain can be expected when using a signal having a faster rise time because of the presence, in the load circuit, of higher peaking transient voltage and current. The transients are generated during turn-off by the rapid interruption of the load current. Their amplitudes are directly proportional to the rate of decay of the load current. The latter, in turn, is directly dependent upon the rise

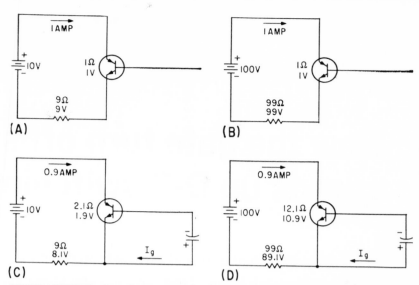

COMPARISON *of resistances and voltage drops of a GTO conducting the same load current at two different supply voltages.. Conditions before turn-off (A) and (B), compared to conditions during turn-off (C) and (D) show an increase in circuit resistance—Fig. 5*

time of the triggering voltage.

Transient voltages are minmum when little or no inductance is present in the load circuit. If the circuit is in this condition and it is desired that the turn-off voltage, not the turn-off current, be kept at a minimum, it will then be advantageous to use a triggering signal having a relatively fast rise time.

Inductance, however small, does appreciably affect the turn-off parameters of a GTO, especially when the triggering signal has a fast rise time. Since the GTO is triggered ON and OFF by the addition and removal of current through the gate, a low impedance voltage source or current source must be used for triggering the device.

LOAD SUPPLY VOLTAGE—Although the junction temperature and triggering signal rise time influence the turn-off parameters of a GTO, their effects are insignificant when compared to that exerted by the magnitude of the load supply voltage, E_{bb}. Differences in the parameters by as much as 100 percent in turn-off current, I_g, and much more in voltage, V_g, are possible with the use of different magnitudes of supply voltages. The relationship, Fig. 4, which is one of more turn-off power for a higher magnitude of supply voltage, is explained by the fact that when operating under the latter condition the device must attain a larger internal resistance. With this, there is an equivalent

reduction in load current.

In Fig. 5A and B, a GTO is shown conducting the same load current supplied by two different magnitudes of supply voltage. Since the current is limited only by load resistance, the resistance of the GTO as well as its forward voltage drop, are in both cases the same.

This, however, is not the case once the process of turn-off is initiated. If turn-off is considered as a continuous reduction of load current brought about by a corresponding increase in circuit resistance, then Fig. 5C and D show that with a larger supply voltage the GTO must attain a larger internal resistance for an equivalent drop in load current. This can only be accomplished by applying more negative power bias on the gate, a method somewhat analogous to imposing a more negative voltage bias on the control grid of a vacuum tube. The same condition applies if the supply voltage is unregulated.

The author thanks General Electric Company for granting permission to include material from the *General Electric Controlled Rectifier Manual* and from reports on Investigation of Electronically Controllable Turn Off Controlled Rectifiers. Thanks also to J. L. Flood, J. Moyson, J. Petruzella of General Electric, William Colletti of the Naval Material Laboratory, and Richard H. Grant of the Naval Material Laboratory for their assistance.

Now the gate turn off switch speeds up D-C switching

A logical development of the silicon controlled rectifier, the gate turn-off switch is out of the experimental stage. Its 10 times faster turn-off speed opens up a variety of applications

By Denis R. Grafham

General Electric Co., Rectifier Components Department, Auburn, N.Y.

Although semiconductor devices, such as the silicon controlled rectifier and the power transistor have simplified switching in power and control circuits, both these devices have serious limitations. The power transistor is inherently a low voltage device while the SCR is difficult to turn-off once it has been triggered in d-c circuits. A new device, the gate turn-off switch, has no such limitations. It can be turned off as well as on from its gate input terminal. And it operates at frequencies up to 100 kilocycles per sec.

The new device is a logical improvement of the SCR. It too is a three-terminal, four layer, pnpn switching device. But its structure is more complex. The gate region has a much larger active area in the GTO than the SCR and it is this change which helps give the GTO its unique characteristic.

In d-c circuits, the disadvantages of the SCR are most evident. Its maximum operating frequency is low because it must be reverse—biased for a relatively long time (10 to 20 microseconds) through an external low impedance circuit which dissipates considerable power. These restrictions confine the SCR to operate at frequencies of a few kilocycles, current ratings from 50 ma to 470 amps rms at d-c voltages of 25 to 1,000 volts.

The biggest advantage of the GTO is its ability to be turned on and off by the gate signal, a low power pulse of less than 10 microsec. A positive pulse of gate current latches the GTO into conduction and, once fired, the switch stays closed. A subsequent negative pulse turns it off again. That's an advantage over the power transistor since the power transistor requires the signal be applied continuously to hold the switch closed.

Current gain exists between anode and gate during turn-off as well as turn-on. Thus the GTO has the advantage over the SCR in d-c switching of faster turn-off and higher speed operation. As a result, commutating components can be smaller and cheaper. Turn-off speed is 10 times faster than that of the SCR, with turn-off gains of 5 to 15. Also, load waveform distortion is minimized because commutation transients are remote from the load carrying circuits.

Compared to switching transistors, the GTO requires much less drive power, because of its true bistable nature. The new device can handle much higher load power for the same current rating, because it is inherently a high voltage device, whereas the transistor is not. In a-c applications, the GTO can be phase-controlled for power factor improvement. The GTO is still a low-power device, however, the largest commercially available GTO being rated at about 7.5 amps at 500 to 600 volts.

GTO characteristics

Like the SCR, the GTO is triggered into conduction by injecting a pulse of forward current across its gate cathode junction. Generally, more gate current is required to trigger the GTO than an equivalently rated SCR. Latching and holding currents are higher, and more power is dissipated during forward conduction. As the potential turn-off capability of the GTO is increased the wider these discrepancies between SCR and GTO become. They are the price paid for gate turn-off capability. As an illustration, consider the General Electric G5 series GTO and the G6. The G5 series GTO features low trigger, latching and holding currents,

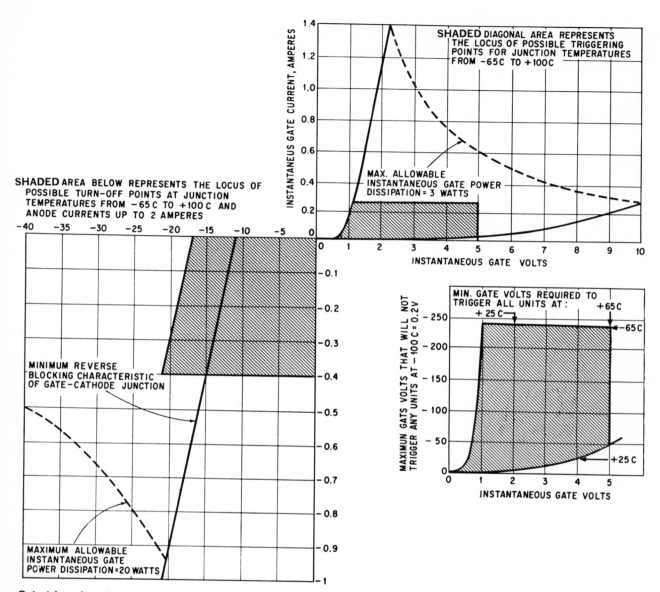

Gate triggering characteristics are needed to design circuits using GTOs. The first quadrant defines the positive gate triggering voltage-current relationship while the third quadrant displays the equivalent negative turn-off data

with gate turn-off up to one ampere. The G6 series requires higher trigger, latching and holding current, but has turn-off capability up to two amperes.

Since the GTO is intended primarily for d-c switching applications, a high reverse voltage rating is unnecessary in most applications so all standard G5 and G6 devices have a nominal 25 volt reverse rating only. When a higher reverse voltage capability is required a conventional silicon diode may be connected in series.

The GTO is charge-operated in the sense that positive gate current must flow for a finite time to trigger the device "on", while negative gate current must flow to turn it off again. In either case gate voltage must be provided to force the gate current through the GTO's internal gate impedance. Since the gate impedance is not constant, it is most convenient to display the gate volt-ampere characteristics of the GTO in graphical form.

The first quadrant defines the positive gate triggering voltage-current relationship, while the third quadrant displays the equivalent negative turn-off data. To ensure turn-off, negative gate voltages in excess of the static gate cathode avalanche voltage of some units must be provided. This characteristic precludes the use of d-c or long duration gate turn-off pulses, unless a silicon diode is connected in series with the GTO cathode lead. Without such a diode, overheating of the gate-cathode junction after turn-off might result. If the diode is not used, gate pulse duration must be less than specified (see chart) for a given gate pulse magnitude.

Turn-off characteristics

To turn off a conducting GTO, sufficient charge must be extracted from its gate to stop internal regeneration. The charge required can be computed from minimum turn-off gain (G_1) and the gate pulse width at which G_1 is specified. (G_1 is defined as the ratio of anode current being turned off to the negative gate current required to effect turn-off.) Since gain is a function of several variables, including pulse width, G_1 is specified for worst case conditions. The major factors affecting turn-off gain are:

(a) Gate pulse width—As the turn-off gate pulse duration is decreased, gate current magnitude must be increased to maintain the correct charge relationship. The relationship between turn-off gain and pulse duration is shown in chart (A).

(b) Anode current—turn-off gain is dependent on the magnitude of anode current being turned off. As anode current is increased above the holding current level, turn-off drops rapidly from infinity to I_H to some minimum value, and then climbs steadily upward again. At slightly above the maximum anode current that can be gate-commutated, turn-off gain drops suddenly to zero. This effect is caused by the inability of the gate to maintain control over the entire GTO cathode region at high current levels, and is a characteristic of all gate turn-off switches. It is possible to destroy a GTO by attempting to gate-commutate more than the design level of anode current. Chart (B) shows the variation in turn-off gain with anode current for the G6 GTO.

(c) Junction temperature—in general, gain decreases as junction temperature increases. Minimum turn-off gain is usually specified, therefore, at maximum rated junction temperature.

(d) Anode voltage and load impedance—turn-off gain is somewhat dependent on the anode supply voltage, and the nature of the load impedance in the anode circuit. As anode current starts to fall during the final phase of turn-off, the magnitude of the resultant voltage that develops across the center blocking junction of the GTO affects the ability of the gate to complete its job. The higher the voltage, the more difficult it becomes to complete commutation. An unclamped inductive load can generate a high forward anode voltage during turn-off, which will affect gain the same way as does a high supply voltage.

(e) Turn-off gate pulse rise and fall times—a fast-rising negative gate pulse is beneficial to the turn-off process, but too rapid a pulse decay time can degrade the GTO's turn-off gain. Both these effects are associated with the GTO's gate-cathode capacitance. While the negative dv/dt of the pulse leading edge speeds up turn-off by discharging the gate capacitance out of the gate, the positive dv/dt of its trailing edge tends to recharge the capacitance in a direction to retrigger the GTO. A similar phenomenon affects the GTO during turn-on. Here a fast rising trigger pulse facilitates turn-on and a rapid decay encourages subsequent turn-off. The effect manifests itself during turn-on as an apparent decrease in gate trigger sensitivity and as an increase in anode latching current.

Turn-off methods

The GTO may be turned on and off by alternately charging and discharging a capacitor connected in series with its gate lead. When switch S_1 is opened, capacitor C_1 charges to E_1 through R_1 and the GTO's internal gate impedance. For the GTO to trigger, the following equations must be satisfied:

$$R_1 \leq (E_1 - V_{GTM})/3\,I_{GTM} \tag{1}$$
$$C_1 \geq t_1/(R_1 + V_{GTM}/I_{GTM}) \tag{2}$$

where V_{GTM} = maximum gate voltage to trigger (volts), I_{GTM} = maximum gate current to trigger (amps), t_1 = pulse duration at which I_{GTM} is specified (seconds).

When S_1 is closed, the charged capacitor C_1 discharges through R_2 and the GTO's gate impedance, and the GTO will turn-off providing:

$$R_2 \leq (E_1 - V_{GTO})/(2\,I_{GTO}) \tag{3}$$
$$C_1 \geq t_2/(R_2 + V_{GTO}/I_{GTO}) \tag{4}$$

where V_{GTO} = maximum gate voltage to turn-off (volts), I_{GTO} = maximum gate current to turn-off I_L amps (amps), t_2 = time duration at which I_{GTO} is specified (seconds), I_L = anode current following at instant of commutation (amps).

Equation 3 defines only the maximum value of R_2 for guaranteed commutation. In most practical circuits, for more rapid turn-off, R_2 can be made much smaller than its calculated value. The lower limit on R_2 is determined either by the peak reverse gate power rating of the GTO, or by some other limiting circuit consideration, such as the current rating of S_1.

Series capacitor turn-off

To select R_1, R_2 and C_1 for a G6F GTO operating in the circuit of (A), where $E_1 = E_2 = 28$ V (d-c); $T_A = 25$ C; $R_L = 28$ ohms, equations 1 to 4 are used. Assume $V_{GTM} = 2$ V, $I_{GTM} = 20$ ma, $t_1 = 20\ \mu S$ and $I_L = 1$ amp.

From Eq. 1, $R_1 \leq 430$ ohms. If $R_1 = 390$ ohms (nearest 10 percent value) Eq. 2 gives $C_1 = 0.0235$ μf. From G6 specifications, minimum turn-off gain $C_1 = 5$ for 500 ma $\leq I_L \leq 2$ amps; $T_J \leq 100$ C; $t_2 \geq 10\ \mu S$.

The maximum gate current to turn-off, I_{GTO} is given by: $I_{GTO} = I_L/G_I = 1/5 = 200$ ma. From G6 specifications, maximum gate voltage to turn-off, $V_{GTO} = 21$ volts. Equation 3 gives $R_2 \leq 17.5$ ohms

The author

Denis R. Grafham joined GE's Rectifier Components Department in 1960. He has specialized in application work and preparation of technical literature in connection with SCRs, rectifiers, light activated switches and gate turn-off switches.

A native of England, he was educated at Churcher's College and the Royal Aircraft Establishment and holds degrees in mechanical and electrical engineering.

Prior to joining GE, he served as a development engineer with aviation firms in Canada and Seattle, Washington

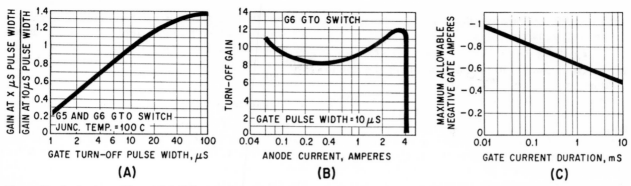

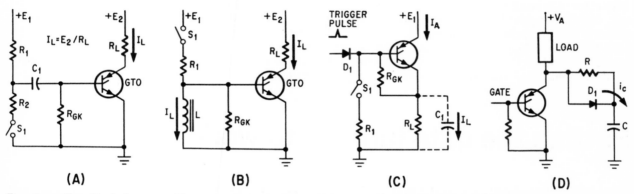

Turn-off gain for type G5 and G6 GTO as a function of the turn-off pulse width (A) and load current (B). Avalanche gate current is plotted as a function of gate pulse width in (C)

Four turn-off methods for controlling the GTO. Device may be turned on and off by charging and discharging a capacitor in series with gate lead (A). Turn-off is achieved by interrupting d-c current in inductor between gate and cathode (B). Load impedance is connected between the GTO's cathode terminal and ground (C). Use of capacitor C allows higher anode current switching by diverting part of the anode current (D)

and eq. 4 gives $C_1 = 0.129 \ \mu F$. Since the value of C_1 calculated for proper turn-off is higher than that required for turn-on, the higher of the two values must be used or let $C_1 = 0.15 \ \mu f$ which is the nearest standard value. Using G6 specified peak reverse gate power of 20 watts, the locus of all possible $(V_G \cdot I_G = 20 \text{ watts})$ is plotted on the gate volt-ampere characteristics. The gate turn-off source load line must lie to the right of this curve. The open circuit gate source voltage $E_1 = 28$ volts. The maximum permissible short circuit current $I_{sc} = E_1/R_2$ where R_2 is the slope of the line drawn on the V-A characteristic from $E_1 = 28$ volts tangential to the 20-watt peak power locus. The slope of such a line is 10 ohms. Thus $R_{2 \ (MIN)} = 10$ ohms.

Parallel inductor turn-off

The GTO can be turned off by attempting to interrupt direct current flowing in an inductor connected between its gate and cathode terminals. In circuit (B) when switch S_1 is closed, current will flow through resistor R_1 and into the GTO gate. If the peak value of gate current $(E_1 = V_{GTM})/R_1 \gg I_{GTM}$, the GTO will trigger. Assuming the GTO gate impedance is high compared to the d-c resistance

of inductor L, in the steady state $i_L - E_1/R_1$. If switch S_1 is now opened, the current i_L must transfer from R_1 to the gate, and the GTO will turn off provided: $E_1/R_1 \geq 2I_{GTO}$ and $(L)(I_{GTO})/C_{GTO} \geq t_2$.

Because the switch S_1 is required to carry the peak turn-off current i_L for as long as the GTO is in conduction, it is usually necessary to select R_1 for minimum permissible turn-off current. In low speed circuits i_L can be minimized by stretching out the turn-off pulse time constant.

Load in cathode commutation

In the next circuit of the figure the load impedance is connected between the GTO cathode terminal and ground. A short positive pulse of gate current applied to the gate terminal through diode D_1 will trigger the GTO and energize the load. Diode D_1, a fast recovery type, decouples the gate triggering source as the gate and cathode terminals jump up to the supply voltage. The GTO can be turned off now by closing switch S_1, when current is diverted out of the gate terminal to ground through current limiting resistor R_1. The value of R_1 is selected so that as the load cathode current and voltage decay during the final phase of turn-off, sufficient current always flows out of the gate to satisfy relationship:

$$R_1 \geq R_L (G_1 - 1) - (V_{GTO} - G_I)/I_A$$

where G_1 = minimum turn-off gain over the anode current range I_A to holding current; V_{GTO} = maximum turn-off gate voltage (volts); I_A = peak anode current during commutation = $I_L/(1 - 1/G_1)$ amps.

Capacitor C_1, which provides a low impedance bypass around the load for the triggering pulse, also aids the turn-off process by "holding up" the load voltage as cathode current falls. In circuits where the load impedance presents a sufficiently low impedance to the trigger pulse, C_1 can often be eliminated.

Because there is no energy storage needed in reactive commutating elements, as in the two previous turn-off methods, GTO circuits employing cathode commutation are inherently capable of very high speed operation. The main disadvantage of the method is that during the turn-off interval anode current is increased by the amount of gate current flowing through R_1. As a consequence the allowable load cathode current must be reduced by a like amount so that the total peak anode current rating of the GTO is not exceeded during turn-off.

Special turn-off circuitry

In some GTO applications it is possible to aid the gate turn-off action by means of a special circuit.[2] As the GTO starts to turn off under the influence of a negative gate signal, part of the diminishing anode current is diverted away from the GTO as charging current to capacitor C_1. The amount of current diverted depends on the size of C_1 and on the rate of rise of anode voltage during turn-off thus: $I_c = C \cdot dr/dt$. This circuit allows higher than rated anode current to be gate commutated, although at the expense of load turn-off speed. Resistor R is added to limit capacitor discharge current through the GTO during turn-on. Diode D_1 bypasses R for maximum current diversion during turn-off.

Putting the gate turn-off to work

Here are six applications that make good advantage of the GTO: a flip-flop, ring counter, sawtooth generator, voltage regulator, high frequency chopper, and high voltage generator

The circuit P. 69 is a GTO adaptation of the SCR capacitor—commutated flip-flop. The diodes are GE1N2613s and the GTOs are GE G611Bs with suitable heat sinks. The circuit transfers load current from one load to the other each time a positive trigger pulse is applied to the common input line. Operation to over 10 kc is possible, and the circuit will accommodate a wide range of load voltages and currents, with suitable component selection.

Assume GTO_1 is conducting load current, and GTO_2 is blocking. Capacitor C_2 charges to the supply voltage through load R_{L2} and resistor R_4. When GTO_2 is turned on by the next positive trigger pulse through R_6 and D_4 the gate of GTO_1 is driven negative by the voltage on C_2 and GTO_1 turns off. Peak negative gate current is limited by resistor R_2. GTO_2 is commutated in turn by capacitor C_1, as GTO_1 is triggered on again.

The flip-flop configuration can be used as a trigger pulse generator for high power SCRs in inverter circuits, or in other applications where high peak pulse power is required. The next circuit illustrates such a trigger circuit that incorporates means for positive starting when power is first applied. Each of the four output windings will deliver more than 1 amp peak into a 10 ohm load. But pulse rise time is approximately 1 microsecond and pulse width is around 20 microseconds. The circuit has operated to 10 kc.

Each time the unijunction transistor Q_1 fires, the GTOs change their state. When GTO_1 turns on, a pulse of current flows in the primary winding of transformer T_1 to charge capacitor C_1; similarly when GTO_2 turns on, current flows in T_2 to charge C_2. These pulses appear as outputs in the transformer secondaries. The positive start feature works as follows: When power is first applied to the circuit both GTO_1 and GTO_2 are off. Diodes D_5 and D_6 are both back biased, interbase current is unable to flow in Q_1, and Q_1 cannot fire. Capacitor C_5 meanwhile charges towards the supply voltage through resistor R_9. As soon as the voltage on C_5 exceeds the breakdown voltage of zener diode D_7, SCR_1 turns on and allows C_7 to charge. The charging current of C_7 then triggers GTO_1. With GTO_1 on, interbase current for Q_1 can flow through D_5 and the conducting GTO, and the unijunction transistor takes over the triggering.

Ring counter

A ring counter may be considered as a circuit that sequentially transfers voltage from one load to

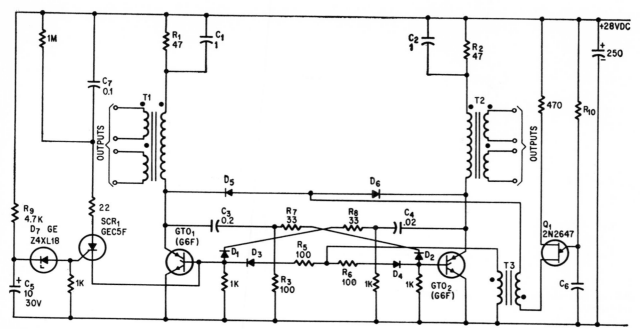

Positive-starting flip-flop may be used in high peak pulse power applications

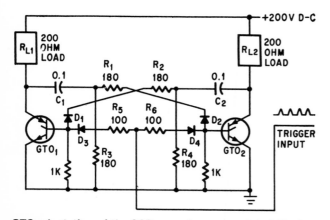

GTO adaptation of the SCR capacitor-commutated flip-flop transfers load current each time a positive trigger pulse is applied

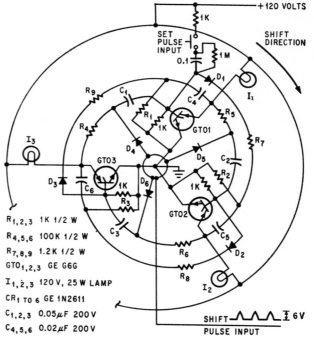

R$_{1,2,3}$ 1K 1/2 W
R$_{4,5,6}$ 100K 1/2 W
R$_{7,8,9}$ 1.2K 1/2 W
GTO$_{1,2,3}$ GE G6G
I$_{1,2,3}$ 120 V, 25 W LAMP
CR$_1$ TO 6 GE 1N2611
C$_{1,2,3}$ 0.05 μF 200 V
C$_{4,5,6}$ 0.02 μF 200 V

Ring counter may function as decade counter with direct lamp readout

the next, when a number of loads are connected to form a closed loop. Transfer around the loop proceeds always in the same direction, and is initiated by pulsing a common shift line. The ring counter is actually an extension of the basic flip-flop circuit, a flip-flop being a two stage ring counter. In this circuit three GTOs drive a trio of incandescent lamps, but other types of load may be substituted and more stages added as desired. A ten-stage circuit using 10 GTOs can perform the function of a decade counter with direct lamp readout.

When power is first applied to the circuit none of the GTOs will turn on. To start the circuit, the set pulse input button is closed, turning on GTO$_1$ and applying voltage to the lamp load I$_1$. At this point diodes D$_4$ and D$_6$ will be reverse biased by the full supply voltage while diode D$_5$ will be reverse biased by less than 2 volts, as determined by the respective anode voltages of the GTOs. If a

positive pulse having amplitude greater than 4 volts, but less than the supply voltage, is applied to the shift line, D$_4$ and D$_6$ will block the pulse from the gates of GTO$_1$ and GTO$_3$ while the pulse will be transmitted to the gate of GTO$_2$ through D$_5$ and C$_2$, causing GTO$_2$ to turn on. As GTO$_2$ turns on, GTO$_1$ is turned off by the negative gate transient coupled into its gate via C$_5$, R$_7$ and diode D$_1$. When the next pulse arrives at the shift line, GTO$_3$

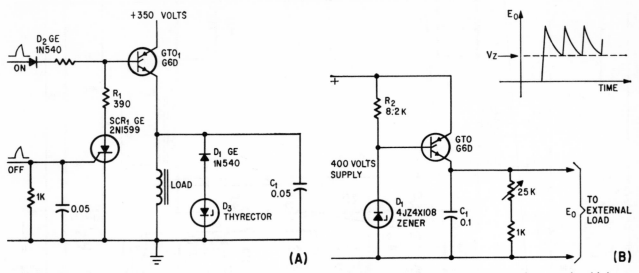

GTO can be used as a high speed hammer driver for a computer readout mechanism (A) and as a free-running high voltage sawtooth generator (B)

turns on and GTO_2 turns off.

The next figure (A) shows how the GTO can be used as a high speed "hammer" driver for a computer or similar readout mechanism. Since speed is the primary objective here, the load solenoid is deliberately overdriven for a short time by connecting it suddenly across a high voltage bus, and then disconnecting it again before overheating can occur. The GTO has both the switching speed and high voltage ability for this type of duty. Load current rise and fall times for this circuit are both considerably less than one millisecond.

Sawtooth generator

The adjacent circuit (B) illustrates a free-running high voltage sawtooth generator. When power is applied to the circuit, the GTO will trigger and connect the supply across C_1. As the voltage across C_1 rises above V_z (the avalanche voltage of D_1), GTO's gate becomes reverse-biased, current in the gate lead reverses, and the device turns off. C_1 then discharges through R_1 and the parallel external load impedance, if any. GTO will turn on and repeat the cycle when the voltage across C_1 decays sufficiently below V_z for positive gate current to flow again.

Voltage regulator

The GTO is an ideal device for d-c to d-c step-down transformer applications. It has the necessary

Editor's note

In addition to General Electric, other companies supply turn-off SCRs (or gate controlled switches): Motorola Semiconductor Products, Inc., Texas Instruments, Inc., Westinghouse Electric, Solid State Products, Inc. and Transitron Electronics Corp. Some typical devices with manufacturer's ratings:

Mfgr:	Type Series	Package	Max rms fwd curr.	Fwd blocking voltage	Max gate turnoff curr.
Motorola	MGCS 821	TO-41	5 amps	25–200 V	500 ma @ 5 a
	"		"	300–400	1 a @ 5 a
	MGCS 924 & 925		"	25–400	500 ma @ 5 a
Texas Instruments	X120A0	Stud mounted	5 amps	50 V	360 ma @ 5 a
	X120A1		"	100	"
	X120A2		"	200	"
Westinghouse Electric	241 U	Same as	5 amps	50–700 V	1.5 a @ 4 a
	241 W	JEDEC 2N1770	"	"	1.5 a @ 5 a
	242 X	TO-48 stud	7.5	50–800	1.5 a @ 6 a
	242 Y		"	"	1.0 a @ 6 a
	242 Z		10	"	1.0 a @ 8 a
	243 X, Y, Z	TO-3 diamond		same as 242 series	
Solid-State Products	2N892	TO-18	8 ma	15–200 V	2 ma @ 4 ma
	2C1030	TO-9	100	30–200	1.5 a @ 100 ma
	3C020		200	"	20 ma @ 200 ma
Transitron	TSW30	TO-5	50 ma	30–200 V	10 ma @ 50 ma
	TSW31	TO-18	"	"	"
	TSW31a		100	"	20 ma @ 100 ma
	2N764		200	"	40 ma @ 200 ma
	2N1686	TO-5	700	"	100 ma @ 500 ma
	SW30	TO-18	30	30	8 ma @ 30 ma

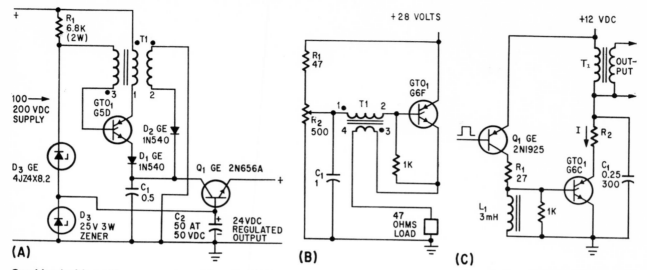

Combined with a silicon power transistor, the GTO operates as a prime switching and regulating element (A). The 100-kc chopper circuit (B) is notable for its versatility and simplicity. Circuit (C) may be used in a very high voltage pulse generator or as d-c step up transformer

voltage capability to work from high voltage d-c power sources, is able to switch efficiently at high frequency for good transformer use, is small, rugged and has silicon reliability. A single GTO (A), operating as the prime switching and regulating element, is combined with a silicon power transistor to form a high performance 200 volt d-c to 24 volt d-c regulated power supply. This type of circuit by virtue of its low weight, small size and efficiency is adaptable to many computer, missile, and airborne power supplies, test equipment and various other industrial applications.

In this circuit, with input voltage varying between 100 and 200 volts d-c, and/or load current-varying between 0-100 milliamperes, output voltage regulation is less than three percent. Ripple at full load is less than 300 millivolts. Circuit efficiency is around 50 percent with the components shown. Most of the circuit losses occur in resistor R_1, which has to provide gate trigger current for the GTO at the lowest expected supply voltage. For optimum efficiency with other supply voltages, R_1 should be selected to provide 10 milliamperes to the GTO gate.

The chopper circuit (B) is notable both for its versatility and simplicity. When power is applied, GTO_1 stays off until the volt-second integral across winding 1-2 of transformer T_1 is sufficient to cause T_1 to saturate. As T_1 saturates, its impedance falls and positive gate current flows through R_1 and R_2 to trigger the GTO. Winding 3-4 provides regeneration to speed up the turn-on process. With the GTO conducting load current, the voltage across winding 1-2 reverses, since the gate and cathode terminals are at + 28 volts, and T_1 comes out of saturation. GTO_1 continues to conduct until T_1 saturates in the reverse direction, when negative gate current flows to ground through R_2 and the GTO turns off. On-to-off time is determined by the setting of potentiometer R_2; alternatively a third bias winding may be added to T_1 to effect control of the duty cycle electrically.

With a third winding added, d-c control current in one direction will increase the duty cycle, while control current in the opposite direction will decrease the duty cycle. By applying a-c to the control winding it is possible to modulate the average output load current. With the components the circuit operates at approximately 100 kc.

High voltage generator

Circuit (C) may be used as a very high voltage pulse generator, or as a d-c step up transformer. Operation is as follows: with transistor Q_1 biased on, current flows through R_1 to trigger the GTO on, current builds up both in the primary of transformer T_1 and in the inductor L_1. When Q_1 is shut off, the current flowing in L_1 transfers to the GTO gate, and the GTO turns off. As the GTO turns off, a high voltage pulse is induced in the secondary of T_1. The pulse is in the form of damped oscillation, of frequency determined by T_1 and capacitor C_1. The output may be rectified and integrated if desired. With the components shown, 3 to 5 kv peak is available at the output terminals of T_1.

With suitable components this circuit forms the basis of an extremely high performance automotive-type ignition system. Using a low-inductance ignition coil in conjunction with an experimental 7 ampere GTO, the circuit develops 25-30 kv with minimal output drop from 0 to 400 pps, equivalent to 0-6000 RPM for a four-stroke V8 auto engine.

References

1. GE SCR Manual 3rd Edition, March, 1964
2. H. F. Storm, Introduction to Turn-Off Silicon Controlled rectifiers, IEEE Conference Paper CP 63-321.
3. J.W. Motto, Jr., Characteristics of the Gate Controlled Turn-Off Transistor Controlled Rectifier, IEEE Conference Paper CP 63-510.

Index